Finite Mathematics

Custom Edition for Northeastern Illinois University

Taken from:

Finite Mathematics and Calculus with Applications, Eighth Edition
by Margaret L. Lial, Raymond N. Greenwell and Nathan P. Ritchey

D1318685

Custom Publishing

New York   Boston   San Francisco
London   Toronto   Sydney   Tokyo   Singapore   Madrid
Mexico City   Munich   Paris   Cape Town   Hong Kong   Montreal

Cover Art: Courtesy of PhotoDisc/Getty Images

Taken from:

Finite Mathematics and Calculus with Applications, Eighth Edition
by Margaret L. Lial, Raymond N. Greenwell and Nathan P. Ritchey
Copyright © 2009 by Pearson Education, Inc.
Published by Addison-Wesley
Boston, Massachusetts 02116

This special edition published in cooperation with Pearson Custom Publishing.

Printed in the United States of America

10 9 8 7 6 5 4 3 2 1

2009361418

LB

Pearson
Custom Publishing
is a division of

www.pearsonhighered.com

ISBN 10: 0-558-44717-1
ISBN 13: 978-0-558-44717-5

Contents

Tables

*Instructor's Edition contains all answers.

2

Systems of Linear Equations and Matrices

The synchronized movements of band members marching on a field can be modeled using matrix arithmetic. An exercise in Section 5 in this chapter shows how multiplication by a matrix inverse transforms the original positions of the marchers into their new coordinates as they change direction.

Many mathematical models require finding the solutions of two or more equations. The solutions must satisfy *all* of the equations in the model. A set of equations related in this way is called a **system of equations**. In this chapter we will discuss systems of equations, introduce the idea of a *matrix*, and then show how matrices are used to solve systems of equations.

2.1 Solution of Linear Systems by the Echelon Method

? THINK ABOUT IT

How much of each ingredient should be used in an animal feed to meet dietary requirements?

Suppose that an animal feed is made from three ingredients: corn, soybeans, and cottonseed. One gram of each ingredient provides the number of grams of protein, fat, and fiber shown in the table. For example, the entries in the first column, 0.25, 0.4, and 0.3, indicate that one gram of corn provides twenty-five hundredths (one-fourth) of a gram of protein, four-tenths of a gram of fat, and three-tenths of a gram of fiber.

	Corn	**Soybeans**	**Cottonseed**
Protein	0.25	0.4	0.2
Fat	0.4	0.2	0.3
Fiber	0.3	0.2	0.1

?

Now suppose we need to know the number of grams of each ingredient that should be used to make a feed that contains 22 g of protein, 28 g of fat, and 18 g of fiber. To find out, we let x represent the required number of grams of corn, y the number of grams of soybeans, and z the number of grams of cottonseed. Each gram of corn provides 0.25 g of protein, so the amount of protein provided by x grams of corn is $0.25x$. Similarly, the amount of protein provided by y grams of soybeans is $0.4y$, and the amount of protein provided by z grams of cottonseed is $0.2z$. Since the total amount of protein is to be 22 g,

$$0.25x + 0.4y + 0.2z = 22.$$

The feed must supply 28 g of fat, so

$$0.4x + 0.2y + 0.3z = 28,$$

and 18 g of fiber, so

$$0.3x + 0.2y + 0.1z = 18.$$

To solve this problem, we must find values of x, y, and z that satisfy this system of equations. Verify that $x = 40$, $y = 15$, and $z = 30$ is a solution of the system, since these numbers satisfy all three equations. In fact, this is the only solution of this system. Many practical problems lead to such systems of *first-degree equations*.

A **first-degree equation in n unknowns** is any equation of the form

$$a_1x_1 + a_2x_2 + \cdots + a_nx_n = k,$$

where $a_1, a_2, \ldots, a_n$ and k are real numbers and $x_1, x_2, \ldots, x_n$ represent variables.* Each of the three equations from the animal feed problem is a first-degree equation. For example, the first equation

$$0.25x + 0.4y + 0.2z = 22$$

is a first-degree equation where

$$a_1 = 0.25, \qquad a_2 = 0.4, \qquad a_3 = 0.2, \qquad k = 22$$

and the variables are x, y, and z.

A *solution* of the first-degree equation

$$a_1x_1 + a_2x_2 + \cdots + a_nx_n = k$$

is a sequence of numbers $s_1, s_2, \ldots, s_n$ such that

$$a_1s_1 + a_2s_2 + \cdots + a_ns_n = k.$$

A solution of an equation is usually written in parentheses as $(s_1, s_2, \ldots, s_n)$. For example, $(1, 6, 2)$ is a solution of the equation $3x_1 + 2x_2 - 4x_3 = 7$, since $3(1) + 2(6) - 4(2) = 7$. This is an extension of the idea of an ordered pair, which was introduced in Chapter 1. A solution of a first-degree equation in two unknowns is an ordered pair, and the graph of the equation is a straight line. For this reason, all first-degree equations are also called linear equations.

Because the graph of a linear equation in two unknowns is a straight line, there are three possibilities for the solutions of a system of two linear equations in two unknowns.

POSSIBLE TYPES OF SOLUTIONS

1. The two graphs are lines intersecting at a single point. The system has a **unique solution**, and it is given by the coordinates of this point. See Figure 1(a).

2. The graphs are distinct parallel lines. When this is the case, the system is **inconsistent**; that is, there is no solution common to both equations. See Figure 1(b).

3. The graphs are the same line. In this case, the equations are said to be **dependent**, since any solution of one equation is also a solution of the other. There are infinitely many solutions. See Figure 1(c).

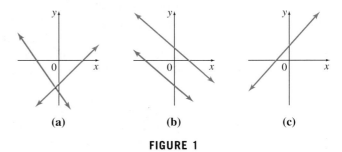

(a)   (b)   (c)

FIGURE 1

---

*a_1 is read "a-sub-one." The notation $a_1, a_2, \ldots, a_n$ represents n real-number coefficients (some of which may be equal), and the notation $x_1, x_2, \ldots, x_n$ represents n different variables, or unknowns.

In larger systems, with more equations and more variables, there also may be exactly one solution, no solutions, or infinitely many solutions. If no solution satisfies every equation in the system, the system is inconsistent, and if there are infinitely many solutions that satisfy all the equations in the system, the equations are dependent.

Methods for solving systems of linear equations with two unknowns are usually introduced in algebra courses. The graphing method shows geometrically how solutions are found, but it may not be possible to determine the exact solution from the graph, especially if the answer does not involve integers. The substitution method, which we used in Chapter 1 to find the equilibrium point, determines the solution algebraically but becomes too difficult with larger systems with many unknowns. The elimination method determines solutions by using the addition property of equality to eliminate variables. We will expand this method to solve systems of linear equations. Although the discussion will be confined to equations with only a few variables, the method of solution can be extended to systems with many variables.

Transformations

To solve a linear system of equations, we use properties of algebra to change, or transform, the system into a simpler *equivalent* system. An **equivalent system** is one that has the same solutions as the given system. Algebraic properties are the basis of the following transformations.

TRANSFORMATIONS OF A SYSTEM

The following transformations can be applied to a system of equations to get an equivalent system:

1. exchanging any two equations;
2. multiplying both sides of an equation by any nonzero real number;
3. replacing any equation by a nonzero multiple of that equation plus a nonzero multiple of any other equation.

Use of these transformations leads to an equivalent system because each transformation can be reversed or "undone," allowing a return to the original system.

The Echelon Method

A systematic approach for solving systems of equations using the three transformations is called the **echelon method**. The goal of the echelon method is to use the transformations to rewrite the equations of the system until the system has a triangular form. For a system of three equations in three variables, for example, the system should have the form

$$x + ay + bz = c$$
$$y + dz = e$$
$$z = f,$$

where a, b, c, d, e, and f are constants. Then the value of z from the third equation can be substituted into the second equation to find y, and the values of y and z can be substituted into the first equation to find x. This is called **back-substitution**.

EXAMPLE 1

Solving a System of Equations with a Unique Solution

Solve the system

$$2x + 3y = 12 \tag{1}$$

$$3x - 4y = 1. \tag{2}$$

▶**Solution** We will first use transformation 3 to eliminate the x-term from equation (2). We multiply equation (1) by 3 and add the results to -2 times equation (2).

$$3(2x + 3y) = 3 \cdot 12 \qquad\qquad 6x + 9y = 36$$

$$-2(3x - 4y) = -2 \cdot 1 \qquad \rightarrow \qquad \underline{-6x + 8y = -2}$$

$$17y = 34$$

We will indicate this process by the notation $3R_1 + (-2)R_2 \rightarrow R_2$. (R stands for row.) The new system is

$$2x + 3y = 12 \tag{1}$$

$$3R_1 + (-2)R_2 \rightarrow R_2 \qquad 17y = 34. \tag{3}$$

Now we use transformation 2 to make the coefficient of the first term in each row equal to 1. Here, we must multiply equation (1) by $1/2$ and equation (3) by $1/17$ to accomplish this.

We get the system

$$\tfrac{1}{2}R_1 \rightarrow R_1 \qquad x + \frac{3}{2}y = 6$$

$$\tfrac{1}{17}R_2 \rightarrow R_2 \qquad y = 2.$$

Back-substitution gives

$$x + \frac{3}{2}(2) = 6 \qquad \text{Substitute } y = 2.$$

$$x + 3 = 6$$

$$x = 3.$$

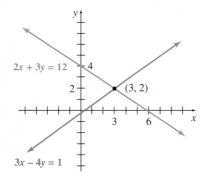

$2x + 3y = 12$

$3x - 4y = 1$

$(3, 2)$

FIGURE 2

The solution of the system is (3, 2). The graphs of the two equations in Figure 2 suggest that (3, 2) satisfies both equations in the system. Verify that (3, 2) does indeed satisfy both original equations.

EXAMPLE 2

Solving a System of Equations with No Solution

Solve the system

$$2x - 3y = 6 \tag{1}$$

$$-4x + 6y = 8. \tag{2}$$

▶**Solution** Eliminate x in equation (2) to get the system

$$2x - 3y = 6 \tag{1}$$

$$2R_1 + R_2 \rightarrow R_2 \qquad 0 = 20. \tag{3}$$

In equation (3), both variables have been eliminated, leaving a *false statement*. This is a signal that these two equations have no common solution. This system is

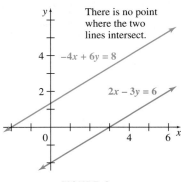

FIGURE 3

inconsistent and has no solution, As Figure 3 shows, the graph of the system is made up of two distinct parallel lines.

EXAMPLE 3 **Solving a System of Equations with an Infinite Number of Solutions**
Solve the system

$$3x - y = 4 \tag{1}$$

$$-6x + 2y = -8. \tag{2}$$

▶**Solution** We use transformation 3 to eliminate x in equation (2), getting the system

$$3x - y = 4 \tag{1}$$

$$2R_1 + R_2 \to R_2 \qquad 0 = 0. \tag{3}$$

The system becomes

$$\frac{1}{3}R_1 \to R_1 \qquad x - \frac{1}{3}y = \frac{4}{3} \tag{4}$$

$$0 = 0. \tag{3}$$

In equation (3), both variables have been eliminated, leaving a *true statement*. If we graph the original equations of the system on the same axes, as shown in Figure 4, we see that the graphs are the same line, and any point on the line will satisfy the system. This system is dependent and has an infinite number of solutions.

We will express the solutions in terms of y, where y can be any real number. The variable y in this case is called a **parameter**. (We could also let x be the parameter. In this text, we will follow the common practice of letting the rightmost variable be the parameter.) Solving equation (4) for x gives $x = (1/3)y + 4/3 = (y + 4)/3$, and all ordered pairs of the form

$$\left(\frac{y + 4}{3}, y \right)$$

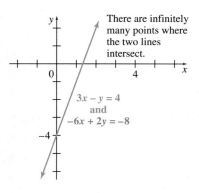

FIGURE 4

are solutions. For example, if we let $y = 5$, then $x = (5 + 4)/3 = 3$ and one solution is $(3, 5)$. Similarly, letting $y = -10$ and $y = 3$ gives the solutions $(-2, -10)$ and $(7/3, 3)$.

Note that the original two equations are solved not only by the particular solutions like $(3, 5)$, $(-2, -10)$, and $(7/3, 3)$, but also by the general solution $(x, y) = ((y + 4)/3, y)$. For example, substituting this general solution into the first equation gives

$$3\left(\frac{y + 4}{3}\right) - y = y + 4 - y = 4,$$

which verifies that this general solution is indeed a solution.

In some applications, x and y must be nonnegative integers. For instance, in Example 3, if x and y represent the number of male and female workers in a factory, it makes no sense to have $x = 7/3$ or $x = -2$. To make both x and y nonnegative, we solve the inequalities

$$\frac{y + 4}{3} \geq 0 \qquad \text{and} \qquad y \geq 0,$$

yielding

$$y \geq -4 \qquad \text{and} \qquad y \geq 0.$$

To make these last two inequalities true, we require $y \geq 0$, from which $y \geq -4$ automatically follows. Furthermore, to ensure $(y + 4)/3$ is an integer, it is necessary that y be 2 more than a whole-number multiple of 3. Therefore, the possible values of y are 2, 5, 8, 11, and so on, and the corresponding values of x are 2, 3, 4, 5, and so on.

The echelon method can be generalized to systems with more equations and unknowns. Because systems with three or more unknowns are complicated, however, we will only do a few in this section. In the next section, we will show a procedure based on the echelon method that is useful for solving large systems of equations. Meanwhile, the following example illustrates the additional steps needed to solve a system with three equations in three unknowns by the echelon method.

EXAMPLE 4   **Solving a System of Equations**

Solve the system

$$2x + y - z = 2 \tag{1}$$
$$x + 3y + 2z = 1 \tag{2}$$
$$x + y + z = 2. \tag{3}$$

▶**Solution**   As in the previous examples, begin by eliminating the term with x, this time from equations (2) and (3), as follows.

$$2x + y - z = 2 \tag{1}$$
$$R_1 + (-2)R_2 \rightarrow R_2 \qquad -5y - 5z = 0 \tag{4}$$
$$R_1 + (-2)R_3 \rightarrow R_3 \qquad -y - 3z = -2 \tag{5}$$

In the same way, use equation (4) to eliminate y in equation (5). The new system is

$$2x + y - z = 2$$
$$-5y - 5z = 0$$
$$R_2 + (-5)R_3 \rightarrow R_3 \qquad 10z = 10.$$

Make the coefficient of the first term in each equation equal to 1.

$$\tfrac{1}{2}R_1 \rightarrow R_1 \qquad x + \frac{1}{2}y - \frac{1}{2}z = 1 \tag{6}$$

$$(-\tfrac{1}{5})R_2 \rightarrow R_2 \qquad y + z = 0 \tag{7}$$

$$\tfrac{1}{10}R_3 \rightarrow R_3 \qquad z = 1 \tag{8}$$

Substitute 1 for z in equation (7) to get $y = -1$. Finally, substitute 1 for z and -1 for y in equation (6) to get $x = 2$. The solution of the system is $(2, -1, 1)$. Verify that $(2, -1, 1)$ satisfies all three equations in the original system. Note the triangular form of the last system. This is the typical echelon form. ▬

In summary, to solve a linear system in n variables by the echelon method, perform the following steps using the three transformations given earlier.

ECHELON METHOD OF SOLVING A LINEAR SYSTEM

1. If possible, arrange the equations so that there is an x_1-term in the first equation, an x_2-term in the second equation, and so on.

2. Eliminate the x_1-term in all equations after the first equation.

3. Eliminate the x_2-term in all equations after the second equation.

4. Eliminate the x_3-term in all equations after the third equation.

5. Continue in this way until the last equation has the form $ax_n = k$, for constants a and k, if possible.

6. Multiply each equation by the reciprocal of the coefficient of its first term.

7. Use back-substitution to find the value of each variable.

Applications   The mathematical techniques in this text will be useful to you only if you are able to apply them to practical problems. To do this, always begin by reading the problem carefully. Next, identify what must be found. Let each unknown quantity be represented by a variable. (It is a good idea to *write down* exactly what each variable represents.) Now reread the problem, looking for all necessary data. Write those down, too. Finally, look for one or more sentences that lead to equations or inequalities. The next example illustrates these steps.

EXAMPLE 5 **Flight Time**
A flight leaves New York at 8 P.M. and arrives in Paris at 9 A.M. (Paris time). This 13-hour difference includes the flight time plus the change in time zones. The

return flight leaves Paris at 1 P.M. and arrives in New York at 3 P.M. (New York time). This 2-hour difference includes the flight time *minus* time zones, plus an extra hour due to the fact that flying westward is against the wind. Find the actual flight time eastward and the difference in time zones.

▶**Solution** Let x be the flight time and y be the difference in time zones. For the trip east, the flight time plus the change in time zones is 13 hours, so

$$x + y = 13.$$

For the trip west, the flight time (which is $x + 1$ hours due to the wind) minus the time zone is 2 hours, so

$$(x + 1) - y = 2.$$

Subtract 1 from both sides of this equation, and then solve the system

$$x + y = 13$$
$$x - y = 1$$

using the echelon method.

$$x + y = 13$$
$$R_1 + (-1)R_2 \rightarrow R_2 \qquad 2y = 12$$

Dividing the last equation by 2 gives $y = 6$. Substituting this into the first equation gives $x + 6 = 13$, so $x = 7$. Therefore, the flight time eastward is 7 hours, and the difference in time zones is 6 hours.

EXAMPLE 6

Integral Solutions
A restaurant owner orders a replacement set of knives, forks, and spoons. The box arrives containing 40 utensils and weighing 141.3 oz (ignoring the weight of the box). A knife, fork, and spoon weigh 3.9 oz, 3.6 oz, and 3.0 oz, respectively.

(a) How many solutions are there for the number of knives, forks, and spoons in the box?

▶**Solution** Let

$$x = \text{the number of knives;}$$
$$y = \text{the number of forks;}$$
$$z = \text{the number of spoons.}$$

A chart is useful for organizing the information in a problem of this type.

	Knives	Forks	Spoons	Total
Number	x	y	z	40
Weight	3.9	3.6	3.0	141.3

Because the box contains 40 utensils,

$$x + y + z = 40.$$

The x knives weigh $3.9x$ ounces, the y forks weigh $3.6y$ ounces, and the z spoons weigh $3.0z$ ounces. Since the total weight is 141.3 oz, we have the system

$$x + y + z = 40$$
$$3.9x + 3.6y + 3.0z = 141.3.$$

Solve using the echelon method.

$$x + y + z = 40$$
$$3.9R_1 + (-1)R_2 \rightarrow R_2 \qquad 0.3y + 0.9z = 14.7$$

We do not have a third equation to solve for z, as we did in Example 4. This system, then, has an infinite number of solutions. Letting z be the parameter, solve the second equation for y to get

$$y = \frac{14.7 - 0.9z}{0.3} = 49 - 3z.$$

Substituting this into the first equation, we get

$$x + (49 - 3z) + z = 40.$$

Solving this for x gives

$$x = 2z - 9.$$

Thus, the solutions are $(2z - 9, 49 - 3z, z)$, where z is any real number.

Now that we have solved for x and y in terms of z, let us investigate what values z can take on. This application demands that the solutions be non-negative integers. The number of forks cannot be negative, so set

$$49 - 3z \geq 0.$$

Solving for z gives

$$z \leq \frac{49}{3} \approx 16.33.$$

Also, the number of knives cannot be negative, so set

$$2z - 9 \geq 0.$$

Solving for z gives

$$z \geq \frac{9}{2} = 4.5.$$

Therefore, the permissible values of z are 5, 6, 7, . . . , 16, for a total of 12 solutions.

(b) Find the solution with the smallest number of spoons.

▶**Solution**   The smallest value of z is $z = 5$, from which we find $x = 2(5) - 9 = 1$ and $y = 49 - 3(5) = 34$. This solution has 1 knife, 34 forks, and 5 spoons.

2.1 Exercises

Use the echelon method to solve each system of two equations in two unknowns. Check your answers.

1. $x + y = 5$
  $2x - 2y = 2$

2. $4x + y = 9$
  $3x - y = 5$

3. $3x - 2y = -3$
  $5x - y = 2$

4. $2x + 7y = -8$
  $-2x + 3y = -12$

5. $3x + 2y = -6$
  $5x - 2y = -10$

6. $-3x + y = 4$
  $2x - 2y = -4$

7. $6x - 2y = -4$
  $3x + 4y = 8$

8. $4m + 3n = -1$
  $2m + 5n = 3$

9. $5p + 11q = -7$
  $3p - 8q = 25$

10. $12s - 5t = 9$
  $3s - 8t = -18$

11. $6x + 7y = -2$
  $7x - 6y = 26$

12. $3a - 8b = 14$
  $a - 2b = 2$

13. $3x + 2y = 5$
  $6x + 4y = 8$

14. $9x - 5y = 1$
  $-18x + 10y = 1$

15. $3x - 2y = -4$
  $-6x + 4y = 8$

16. $3x + 5y + 2 = 0$
  $9x + 15y + 6 = 0$

17. An inconsistent system has _____ solutions.

18. The solution of a system with two dependent equations in two variables is _____.

Use the echelon method to solve each system. Check your answers.

19. $x - \dfrac{3y}{2} = \dfrac{5}{2}$
  $\dfrac{4x}{3} + \dfrac{2y}{3} = 6$

20. $\dfrac{x}{5} + 3y = 31$
  $2x - \dfrac{y}{5} = 8$

21. $\dfrac{x}{2} + y = \dfrac{3}{2}$
  $\dfrac{x}{3} + y = \dfrac{1}{3}$

22. $\dfrac{x}{9} + \dfrac{y}{6} = \dfrac{1}{3}$
  $2x + \dfrac{8y}{5} = \dfrac{2}{5}$

Use the echelon method to solve each system of three equations in three unknowns. Check your answers.

23. $x + y + z = 2$
  $2x + y - z = 5$
  $x - y + z = -2$

24. $2x + y + z = 9$
  $-x - y + z = 1$
  $3x - y + z = 9$

25. $x + 3y + 4z = 14$
  $2x - 3y + 2z = 10$
  $3x - y + z = 9$

26. $4x - y + 3z = -2$
  $3x + 5y - z = 15$
  $-2x + y + 4z = 14$

27. $2x + 5y + 4z = 10$
  $8x + 2y + 3z = 27$
  $4x + y + z = 13$

28. $2x + y + 4z = 5$
  $-3x + y + 3z = 14$
  $4x + 2y + z = 3$

29. In your own words, describe the echelon method as used to solve a system of three equations in three variables.

Solve each system of equations. Let z be the parameter.

30. $2x + 3y - z = 1$
  $3x + 5y + z = 3$

31. $3x + y - z = 0$
  $2x - y + 3z = -7$

32. $x + 2y + 3z = 11$
  $2x - y + z = 2$

33. $-x + y - z = -7$
  $2x + 3y + z = 7$

34. In an exercise in Section 1.3, you were asked to solve the system of least squares line equations

$$nb + (\Sigma x)m = \Sigma y$$
$$(\Sigma x)b + (\Sigma x^2)m = \Sigma xy$$

by the method of substitution. Now solve the system by the echelon method to get

$$m = \frac{n(\Sigma xy) - (\Sigma x)(\Sigma y)}{n(\Sigma x^2) - (\Sigma x)^2}$$

$$b = \frac{\Sigma y - m(\Sigma x)}{n}.$$

35. The examples in this section did not use the first transformation. How might this transformation be used in the echelon method?

▶ Applications

BUSINESS AND ECONOMICS

36. *Groceries* If 20 lb of rice and 10 lb of potatoes cost $16.20, and 30 lb of rice and 12 lb of potatoes cost $23.04, how much will 10 lb of rice and 50 lb of potatoes cost?

37. *Sales* An apparel shop sells skirts for $45 and blouses for $35. Its entire stock is worth $51,750. But sales are slow and only half the skirts and two-thirds of the blouses are sold, for a total of $30,600. How many skirts and blouses are left in the store?

38. *Sales* A theater charges $8 for main floor seats and $5 for balcony seats. If all seats are sold, the ticket income is $4200. At one show, 25% of the main floor seats and 40% of the balcony seats were sold and ticket income was $1200. How many seats are on the main floor and how many are in the balcony?

39. *Stock* Lorri Morgan has $16,000 invested in Disney and Exxon stock. The Disney stock currently sells for $30 a share and the Exxon stock for $70 a share. Her stockbroker points out that if Disney stock goes up 50% and Exxon stock goes up by $35 a share, her stock will be worth $25,500. Is this possible? If so, tell how many shares of each stock she owns. If not, explain why not.

40. *Production* A company produces two models of bicycles, model 201 and model 301. Model 201 requires 2 hours of assembly time and model 301 requires 3 hours of assembly time. The parts for model 201 cost $18 per bike and the parts for model 301 cost $27 per bike. If the company has a total of 34 hours of assembly time and $335 available per day for these two models, how many of each should be made in a day to use up all available time and money? If it is not possible, explain why not.

41. *Banking* A bank teller has a total of 70 bills in five-, ten-, and twenty-dollar denominations. The number of fives is three times the number of tens, while the total value of the money is $960. Find the number of each type of bill.

42. *Investments* Katherine Chong invests $10,000 received from her grandmother in three ways. With one part, she buys U.S. savings bonds at an interest rate of 2.5% per year. She uses the second part, which amounts to twice the first, to buy mutual funds that offer a return of 6% per year. She puts the rest of the money into a money market account paying 4.5% annual interest. The first year her investments bring a return of $470. How much did she invest in each way?

43. *Production* Felsted Furniture makes dining room furniture. A buffet requires 30 hours for construction and 10 hours for finishing. A chair requires 10 hours for construction and 10 hours for finishing. A table requires 10 hours for construction and 30 hours for finishing. The construction department has 350 hours of labor and the finishing department has 150 hours of labor available each week. How many pieces of each type of furniture should be produced each week if the factory is to run at full capacity?

44. *Rug Cleaning Machines* Kelly Karpet Kleaners sells rug cleaning machines. The EZ model weighs 10 lb and comes in a 10-cubic-ft box. The compact model weighs 20 lb and comes in an 8-cubic-ft box. The commercial model weighs 60 lb and comes in a 28-cubic-ft box. Each of their delivery vans has 248 cubic ft of space and can hold a maximum of 440 lb. In order for a van to be fully loaded, how many of each model should it carry?

45. *Production* Turley Tailor Inc. makes long-sleeve, short-sleeve, and sleeveless blouses. A long-sleeve blouse requires 1.5 hours of cutting and 1.2 hours of sewing. A short-sleeve blouse requires 1 hour of cutting and 0.9 hour of sewing. A sleeveless blouse requires 0.5 hour of cutting and 0.6 hour of sewing. There are 380 hours of labor available in the cutting department each day and 330 hours in the sewing department. If the plant is to run at full capacity, how many of each type of blouse should be made each day?

46. *Broadway Economics* When Neil Simon opens a new play, he has to decide whether to open the show on Broadway or Off Broadway. For example, in his play *London Suite*, he decided to open it Off Broadway. From information provided by Emanuel Azenberg, his producer, the following equations were developed:

$$43{,}500x - y = 1{,}295{,}000$$
$$27{,}000x - y = 440{,}000,$$

where x represents the number of weeks that the show has run and y represents the profit or loss from the show (first equation is for Broadway and second equation is for Off Broadway).*

a. Solve this system of equations to determine when the profit/loss from the show will be equal for each venue. What is the profit at that point?

b. Discuss which venue is favorable for the show.

LIFE SCIENCES

47. *Birds* The date of the first sighting of robins has been occurring earlier each spring over the past 25 years at the Rocky Mountain Biological Laboratory. Scientists from this laboratory have developed two linear equations that estimate the date of the first sighting of robins:

$$y = 759 - 0.338x$$
$$y = 1637 - 0.779x,$$

where x is the year and y is the estimated number of days into the year when a robin can be expected.[†]

a. Compare the date of first sighting in 2000 for each of these equations. (*Hint:* 2000 was a leap year.)

b. Solve this system of equations to find the year in which the two estimates agree.

PHYSICAL SCIENCES

48. *Stopping Distance* The stopping distance of a car traveling 25 mph is 61.7 ft, and for a car traveling 35 mph it is 106 ft.[‡] The stopping distance in feet can be described by the equation $y = ax^2 + bx + c$, where x is the speed in mph.

a. Find the values of a and b.

b. Use your answers from part a to find the stopping distance for a car traveling 55 mph.

GENERAL INTEREST

49. *Basketball* Wilt Chamberlain holds the record for the highest number of points scored in a single NBA basketball game. Chamberlain scored 100 points for Philadelphia against the New York Knicks on March 2, 1962. This is an amazing feat, considering he scored all of his points without the help of three-point shots. Chamberlain made a total of 64 baskets, consisting of free throws (worth two points) and foul shots (worth one point).[§] Find the number of free throws and the number of foul shots that Chamberlain made.

50. *Basketball* Kobe Bryant has the second highest single game point total in the NBA. Bryant scored 81 points for the Los Angeles Lakers on January 22, 2006, against the Toronto Raptors. Bryant made a total of 46 baskets, including foul shots (worth one point), free throws (worth two points), and three-point shots (worth three points). The number of free throw shots he made is equal to three times the number of three pointers he made.[§] Find the number of foul shots, free throws, and three pointers Bryant made.

51. *The 24® Game* The object of the 24® Game, created by Robert Sun, is to combine four numbers, using addition, subtraction, multiplication, and/or division, to get the number 24.[‖] For example, the numbers 2, 5, 5, 4 can be combined as $2(5 + 5) + 4 = 24$. For the algebra edition of the game and the game card shown below, the object is to find single-digit positive integer values x and y so the four numbers $x + y$, $3x + 2y$, 8, and 9 can be combined to make 24.

a. Using the game card, write a system of equations that, when solved, can be used to make 24 from the game card. What is the solution to this system, and how can it be used to make 24 on the game card?

b. Repeat part a and develop a second system of equations.

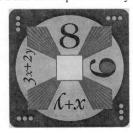

*Goetz, Albert, "Basic Economics: Calculating Against Theatrical Disaster," *The Mathematics Teacher*, Vol. 89, No. 1, Jan. 1996, pp. 30–32.
[†]Inouye, David, Billy Barr, Kenneth Armitage, and Brian Inouye, "Climate Change Is Affecting Altitudinal Migrants and Hibernating Species," *Proceedings of the National Academy of Science*, Vol. 97, No. 4, Feb. 15, 2000, pp. 1630–1633.
[‡]*National Traffic Safety Institute Student Workbook*, 1993, p. 7.
[§]"Kobe's 81-Point Game Second Only to Wilt," http://sports.espn.go.com.
[‖]Source: Copied with permission. 24® is a registered trademark of Suntex International Inc., all rights reserved. Suntex Int. Inc., Easton, PA, http://www.24game.com.

2.2 Solution of Linear Systems by the Gauss-Jordan Method

How can an auto manufacturer with more than one factory and several dealers decide how many cars to send to each dealer from each factory?

Questions like this are called *transportation problems*; they frequently lead to a system of equations that must be satisfied. In this section we use a further refinement of the echelon method to answer this question. When we use the echelon method, since the variables are in the same order in each equation, we really need to keep track of just the coefficients and the constants. For example, look at the system solved in Example 4 of the previous section.

$$2x + y - z = 2$$
$$x + 3y + 2z = 1$$
$$x + y + z = 2$$

This system can be written in an abbreviated form as

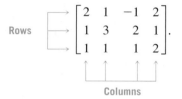

Rows
Columns

Such a rectangular array of numbers enclosed by brackets is called a **matrix** (plural: **matrices**).* Each number in the array is an **element** or **entry**. To separate the constants in the last column of the matrix from the coefficients of the variables, we use a vertical line, producing the following **augmented matrix**.

$$\left[\begin{array}{ccc|c} 2 & 1 & -1 & 2 \\ 1 & 3 & 2 & 1 \\ 1 & 1 & 1 & 2 \end{array}\right]$$

The rows of the augmented matrix can be transformed in the same way as the equations of the system, since the matrix is just a shortened form of the system. The following **row operations** on the augmented matrix correspond to the transformations of systems of equations given earlier.

---

*The word matrix, Latin for "womb," was coined by James Joseph Sylvester (1814–1897) and made popular by his friend Arthur Cayley (1821–1895). Both mathematicians were English, although Sylvester spent much of his life in the United States.

> ## ROW OPERATIONS
>
> For any augmented matrix of a system of equations, the following operations produce the augmented matrix of an equivalent system:
>
> **1.** interchanging any two rows;
>
> **2.** multiplying the elements of a row by any nonzero real number;
>
> **3.** adding a nonzero multiple of the elements of one row to the corresponding elements of a nonzero multiple of some other row.

In steps 2 and 3, we are replacing a row with a new, modified row, which the old row helped to form, just as we replaced an equation with a new, modified equation in the previous section.

Row operations, like the transformations of systems of equations, are reversible. If they are used to change matrix A to matrix B, then it is possible to use row operations to transform B back into A. In addition to their use in solving equations, row operations are very important in the simplex method to be described in Chapter 4.

In the examples in this section, we will use the same notation as in Section 1 to show the row operation used. For example, the notation R_1 indicates row 1 of the previous matrix, and $-3R_1 + R_2$ means that row 1 is multiplied by -3 and added to row 2.

By the first row operation, interchanging two rows, the matrix

$$\begin{bmatrix} 0 & 1 & 2 & 3 \\ -2 & -6 & -10 & -12 \\ 2 & 1 & -2 & -5 \end{bmatrix} \quad \text{becomes} \quad \begin{bmatrix} -2 & -6 & -10 & -12 \\ 0 & 1 & 2 & 3 \\ 2 & 1 & -2 & -5 \end{bmatrix} \quad \begin{array}{l} \text{Interchange } R_1 \\ \text{and } R_2 \end{array}$$

by interchanging the first two rows. Row 3 is left unchanged.

The second row operation, multiplying a row by a number, allows us to change

$$\begin{bmatrix} -2 & -6 & -10 & -12 \\ 0 & 1 & 2 & 3 \\ 2 & 1 & -2 & -5 \end{bmatrix} \quad \text{to} \quad \begin{bmatrix} 1 & 3 & 5 & 6 \\ 0 & 1 & 2 & 3 \\ 2 & 1 & -2 & -5 \end{bmatrix} \quad (-1/2)R_1 \rightarrow R_1$$

by multiplying the elements of row 1 of the original matrix by $-1/2$. Note that rows 2 and 3 are left unchanged.

Using the third row operation, adding a multiple of one row to another, we change

$$\begin{bmatrix} 1 & 3 & 5 & 6 \\ 0 & 1 & 2 & 3 \\ 2 & 1 & -2 & -5 \end{bmatrix} \quad \text{to} \quad \begin{bmatrix} 1 & 3 & 5 & 6 \\ 0 & 1 & 2 & 3 \\ 0 & -5 & -12 & -17 \end{bmatrix} \quad -2R_1 + R_3 \rightarrow R_3$$

by first multiplying each element in row 1 of the original matrix by -2 and then adding the results to the corresponding elements in the third row of that matrix. Work as follows.

$$\begin{bmatrix} 1 & 3 & 5 & 6 \\ 0 & 1 & 2 & 3 \\ (-2)1+2 & (-2)3+1 & (-2)5-2 & (-2)6-5 \end{bmatrix} = \begin{bmatrix} 1 & 3 & 5 & 6 \\ 0 & 1 & 2 & 3 \\ 0 & -5 & -12 & -17 \end{bmatrix}$$

Notice that rows 1 and 2 are left unchanged, *even though the elements of row 1 were used to transform row 3.*

The Gauss-Jordan Method

The **Gauss-Jordan method** is an extension of the echelon method of solving systems.* Before the Gauss-Jordan method can be used, the system must be in proper form: the terms with variables should be on the left and the constants on the right in each equation, with the variables in the same order in each equation.

The system is then written as an augmented matrix. Using row operations, the goal is to transform the matrix so that it has zeros above and below a diagonal of 1's on the left of the vertical bar. Once this is accomplished, the final solution can be read directly from the last matrix. The following example illustrates the use of the Gauss-Jordan method to solve a system of equations.

EXAMPLE 1 Gauss-Jordan Method
Solve the system

$$3x - 4y = 1 \tag{1}$$
$$5x + 2y = 19. \tag{2}$$

▶**Solution**

METHOD 1
1's on Diagonal

The system is already in the proper form to use the Gauss-Jordan method. To begin, we change the 3 in the first row to 1 using the second row operation. (Notice that the same notation is used to indicate each transformation, as in the previous section.)

$$\begin{bmatrix} 3 & -4 & | & 1 \\ 5 & 2 & | & 19 \end{bmatrix} \qquad \text{Augmented matrix}$$

$$\frac{1}{3}R_1 \to R_1 \quad \begin{bmatrix} 1 & -\frac{4}{3} & | & \frac{1}{3} \\ 5 & 2 & | & 19 \end{bmatrix}$$

Using the third row operation, we change the 5 in row 2 to 0.

$$-5R_1 + R_2 \to R_2 \quad \begin{bmatrix} 1 & -\frac{4}{3} & | & \frac{1}{3} \\ 0 & \frac{26}{3} & | & \frac{52}{3} \end{bmatrix}$$

*The great German mathematician Carl Friedrich Gauss (1777–1855), sometimes referred to as the "Prince of Mathematicians," originally developed his elimination method for use in finding least squares coefficients. (See Section 1.3.) The German geodesist Wilhelm Jordan (1842–1899) improved his method and used it in surveying problems. Gauss's method had been known to the Chinese at least 1800 years earlier and was described in the *Jiuahang Suanshu (Nine Chapters on the Mathematical Art)*.

We now change 26/3 in row 2 to 1 to complete the diagonal of 1's.

$$\frac{3}{26}R_2 \rightarrow R_2 \qquad \begin{bmatrix} 1 & -\frac{4}{3} & \Big| & \frac{1}{3} \\ 0 & 1 & \Big| & 2 \end{bmatrix}$$

The final transformation is to change the $-4/3$ in row 1 to 0.

$$\frac{4}{3}R_2 + R_1 \rightarrow R_1 \qquad \begin{bmatrix} 1 & 0 & \Big| & 3 \\ 0 & 1 & \Big| & 2 \end{bmatrix}$$

The last matrix corresponds to the system

$$x = 3$$
$$y = 2,$$

so we can read the solution directly from the last column of the final matrix. Check that (3, 2) is the solution by substitution in the equations of the original matrix.

METHOD 2
Fraction-Free

An alternate form of Gauss-Jordan is to first transform the matrix so that it contains zeros above and below the main diagonal. Then, use the second transformation to get the required 1's. When doing calculations by hand, this second method simplifies the calculations by avoiding fractions and decimals. We will use this method when doing calculations by hand throughout the remainder of this chapter.

To begin, we change the 5 in row 2 to 0.

$$\begin{bmatrix} 3 & -4 & \Big| & 1 \\ 5 & 2 & \Big| & 19 \end{bmatrix} \qquad \text{Augmented matrix}$$

$$5R_1 + (-3)R_2 \rightarrow R_2 \qquad \begin{bmatrix} 3 & -4 & \Big| & 1 \\ 0 & -26 & \Big| & -52 \end{bmatrix}$$

We change the -4 in row 1 to 0.

$$-4R_2 + 26R_1 \rightarrow R_1 \qquad \begin{bmatrix} 78 & 0 & \Big| & 234 \\ 0 & -26 & \Big| & -52 \end{bmatrix}$$

Then we change the first nonzero number in each row to 1.

$$\begin{matrix} \frac{1}{78}R_1 \rightarrow R_1 \\ -\frac{1}{26}R_2 \rightarrow R_2 \end{matrix} \qquad \begin{bmatrix} 1 & 0 & \Big| & 3 \\ 0 & 1 & \Big| & 2 \end{bmatrix}$$

The solution is read directly from this last matrix: $x = 3$ and $y = 2$, or (3, 2).

NOTE If your solution does not check, the most efficient way to find the error is to substitute back through the equations that correspond to each matrix, starting with the last matrix. When you find a system that is not satisfied by your (incorrect) answers, you have probably reached the matrix just before the error occurred. Look for the error in the transformation to the next matrix. ∎

When the Gauss-Jordan method is used to solve a system, the final matrix always will have zeros above and below the diagonal of 1's on the left of the vertical bar. To transform the matrix, it is best to work column by column from left to right. Such an orderly method avoids confusion and going around in circles. For each column, first perform the steps that give the zeros. When all columns have zeros in place, multiply each row by the reciprocal of the coefficient of the remaining nonzero number in that row to get the required 1's. With dependent equations or inconsistent systems, it will not be possible to get the complete diagonal of 1's.

EXAMPLE 2 **Gauss-Jordan Method**

Use the Gauss-Jordan method to solve the system

$$x + 5z = -6 + y$$
$$3x + 3y = 10 + z$$
$$x + 3y + 2z = 5.$$

▶**Solution**

METHOD 1
Calculating by Hand

First, rewrite the system in proper form, as follows.

$$x - y + 5z = -6$$
$$3x + 3y - z = 10$$
$$x + 3y + 2z = 5$$

Begin to find the solution by writing the augmented matrix of the linear system.

$$\begin{bmatrix} 1 & -1 & 5 & | & -6 \\ 3 & 3 & -1 & | & 10 \\ 1 & 3 & 2 & | & 5 \end{bmatrix}$$

Row transformations will be used to rewrite this matrix in the form

$$\begin{bmatrix} 1 & 0 & 0 & | & m \\ 0 & 1 & 0 & | & n \\ 0 & 0 & 1 & | & p \end{bmatrix},$$

where m, n, and p are real numbers (if this form is possible). From this final form of the matrix, the solution can be read: $x = m$, $y = n$, $z = p$, or (m, n, p).

In the first column, we need zeros in the second and third rows. Multiply the first row by -3 and add to the second row to get a zero there. Then multiply the first row by -1 and add to the third row to get that zero.

$$\begin{matrix} \\ -3R_1 + R_2 \rightarrow R_2 \\ -1R_1 + R_3 \rightarrow R_3 \end{matrix} \begin{bmatrix} 1 & -1 & 5 & | & -6 \\ 0 & 6 & -16 & | & 28 \\ 0 & 4 & -3 & | & 11 \end{bmatrix}$$

Now get zeros in the second column in a similar way. We want zeros in the first and third rows. Row 2 will not change.

$$R_2 + 6R_1 \rightarrow R_1 \qquad \begin{bmatrix} 6 & 0 & 14 & -8 \\ 0 & 6 & -16 & 28 \\ 0 & 0 & -23 & 23 \end{bmatrix}$$
$$2R_2 + (-3)R_3 \rightarrow R_3$$

In transforming the third row, you may have used the operation $4R_2 + (-6)R_3 \rightarrow R_3$ instead of $2R_2 + (-3)R_3 \rightarrow R_3$. This is perfectly fine; the last row would then have -46 and 46 in place of -23 and 23. To avoid errors, it helps to keep the numbers as small as possible. We observe at this point that all of the numbers can be reduced in size by multiplying each row by an appropriate constant. This next step is not essential, but it simplifies the arithmetic.

$$\tfrac{1}{2}R_1 \rightarrow R_1 \qquad \begin{bmatrix} 3 & 0 & 7 & -4 \\ 0 & 3 & -8 & 14 \\ 0 & 0 & 1 & -1 \end{bmatrix}$$
$$\tfrac{1}{2}R_2 \rightarrow R_2$$
$$-\tfrac{1}{23}R_3 \rightarrow R_3$$

Next, we want zeros in the first and second rows of the third column. Row 3 will not change.

$$-7R_3 + R_1 \rightarrow R_1 \qquad \begin{bmatrix} 3 & 0 & 0 & 3 \\ 0 & 3 & 0 & 6 \\ 0 & 0 & 1 & -1 \end{bmatrix}$$
$$8R_3 + R_2 \rightarrow R_2$$

Finally, get 1's in each row by multiplying the row by the reciprocal of (or dividing the row by) the number in the diagonal position.

$$\tfrac{1}{3}R_1 \rightarrow R_1 \qquad \begin{bmatrix} 1 & 0 & 0 & 1 \\ 0 & 1 & 0 & 2 \\ 0 & 0 & 1 & -1 \end{bmatrix}$$
$$\tfrac{1}{3}R_2 \rightarrow R_2$$

The linear system associated with the final augmented matrix is

$$x = 1$$
$$y = 2$$
$$z = -1,$$

and the solution is $(1, 2, -1)$. Verify that this is the solution to the original system of equations.

CAUTION   Notice that we have performed two or three operations on the same matrix in one step. This is permissible as long as we do not use a row that we are changing as part of another row operation. For example, when we changed row 2 in the first step, we could not use row 2 to transform row 3 in the same step. To avoid difficulty, use *only* row 1 to get zeros in column 1, row 2 to get zeros in column 2, and so on. ∎

METHOD 2
Graphing Calculators

The row operations of the Gauss-Jordan method can also be done on a graphing calculator. For example, Figure 5 shows the result when the augmented matrix is entered into a TI-83/84 Plus. Figures 6 and 7 show how row operations can be used to get zeros in rows 2 and 3 of the first column.

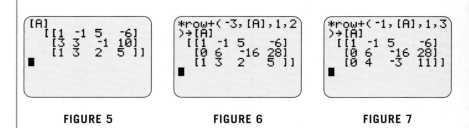

| FIGURE 5 | FIGURE 6 | FIGURE 7 |

Calculators typically do not allow any multiple of a row to be added to any multiple of another row, such as in the operation $2R_2 + 6R_1 \rightarrow R_1$. They normally allow a multiple of a row to be added only to another unmodified row. To get around this restriction, we can convert the diagonal element to a 1 before changing the other elements in the column to 0, as we did in the first method of Example 1. In this example, we change the 6 in row 2, column 2, to a 1 by dividing by 6. The result is shown in Figure 8. (The right side of the matrix is not visible, but can be seen by pressing the right arrow key.) Notice that this operation introduces decimals. Converting to fractions is preferable on calculators that have that option; 1/3 is certainly more concise than 0.3333333333. Figure 9 shows such a conversion on the TI-83/84 Plus.

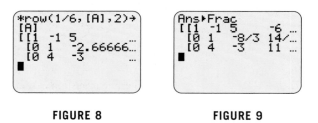

| FIGURE 8 | FIGURE 9 |

When performing row operations without a graphing calculator, it is best to avoid fractions and decimals, because these make the operations more difficult and more prone to error. A calculator, on the other hand, encounters no such difficulties.

Continuing in the same manner, the solution $(1, 2, -1)$ is found as shown in Figure 10.

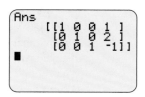

FIGURE 10

Some calculators can do the entire Gauss-Jordan process with a single command; on the TI-83/84 Plus, for example, this is done with the `rref` command. This is very useful in practice, although it does not show any of the intermediate steps.

METHOD 3
Spreadsheets

The Gauss-Jordan method can be done using a spreadsheet either by using a macro or by developing the pivot steps using formulas with the copy and paste commands. However, spreadsheets also have built-in methods to solve systems of equations. Although these solvers do not usually employ the Gauss-Jordan method for solving systems of equations, they are, nonetheless, efficient and practical to use.

The Solver included with Excel can solve systems of equations that are both linear and nonlinear. The Solver is located in the Tools menu and requires that cells be identified ahead of time for each variable in the problem. It also requires that the left-hand side of each equation be placed in the spreadsheet as a formula. For example, to solve the above problem, we could identify cells A1, B1, and C1 for the variables x, y, and z, respectively. The Solver requires that we place a guess for the answer in these cells. It is convenient to place a zero in each of these cells. The left-hand side of each equation must be placed in a cell. We could choose A3, A4, and A5 to hold each of these formulas. Thus, in cell A3, we would type "=A1 - B1 + 5*C1" and put the other two equations in cells A4 and A5.

We now click on the Tools menu and choose Solver. Since this solver attempts to find a solution that is best in some way, we are required to identify a cell with a formula in it that we want to optimize. In this case, it is convenient to use the cell with the left-hand side of the first constraint in it, A3. Figure 11 illustrates the Solver box and the items placed in it.

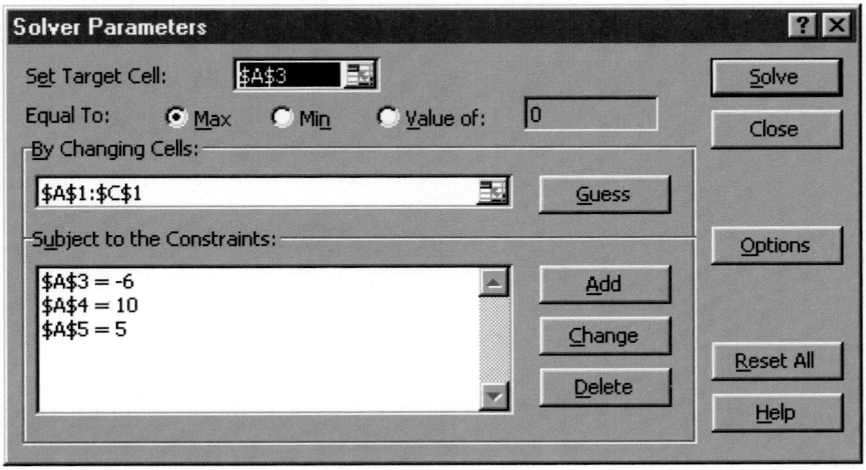

FIGURE 11

To obtain a solution, click on Solve. The solution is located in cells A1, B1, and C1, and these correspond to x, y, and z, respectively.

In summary, the Gauss-Jordan method of solving a linear system requires the following steps.

GAUSS-JORDAN METHOD OF SOLVING A LINEAR SYSTEM

1. Write each equation so that variable terms are in the same order on the left side of the equals sign and constants are on the right.

2. Write the augmented matrix that corresponds to the system.

3. Use row operations to transform the first column so that all elements except the element in the first row are zero.

4. Use row operations to transform the second column so that all elements except the element in the second row are zero.

5. Use row operations to transform the third column so that all elements except the element in the third row are zero.

6. Continue in this way, when possible, until the last row is written in the form

$$[0 \quad 0 \quad 0 \quad \cdots \quad 0 \quad j \mid k],$$

where j and k are constants with $j \neq 0$. When this is not possible, continue until every row has more zeros on the left than the previous row (except possibly for any rows of all zero at the bottom of the matrix), and the first nonzero entry in each row is the only nonzero entry in its column.

7. Multiply each row by the reciprocal of the nonzero element in that row.

Systems without a Unique Solution   In the previous examples, we were able to get the last row in the form $[0 \quad 0 \quad 0 \quad \cdots \quad 0 \quad j \mid k]$, where j and k are constants with $j \neq 0$. We will now look at examples where this is not the case.

EXAMPLE 3   **Solving a System of Equations with No Solution**
Use the Gauss-Jordan method to solve the system

$$x - 2y = 2$$
$$3x - 6y = 5.$$

▶**Solution** Begin by writing the augmented matrix.

$$\begin{bmatrix} 1 & -2 & \mid & 2 \\ 3 & -6 & \mid & 5 \end{bmatrix}$$

To get a zero for the second element in column 1, multiply the numbers in row 1 by -3 and add the results to the corresponding elements in row 2.

$$-3R_1 + R_2 \rightarrow R_2 \quad \begin{bmatrix} 1 & -2 & \mid & 2 \\ 0 & 0 & \mid & -1 \end{bmatrix}$$

This matrix corresponds to the system

$$x - 2y = 2$$
$$0x + 0y = -1.$$

Since the second equation is $0 = -1$, the system is inconsistent and therefore has no solution. The row $[0 \quad 0 \mid k]$ for any nonzero k is a signal that the given system is inconsistent.

EXAMPLE 4

Solving a System of Equations with an Infinite Number of Solutions
Use the Gauss-Jordan method to solve the system

$$x + 2y - z = 0$$
$$3x - y + z = 6$$
$$-2x - 4y + 2z = 0.$$

▶**Solution** The augmented matrix is

$$\begin{bmatrix} 1 & 2 & -1 & \mid & 0 \\ 3 & -1 & 1 & \mid & 6 \\ -2 & -4 & 2 & \mid & 0 \end{bmatrix}.$$

We first get zeros in the second and third rows of column 1.

$$\begin{array}{c} -3R_1 + R_2 \to R_2 \\ 2R_1 + R_3 \to R_3 \end{array} \quad \begin{bmatrix} 1 & 2 & -1 & \mid & 0 \\ 0 & -7 & 4 & \mid & 6 \\ 0 & 0 & 0 & \mid & 0 \end{bmatrix}$$

To continue, we get a zero in the first row of column 2 using the second row, as usual.

$$2R_2 + 7R_1 \to R_1 \quad \begin{bmatrix} 7 & 0 & 1 & \mid & 12 \\ 0 & -7 & 4 & \mid & 6 \\ 0 & 0 & 0 & \mid & 0 \end{bmatrix}$$

We cannot get a zero for the first-row, third-column element without changing the form of the first two columns. We must multiply each of the first two rows by the reciprocal of the first nonzero number.

$$\begin{array}{c} \frac{1}{7}R_1 \to R_1 \\ -\frac{1}{7}R_2 \to R_2 \end{array} \quad \begin{bmatrix} 1 & 0 & \frac{1}{7} & \mid & \frac{12}{7} \\ 0 & 1 & -\frac{4}{7} & \mid & -\frac{6}{7} \\ 0 & 0 & 0 & \mid & 0 \end{bmatrix}$$

To complete the solution, write the equations that correspond to the first two rows of the matrix.

$$x + \frac{1}{7}z = \frac{12}{7}$$
$$y - \frac{4}{7}z = -\frac{6}{7}$$

Because both equations involve z, let z be the parameter. There are an infinite number of solutions, corresponding to the infinite number of values of z. Solve the first equation for x and the second for y to get

$$x = \frac{12 - z}{7} \quad \text{and} \quad y = \frac{4z - 6}{7}.$$

As shown in the previous section, the general solution is written

$$\left(\frac{12-z}{7}, \frac{4z-6}{7}, z\right),$$

where z is any real number. For example, $z = 2$ and $z = 12$ lead to the solutions $(10/7, 2/7, 2)$ and $(0, 6, 12)$.

EXAMPLE 5   **Solving a System of Equations with an Infinite Number of Solutions**
Consider the following system of equations.

$$x + 2y + 3z - w = 4$$
$$2x + 3y + w = -3$$
$$3x + 5y + 3z = 1$$

(a) Set this up as an augmented matrix, and verify that the result after the Gauss-Jordan method is

$$\begin{bmatrix} 1 & 0 & -9 & 5 & | & -18 \\ 0 & 1 & 6 & -3 & | & 11 \\ 0 & 0 & 0 & 0 & | & 0 \end{bmatrix}$$

(b) Find the solution to this system of equations.

▶**Solution**   To complete the solution, write the equations that correspond to the first two rows of the matrix.

$$x \quad - 9z + 5w = -18$$
$$y + 6z - 3w = 11$$

Because both equations involve both z and w, let z and w be parameters. There are an infinite number of solutions, corresponding to the infinite number of values of z and w. Solve the first equation for x and the second for y to get

$$x = -18 + 9z - 5w \qquad \text{and} \qquad y = 11 - 6z + 3w.$$

In an analogous manner to problems with a single parameter, the general solution is written

$$(-18 + 9z - 5w, 11 - 6z + 3w, z, w),$$

where z and w are any real numbers. For example, $z = 1$ and $w = -2$ leads to the solution $(1, -1, 1, -2)$.

Although the examples have used only systems with two equations in two unknowns, three equations in three unknowns, or three equations in four unknowns, the Gauss-Jordan method can be used for any system with n equations and m unknowns. The method becomes tedious with more than three equations in three unknowns; on the other hand, it is very suitable for use with graphing calculators and computers, which can solve fairly large systems quickly. Sophisticated computer programs modify the method to reduce round-off error. Other methods used for special types of large matrices are studied in a course on numerical analysis.

EXAMPLE 6   Soda Sales
A convenience store sells 23 sodas one summer afternoon in 12-, 16-, and 20-oz cups (small, medium, and large). The total volume of soda sold was 376 oz.

(a) Suppose that the prices for a small, medium, and large soda are $1, $1.25, and $1.40, respectively, and that the total sales were $28.45. How many of each size did the store sell?

▶**Solution** As in Example 6 of the previous section, we will organize the information in a table.

	Small	Medium	Large	Total
Number	x	y	z	23
Volume	12	16	20	376
Price	1.00	1.25	1.40	28.45

The three rows of the table lead to three equations: one for the total number of sodas, one for the volume, and one for the price.

$$\begin{aligned} x + y + z &= 23 \\ 12x + 16y + 20z &= 376 \\ 1.00x + 1.25y + 1.40z &= 28.45 \end{aligned}$$

Set this up as an augmented matrix, and verify that the result after the Gauss-Jordan method is

$$\begin{bmatrix} 1 & 0 & 0 & 6 \\ 0 & 1 & 0 & 9 \\ 0 & 0 & 1 & 8 \end{bmatrix}.$$

The store sold 6 small, 9 medium, and 8 large sodas.

(b) Suppose the prices for small, medium, and large sodas are changed to $1, $2, and $3, respectively, but all other information is kept the same. How many of each size did the store sell?

▶**Solution** Change the third equation to

$$x + 2y + 3z = 28.45$$

and go through the Gauss-Jordan method again. The result is

$$\begin{bmatrix} 1 & 0 & -1 & 2 \\ 0 & 1 & 2 & 25 \\ 0 & 0 & 0 & -19.55 \end{bmatrix}.$$

(If you do the row operations in a different order in this example, you will have different numbers in the last column.) The last row of this matrix says that $0 = -19.55$, so the system is inconsistent and has no solution. (In retrospect, this is clear, because each soda sells for a whole number of dollars, and the total amount of money is not a whole number of dollars. In general, however, it is not easy to tell whether a system of equations has a solution or not by just looking at it.)

(c) Suppose the prices are the same as in part (b), but the total revenue is $48. Now how many of each size did the store sell?

▶**Solution** The third equation becomes

$$x + 2y + 3z = 48,$$

and the Gauss-Jordan method leads to

$$\begin{bmatrix} 1 & 0 & -1 & | & -2 \\ 0 & 1 & 2 & | & 25 \\ 0 & 0 & 0 & | & 0 \end{bmatrix}.$$

The system is dependent, similar to Example 4. Let z be the parameter, and solve the first two equations for x and y, yielding

$$x = z - 2 \quad \text{and} \quad y = 25 - 2z.$$

Remember that in this problem, x, y, and z must be nonnegative integers. From the equation for x, we must have

$$z \geq 2,$$

and from the equation for y, we must have

$$25 - 2z \geq 0,$$

from which we find

$$z \leq 12.5.$$

We therefore have 11 solutions corresponding to $z = 2, 3, \ldots, 12$.

(d) Give the solutions from part (c) that have the smallest and largest numbers of large sodas.

▶**Solution** For the smallest number of large sodas, let $z = 2$, giving $x = 2 - 2 = 0$ and $y = 25 - 2(2) = 21$. There are 0 small, 21 medium, and 2 large sodas.

For the largest number of large sodas, let $z = 12$, giving $x = 12 - 2 = 10$ and $y = 25 - 2(12) = 1$. There are 10 small, 1 medium, and 12 large sodas.

▶ 2.2 Exercises

Write the augmented matrix for each system. **Do not solve.**

1. $3x + y = 6$
$2x + 5y = 15$

2. $4x - 2y = 8$
$-7y = -12$

3. $2x + y + z = 3$
$3x - 4y + 2z = -7$
$x + y + z = 2$

4. $2x - 5y + 3z = 4$
$-4x + 2y - 7z = -5$
$3x - y = 8$

Write the system of equations associated with each augmented matrix.

5. $\begin{bmatrix} 1 & 0 & | & 2 \\ 0 & 1 & | & 3 \end{bmatrix}$

6. $\begin{bmatrix} 1 & 0 & | & 5 \\ 0 & 1 & | & -3 \end{bmatrix}$

7. $\begin{bmatrix} 1 & 0 & 0 & | & 4 \\ 0 & 1 & 0 & | & -5 \\ 0 & 0 & 1 & | & 1 \end{bmatrix}$

8. $\begin{bmatrix} 1 & 0 & 0 & | & 4 \\ 0 & 1 & 0 & | & 2 \\ 0 & 0 & 1 & | & 3 \end{bmatrix}$

9. _____ on a matrix correspond to transformations of a system of equations.

10. Describe in your own words what $2R_1 + R_3 \rightarrow R_3$ means.

Use the indicated row operations to change each matrix.

11. Replace R_2 by $R_1 + (-3)R_2$.

$$\begin{bmatrix} 3 & 7 & 4 & | & 10 \\ 1 & 2 & 3 & | & 6 \\ 0 & 4 & 5 & | & 11 \end{bmatrix}$$

12. Replace R_3 by $(-1)R_1 + 3R_3$.

$$\begin{bmatrix} 3 & 2 & 6 & | & 18 \\ 2 & -2 & 5 & | & 7 \\ 1 & 0 & 5 & | & 20 \end{bmatrix}$$

13. Replace R_1 by $(-2)R_2 + R_1$.

$$\begin{bmatrix} 1 & 6 & 4 & | & 7 \\ 0 & 3 & 2 & | & 5 \\ 0 & 5 & 3 & | & 7 \end{bmatrix}$$

14. Replace R_1 by $R_3 + (-3)R_1$.

$$\begin{bmatrix} 1 & 0 & 4 & | & 21 \\ 0 & 6 & 5 & | & 30 \\ 0 & 0 & 12 & | & 15 \end{bmatrix}$$

15. Replace R_1 by $\frac{1}{3}R_1$.

$$\begin{bmatrix} 3 & 0 & 0 & | & 18 \\ 0 & 5 & 0 & | & 9 \\ 0 & 0 & 4 & | & 8 \end{bmatrix}$$

16. Replace R_3 by $\frac{1}{6}R_3$.

$$\begin{bmatrix} 1 & 0 & 0 & | & 30 \\ 0 & 1 & 0 & | & 17 \\ 0 & 0 & 6 & | & 162 \end{bmatrix}$$

Use the Gauss-Jordan method to solve each system of equations.

17. $x + y = 5$
$3x + 2y = 12$

18. $x + 2y = 5$
$2x + y = -2$

19. $x + y = 7$
$4x + 3y = 22$

20. $4x - 2y = 3$
$-2x + 3y = 1$

21. $2x - 3y = 2$
$4x - 6y = 1$

22. $2x + 3y = 9$
$4x + 6y = 7$

23. $6x - 3y = 1$
$-12x + 6y = -2$

24. $x - y = 1$
$-x + y = -1$

25. $y = x - 3$
$y = 1 + z$
$z = 4 - x$

26. $x = 1 - y$
$2x = z$
$2z = -2 - y$

27. $2x - 2y = -5$
$2y + z = 0$
$2x + z = -7$

28. $x - z = -3$
$y + z = 9$
$-2x + 3y + 5z = 33$

29. $4x + 4y - 4z = 24$
$2x - y + z = -9$
$x - 2y + 3z = 1$

30. $x + 2y - 7z = -2$
$-2x - 5y + 2z = 1$
$3x + 5y + 4z = -9$

31. $3x + 5y - z = 0$
$4x - y + 2z = 1$
$7x + 4y + z = 1$

32. $3x - 6y + 3z = 11$
$2x + y - z = 2$
$5x - 5y + 2z = 6$

33. $5x - 4y + 2z = 6$
$5x + 3y - z = 11$
$15x - 5y + 3z = 23$

34. $3x + 2y - z = -16$
$6x - 4y + 3z = 12$
$5x - 2y + 2z = 4$

35. $2x + 3y + z = 9$
$4x + 6y + 2z = 18$
$-\dfrac{1}{2}x - \dfrac{3}{4}y - \dfrac{1}{4}z = -\dfrac{9}{4}$

36. $3x - 5y - 2z = -9$
$-4x + 3y + z = 11$
$8x - 5y + 4z = 6$

37. $x + 2y - w = 3$
$2x + 4z + 2w = -6$
$x + 2y - z = 6$
$2x - y + z + w = -3$

38. $x + 3y - 2z - w = 9$
$2x + 4y + 2w = 10$
$-3x - 5y + 2z - w = -15$
$x - y - 3z + 2w = 6$

39. $x + y - z + 2w = -20$
$2x - y + z + w = 11$
$3x - 2y + z - 2w = 27$

40. $4x - 3y + z + w = 21$
$-2x - y + 2z + 7w = 2$
$10x - 5z - 20w = 15$

41. $10.47x + 3.52y + 2.58z - 6.42w = 218.65$
$8.62x - 4.93y - 1.75z + 2.83w = 157.03$
$4.92x + 6.83y - 2.97z + 2.65w = 462.3$
$2.86x + 19.10y - 6.24z - 8.73w = 398.4$

42. $28.6x + 94.5y + 16.0z - 2.94w = 198.3$
$16.7x + 44.3y - 27.3z + 8.9w = 254.7$
$12.5x - 38.7y + 92.5z + 22.4w = 562.7$
$40.1x - 28.3y + 17.5z - 10.2w = 375.4$

43. On National Public Radio, the "Weekend Edition" program on Sunday, July 29, 2001, posed the following puzzle: Draw a three-by-three square (three boxes across by three boxes down). Put the fraction 3/8 in the first square in the first row. Put the fraction 1/4 in the last square in the second row. The object is to put a fraction in each of the remaining boxes, so the three numbers in each row, each column, and each of the long diagonals add up to 1. Solve this puzzle by letting seven variables represent the seven unknown fractions, writing eight equations for the eight sums, and solving by the Gauss-Jordan method.

▶ Applications

BUSINESS AND ECONOMICS

44. *Surveys* The president of Sam's Supermarkets plans to hire two public relations firms to survey 500 customers by phone, 750 by mail, and 250 by in-person interviews. The Garcia firm has personnel to do 10 phone surveys, 30 mail surveys, and 5 interviews per hour. The Wong firm can handle 20 phone surveys, 10 mail surveys, and 10 interviews per hour. For how many hours should each firm be hired to produce the exact number of surveys needed?

45. *Transportation* A knitting shop orders yarn from three suppliers in Toronto, Montreal, and Ottawa. One month the shop ordered a total of 100 units of yarn from these suppliers. The delivery costs were $80, $50, and $65 per unit for the orders from Toronto, Montreal, and Ottawa, respectively, with total delivery costs of $5990. The shop ordered the same amount from Toronto and Ottawa. How many units were ordered from each supplier?

46. *Manufacturing* Fred's Furniture Factory has 1950 machine hours available each week in the cutting department, 1490 hours in the assembly department, and 2160 in the finishing department. Manufacturing a chair requires 0.2 hours of cutting, 0.3 hours of assembly, and 0.1 hours of finishing. A cabinet requires 0.5 hours of cutting, 0.4 hours of assembly, and 0.6 hours of finishing. A buffet requires 0.3 hours of cutting, 0.1 hours of assembly, and 0.4 hours of finishing. How many chairs, cabinets, and buffets should be produced in order to use all the available production capacity?

47. *Manufacturing* Nadir Inc. produces three models of television sets: deluxe, super-deluxe, and ultra. Each deluxe set requires 2 hours of electronics work, 2 hours of assembly time, and 1 hour of finishing time. Each super-deluxe requires 1, 3, and 1 hour of electronics, assembly, and finishing time, respectively. Each ultra requires 3, 2, and 2 hours of the same work, respectively.

a. There are 100 hours available for electronics, 100 hours available for assembly, and 65 hours available for finish-

ing per week. How many of each model should be produced each week if all available time is to be used?

b. Suppose everything is the same as in part a, but an ultra set requires 6, rather than 3, hours of electronics work. How many solutions are there now?

c. Suppose everything is the same as in part b, but the total hours available for electronics changes from 100 hours to 160 hours. Now how many solutions are there?

48. *Transportation* An electronics company produces three models of stereo speakers, models A, B, and C, and can deliver them by truck, van, or station wagon. A truck holds 2 boxes of model A, 2 of model B, and 3 of model C. A van holds 3 boxes of model A, 4 boxes of model B, and 2 boxes of model C. A station wagon holds 3 boxes of model A, 5 boxes of model B, and 1 box of model C.

a. If 25 boxes of model A, 33 boxes of model B, and 22 boxes of model C are to be delivered, how many vehicles of each type should be used so that all operate at full capacity?

b. Model C has been discontinued. If 25 boxes of model A and 33 boxes of model B are to be delivered, how many vehicles of each type should be used so that all operate at full capacity?

49. *Truck Rental* The U-Drive Rent-A-Truck company plans to spend $7 million on 200 new vehicles. Each commercial van will cost $35,000, each small truck $30,000, and each large truck $50,000. Past experience shows that they need twice as many vans as small trucks. How many of each type of vehicle can they buy?

50. *Loans* To get the necessary funds for a planned expansion, a small company took out three loans totaling $25,000. Company owners were able to get interest rates of 8%, 9%, and 10%. They borrowed $1000 more at 9% than they borrowed at 10%. The total annual interest on the loans was $2190.

a. How much did they borrow at each rate?

b. Suppose we drop the condition that they borrowed $1000 more at 9% than at 10%. What can you say about the amount borrowed at 10%? What is the solution if the amount borrowed at 10% is $5000?

c. Suppose the bank sets a maximum of $10,000 at the lowest interest rate of 8%. Is a solution possible that still meets all of the original conditions?

d. Explain why $10,000 at 8%, $8000 at 9%, and $7000 at 10% is not a feasible solution for part c.

51. *Transportation* An auto manufacturer sends cars from two plants, I and II, to dealerships A and B located in a midwestern city. Plant I has a total of 28 cars to send, and plant II has 8. Dealer A needs 20 cars, and dealer B needs 16. Transportation costs per car, based on the distance of each dealership from each plant, are $220 from I to A, $300 from I to B, $400 from II to A, and $180 from II to B. The manufacturer wants to limit transportation costs to $10,640. How many cars should be sent from each plant to each of the two dealerships?

52. *Transportation* A manufacturer purchases a part for use at both of its plants—one at Roseville, California, the other at Akron, Ohio. The part is available in limited quantities from two suppliers. Each supplier has 75 units available. The Roseville plant needs 40 units, and the Akron plant requires 75 units. The first supplier charges $70 per unit delivered to Roseville and $90 per unit delivered to Akron. Corresponding costs from the second supplier are $80 and $120. The manufacturer wants to order a total of 75 units from the first, less expensive supplier, with the remaining 40 units to come from the second supplier. If the company spends $10,750 to purchase the required number of units for the two plants, find the number of units that should be sent from each supplier to each plant.

53. *Packaging* A company produces three combinations of mixed vegetables that sell in 1-kg packages. Italian style combines 0.3 kg of zucchini, 0.3 of broccoli, and 0.4 of carrots. French style combines 0.6 kg of broccoli and 0.4 of carrots. Oriental style combines 0.2 kg of zucchini, 0.5 of broccoli, and 0.3 of carrots. The company has a stock of 16,200 kg of zucchini, 41,400 kg of broccoli, and 29,400 kg of carrots. How many packages of each style should it prepare to use up existing supplies?

54. *Tents* L. L. Bean makes three sizes of Ultra Dome tents: two-person, four-person, and six-person models, which cost $129, $179, and $229, respectively. A two-person tent provides 40 ft^2 of floor space, while a four-person and a six-person model provide 64 ft^2 and 88 ft^2 of floor space, respectively.* A recent order by an organization that takes children camping ordered enough tents to hold 200 people and provide 3200 ft^2 of floor space. The total cost was $8950, and we wish to know how many tents of each size were ordered.

a. How many solutions are there to this problem?

b. What is the solution with the most four-person tents?

c. What is the solution with the most two-person tents?

d. Discuss the company's pricing strategy that led to a system of equations that is dependent. Do you think that this is a coincidence or an example of logical thinking?

LIFE SCIENCES

55. *Animal Breeding* An animal breeder can buy four types of food for Vietnamese pot-bellied pigs. Each case of Brand A contains 25 units of fiber, 30 units of protein, and 30 units of fat. Each case of Brand B contains 50 units of fiber, 30 units of protein, and 20 units of fat. Each case of Brand C contains 75 units of fiber, 30 units of protein, and 20 units of fat. Each case of Brand D contains 100 units of fiber, 60 units of protein, and 30 units of fat. How many cases of each should the breeder mix together to obtain a food that provides 1200 units of fiber, 600 units of protein, and 400 units of fat?

56. *Dietetics* A hospital dietician is planning a special diet for a certain patient. The total amount per meal of food groups A, B, and C must equal 400 grams. The diet should include one-third as much of group A as of group B, and the sum of the amounts of group A and group C should equal twice the amount of group B.

a. How many grams of each food group should be included?

b. Suppose we drop the requirement that the diet include one-third as much of group A as of group B. Describe the set of all possible solutions.

c. Suppose that, in addition to the conditions given in the original problem, foods A and B cost 2 cents per gram and food C costs 3 cents per gram, and that a meal must cost $8. Is a solution possible?

57. *Bacterial Food Requirements* Three species of bacteria are fed three foods, I, II, and III. A bacterium of the first species consumes 1.3 units each of foods I and II and 2.3 units of food III each day. A bacterium of the second species consumes 1.1 units of food I, 2.4 units of food II, and 3.7 units of food III each day. A bacterium of the third species consumes 8.1 units of I, 2.9 units of II, and 5.1 units of III each day. If 16,000 units of I, 28,000 units of II, and 44,000 units of III are supplied each day, how many of each species can be maintained in this environment?

58. *Fish Food Requirements* A lake is stocked each spring with three species of fish, A, B, and C. Three foods, I, II, and III, are available in the lake. Each fish of species A requires an average of 1.32 units of food I, 2.9 units of food II, and 1.75 units of food III each day. Species B fish each require 2.1 units of food I, 0.95 unit of food II, and 0.6 unit of food III daily. Species C fish require 0.86, 1.52, and 2.01 units of I, II, and III per day, respectively. If 490 units of food I, 897 units of food II, and 653 units of food III are available daily, how many of each species should be stocked?

*L. L. Bean, http://www.llbean.com.

59. *Agriculture* According to data from a Texas agricultural report, the amount of nitrogen (in lb/acre), phosphate (in lb/acre), and labor (in hr/acre) needed to grow honeydews, yellow onions, and lettuce is given by the following table.*

	Honeydews	Yellow Onions	Lettuce
Nitrogen	120	150	180
Phosphate	180	80	80
Labor	4.97	4.45	4.65

a. If the farmer has 220 acres, 29,100 lb of nitrogen, 32,600 lb of phosphate, and 480 hours of labor, is it possible to use all resources completely? If so, how many acres should he allot for each crop?

b. Suppose everything is the same as in part a, except that 1061 hours of labor are available. Is it possible to use all resources completely? If so, how many acres should he allot for each crop?

60. *Archimedes' Problem Bovinum* Archimedes is credited with the authorship of a famous problem involving the number of cattle of the sun god. A simplified version of the problem is stated as follows:[†]

> The sun god had a herd of cattle consisting of bulls and cows, one part of which was white, a second black, a third spotted, and a fourth brown.
> Among the bulls, the number of white ones was one half plus one third the number of the black greater than the brown; the number of the black, one quarter plus one fifth the number of the spotted greater than the brown; the number of the spotted, one sixth and one seventh the number of the white greater than the brown.
> Among the cows, the number of white ones was one third plus one quarter of the total black cattle; the number of the black, one quarter plus one fifth the total of the spotted cattle; the number of the spotted, one fifth plus one sixth the total of the brown cattle; the number of the brown, one sixth plus one seventh the total of the white cattle.
> What was the composition of the herd?

The problem can be solved by converting the statements into two systems of equations, using X, Y, Z, and T for the number of white, black, spotted, and brown bulls, respectively, and x, y, z, and t for the number of white, black, spotted, and brown cows, respectively. For example, the first statement can be written as $X = (1/2 + 1/3)Y + T$

and then reduced. The result is the following two systems of equations:

$$6X - 5Y = 6T$$
$$20Y - 9Z = 20T$$
$$42Z - 13X = 42T$$

and

$$12x - 7y = 7Y$$
$$20y - 9z = 9Z$$
$$30z - 11t = 11T$$
$$-13x + 42t = 13X$$

a. Show that these two systems of equations represent Archimedes' Problem Bovinum.

b. If it is known that the number of brown bulls, T, is 4,149,387, use the Gauss-Jordan method to first find a solution to the 3×3 system and then use these values and the Gauss-Jordan method to find a solution to the 4×4 system of equations.

61. *Health* The U.S. National Center for Health Statistics tracks the major causes of death in the United States. After a steady increase, the death rate by cancer has decreased since the early 1990s. The table lists the age-adjusted death rate per 1,000,000 people for 4 years.[‡]

Year	Rate
1980	207.9
1990	216.0
2000	199.6
2003	190.1

a. If the relationship between the death rate R and the year t is expressed as $R = at^2 + bt + c$, where $t = 0$ corresponds to 1980, use data from 1980, 1990, and 2000 and a linear system of equations to determine the constants a, b, and c.

b. Use the equation from part a to predict the rate in 2003, and compare the result with the actual data.

c. If the relationship between the death rate R and the year t is expressed as $R = at^3 + bt^2 + ct + d$, where $t = 0$ corresponds to 1980, use all four data points and a linear system of equations to determine the constants a, b, c, and d.

d. Discuss the appropriateness of the functions used in parts a and c to model this data.

SOCIAL SCIENCES

62. *Modeling War* One of the factors that contribute to the success or failure of a particular army during war is its abil-

---

*Paredes, Miguel, Mohammad Fatehi, and Richard Hinthorn, "The Transformation of an Inconsistent Linear System into a Consistent System," *The AMATYC Review*, Vol. 13, No. 2, Spring 1992.

†Dorrie, Heinrich, *100 Great Problems of Elementary Mathematics, Their History and Solution*, New York: Dover Publications, 1965, pp. 3–7.

‡http://www.cdc.gov/nchs/data, and *Time Almanac 2006*, p. 135.

ity to get new troops ready for service. It is possible to analyze the rate of change in the number of troops of two hypothetical armies with the following simplified model,

Rate of increase (RED ARMY) $= 200{,}000 - 0.5r - 0.3b$

Rate of increase (BLUE ARMY) $= 350{,}000 - 0.5r - 0.7b$,

where r is the number of soldiers in the Red Army at a given time and b is the number of soldiers in the Blue Army at a given time. The factors 0.5 and 0.7 represent each army's efficiency of bringing new soldiers to the fight.*

a. Solve this system of equations to determine the number of soldiers in each army when the rate of increase for each is zero.

b. Describe what might be going on in a war when the rate of increase is zero.

63. *Traffic Control* At rush hours, substantial traffic congestion is encountered at the traffic intersections shown in the figure. (The streets are one-way, as shown by the arrows.)

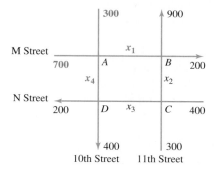

The city wishes to improve the signals at these corners so as to speed the flow of traffic. The traffic engineers first gather data. As the figure shows, 700 cars per hour come down M Street to intersection A, and 300 cars per hour come down 10th Street to intersection A. A total of x_1 of these cars leave A on M Street, and x_4 cars leave A on 10th Street. The number of cars entering A must equal the number leaving, so that

$$x_1 + x_4 = 700 + 300$$

or

$$x_1 + x_4 = 1000.$$

For intersection B, x_1 cars enter on M Street and x_2 on 11th Street. The figure shows that 900 cars leave B on 11th and 200 on M. Thus,

$$x_1 + x_2 = 900 + 200$$
$$x_1 + x_2 = 1100.$$

a. Write two equations representing the traffic entering and leaving intersections C and D.

b. Use the four equations to set up an augmented matrix, and solve the system by the Gauss-Jordan method, using x_4 as the parameter.

c. Based on your solution to part b, what are the largest and smallest possible values for the number of cars leaving intersection A on 10th Street?

d. Answer the question in part c for the other three variables.

e. Verify that you could have discarded any one of the four original equations without changing the solution. What does this tell you about the original problem?

GENERAL INTEREST

64. *Ice Cream* Researchers have determined that the amount of sugar contained in ice cream helps to determine the overall "degree of like" that a consumer has toward that particular flavor. They have also determined that too much or too little sugar will have the same negative affect on the "degree of like" and that this relationship follows a quadratic function. In an experiment conducted at Pennsylvania State University, the following condensed table was obtained.[†]

Percentage of Sugar	Degree of Like
8	5.4
13	6.3
18	5.6

a. Use this information and the Gauss-Jordan method to determine the coefficients a, b, c, of the quadratic equation

$$y = ax^2 + bx + c,$$

---

*Bellany, Ian, "Modeling War," *Journal of Peace Research*, Vol. 36, No. 6, 1999, pp. 729–739.
†Guinard, J., C. Zoumas-Morse, L. Mori, B. Uatoni, D. Panyam, and A. Kilar, "Sugar and Fat Effects on Sensory Properties of Ice Cream," *Journal of Food Science*, Vol. 62, No. 4, Sept./Oct. 1997, pp. 1087–1094.

where y is the "degree of like" and x is the percentage of sugar in the ice cream mix.

b. Repeat part a by using the quadratic regression feature on a graphing calculator. Compare your answers.

65. *Toys* One hundred toys are to be given out to a group of children. A ball costs $2, a doll costs $3, and a car costs $4. A total of $295 was spent on the toys.

   a. A ball weighs 12 oz, a doll 16 oz, and a car 18 oz. The total weight of all the toys is 1542 oz. Find how many of each toy there are.

   b. Now suppose the weight of a ball, doll, and car are 11, 15, and 19 oz, respectively. If the total weight is still 1542 oz, how many solutions are there now?

   c. Keep the weights as in part b, but change the total weight to 1480 oz. How many solutions are there?

   d. Give the solution to part c that has the smallest number of cars.

   e. Give the solution to part c that has the largest number of cars.

66. *Lights Out* The Tiger Electronics' game, Lights Out, consists of five rows of five lighted buttons. When a button is pushed, it changes the on/off status of it and the status of all of its vertical and horizontal neighbors. For any given situation where some of the lights are on and some are off, the goal of the game is to push buttons until all of the lights are turned off. It turns out that for any given array of lights, solving a system of equations can be used to develop a strategy for turning the lights out.* The follow-

ing system of equations can be used to solve the problem for a simplified version of the game with 2 rows of 2 buttons where all of the lights are initially turned on.

$$x_{11} + x_{12} + x_{21} = 1$$
$$x_{11} + x_{12} + x_{22} = 1$$
$$x_{11} + x_{21} + x_{22} = 1$$
$$x_{12} + x_{21} + x_{22} = 1,$$

where $x_{ij} = 1$ if the light in row i, column j, is on and $x_{ij} = 0$ when it is off. The order in which the buttons are pushed does not matter, so we are only seeking which buttons should be pushed.

   a. Solve this system of equations and determine a strategy to turn the lights out. (*Hint:* While doing row operations, if an odd number is found, immediately replace this value with a 1; if an even number is found, then immediately replace that number with a zero. This is called modulo 2 arithmetic, and it is necessary in problems dealing with on/off switches.)

   b. Resolve the equation with the right side changed to (0, 1, 1, 0).

67. *Baseball* Ichiro Suzuki holds the American League record for the most hits in a single baseball season. In 2004, Suzuki had a total of 262 hits for the Seattle Mariners. He hit three fewer triples than home runs, and he hit three times as many doubles as home runs. Suzuki also hit 45 times as many singles as triples.[†] Find the number of singles, doubles, triples, and home runs hit by Suzuki during the season.

2.3 Addition and Subtraction of Matrices

? THINK ABOUT IT **A company sends monthly shipments to its warehouses in several cities. How might the company keep track of the shipments to each warehouse most efficiently?**

In the previous section, matrices were used to store information about systems of linear equations. In this section, we begin a study of matrices and show additional uses of matrix notation that will answer the question posed above. The use of matrices has gained increasing importance in the fields of management, natural science, and social science because matrices provide a convenient way to organize data, as Example 1 demonstrates.

EXAMPLE 1 **Furniture Shipments**
The EZ Life Company manufactures sofas and armchairs in three models, A, B, and C. The company has regional warehouses in New York, Chicago, and San

*Anderson, Marlow and Todd Feil, "Turning Lights Out with Linear Algebra," *Mathematics Magazine*, Vol. 71, No. 4, 1998, pp. 300–303.
[†]http://www.baseball-almanac.com.

Francisco. In its August shipment, the company sends 10 model-A sofas, 12 model-B sofas, 5 model-C sofas, 15 model-A chairs, 20 model-B chairs, and 8 model-C chairs to each warehouse. Use a matrix to organize this information.

▶Solution To organize this data, we might first list it as follows.

| Sofas | 10 model-A | 12 model-B | 5 model-C |
| Chairs | 15 model-A | 20 model-B | 8 model-C |

Alternatively, we might tabulate the data in a chart.

		Model		
		A	**B**	**C**
Furniture Type	*Sofas*	10	12	5
	Chairs	15	20	8

With the understanding that the numbers in each row refer to the furniture type (sofa, chair) and the numbers in each column refer to the model (A, B, C), the same information can be given by a matrix, as follows.

$$M = \begin{bmatrix} 10 & 12 & 5 \\ 15 & 20 & 8 \end{bmatrix}$$

Matrices often are named with capital letters, as in Example 1. Matrices are classified by **size**; that is, by the number of rows and columns they contain. For example, matrix M above has two rows and three columns. This matrix is a 2×3 (read "2 by 3") matrix. By definition, a matrix with m rows and n columns is an $m \times n$ matrix. The number of rows is always given first.

EXAMPLE 2 **Matrix Size**

(a) The matrix $\begin{bmatrix} -3 & 5 \\ 2 & 0 \\ 5 & -1 \end{bmatrix}$ is a 3×2 matrix.

(b) $\begin{bmatrix} 0.5 & 8 & 0.9 \\ 0 & 5.1 & -3 \\ -4 & 0 & 5 \end{bmatrix}$ is a 3×3 matrix.

(c) $\begin{bmatrix} 1 & 6 & 5 & -2 & 5 \end{bmatrix}$ is a 1×5 matrix.

(d) $\begin{bmatrix} 3 \\ -5 \\ 0 \\ 2 \end{bmatrix}$ is a 4×1 matrix.

A matrix with the same number of rows as columns is called a **square matrix**. The matrix in Example 2(b) is a square matrix.

A matrix containing only one row is called a **row matrix** or a **row vector**. The matrix in Example 2(c) is a row matrix, as are

$$[5 \quad 8], \qquad [6 \quad -9 \quad 2], \qquad \text{and} \qquad [-4 \quad 0 \quad 0 \quad 0].$$

A matrix of only one column, as in Example 2(d), is a **column matrix** or a **column vector**.

Equality for matrices is defined as follows.

MATRIX EQUALITY

Two matrices are equal if they are the same size and if each pair of corresponding elements is equal.

By this definition,

$$\begin{bmatrix} 2 & 1 \\ 3 & -5 \end{bmatrix} \qquad \text{and} \qquad \begin{bmatrix} 1 & 2 \\ -5 & 3 \end{bmatrix}$$

are not equal (even though they contain the same elements and are the same size) since the corresponding elements differ.

EXAMPLE 3 **Matrix Equality**

(a) From the definition of matrix equality given above, the only way that the statement

$$\begin{bmatrix} 2 & 1 \\ p & q \end{bmatrix} = \begin{bmatrix} x & y \\ -1 & 0 \end{bmatrix}$$

can be true is if $2 = x$, $1 = y$, $p = -1$, and $q = 0$.

(b) The statement

$$\begin{bmatrix} x \\ y \end{bmatrix} = \begin{bmatrix} 1 \\ -3 \\ 0 \end{bmatrix}$$

can never be true, since the two matrices are different sizes. (One is 2×1 and the other is 3×1.)

Addition The matrix given in Example 1,

$$M = \begin{bmatrix} 10 & 12 & 5 \\ 15 & 20 & 8 \end{bmatrix},$$

shows the August shipment from the EZ Life plant to each of its warehouses. If matrix N below gives the September shipment to the New York warehouse, what is the total shipment of each item of furniture to the New York warehouse for these two months?

$$N = \begin{bmatrix} 45 & 35 & 20 \\ 65 & 40 & 35 \end{bmatrix}$$

If 10 model-A sofas were shipped in August and 45 in September, then altogether $10 + 45 = 55$ model-A sofas were shipped in the two months. The other corresponding entries can be added in a similar way to get a new matrix Q, which represents the total shipment for the two months.

$$Q = \begin{bmatrix} 55 & 47 & 25 \\ 80 & 60 & 43 \end{bmatrix}$$

It is convenient to refer to Q as the sum of M and N.

The way these two matrices were added illustrates the following definition of addition of matrices.

ADDING MATRICES

The sum of two $m \times n$ matrices X and Y is the $m \times n$ matrix $X + Y$ in which each element is the sum of the corresponding elements of X and Y.

CAUTION It is important to remember that only matrices that are the same size can be added. ∎

EXAMPLE 4 **Adding Matrices**
Find each sum, if possible.

▶**Solution**

(a) $\begin{bmatrix} 5 & -6 \\ 8 & 9 \end{bmatrix} + \begin{bmatrix} -4 & 6 \\ 8 & -3 \end{bmatrix} = \begin{bmatrix} 5 + (-4) & -6 + 6 \\ 8 + 8 & 9 + (-3) \end{bmatrix} = \begin{bmatrix} 1 & 0 \\ 16 & 6 \end{bmatrix}$

(b) The matrices

$$A = \begin{bmatrix} 5 & -8 \\ 6 & 2 \end{bmatrix} \quad \text{and} \quad B = \begin{bmatrix} 3 & -9 & 1 \\ 4 & 2 & -5 \end{bmatrix}$$

are different sizes. Therefore, the sum $A + B$ does not exist.

EXAMPLE 5 **Furniture Shipments**
The September shipments from the EZ Life Company to the New York, San Francisco, and Chicago warehouses are given in matrices N, S, and C below.

$$N = \begin{bmatrix} 45 & 35 & 20 \\ 65 & 40 & 35 \end{bmatrix} \quad S = \begin{bmatrix} 30 & 32 & 28 \\ 43 & 47 & 30 \end{bmatrix} \quad C = \begin{bmatrix} 22 & 25 & 38 \\ 31 & 34 & 35 \end{bmatrix}$$

What was the total amount shipped to the three warehouses in September?

▶**Solution** The total of the September shipments is represented by the sum of the three matrices N, S, and C.

$$N + S + C = \begin{bmatrix} 45 & 35 & 20 \\ 65 & 40 & 35 \end{bmatrix} + \begin{bmatrix} 30 & 32 & 28 \\ 43 & 47 & 30 \end{bmatrix} + \begin{bmatrix} 22 & 25 & 38 \\ 31 & 34 & 35 \end{bmatrix}$$

$$= \begin{bmatrix} 97 & 92 & 86 \\ 139 & 121 & 100 \end{bmatrix}$$

For example, this sum shows that the total number of model-C sofas shipped to the three warehouses in September was 86.

The additive inverse of the real number a is $-a$; a similar definition applies to matrices.

ADDITIVE INVERSE

The **additive inverse** (or **negative**) of a matrix X is the matrix $-X$ in which each element is the additive inverse of the corresponding element of X.

If

$$A = \begin{bmatrix} 1 & 2 & 3 \\ 0 & -1 & 5 \end{bmatrix} \quad \text{and} \quad B = \begin{bmatrix} -2 & 3 & 0 \\ 1 & -7 & 2 \end{bmatrix},$$

then by the definition of the additive inverse of a matrix,

$$-A = \begin{bmatrix} -1 & -2 & -3 \\ 0 & 1 & -5 \end{bmatrix} \quad \text{and} \quad -B = \begin{bmatrix} 2 & -3 & 0 \\ -1 & 7 & -2 \end{bmatrix}.$$

By the definition of matrix addition, for each matrix X the sum $X + (-X)$ is a **zero matrix**, O, whose elements are all zeros. For the matrix A above,

$$A + (-A) = \begin{bmatrix} 0 & 0 & 0 \\ 0 & 0 & 0 \end{bmatrix}.$$

There is an $m \times n$ zero matrix for each pair of values of m and n. Such a matrix serves as an $m \times n$ **additive identity**, similar to the additive identity 0 for any real number. Zero matrices have the following identity property.

FOR REVIEW

Compare this with the identity property for real numbers: for any real number a, we have $a + 0 = 0 + a = a$. Exercises 34–37 give other properties of matrices that are parallel to the properties of real numbers.

ZERO MATRIX

If O is an $m \times n$ zero matrix, and A is any $m \times n$ matrix, then

$$A + O = O + A = A.$$

Subtraction   The subtraction of matrices is defined in a manner comparable to subtraction of real numbers.

SUBTRACTING MATRICES

For two $m \times n$ matrices X and Y, the difference $X - Y$ is the $m \times n$ matrix defined by

$$X - Y = X + (-Y).$$

This definition means that matrix subtraction can be performed by subtracting corresponding elements. For example, with A, B, and $-B$ as defined above,

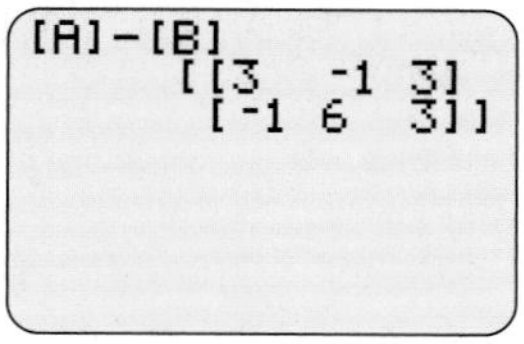

```
[A]-[B]
   [[3  -1  3]
    [-1  6  3]]
```

FIGURE 12

$$A - B = A + (-B) = \begin{bmatrix} 1 & 2 & 3 \\ 0 & -1 & 5 \end{bmatrix} + \begin{bmatrix} 2 & -3 & 0 \\ -1 & 7 & -2 \end{bmatrix}$$

$$= \begin{bmatrix} 3 & -1 & 3 \\ -1 & 6 & 3 \end{bmatrix}.$$

Matrix operations are easily performed on a graphing calculator. Figure 12 shows the previous operation; the matrices A and B were already entered into the calculator.

Spreadsheet programs are designed to effectively organize data that can be represented in rows and columns. Accordingly, matrix operations are also easily performed on spreadsheets. See *The Spreadsheet Manual* available with this book for details.

EXAMPLE 6   **Subtracting Matrices**

(a) $\begin{bmatrix} 8 & 6 & -4 \end{bmatrix} - \begin{bmatrix} 3 & 5 & -8 \end{bmatrix} = \begin{bmatrix} 5 & 1 & 4 \end{bmatrix}$

(b) The matrices

$$\begin{bmatrix} -2 & 5 \\ 0 & 1 \end{bmatrix} \quad \text{and} \quad \begin{bmatrix} 3 \\ 5 \end{bmatrix}$$

are different sizes and cannot be subtracted.

EXAMPLE 7   **Furniture Shipments**

During September the Chicago warehouse of the EZ Life Company shipped out the following numbers of each model.

$$K = \begin{bmatrix} 5 & 10 & 8 \\ 11 & 14 & 15 \end{bmatrix}$$

What was the Chicago warehouse inventory on October 1, taking into account only the number of items received and sent out during the month?

?   ▶**Solution** The number of each kind of item received during September is given by matrix C from Example 5; the number of each model sent out during September is given by matrix K. The October 1 inventory will be represented by the matrix $C - K$:

$$\begin{bmatrix} 22 & 25 & 38 \\ 31 & 34 & 35 \end{bmatrix} - \begin{bmatrix} 5 & 10 & 8 \\ 11 & 14 & 15 \end{bmatrix} = \begin{bmatrix} 17 & 15 & 30 \\ 20 & 20 & 20 \end{bmatrix}.$$

➔ 2.3 Exercises

Decide whether each statement is true or false. If false, tell why.

1. $\begin{bmatrix} 1 & 3 \\ 5 & 7 \end{bmatrix} = \begin{bmatrix} 1 & 5 \\ 3 & 7 \end{bmatrix}$

2. $\begin{bmatrix} 1 \\ 2 \\ 3 \end{bmatrix} = \begin{bmatrix} 1 & 2 & 3 \end{bmatrix}$

3. $\begin{bmatrix} x \\ y \end{bmatrix} = \begin{bmatrix} -2 \\ 8 \end{bmatrix}$ if $x = -2$ and $y = 8$.

4. $\begin{bmatrix} 3 & 5 & 2 & 8 \\ 1 & -1 & 4 & 0 \end{bmatrix}$ is a 4 × 2 matrix.

5. $\begin{bmatrix} 1 & 9 & -4 \\ 3 & 7 & 2 \\ -1 & 1 & 0 \end{bmatrix}$ is a square matrix.

6. $\begin{bmatrix} 2 & 4 & -1 \\ 3 & 7 & 5 \\ 0 & 0 & 0 \end{bmatrix} = \begin{bmatrix} 2 & 4 & -1 \\ 3 & 7 & 5 \end{bmatrix}$

Find the size of each matrix. Identify any square, column, or row matrices. Give the additive inverse of each matrix.

7. $\begin{bmatrix} -4 & 8 \\ 2 & 3 \end{bmatrix}$

8. $\begin{bmatrix} 2 & -3 & 7 \\ 1 & 0 & 4 \end{bmatrix}$

9. $\begin{bmatrix} -6 & 8 & 0 & 0 \\ 4 & 1 & 9 & 2 \\ 3 & -5 & 7 & 1 \end{bmatrix}$

10. $\begin{bmatrix} 8 & -2 & 4 & 6 & 3 \end{bmatrix}$

11. $\begin{bmatrix} -7 \\ 5 \end{bmatrix}$

12. $\begin{bmatrix} -9 \end{bmatrix}$

13. The sum of an $n \times m$ matrix and its additive inverse is _____.

14. If A is a 5 × 2 matrix and $A + K = A$, what do you know about K?

Find the values of the variables in each equation.

15. $\begin{bmatrix} 3 & 4 \\ -8 & 1 \end{bmatrix} = \begin{bmatrix} 3 & x \\ y & z \end{bmatrix}$

16. $\begin{bmatrix} -5 \\ y \end{bmatrix} = \begin{bmatrix} -5 \\ 8 \end{bmatrix}$

17. $\begin{bmatrix} s - 4 & t + 2 \\ -5 & 7 \end{bmatrix} = \begin{bmatrix} 6 & 2 \\ -5 & r \end{bmatrix}$

18. $\begin{bmatrix} 9 & 7 \\ r & 0 \end{bmatrix} = \begin{bmatrix} m - 3 & n + 5 \\ 8 & 0 \end{bmatrix}$

19. $\begin{bmatrix} a + 2 & 3b & 4c \\ d & 7f & 8 \end{bmatrix} + \begin{bmatrix} -7 & 2b & 6 \\ -3d & -6 & -2 \end{bmatrix} = \begin{bmatrix} 15 & 25 & 6 \\ -8 & 1 & 6 \end{bmatrix}$

20. $\begin{bmatrix} a + 2 & 3z + 1 & 5m \\ 4k & 0 & 3 \end{bmatrix} + \begin{bmatrix} 3a & 2z & 5m \\ 2k & 5 & 6 \end{bmatrix} = \begin{bmatrix} 10 & -14 & 80 \\ 10 & 5 & 9 \end{bmatrix}$

Perform the indicated operations, where possible.

21. $\begin{bmatrix} 2 & 4 & -5 & -7 \\ 6 & -3 & 12 & 0 \end{bmatrix} + \begin{bmatrix} 8 & 0 & -10 & 1 \\ -2 & 8 & -9 & 11 \end{bmatrix}$

22. $\begin{bmatrix} 1 & 5 \\ 2 & -3 \\ 3 & 7 \end{bmatrix} + \begin{bmatrix} 2 & 3 \\ 8 & 5 \\ -1 & 9 \end{bmatrix}$

23. $\begin{bmatrix} 1 & 3 & -2 \\ 4 & 7 & 1 \end{bmatrix} + \begin{bmatrix} 3 & 0 \\ 6 & 4 \\ -5 & 2 \end{bmatrix}$

24. $\begin{bmatrix} 8 & 0 & -3 \\ 1 & 19 & -5 \end{bmatrix} - \begin{bmatrix} 1 & -5 & 2 \\ 3 & 9 & -8 \end{bmatrix}$

25. $\begin{bmatrix} 2 & 8 & 12 & 0 \\ 7 & 4 & -1 & 5 \\ 1 & 2 & 0 & 10 \end{bmatrix} - \begin{bmatrix} 1 & 3 & 6 & 9 \\ 2 & -3 & -3 & 4 \\ 8 & 0 & -2 & 17 \end{bmatrix}$

26. $\begin{bmatrix} 2 & 1 \\ 5 & -3 \\ -7 & 2 \\ 9 & 0 \end{bmatrix} + \begin{bmatrix} 1 & -8 & 0 \\ 5 & 3 & 2 \\ -6 & 7 & -5 \\ 2 & -1 & 0 \end{bmatrix}$

27. $\begin{bmatrix} 2 & 3 \\ -2 & 4 \end{bmatrix} + \begin{bmatrix} 4 & 3 \\ 7 & 8 \end{bmatrix} - \begin{bmatrix} 3 & 2 \\ 1 & 4 \end{bmatrix}$

28. $\begin{bmatrix} 4 & 3 \\ 1 & 2 \end{bmatrix} - \begin{bmatrix} 1 & 1 \\ 1 & 0 \end{bmatrix} + \begin{bmatrix} 1 & 1 \\ 1 & 4 \end{bmatrix}$

29. $\begin{bmatrix} 2 & -1 \\ 0 & 13 \end{bmatrix} - \begin{bmatrix} 4 & 8 \\ -5 & 7 \end{bmatrix} + \begin{bmatrix} 12 & 7 \\ 5 & 3 \end{bmatrix}$

30. $\begin{bmatrix} 5 & 8 \\ -3 & 1 \end{bmatrix} + \begin{bmatrix} 0 & 1 \\ -2 & -2 \end{bmatrix} + \begin{bmatrix} -5 & -8 \\ 6 & 1 \end{bmatrix}$

31. $\begin{bmatrix} -4x + 2y & -3x + y \\ 6x - 3y & 2x - 5y \end{bmatrix} + \begin{bmatrix} -8x + 6y & 2x \\ 3y - 5x & 6x + 4y \end{bmatrix}$

32. $\begin{bmatrix} 4k - 8y \\ 6z - 3x \\ 2k + 5a \\ -4m + 2n \end{bmatrix} - \begin{bmatrix} 5k + 6y \\ 2z + 5x \\ 4k + 6a \\ 4m - 2n \end{bmatrix}$

33. For matrix $X = \begin{bmatrix} x & y \\ z & w \end{bmatrix}$, find the matrix $-X$.

Using matrices $O = \begin{bmatrix} 0 & 0 \\ 0 & 0 \end{bmatrix}$, $P = \begin{bmatrix} m & n \\ p & q \end{bmatrix}$, $T = \begin{bmatrix} r & s \\ t & u \end{bmatrix}$, and $X = \begin{bmatrix} x & y \\ z & w \end{bmatrix}$, verify the statements in Exercises 34–37.

34. $X + T = T + X$ (commutative property of addition of matrices)

35. $X + (T + P) = (X + T) + P$ (associative property of addition of matrices)

36. $X + (-X) = O$ (inverse property of addition of matrices)

37. $P + O = P$ (identity property of addition of matrices)

38. Which of the above properties are valid for matrices that are not square?

→ Applications

BUSINESS AND ECONOMICS

39. *Management* A toy company has plants in Boston, Chicago, and Seattle that manufacture toy phones and calculators. The following matrix gives the production costs (in dollars) for each item at the Boston plant:

	Phones	Calculators
Material	4.27	6.94
Labor	3.45	3.65

a. In Chicago, a phone costs $4.05 for material and $3.27 for labor; a calculator costs $7.01 for material and $3.51 for labor. In Seattle, material costs are $4.40 for a phone and $6.90 for a calculator; labor costs are $3.54 for a phone and $3.76 for a calculator. Write the production cost matrices for Chicago and Seattle.

b. Suppose labor costs increase by $0.11 per item in Chicago and material costs there increase by $0.37 for a phone and $0.42 for a calculator. What is the new production cost matrix for Chicago?

40. *Management* There are three convenience stores in Folsom. This week, store I sold 88 loaves of bread, 48 qt of milk, 16 jars of peanut butter, and 112 lb of cold cuts. Store II sold 105 loaves of bread, 72 qt of milk, 21 jars of peanut butter, and 147 lb of cold cuts. Store III sold 60 loaves of bread, 40 qt of milk, no peanut butter, and 50 lb of cold cuts.

a. Use a 4 × 3 matrix to express the sales information for the three stores.

b. During the following week, sales on these products at store I increased by 25%; sales at store II increased by 1/3; and sales at store III increased by 10%. Write the sales matrix for that week.

c. Write a matrix that represents total sales over the two-week period.

LIFE SCIENCES

41. *Dietetics* A dietician prepares a diet specifying the amounts a patient should eat of four basic food groups: group I, meats; group II, fruits and vegetables; group III, breads and starches; group IV, milk products. Amounts are given in "exchanges" that represent 1 oz (meat), 1/2 cup (fruits and vegetables), 1 slice (bread), 8 oz (milk), or other suitable measurements.

a. The number of "exchanges" for breakfast for each of the four food groups, respectively, are 2, 1, 2, and 1; for lunch, 3, 2, 2, and 1; and for dinner, 4, 3, 2, and 1. Write a 3 × 4 matrix using this information.

b. The amounts of fat, carbohydrates, and protein (in appropriate units) in each food group, respectively, are as follows.

  Fat: 5, 0, 0, 10

  Carbohydrates: 0, 10, 15, 12

  Protein: 7, 1, 2, 8

  Use this information to write a 4 × 3 matrix.

c. There are 8 calories per exchange of fat, 4 calories per exchange of carbohydrates, and 5 calories per exchange of protein. Summarize this data in a 3 × 1 matrix.

42. *Animal Growth* At the beginning of a laboratory experiment, five baby rats measured 5.6, 6.4, 6.9, 7.6, and 6.1 cm in length, and weighed 144, 138, 149, 152, and 146 g, respectively.

a. Write a 2 × 5 matrix using this information.

b. At the end of two weeks, their lengths (in centimeters) were 10.2, 11.4, 11.4, 12.7, and 10.8 and their weights (in grams) were 196, 196, 225, 250, and 230. Write a 2 × 5 matrix with this information.

c. Use matrix subtraction and the matrices found in parts a and b to write a matrix that gives the amount of change in length and weight for each rat.

d. During the third week, the rats grew by the amounts shown in the matrix below.

Length	1.8	1.5	2.3	1.8	2.0
Weight	25	22	29	33	20

What were their lengths and weights at the end of this week?

43. *Testing Medication* A drug company is testing 200 patients to see if Painfree (a new headache medicine) is effective. Half the patients receive Painfree and half receive a placebo. The data on the first 50 patients is summarized in this matrix:

Pain Relief Obtained

Yes No

Painfree $\begin{bmatrix} 22 & 3 \\ 8 & 17 \end{bmatrix}$
Placebo

a. Of those who took the placebo, how many got relief?

b. Of those who took the new medication, how many got no relief?

c. The test was repeated on three more groups of 50 patients each, with the results summarized by these matrices.

$$\begin{bmatrix} 21 & 4 \\ 6 & 19 \end{bmatrix} \quad \begin{bmatrix} 19 & 6 \\ 10 & 15 \end{bmatrix} \quad \begin{bmatrix} 23 & 2 \\ 3 & 22 \end{bmatrix}$$

Find the total results for all 200 patients.

d. On the basis of these results, does it appear that Painfree is effective?

44. *Driving Habits* The following tables give the percentages of male and female high school students who rarely or never wore a seatbelt, rode with drivers who had been drinking, and drove after drinking for various years from 1997 to 2003.*

Male	1997	1999	2001	2003
Rarely or never wore seatbelt	23.2	20.8	18.1	21.5
Rode with drinking driver	38.3	34.4	31.8	29.2
Drove after drinking	27.9	25.5	24.6	22.4

Female	1997	1999	2001	2003
Rarely or never wore seatbelt	14.5	11.9	10.2	14.6
Rode with drinking driver	34.5	31.7	29.6	31.1
Drove after drinking	16.2	13.3	14.1	12.3

a. Write a matrix for the driving habits of male drivers.

b. Write a matrix for the driving habits of female drivers.

c. Use the matrices from parts a and b to write a matrix showing the difference between the driving habits of males and females.

d. Analyze the results from part c and discuss any noticeable trends.

45. *Life Expectancy* The following table gives the life expectancy of African American males and females and white American males and females at the beginning of each decade since 1970.[†]

	African American		White American	
Year	Male	Female	Male	Female
1970	60.0	68.3	68.0	75.6
1980	63.8	72.5	70.7	78.1
1990	64.5	73.6	72.7	79.4
2000	68.2	74.9	74.8	80.0

a. Write a matrix for the life expectancy of African Americans.

b. Write a matrix for the life expectancy of white Americans.

c. Use the matrices from parts a and b to write a matrix showing the difference between the two groups.

d. Analyze the results from part c and discuss any noticeable trends.

46. *Educational Attainment* The table on the next page gives the educational attainment of the U.S. population 25 years and older since 1960.[‡]

a. Write a matrix for the educational attainment of males.

b. Write a matrix for the educational attainment of females.

c. Use the matrices from parts a and b to write a matrix showing the difference in educational attainment between males and females since 1960.

---

*National Highway Traffic Safety Administration, Traffic Safety Facts 2003 (Table 63, issued January 2005), http:www-nrd.nhtsa.dot.gov.

[†]*The World Almanac and Book of Facts 2006*, p. 181.

[‡]U.S. Department of Commerce, Census Bureau, Current Population Reports, "Educational Attainment in the United States, 2004." March 25, 2005;
http://www.census.gov/population/www/socdemo/education/cps2004.

	Male		Female	
Year	Percentage with 4 Years of High School or More	Percentage with 4 Years of College or More	Percentage with 4 Years of High School or More	Percentage with 4 Years of College or More
1960	39.5	9.7	42.5	5.8
1970	51.9	13.5	52.8	8.1
1980	67.3	20.1	65.8	12.8
1990	77.7	24.4	77.5	18.4
2000	84.2	27.8	84.0	23.6
2004	84.8	29.4	85.4	26.1

47. *Educational Attainment* The following table gives the educational attainment of African Americans and Hispanic Americans 25 years and older since 1980.*

	African American		Hispanic American	
Year	Percentage with 4 Years of High School or More	Percentage with 4 Years of College or More	Percentage with 4 Years of High School or More	Percentage with 4 Years of College or More
1980	51.4	7.9	44.5	7.6
1985	59.9	11.1	47.9	8.5
1990	66.2	11.3	50.8	9.2
1995	73.8	13.3	53.4	9.3
2000	78.9	16.6	57.0	10.6
2004	80.6	17.6	58.4	12.1

a. Write a matrix for the educational attainment of African Americans.

b. Write a matrix for the educational attainment of Hispanic Americans.

c. Use the matrices from parts a and b to write a matrix showing the difference in educational attainment between African and Hispanic Americans.

GENERAL INTEREST

48. *Animal Interactions* When two kittens named Cauchy and Cliché were introduced into a household with Jamie (an older cat) and Musk (a dog), the interactions among animals were complicated. The two kittens liked each other and Jamie, but didn't like Musk. Musk liked everybody, but Jamie didn't like any of the other animals.

a. Write a 4 × 4 matrix in which rows (and columns) 1, 2, 3, and 4 refer to Musk, Jamie, Cauchy, and Cliché. Make an element a 1 if the animal for that row likes the animal for that column, and otherwise make the element a 0. Assume every animal likes herself.

b. Within a few days, Cauchy and Cliché decided that they liked Musk after all. Write a 4 × 4 matrix, as you did in part a, representing the new situation.

*U.S. Department of Commerce, Bureau of the Census, U.S. Census of Population, 1960, Vol. 1, part 1; *Current Population Reports*, Series P-20 and unpublished data; and Folger, John K. and Charles B. Nam, "Education of the American Population," *1960 Census Monograph*, from U.S. Dept. of Education, National Center for Education Statistics, *Digest of Education Statistics 2003*, and U.S. Census Bureau, *Current Population Survey*, March 2005.

2.4 Multiplication of Matrices

? THINK ABOUT IT

What is a contractor's total cost for materials required for various types of model homes?

Matrix multiplication will be used to answer this question in Example 5. We begin by defining the product of a real number and a matrix. In work with matrices, a real number is called a **scalar**.

PRODUCT OF A MATRIX AND A SCALAR

The product of a scalar k and a matrix X is the matrix kX, each of whose elements is k times the corresponding element of X.

For example,

$$(-5)\begin{bmatrix} 3 & 4 \\ 0 & -1 \end{bmatrix} = \begin{bmatrix} -15 & -20 \\ 0 & 5 \end{bmatrix}.$$

Finding the product of two matrices is more involved, but such multiplication is important in solving practical problems. To understand the reasoning behind matrix multiplication, it may be helpful to consider another example concerning EZ Life Company discussed in the previous section. Suppose sofas and chairs of the same model are often sold as sets. Matrix W shows the number of sets of each model in each warehouse.

$$\begin{array}{c} \\ \text{New York} \\ \text{Chicago} \\ \text{San Francisco} \end{array} \begin{array}{c} \begin{array}{ccc} A & B & C \end{array} \\ \begin{bmatrix} 10 & 7 & 3 \\ 5 & 9 & 6 \\ 4 & 8 & 2 \end{bmatrix} \end{array} = W$$

If the selling price of a model-A set is $1000, of a model-B set $1200, and of a model-C set $1400, the total value of the sets in the New York warehouse is found as follows.

Type	Number of Sets		Price of Set		Total
A	10	×	$1000	=	$10,000
B	7	×	$1200	=	$8400
C	3	×	$1400	=	$4200
			(Total for New York)		$22,600

The total value of the three kinds of sets in New York is $22,600.

The work done in the table above is summarized as follows:

$$10(\$1000) + 7(\$1200) + 3(\$1400) = \$22,600.$$

In the same way, we find that the Chicago sets have a total value of

$$5(\$1000) + 9(\$1200) + 6(\$1400) = \$24{,}200,$$

and in San Francisco, the total value of the sets is

$$4(\$1000) + 8(\$1200) + 2(\$1400) = \$16{,}400.$$

The selling prices can be written as a column matrix P, and the total value in each location as another column matrix, V.

$$\begin{bmatrix} 1000 \\ 1200 \\ 1400 \end{bmatrix} = P \qquad \begin{bmatrix} 22{,}600 \\ 24{,}200 \\ 16{,}400 \end{bmatrix} = V$$

Look at the elements of W and P below; multiplying the first, second, and third elements of the first row of W by the first, second, and third elements, respectively, of the column matrix P and then adding these products gives the first element in V. Doing the same thing with the second row of W gives the second element of V; the third row of W leads to the third element of V, suggesting that it is reasonable to write the product of matrices

$$W = \begin{bmatrix} 10 & 7 & 3 \\ 5 & 9 & 6 \\ 4 & 8 & 2 \end{bmatrix} \qquad \text{and} \qquad P = \begin{bmatrix} 1000 \\ 1200 \\ 1400 \end{bmatrix}$$

as

$$WP = \begin{bmatrix} 10 & 7 & 3 \\ 5 & 9 & 6 \\ 4 & 8 & 2 \end{bmatrix} \begin{bmatrix} 1000 \\ 1200 \\ 1400 \end{bmatrix} = \begin{bmatrix} 22{,}600 \\ 24{,}200 \\ 16{,}400 \end{bmatrix} = V.$$

The product was found by multiplying the elements of *rows* of the matrix on the left and the corresponding elements of the *column* of the matrix on the right, and then finding the sum of these separate products. Notice that the product of a 3×3 matrix and a 3×1 matrix is a 3×1 matrix.

The product AB of an $m \times n$ matrix A and an $n \times k$ matrix B is found as follows. Multiply each element of the first row of A by the corresponding element of the *first column* of B. The sum of these n products is the *first-row, first-column* element of AB. Similarly, the sum of the products found by multiplying the elements of the *first row* of A by the corresponding elements of the *second column* of B gives the *first-row, second-column* element of AB, and so on.

> **PRODUCT OF TWO MATRICES**
>
> Let A be an $m \times n$ matrix and let B be an $n \times k$ matrix. To find the element in the ith row and jth column of the **product matrix** AB, multiply each element in the ith row of A by the corresponding element in the jth column of B, and then add these products. The product matrix AB is an $m \times k$ matrix.

EXAMPLE 1 **Matrix Product**
Find the product AB of matrices

$$A = \begin{bmatrix} 2 & 3 & -1 \\ 4 & 2 & 2 \end{bmatrix} \qquad \text{and} \qquad B = \begin{bmatrix} 1 \\ 8 \\ 6 \end{bmatrix}.$$

▶**Solution** Since A is 2×3 and B is 3×1, we can find the product matrix AB.

Step 1 Multiply the elements of the first row of A and the corresponding elements of the column of B.

$$\begin{bmatrix} \mathbf{2} & \mathbf{3} & \mathbf{-1} \\ 4 & 2 & 2 \end{bmatrix} \begin{bmatrix} \mathbf{1} \\ \mathbf{8} \\ \mathbf{6} \end{bmatrix} \qquad \mathbf{2} \cdot \mathbf{1} + \mathbf{3} \cdot \mathbf{8} + (\mathbf{-1}) \cdot \mathbf{6} = 20$$

Thus, 20 is the first-row entry of the product matrix AB.

Step 2 Multiply the elements of the second row of A and the corresponding elements of B.

$$\begin{bmatrix} 2 & 3 & -1 \\ \mathbf{4} & \mathbf{2} & \mathbf{2} \end{bmatrix} \begin{bmatrix} \mathbf{1} \\ \mathbf{8} \\ \mathbf{6} \end{bmatrix} \qquad \mathbf{4} \cdot \mathbf{1} + \mathbf{2} \cdot \mathbf{8} + \mathbf{2} \cdot \mathbf{6} = 32$$

The second-row entry of the product matrix AB is 32.

Step 3 Write the product as a column matrix using the two entries found above.

$$AB = \begin{bmatrix} 2 & 3 & -1 \\ 4 & 2 & 2 \end{bmatrix} \begin{bmatrix} 1 \\ 8 \\ 6 \end{bmatrix} = \begin{bmatrix} 20 \\ 32 \end{bmatrix}$$

Note that the product of a 2×3 matrix and a 3×1 matrix is a 2×1 matrix.

EXAMPLE 2 **Matrix Product**

Find the product CD of matrices

$$C = \begin{bmatrix} -3 & 4 & 2 \\ 5 & 0 & 4 \end{bmatrix} \qquad \text{and} \qquad D = \begin{bmatrix} -6 & 4 \\ 2 & 3 \\ 3 & -2 \end{bmatrix}.$$

▶**Solution** Since C is 2×3 and D is 3×2, we can find the product matrix CD.

Step 1
$$\begin{bmatrix} \mathbf{-3} & \mathbf{4} & \mathbf{2} \\ 5 & 0 & 4 \end{bmatrix} \begin{bmatrix} \mathbf{-6} & 4 \\ \mathbf{2} & 3 \\ \mathbf{3} & -2 \end{bmatrix} \qquad (\mathbf{-3}) \cdot (\mathbf{-6}) + \mathbf{4} \cdot \mathbf{2} + \mathbf{2} \cdot \mathbf{3} = 32$$

Step 2
$$\begin{bmatrix} \mathbf{-3} & \mathbf{4} & \mathbf{2} \\ 5 & 0 & 4 \end{bmatrix} \begin{bmatrix} -6 & \mathbf{4} \\ 2 & \mathbf{3} \\ 3 & \mathbf{-2} \end{bmatrix} \qquad (\mathbf{-3}) \cdot \mathbf{4} + \mathbf{4} \cdot \mathbf{3} + \mathbf{2} \cdot (\mathbf{-2}) = -4$$

Step 3
$$\begin{bmatrix} -3 & 4 & 2 \\ \mathbf{5} & \mathbf{0} & \mathbf{4} \end{bmatrix} \begin{bmatrix} \mathbf{-6} & 4 \\ \mathbf{2} & 3 \\ \mathbf{3} & -2 \end{bmatrix} \qquad \mathbf{5} \cdot (\mathbf{-6}) + \mathbf{0} \cdot \mathbf{2} + \mathbf{4} \cdot \mathbf{3} = -18$$

Step 4
$$\begin{bmatrix} -3 & 4 & 2 \\ \mathbf{5} & \mathbf{0} & \mathbf{4} \end{bmatrix} \begin{bmatrix} -6 & \mathbf{4} \\ 2 & \mathbf{3} \\ 3 & \mathbf{-2} \end{bmatrix} \qquad \mathbf{5} \cdot \mathbf{4} + \mathbf{0} \cdot \mathbf{3} + \mathbf{4} \cdot (\mathbf{-2}) = 12$$

Step 5 The product is

$$CD = \begin{bmatrix} -3 & 4 & 2 \\ 5 & 0 & 4 \end{bmatrix} \begin{bmatrix} -6 & 4 \\ 2 & 3 \\ 3 & -2 \end{bmatrix} = \begin{bmatrix} 32 & -4 \\ -18 & 12 \end{bmatrix}.$$

Here the product of a 2 × 3 matrix and a 3 × 2 matrix is a 2 × 2 matrix.

NOTE One way to avoid errors in matrix multiplication is to lower the first matrix so it is below and to the left of the second matrix, and then write the product in the space between the two matrices. For example, to multiply the matrices in Example 2, we could rewrite the product as shown below.

$$\downarrow$$
$$\begin{bmatrix} -6 & 4 \\ 2 & 3 \\ 3 & -2 \end{bmatrix}$$
$$\rightarrow \begin{bmatrix} -3 & 4 & 2 \\ 5 & 0 & 4 \end{bmatrix} \begin{bmatrix} & \\ * & \end{bmatrix}$$

To find the entry where the * is, for example, multiply the row and the column indicated by the arrows: $5 \cdot (-6) + 0 \cdot 2 + 4 \cdot 3 = -18$. ■

As the definition of matrix multiplication shows,

> the product AB of two matrices A and B can be found only if the number of columns of A is the same as the number of rows of B.

The final product will have as many rows as A and as many columns as B.

EXAMPLE 3 **Matrix Product**

Suppose matrix A is 2 × 2 and matrix B is 2 × 4. Can the products AB and BA be calculated? If so, what is the size of each product?

▶**Solution** The following diagram helps decide the answers to these questions.

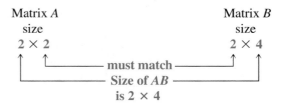

The product of A and B can be found because A has two columns and B has two rows. The size of the product is 2 × 4.

Matrix B Matrix A
size   size
2 × 4   2 × 2

do not match

The product BA cannot be found because B has 4 columns and A has 2 rows.

EXAMPLE 4 **Comparing Matrix Products AB and BA**
Find AB and BA, given

$$A = \begin{bmatrix} 1 & -3 \\ 7 & 2 \\ -2 & 5 \end{bmatrix} \quad \text{and} \quad B = \begin{bmatrix} 1 & 0 & -1 \\ 3 & 1 & 4 \end{bmatrix}.$$

▶**Solution**

METHOD 1
Calculating by Hand

$$AB = \begin{bmatrix} 1 & -3 \\ 7 & 2 \\ -2 & 5 \end{bmatrix} \begin{bmatrix} 1 & 0 & -1 \\ 3 & 1 & 4 \end{bmatrix}$$

$$= \begin{bmatrix} -8 & -3 & -13 \\ 13 & 2 & 1 \\ 13 & 5 & 22 \end{bmatrix}$$

$$BA = \begin{bmatrix} 1 & 0 & -1 \\ 3 & 1 & 4 \end{bmatrix} \begin{bmatrix} 1 & -3 \\ 7 & 2 \\ -2 & 5 \end{bmatrix}$$

$$= \begin{bmatrix} 3 & -8 \\ 2 & 13 \end{bmatrix}$$

METHOD 2
Graphing Calculators

Matrix multiplication is easily performed on a graphing calculator. Figure 13 shows the results. The matrices A and B were already entered into the calculator.

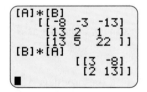

```
[A]*[B]
  [[-8 -3 -13]
   [13 2  1  ]
   [13 5  22 ]]
[B]*[A]
      [[3 -8]
       [2 13]]
■
```

FIGURE 13

Matrix multiplication can also be easily done with a spreadsheet. See *The Spreadsheet Manual* available with this textbook for details.

Notice in Example 4 that $AB \neq BA$; matrices AB and BA aren't even the same size. In Example 3, we showed that they may not both exist. This means that matrix multiplication is *not* commutative. Even if both A and B are square matrices, in general, matrices AB and BA are not equal. (See Exercise 31.) Of course, there may be special cases in which they are equal, but this is not true in general.

CAUTION Since matrix multiplication is not commutative, always be careful to multiply matrices in the correct order. ■

Matrix multiplication *is* associative, however. For example, if

$$C = \begin{bmatrix} 3 & 2 \\ 0 & -4 \\ -1 & 1 \end{bmatrix},$$

then $(AB)C = A(BC)$, where A and B are the matrices given in Example 4. (Verify this.) Also, there is a distributive property of matrices such that, for appropriate matrices A, B, and C,

$$A(B + C) = AB + AC.$$

(See Exercises 32 and 33.) Other properties of matrix multiplication involving scalars are included in the exercises. Multiplicative inverses and multiplicative identities are defined in the next section.

EXAMPLE 5 **Home Construction**

A contractor builds three kinds of houses, models A, B, and C, with a choice of two styles, Spanish and contemporary. Matrix P shows the number of each kind of house planned for a new 100-home subdivision. The amounts for each of the exterior materials depend primarily on the style of the house. These amounts are shown in matrix Q. (Concrete is in cubic yards, lumber in units of 1000 board feet, brick in 1000s, and shingles in units of 100 ft^2.) Matrix R gives the cost in dollars for each kind of material.

$$
\begin{array}{c}
\quad\quad\quad\quad \text{Spanish} \quad \text{Contemporary} \\
\begin{array}{c} \text{Model A} \\ \text{Model B} \\ \text{Model C} \end{array}
\left[\begin{array}{cc} 0 & 30 \\ 10 & 20 \\ 20 & 20 \end{array}\right] = P
\end{array}
$$

$$
\begin{array}{c}
\quad\quad\quad\quad\quad \text{Concrete} \quad \text{Lumber} \quad \text{Brick} \quad \text{Shingles} \\
\begin{array}{c} \text{Spanish} \\ \text{Contemporary} \end{array}
\left[\begin{array}{cccc} 10 & 2 & 0 & 2 \\ 50 & 1 & 20 & 2 \end{array}\right] = Q
\end{array}
$$

$$
\begin{array}{c}
\quad\quad\quad \text{Cost per Unit} \\
\begin{array}{c} \text{Concrete} \\ \text{Lumber} \\ \text{Brick} \\ \text{Shingles} \end{array}
\left[\begin{array}{c} 20 \\ 180 \\ 60 \\ 25 \end{array}\right] = R
\end{array}
$$

(a) What is the total cost of these materials for each model?

▶ **Solution** To find the cost for each model, first find PQ, which shows the amount of each material needed for each model.

$$
PQ = \begin{bmatrix} 0 & 30 \\ 10 & 20 \\ 20 & 20 \end{bmatrix} \begin{bmatrix} 10 & 2 & 0 & 2 \\ 50 & 1 & 20 & 2 \end{bmatrix}
$$

$$
\begin{array}{c}
\quad\quad \text{Concrete} \quad \text{Lumber} \quad \text{Brick} \quad \text{Shingles} \\
= \left[\begin{array}{cccc} 1500 & 30 & 600 & 60 \\ 1100 & 40 & 400 & 60 \\ 1200 & 60 & 400 & 80 \end{array}\right] \begin{array}{c} \text{Model A} \\ \text{Model B} \\ \text{Model C} \end{array}
\end{array}
$$

Now multiply PQ and R, the cost matrix, to get the total cost of the exterior materials for each model.

$$
\begin{array}{c}
\quad\quad\quad\quad\quad\quad\quad\quad\quad\quad \text{Cost} \\
\begin{bmatrix} 1500 & 30 & 600 & 60 \\ 1100 & 40 & 400 & 60 \\ 1200 & 60 & 400 & 80 \end{bmatrix} \begin{bmatrix} 20 \\ 180 \\ 60 \\ 25 \end{bmatrix} = \begin{bmatrix} 72{,}900 \\ 54{,}700 \\ 60{,}800 \end{bmatrix} \begin{array}{c} \text{Model A} \\ \text{Model B} \\ \text{Model C} \end{array}
\end{array}
$$

The total cost of materials is $72,900 for model A, $54,700 for model B, and $60,800 for model C.

(b) How much of each of the four kinds of material must be ordered?

▶**Solution** The totals of the columns of matrix PQ will give a matrix whose elements represent the total amounts of each material needed for the subdivision. Call this matrix T, and write it as a row matrix.

$$T = \begin{bmatrix} 3800 & 130 & 1400 & 200 \end{bmatrix}$$

Thus, 3800 yd³ of concrete, 130,000 board feet of lumber, 1,400,000 bricks, and 20,000 ft² of shingles are needed.

(c) What is the total cost for exterior materials?

▶**Solution** For the total cost of all the exterior materials, find the product of matrix T, the matrix showing the total amount of each material, and matrix R, the cost matrix. (To multiply these and get a 1×1 matrix representing total cost, we need a 1×4 matrix multiplied by a 4×1 matrix. This is why T was written as a row matrix in (b) above.)

$$TR = \begin{bmatrix} 3800 & 130 & 1400 & 200 \end{bmatrix} \begin{bmatrix} 20 \\ 180 \\ 60 \\ 25 \end{bmatrix} = \begin{bmatrix} 188,400 \end{bmatrix}$$

The total cost for exterior materials is $188,400.

(d) Suppose the contractor builds the same number of homes in five subdivisions. Calculate the total amount of each exterior material for each model for all five subdivisions.

▶**Solution** Multiply PQ by the scalar 5, as follows.

$$5(PQ) = 5 \begin{bmatrix} 1500 & 30 & 600 & 60 \\ 1100 & 40 & 400 & 60 \\ 1200 & 60 & 400 & 80 \end{bmatrix} = \begin{bmatrix} 7500 & 150 & 3000 & 300 \\ 5500 & 200 & 2000 & 300 \\ 6000 & 300 & 2000 & 400 \end{bmatrix}$$

The total amount of concrete needed for model A homes, for example, is 7500 yd³.

Choosing Matrix Notation
It is helpful to use a notation that keeps track of the quantities a matrix represents. We will use the notation

meaning of the rows/meaning of the columns,

that is, writing the meaning of the rows first, followed by the meaning of the columns. In Example 5, we would use the notation models/styles for matrix P, styles/materials for matrix Q, and materials/cost for matrix R. In multiplying PQ, we are multiplying models/styles by styles/materials. The result is models/materials. Notice that styles, the common quantity in both P and Q, was eliminated in the product PQ. By this method, the product $(PQ)R$ represents models/cost.

In practical problems this notation helps us decide in which order to multiply matrices so that the results are meaningful. In Example 5(c) either RT or TR can be calculated. Since T represents subdivisions/materials and R represents materials/cost, the product TR gives subdivisions/cost, while the product RT is meaningless.

→ 2.4 Exercises

Let $A = \begin{bmatrix} -2 & 4 \\ 0 & 3 \end{bmatrix}$ and $B = \begin{bmatrix} -6 & 2 \\ 4 & 0 \end{bmatrix}$. Find each value.

1. $2A$

2. $-3B$

3. $-6A$

4. $5B$

5. $-4A + 5B$

6. $7B - 3A$

In Exercises 7–12, the sizes of two matrices A and B are given. Find the sizes of the product AB and the product BA, whenever these products exist.

7. A is 2×2, and B is 2×2.

8. A is 3×3, and B is 3×3.

9. A is 3×4, and B is 4×4.

10. A is 4×3, and B is 3×6.

11. A is 4×2, and B is 3×4.

12. A is 3×2, and B is 1×3.

13. To find the product matrix AB, the number of _____ of A must be the same as the number of _____ of B.

14. The product matrix AB has the same number of _____ as A and the same number of _____ as B.

Find each matrix product, if possible.

15. $\begin{bmatrix} 2 & -1 \\ 5 & 8 \end{bmatrix} \begin{bmatrix} 3 \\ -2 \end{bmatrix}$

16. $\begin{bmatrix} -1 & 5 \\ 7 & 0 \end{bmatrix} \begin{bmatrix} 6 \\ 2 \end{bmatrix}$

17. $\begin{bmatrix} 2 & -1 & 7 \\ -3 & 0 & -4 \end{bmatrix} \begin{bmatrix} 5 \\ 10 \\ 2 \end{bmatrix}$

18. $\begin{bmatrix} 5 & 2 \\ 7 & 6 \\ 1 & 0 \end{bmatrix} \begin{bmatrix} 1 & 4 & 0 \\ 2 & -1 & 2 \end{bmatrix}$

19. $\begin{bmatrix} 2 & -1 \\ 3 & 6 \end{bmatrix} \begin{bmatrix} -1 & 0 & 4 \\ 5 & -2 & 0 \end{bmatrix}$

20. $\begin{bmatrix} 6 & 0 & -4 \\ 1 & 2 & 5 \\ 10 & -1 & 3 \end{bmatrix} \begin{bmatrix} 1 \\ 2 \\ 0 \end{bmatrix}$

21. $\begin{bmatrix} 2 & 2 & -1 \\ 3 & 0 & 1 \end{bmatrix} \begin{bmatrix} 0 & 2 \\ -1 & 4 \\ 0 & 2 \end{bmatrix}$

22. $\begin{bmatrix} -3 & 1 & 0 \\ 6 & 0 & 8 \end{bmatrix} \begin{bmatrix} 3 \\ -1 \\ -2 \end{bmatrix}$

23. $\begin{bmatrix} 1 & 2 \\ 3 & 4 \end{bmatrix} \begin{bmatrix} -1 & 5 \\ 7 & 0 \end{bmatrix}$

24. $\begin{bmatrix} 2 & 8 \\ -7 & 5 \end{bmatrix} \begin{bmatrix} 1 & 0 \\ 0 & 1 \end{bmatrix}$

25. $\begin{bmatrix} -2 & -3 & 7 \\ 1 & 5 & 6 \end{bmatrix} \begin{bmatrix} 1 \\ 2 \\ 3 \end{bmatrix}$

26. $\begin{bmatrix} 2 \\ -9 \\ 12 \end{bmatrix} \begin{bmatrix} 1 & 0 & -1 \end{bmatrix}$

27. $\left(\begin{bmatrix} 2 & 1 \\ -3 & -6 \\ 4 & 0 \end{bmatrix} \begin{bmatrix} 1 & -2 \\ 2 & -1 \end{bmatrix} \right) \begin{bmatrix} 3 \\ 1 \end{bmatrix}$

28. $\begin{bmatrix} 2 & 1 \\ -3 & -6 \\ 4 & 0 \end{bmatrix} \left(\begin{bmatrix} 1 & -2 \\ 2 & -1 \end{bmatrix} \begin{bmatrix} 3 \\ 1 \end{bmatrix} \right)$

29. $\begin{bmatrix} 2 & -2 \\ 1 & -1 \end{bmatrix} \left(\begin{bmatrix} 4 & 3 \\ 1 & 2 \end{bmatrix} + \begin{bmatrix} 7 & 0 \\ -1 & 5 \end{bmatrix} \right)$

30. $\begin{bmatrix} 2 & -2 \\ 1 & -1 \end{bmatrix} \begin{bmatrix} 4 & 3 \\ 1 & 2 \end{bmatrix} + \begin{bmatrix} 2 & -2 \\ 1 & -1 \end{bmatrix} \begin{bmatrix} 7 & 0 \\ -1 & 5 \end{bmatrix}$

31. Let $A = \begin{bmatrix} -2 & 4 \\ 1 & 3 \end{bmatrix}$ and $B = \begin{bmatrix} -2 & 1 \\ 3 & 6 \end{bmatrix}$.

   a. Find AB.

   b. Find BA.

   c. Did you get the same answer in parts a and b?

   d. In general, for matrices A and B such that AB and BA both exist, does AB always equal BA?

Given matrices $P = \begin{bmatrix} m & n \\ p & q \end{bmatrix}$, $X = \begin{bmatrix} x & y \\ z & w \end{bmatrix}$, *and* $T = \begin{bmatrix} r & s \\ t & u \end{bmatrix}$, *verify that the statements in Exercises 32–35 are true. The statements are valid for any matrices whenever matrix multiplication and addition can be carried out. This, of course, depends on the size of the matrices.*

32. $(PX)T = P(XT)$ (associative property: see Exercises 27 and 28)

33. $P(X + T) = PX + PT$ (distributive property: see Exercises 29 and 30)

34. $k(X + T) = kX + kT$ for any real number k.

35. $(k + h)P = kP + hP$ for any real numbers k and h.

36. Let I be the matrix $I = \begin{bmatrix} 1 & 0 \\ 0 & 1 \end{bmatrix}$, and let matrices P, X, and T be defined as for Exercises 32–35.

    a. Find IP, PI, and IX.

    b. Without calculating, guess what the matrix IT might be.

    c. Suggest a reason for naming a matrix such as I an *identity matrix*.

37. Show that the system of linear equations

$$2x_1 + 3x_2 + x_3 = 5$$
$$x_1 - 4x_2 + 5x_3 = 8$$

can be written as the matrix equation

$$\begin{bmatrix} 2 & 3 & 1 \\ 1 & -4 & 5 \end{bmatrix} \begin{bmatrix} x_1 \\ x_2 \\ x_3 \end{bmatrix} = \begin{bmatrix} 5 \\ 8 \end{bmatrix}.$$

38. Let $A = \begin{bmatrix} 1 & 2 \\ -3 & 5 \end{bmatrix}$, $X = \begin{bmatrix} x_1 \\ x_2 \end{bmatrix}$, and $B = \begin{bmatrix} -4 \\ 12 \end{bmatrix}$. Show that the equation $AX = B$ represents a linear system of two equations in two unknowns. Solve the system and substitute into the matrix equation to check your results.

Use a computer or graphing calculator and the following matrices to find the matrix products and sums in Exercises 39–41.

$$A = \begin{bmatrix} 2 & 3 & -1 & 5 & 10 \\ 2 & 8 & 7 & 4 & 3 \\ -1 & -4 & -12 & 6 & 8 \\ 2 & 5 & 7 & 1 & 4 \end{bmatrix} \qquad B = \begin{bmatrix} 9 & 3 & 7 & -6 \\ -1 & 0 & 4 & 2 \\ -10 & -7 & 6 & 9 \\ 8 & 4 & 2 & -1 \\ 2 & -5 & 3 & 7 \end{bmatrix}$$

$$C = \begin{bmatrix} -6 & 8 & 2 & 4 & -3 \\ 1 & 9 & 7 & -12 & 5 \\ 15 & 2 & -8 & 10 & 11 \\ 4 & 7 & 9 & 6 & -2 \\ 1 & 3 & 8 & 23 & 4 \end{bmatrix} \qquad D = \begin{bmatrix} 5 & -3 & 7 & 9 & 2 \\ 6 & 8 & -5 & 2 & 1 \\ 3 & 7 & -4 & 2 & 11 \\ 5 & -3 & 9 & 4 & -1 \\ 0 & 3 & 2 & 5 & 1 \end{bmatrix}$$

39. a. Find AC.   **b.** Find CA.   **c.** Does $AC = CA$?

40. a. Find CD.   **b.** Find DC.   **c.** Does $CD = DC$?

41. a. Find $C + D$.   **b.** Find $(C + D)B$.   **c.** Find CB.

    d. Find DB.   **e.** Find $CB + DB$.   **f.** Does $(C + D)B = CB + DB$?

42. Which property of matrices does Exercise 41 illustrate?

→ Applications

BUSINESS AND ECONOMICS

43. *Cost Analysis* The four departments of Spangler Enterprises need to order the following amounts of the same products.

	Paper	Tape	Binders	Memo Pads	Pens
Department 1	10	4	3	5	6
Department 2	7	2	2	3	8
Department 3	4	5	1	0	10
Department 4	0	3	4	5	5

The unit price (in dollars) of each product is given in the next column for two suppliers.

	Supplier A	Supplier B
Paper	2	3
Tape	1	1
Binders	4	3
Memo Pads	3	3
Pens	1	2

a. Use matrix multiplication to get a matrix showing the comparative costs for each department for the products from the two suppliers.

b. Find the total cost over all departments to buy products from each supplier. From which supplier should the company make the purchase?

44. *Cost Analysis* The Mundo Candy Company makes three types of chocolate candy: Cheery Cherry, Mucho Mocha, and Almond Delight. The company produces its products in San Diego, Mexico City, and Managua using two main ingredients: chocolate and sugar.

a. Each kilogram of Cheery Cherry requires 0.5 kg of sugar and 0.2 kg of chocolate; each kilogram of Mucho Mocha requires 0.4 kg of sugar and 0.3 kg of chocolate; and each kilogram of Almond Delight requires 0.3 kg of sugar and 0.3 kg of chocolate. Put this information into a 2×3 matrix, labeling the rows and columns.

b. The cost of 1 kg of sugar is $4 in San Diego, $2 in Mexico City, and $1 in Managua. The cost of 1 kg of chocolate is $3 in San Diego, $5 in Mexico City, and $7 in Managua. Put this information into a matrix in such a way that when you multiply it with your matrix from part a, you get a matrix representing the ingredient cost of producing each type of candy in each city.

c. Multiply the matrices in parts a and b, labeling the product matrix.

d. From part c, what is the combined sugar-and-chocolate cost to produce 1 kg of Mucho Mocha in Managua?

e. Mundo Candy needs to quickly produce a special shipment of 100 kg of Cheery Cherry, 200 kg of Mucho Mocha, and 500 kg of Almond Delight, and it decides to select one factory to fill the entire order. Use matrix multiplication to determine in which city the total sugar-and-chocolate cost to produce the order is the smallest.

45. *Management* In Exercise 39 from Section 2.3, consider the matrices $\begin{bmatrix} 4.27 & 6.94 \\ 3.45 & 3.65 \end{bmatrix}, \begin{bmatrix} 4.05 & 7.01 \\ 3.27 & 3.51 \end{bmatrix}$, and $\begin{bmatrix} 4.40 & 6.90 \\ 3.54 & 3.76 \end{bmatrix}$ for the production costs at the Boston, Chicago, and Seattle plants, respectively.

a. Assume each plant makes the same number of each item. Write a matrix that expresses the average production costs for all three plants.

b. In part b of Exercise 39 in Section 2.3, cost increases for the Chicago plant resulted in a new production cost matrix $\begin{bmatrix} 4.42 & 7.43 \\ 3.38 & 3.62 \end{bmatrix}$. Following those cost increases the Boston plant was closed and production divided evenly between the Chicago and Seattle plants. What is the matrix that now expresses the average production cost for the entire country?

46. *House Construction* Consider the matrices P, Q, and R given in Example 5.

a. Find and interpret the matrix product QR.

b. Verify that $P(QR)$ is equal to $(PQ)R$ calculated in Example 5.

47. *Shoe Sales* Sal's Shoes and Fred's Footwear both have outlets in California and Arizona. Sal's sells shoes for $80, sandals for $40, and boots for $120. Fred's prices are $60, $30, and $150 for shoes, sandals, and boots, respectively. Half of all sales in California stores are shoes, 1/4 are sandals, and 1/4 are boots. In Arizona the fractions are 1/5 shoes, 1/5 sandals, and 3/5 boots.

a. Write a 2×3 matrix called P representing prices for the two stores and three types of footwear.

b. Write a 3×2 matrix called F representing the fraction of each type of footwear sold in each state.

c. Only one of the two products PF and FP is meaningful. Determine which one it is, calculate the product, and describe what the entries represent.

48. *Management* In Exercise 40 from Section 2.3, consider the matrix

$$\begin{bmatrix} 88 & 105 & 60 \\ 48 & 72 & 40 \\ 16 & 21 & 0 \\ 112 & 147 & 50 \end{bmatrix}$$

expressing the sales information for the three stores.

a. Write a 3 × 1 matrix expressing the factors by which sales in each store should be multiplied to reflect the fact that sales increased during the following week by 25%, 1/3, and 10% in stores I, II, and III, respectively, as described in part b of Exercise 40 from Section 2.3.

b. Multiply the matrix expressing sales information by the matrix found in part a of this exercise to find the sales for all three stores in the second week.

LIFE SCIENCES

49. *Dietetics* In Exercise 41 from Section 2.3, label the matrices

$$\begin{bmatrix} 2 & 1 & 2 & 1 \\ 3 & 2 & 2 & 1 \\ 4 & 3 & 2 & 1 \end{bmatrix}, \quad \begin{bmatrix} 5 & 0 & 7 \\ 0 & 10 & 1 \\ 0 & 15 & 2 \\ 10 & 12 & 8 \end{bmatrix}, \quad \text{and} \quad \begin{bmatrix} 8 \\ 4 \\ 5 \end{bmatrix}$$

found in parts a, b, and c, respectively, X, Y, and Z.

a. Find the product matrix XY. What do the entries of this matrix represent?

b. Find the product matrix YZ. What do the entries represent?

c. Find the products $(XY)Z$ and $X(YZ)$ and verify that they are equal. What do the entries represent?

50. *Driving Habits* In Exercise 44 from Section 2.3, you constructed matrices that represent percentages for various years of male and female high school students who rarely or never wore a seatbelt, rode with drivers who had been drinking, and drove after drinking. Use matrix operations to combine these two matrices to form one matrix that represents the combined percentages of driving habits for males and females. Assume males and females represented are equal in number. (*Hint:* Add the two matrices together and then multiply the resulting matrix by the scalar 1/2.)

51. *Life Expectancy* In Exercise 45 from Section 2.3, you constructed matrices that represent the life expectancy of African American and white American males and females. Use matrix operations to combine these two matrices to form one matrix that represents the combined life expectancy of both races at the beginning of each decade since 1970. Use the fact that of the combined African and white American population, African Americans are about one-sixth of the total and white Americans about five-sixths. (*Hint:* Multiply the matrix for African Americans by 1/6 and the matrix for the white Americans by 5/6, and then add the results.)

52. *Northern Spotted Owl Population** In an attempt to save the endangered northern spotted owl, the U.S. Fish and Wildlife Service imposed strict guidelines for the use of 12 million acres of Pacific Northwest forest. This decision led to a national debate between the logging industry and environmentalists. Mathematical ecologists have created a mathematical model to analyze population dynamics of the northern spotted owl by dividing the female owl population into three categories: juvenile (up to 1 year old), subadult (1 to 2 years), and adult (over 2 years old). By analyzing these three subgroups, it is possible to use the number of females in each subgroup at time n to estimate the number of females in each group at any time $n + 1$ with the following matrix equation:

$$\begin{bmatrix} j_{n+1} \\ s_{n+1} \\ a_{n+1} \end{bmatrix} = \begin{bmatrix} 0 & 0 & 0.33 \\ 0.18 & 0 & 0 \\ 0 & 0.71 & 0.94 \end{bmatrix} \begin{bmatrix} j_n \\ s_n \\ a_n \end{bmatrix},$$

where j_n is the number of juveniles, s_n is the number of subadults, and a_n is the number of adults at time n.[†]

a. If there are currently 4000 female northern spotted owls made up of 900 juveniles, 500 subadults, and 2600 adults, use a graphing calculator or spreadsheet and matrix operations to determine the total number of female owls for each of the next 5 years. (*Hint:* Round each answer to the nearest whole number after each matrix multiplication.)

b. With advanced techniques from linear algebra, it is possible to show that in the long run, the following holds.

$$\begin{bmatrix} j_{n+1} \\ s_{n+1} \\ a_{n+1} \end{bmatrix} \approx 0.98359 \begin{bmatrix} j_n \\ s_n \\ a_n \end{bmatrix}$$

What can we conclude about the long-term survival of the northern spotted owl?

---

*This problem was created by David I. Schneider, University of Maryland.
[†]Lamberson, R., R. McKelvey, B. Noon, and C. Voss, "A Dynamic Analysis of Northern Spotted Owl Viability in a Fragmented Forest Landscape," *Conservation Biology*, Vol. 6, No. 4, Dec. 1992, pp. 505–512.

	Births	Deaths
Africa	0.036	0.014
Asia	0.019	0.008
Latin America	0.021	0.006
North America	0.014	0.008
Europe	0.011	0.011

Year	Africa	Asia	Latin America	North America	Europe
1960	283	1628	218	199	425
1970	361	2038	286	227	460
1980	473	2494	362	252	484
1990	627	2978	443	278	499
2002	839	3518	539	320	513

c. Notice that only 18 percent of the juveniles become subadults. Assuming that, through better habitat management, this number could be increased to 40 percent, rework part a. Discuss possible reasons why only 18 percent of the juveniles become subadults. Under the new assumption, what can you conclude about the long-term survival of the northern spotted owl?

SOCIAL SCIENCES

53. *World Population* The 2002 birth and death rates per million for several regions and the world population (in millions) by region are given in the following tables.*

a. Write the information in each table as a matrix.

b. Use the matrices from part a to find the total number (in millions) of births and deaths in each year.

c. Using the results of part b, compare the number of births in 1960 and in 2002. Also compare the birth rates from part a. Which gives better information?

d. Using the results of part b, compare the number of deaths in 1980 and in 2002. Discuss how this comparison differs from a comparison of death rates from part a.

2.5 Matrix Inverses

? THINK ABOUT IT One top leader needs to get an important message to one of her agents. How can she encrypt the message to ensure secrecy?

This question is answered in Example 6. In this section, we introduce the idea of a matrix inverse, which is comparable to the reciprocal of a real number. This will allow us to solve a matrix equation.

Earlier, we defined a zero matrix as an additive identity matrix with properties similar to those of the real number 0, the additive identity for real numbers. The real number 1 is the *multiplicative* identity for real numbers: for any real number a, we have $a \cdot 1 = 1 \cdot a = a$. In this section, we define a *multiplicative identity matrix I* that has properties similar to those of the number 1. We then use

*"World Population by Region and Development Category, 1950–2050," from U.S. Bureau of the Census, World Population Profile: 2002 (Issued March 2004).

the definition of matrix I to find the *multiplicative inverse* of any square matrix that has an inverse.

If I is to be the identity matrix, both of the products AI and IA must equal A. This means that an identity matrix exists only for square matrices. The 2×2 **identity matrix** that satisfies these conditions is

$$I = \begin{bmatrix} 1 & 0 \\ 0 & 1 \end{bmatrix}.$$

To check that I, as defined above, is really the 2×2 identity, let

$$A = \begin{bmatrix} a & b \\ c & d \end{bmatrix}.$$

Then AI and IA should both equal A.

$$AI = \begin{bmatrix} a & b \\ c & d \end{bmatrix} \begin{bmatrix} 1 & 0 \\ 0 & 1 \end{bmatrix} = \begin{bmatrix} a(1) + b(0) & a(0) + b(1) \\ c(1) + d(0) & c(0) + d(1) \end{bmatrix} = \begin{bmatrix} a & b \\ c & d \end{bmatrix} = A$$

$$IA = \begin{bmatrix} 1 & 0 \\ 0 & 1 \end{bmatrix} \begin{bmatrix} a & b \\ c & d \end{bmatrix} = \begin{bmatrix} 1(a) + 0(c) & 1(b) + 0(d) \\ 0(a) + 1(c) & 0(b) + 1(d) \end{bmatrix} = \begin{bmatrix} a & b \\ c & d \end{bmatrix} = A$$

This verifies that I has been defined correctly.

It is easy to verify that the identity matrix I is unique. Suppose there is another identity; call it J. Then IJ must equal I, because J is an identity, and IJ must also equal J, because I is an identity. Thus $I = J$.

The identity matrices for 3×3 matrices and 4×4 matrices, respectively, are

$$I = \begin{bmatrix} 1 & 0 & 0 \\ 0 & 1 & 0 \\ 0 & 0 & 1 \end{bmatrix} \quad \text{and} \quad I = \begin{bmatrix} 1 & 0 & 0 & 0 \\ 0 & 1 & 0 & 0 \\ 0 & 0 & 1 & 0 \\ 0 & 0 & 0 & 1 \end{bmatrix}.$$

By generalizing, we can find an $n \times n$ identity matrix for any value of n.

Recall that the multiplicative inverse of the nonzero real number a is $1/a$. The product of a and its multiplicative inverse $1/a$ is 1. Given a matrix A, can a **multiplicative inverse matrix** A^{-1} (read "A-inverse") that will satisfy both

$$AA^{-1} = I \quad \text{and} \quad A^{-1}A = I$$

be found? For a given matrix, we often can find an inverse matrix by using the row operations of Section 2.2.

$\boxed{\text{NOTE}}$ A^{-1} does not mean $1/A$; here, A^{-1} is just the notation for the multiplicative inverse of matrix A. Also, only square matrices can have inverses because both $A^{-1}A$ and AA^{-1} must exist and be equal to an identity matrix of the same size. ■

If an inverse exists, it is unique. That is, any given square matrix has no more than one inverse. The proof of this is left to Exercise 50 in this section.

As an example, let us find the inverse of

$$A = \begin{bmatrix} 1 & 3 \\ -1 & 2 \end{bmatrix}.$$

Let the unknown inverse matrix be

$$A^{-1} = \begin{bmatrix} x & y \\ z & w \end{bmatrix}.$$

By the definition of matrix inverse, $AA^{-1} = I$, or

$$AA^{-1} = \begin{bmatrix} 1 & 3 \\ -1 & 2 \end{bmatrix} \begin{bmatrix} x & y \\ z & w \end{bmatrix} = \begin{bmatrix} 1 & 0 \\ 0 & 1 \end{bmatrix}.$$

By matrix multiplication,

$$\begin{bmatrix} x + 3z & y + 3w \\ -x + 2z & -y + 2w \end{bmatrix} = \begin{bmatrix} 1 & 0 \\ 0 & 1 \end{bmatrix}.$$

Setting corresponding elements equal gives the system of equations

$$x + 3z = 1 \qquad \textbf{(1)}$$
$$y + 3w = 0 \qquad \textbf{(2)}$$
$$-x + 2z = 0 \qquad \textbf{(3)}$$
$$-y + 2w = 1. \qquad \textbf{(4)}$$

Since equations (1) and (3) involve only x and z, while equations (2) and (4) involve only y and w, these four equations lead to two systems of equations,

$$\begin{array}{ccc} x + 3z = 1 & & y + 3w = 0 \\ -x + 2z = 0 & \text{and} & -y + 2w = 1. \end{array}$$

Writing the two systems as augmented matrices gives

$$\begin{bmatrix} 1 & 3 & | & 1 \\ -1 & 2 & | & 0 \end{bmatrix} \quad \text{and} \quad \begin{bmatrix} 1 & 3 & | & 0 \\ -1 & 2 & | & 1 \end{bmatrix}.$$

Each of these systems can be solved by the Gauss-Jordan method. Notice, however, that the elements to the left of the vertical bar are identical. The two systems can be combined into the single matrix

$$\begin{bmatrix} 1 & 3 & | & 1 & 0 \\ -1 & 2 & | & 0 & 1 \end{bmatrix}.$$

This is of the form $[A \mid I]$. It is solved simultaneously as follows.

$$R_1 + R_2 \rightarrow R_2 \quad \begin{bmatrix} 1 & 3 & | & 1 & 0 \\ 0 & 5 & | & 1 & 1 \end{bmatrix} \quad \begin{array}{l} \text{Get 0 in the second-row,} \\ \text{first-column position.} \end{array}$$

$$-3R_2 + 5R_1 \rightarrow R_1 \quad \begin{bmatrix} 5 & 0 & | & 2 & -3 \\ 0 & 5 & | & 1 & 1 \end{bmatrix} \quad \begin{array}{l} \text{Get 0 in the first-row,} \\ \text{second-column position.} \end{array}$$

$$\begin{array}{l} \frac{1}{5}R_1 \rightarrow R_1 \\ \frac{1}{5}R_2 \rightarrow R_2 \end{array} \quad \begin{bmatrix} 1 & 0 & | & \frac{2}{5} & -\frac{3}{5} \\ 0 & 1 & | & \frac{1}{5} & \frac{1}{5} \end{bmatrix} \quad \begin{array}{l} \text{Get 1's down the} \\ \text{diagonal.} \end{array}$$

The numbers in the first column to the right of the vertical bar give the values of x and z. The second column gives the values of y and w. That is,

$$\begin{bmatrix} 1 & 0 & | & x & y \\ 0 & 1 & | & z & w \end{bmatrix} = \begin{bmatrix} 1 & 0 & | & \frac{2}{5} & -\frac{3}{5} \\ 0 & 1 & | & \frac{1}{5} & \frac{1}{5} \end{bmatrix}$$

so that

$$A^{-1} = \begin{bmatrix} x & y \\ z & w \end{bmatrix} = \begin{bmatrix} \frac{2}{5} & -\frac{3}{5} \\ \frac{1}{5} & \frac{1}{5} \end{bmatrix}.$$

To check, multiply A by A^{-1}. The result should be I.

$$AA^{-1} = \begin{bmatrix} 1 & 3 \\ -1 & 2 \end{bmatrix} \begin{bmatrix} \frac{2}{5} & -\frac{3}{5} \\ \frac{1}{5} & \frac{1}{5} \end{bmatrix} = \begin{bmatrix} \frac{2}{5} + \frac{3}{5} & -\frac{3}{5} + \frac{3}{5} \\ -\frac{2}{5} + \frac{2}{5} & \frac{3}{5} + \frac{2}{5} \end{bmatrix} = \begin{bmatrix} 1 & 0 \\ 0 & 1 \end{bmatrix} = I$$

Verify that $A^{-1}A = I$, also.

FINDING A MULTIPLICATIVE INVERSE MATRIX

To obtain A^{-1} for any $n \times n$ matrix A for which A^{-1} exists, follow these steps.

1. Form the augmented matrix $[A|I]$, where I is the $n \times n$ identity matrix.
2. Perform row operations on $[A|I]$ to get a matrix of the form $[I|B]$, if this is possible.
3. Matrix B is A^{-1}.

EXAMPLE 1 **Inverse Matrix**

Find A^{-1} if $A = \begin{bmatrix} 1 & 0 & 1 \\ 2 & -2 & -1 \\ 3 & 0 & 0 \end{bmatrix}$.

METHOD 1
Calculating by Hand

▶**Solution** Write the augmented matrix $[A \mid I]$.

$$[A|I] = \begin{bmatrix} 1 & 0 & 1 & | & 1 & 0 & 0 \\ 2 & -2 & -1 & | & 0 & 1 & 0 \\ 3 & 0 & 0 & | & 0 & 0 & 1 \end{bmatrix}$$

Begin by selecting the row operation that produces a zero for the first element in row 2.

$$\begin{matrix} \\ -2R_1 + R_2 \rightarrow R_2 \\ -3R_1 + R_3 \rightarrow R_3 \end{matrix} \begin{bmatrix} 1 & 0 & 1 & | & 1 & 0 & 0 \\ 0 & -2 & -3 & | & -2 & 1 & 0 \\ 0 & 0 & -3 & | & -3 & 0 & 1 \end{bmatrix}$$ Get 0's in the first column.

Column 2 already has zeros in the required positions, so work on column 3.

$$\begin{matrix} R_3 + 3R_1 \rightarrow R_1 \\ R_3 + (-1)R_2 \rightarrow R_2 \\ \\ \end{matrix} \begin{bmatrix} 3 & 0 & 0 & | & 0 & 0 & 1 \\ 0 & 2 & 0 & | & -1 & -1 & 1 \\ 0 & 0 & -3 & | & -3 & 0 & 1 \end{bmatrix}$$ Get 0's in the third column.

Now get 1's down the main diagonal.

$$\begin{matrix} \frac{1}{3}R_1 \rightarrow R_1 \\ \frac{1}{2}R_2 \rightarrow R_2 \\ -\frac{1}{3}R_3 \rightarrow R_3 \end{matrix} \begin{bmatrix} 1 & 0 & 0 & | & 0 & 0 & \frac{1}{3} \\ 0 & 1 & 0 & | & -\frac{1}{2} & -\frac{1}{2} & \frac{1}{2} \\ 0 & 0 & 1 & | & 1 & 0 & -\frac{1}{3} \end{bmatrix}$$ Get 1's down the diagonal.

From the last transformation, the desired inverse is

$$A^{-1} = \begin{bmatrix} 0 & 0 & \frac{1}{3} \\ -\frac{1}{2} & -\frac{1}{2} & \frac{1}{2} \\ 1 & 0 & -\frac{1}{3} \end{bmatrix}.$$

Confirm this by forming the products $A^{-1}A$ and AA^{-1}, both of which should equal I.

METHOD 2
Graphing Calculators

The inverse of A can also be found with a graphing calculator, as shown in Figure 14. (The matrix A had previously been entered into the calculator.) The entire answer can be viewed by pressing the right and left arrow keys on the calculator.

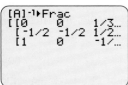

FIGURE 14

Spreadsheets also have the capability of calculating the inverse of a matrix with a simple command. See *The Spreadsheet Manual* available with this book for details.

EXAMPLE 2

Inverse Matrix

Find A^{-1} if $A = \begin{bmatrix} 2 & -4 \\ 1 & -2 \end{bmatrix}$.

▶**Solution** Using row operations to transform the first column of the augmented matrix

$$\begin{bmatrix} 2 & -4 & | & 1 & 0 \\ 1 & -2 & | & 0 & 1 \end{bmatrix}$$

gives the following results.

$$R_1 + (-2)R_2 \rightarrow R_2 \qquad \begin{bmatrix} 2 & -4 & | & 1 & 0 \\ 0 & 0 & | & 1 & -2 \end{bmatrix}$$

Because the last row has all zeros to the left of the vertical bar, there is no way to complete the process of finding the inverse matrix. What is wrong? Just as the real number 0 has no multiplicative inverse, some matrices do not have inverses. Matrix A is an example of a matrix that has no inverse: there is no matrix A^{-1} such that $AA^{-1} = A^{-1}A = I$.

Solving Systems of Equations with Inverses

We used matrices to solve systems of linear equations by the Gauss-Jordan method in Section 2.2. Another way to use matrices to solve linear systems is to write the system as a matrix equation $AX = B$, where A is the matrix of the coefficients of the variables of the system, X is the matrix of the variables, and B is the matrix of the constants. Matrix A is called the **coefficient matrix**.

To solve the matrix equation $AX = B$, first see if A^{-1} exists. Assuming A^{-1} exists and using the facts that $A^{-1}A = I$ and $IX = X$ gives

$$
\begin{aligned}
AX &= B \\
A^{-1}(AX) &= A^{-1}B \qquad \text{Multiply both sides by } A^{-1}. \\
(A^{-1}A)X &= A^{-1}B \qquad \text{Associative property} \\
IX &= A^{-1}B \qquad \text{Multiplicative inverse property} \\
X &= A^{-1}B. \qquad \text{Identity property}
\end{aligned}
$$

CAUTION When multiplying by matrices on both sides of a matrix equation, be careful to multiply in the same order on both sides of the equation, since multiplication of matrices is not commutative (unlike multiplication of real numbers). ■

The work above leads to the following method of solving a system of equations written as a matrix equation.

SOLVING A SYSTEM $AX = B$ USING MATRIX INVERSES

To solve a system of equations $AX = B$, where A is the matrix of coefficients, X is the matrix of variables, and B is the matrix of constants, first find A^{-1}. Then $X = A^{-1}B$.

This method is most practical in solving several systems that have the same coefficient matrix but different constants, as in Example 4 in this section. Then just one inverse matrix must be found.

EXAMPLE 3 **Inverse Matrices and Systems of Equations**
Use the inverse of the coefficient matrix to solve the linear system

$$2x - 3y = 4$$
$$x + 5y = 2.$$

▶**Solution** To represent the system as a matrix equation, use the coefficient matrix of the system together with the matrix of variables and the matrix of constants:

$$A = \begin{bmatrix} 2 & -3 \\ 1 & 5 \end{bmatrix}, \qquad X = \begin{bmatrix} x \\ y \end{bmatrix}, \qquad \text{and} \qquad B = \begin{bmatrix} 4 \\ 2 \end{bmatrix}.$$

The system can now be written in matrix form as the equation $AX = B$ since

$$AX = \begin{bmatrix} 2 & -3 \\ 1 & 5 \end{bmatrix} \begin{bmatrix} x \\ y \end{bmatrix} = \begin{bmatrix} 2x - 3y \\ x + 5y \end{bmatrix} = \begin{bmatrix} 4 \\ 2 \end{bmatrix} = B.$$

To solve the system, first find A^{-1}. Do this by using row operations on matrix $[A|I]$ to get

$$\begin{bmatrix} 1 & 0 & | & \frac{5}{13} & \frac{3}{13} \\ 0 & 1 & | & -\frac{1}{13} & \frac{2}{13} \end{bmatrix}.$$

From this result,

$$A^{-1} = \begin{bmatrix} \frac{5}{13} & \frac{3}{13} \\ -\frac{1}{13} & \frac{2}{13} \end{bmatrix}.$$

Next, find the product $A^{-1}B$.

$$A^{-1}B = \begin{bmatrix} \frac{5}{13} & \frac{3}{13} \\ -\frac{1}{13} & \frac{2}{13} \end{bmatrix} \begin{bmatrix} 4 \\ 2 \end{bmatrix} = \begin{bmatrix} 2 \\ 0 \end{bmatrix}.$$

Since $X = A^{-1}B$,

$$X = \begin{bmatrix} x \\ y \end{bmatrix} = \begin{bmatrix} 2 \\ 0 \end{bmatrix}.$$

The solution of the system is $(2, 0)$.

EXAMPLE 4 **Fertilizer**

Three brands of fertilizer are available that provide nitrogen, phosphoric acid, and soluble potash to the soil. One bag of each brand provides the following units of each nutrient.

		Brand		
		Fertifun	**Big Grow**	**Soakem**
	Nitrogen	1	2	3
Nutrient	*Phosphoric Acid*	3	1	2
	Potash	2	0	1

For ideal growth, the soil on a Michigan farm needs 18 units of nitrogen, 23 units of phosphoric acid, and 13 units of potash per acre. The corresponding numbers for a California farm are 31, 24, and 11, and for a Kansas farm are 20, 19, and 15. How many bags of each brand of fertilizer should be used per acre for ideal growth on each farm?

▶**Solution**   Rather than solve three separate systems, we consider the single system

$$x + 2y + 3z = a$$
$$3x + y + 2z = b$$
$$2x + z = c,$$

where a, b, and c represent the units of nitrogen, phosphoric acid, and potash needed for the different farms. The system of equations is then of the form $AX = B$, where

$$A = \begin{bmatrix} 1 & 2 & 3 \\ 3 & 1 & 2 \\ 2 & 0 & 1 \end{bmatrix} \quad \text{and} \quad X = \begin{bmatrix} x \\ y \\ z \end{bmatrix}.$$

B has different values for the different farms. We find A^{-1} first, then use it to solve all three systems.

To find A^{-1}, we start with the matrix

$$[A|I] = \begin{bmatrix} 1 & 2 & 3 & | & 1 & 0 & 0 \\ 3 & 1 & 2 & | & 0 & 1 & 0 \\ 2 & 0 & 1 & | & 0 & 0 & 1 \end{bmatrix}$$

and use row operations to get $[I|A^{-1}]$. The result is

$$A^{-1} = \begin{bmatrix} -\frac{1}{3} & \frac{2}{3} & -\frac{1}{3} \\ -\frac{1}{3} & \frac{5}{3} & -\frac{7}{3} \\ \frac{2}{3} & -\frac{4}{3} & \frac{5}{3} \end{bmatrix}.$$

Now we can solve each of the three systems by using $X = A^{-1}B$.

For the Michigan farm, $B = \begin{bmatrix} 18 \\ 23 \\ 13 \end{bmatrix}$, and

$$X = \begin{bmatrix} -\frac{1}{3} & \frac{2}{3} & -\frac{1}{3} \\ -\frac{1}{3} & \frac{5}{3} & -\frac{7}{3} \\ \frac{2}{3} & -\frac{4}{3} & \frac{5}{3} \end{bmatrix} \begin{bmatrix} 18 \\ 23 \\ 13 \end{bmatrix} = \begin{bmatrix} 5 \\ 2 \\ 3 \end{bmatrix}.$$

Therefore, $x = 5$, $y = 2$, and $z = 3$. Buy 5 bags of Fertifun, 2 bags of Big Grow, and 3 bags of Soakem.

For the California farm, $B = \begin{bmatrix} 31 \\ 24 \\ 11 \end{bmatrix}$, and

$$X = \begin{bmatrix} -\frac{1}{3} & \frac{2}{3} & -\frac{1}{3} \\ -\frac{1}{3} & \frac{5}{3} & -\frac{7}{3} \\ \frac{2}{3} & -\frac{4}{3} & \frac{5}{3} \end{bmatrix} \begin{bmatrix} 31 \\ 24 \\ 11 \end{bmatrix} = \begin{bmatrix} 2 \\ 4 \\ 7 \end{bmatrix}.$$

Buy 2 bags of Fertifun, 4 bags of Big Grow, and 7 bags of Soakem.

For the Kansas farm, $B = \begin{bmatrix} 20 \\ 19 \\ 15 \end{bmatrix}$. Verify that this leads to $x = 1$, $y = -10$, and $z = 13$. We cannot have a negative number of bags, so this solution is impossible. In buying enough bags to meet all of the nutrient requirements, the farmer must purchase an excess of some nutrients. In the next two chapters, we will study a method of solving such problems at a minimum cost.

In Example 4, using the matrix inverse method of solving the systems involved considerably less work than using row operations for each of the three systems.

EXAMPLE 5 Solving an Inconsistent System of Equations
Use the inverse of the coefficient matrix to solve the system

$$2x - 4y = 13$$
$$x - 2y = 1.$$

▶**Solution** We saw in Example 2 that the coefficient matrix $\begin{bmatrix} 2 & -4 \\ 1 & -2 \end{bmatrix}$ does not have an inverse. This means that the given system either has no solution or has an infinite number of solutions. Verify that this system is inconsistent and has no solution.

EXAMPLE 6 Cryptography
Throughout the Cold War and as the Internet has grown and developed, the need for sophisticated methods of coding and decoding messages has increased. Although there are many methods of encrypting messages, one fairly sophisti-

cated method uses matrix operations. This method first assigns a number to each letter of the alphabet. The simplest way to do this is to assign the number 1 to A, 2 to B, and so on, with the number 27 used to represent a space between words.

For example, the message *math is cool* can be divided into groups of three letters each and then converted into numbers as follows

$$\begin{bmatrix} m \\ a \\ t \end{bmatrix} = \begin{bmatrix} 13 \\ 1 \\ 20 \end{bmatrix}.$$

The entire message would then consist of four 3×1 columns of numbers:

$$\begin{bmatrix} 13 \\ 1 \\ 20 \end{bmatrix}, \quad \begin{bmatrix} 8 \\ 27 \\ 9 \end{bmatrix}, \quad \begin{bmatrix} 19 \\ 27 \\ 3 \end{bmatrix}, \quad \begin{bmatrix} 15 \\ 15 \\ 12 \end{bmatrix}.$$

This code is easy to break, so we further complicate the code by choosing a matrix that has an inverse (in this case a 3×3 matrix) and calculate the products of the matrix and each of the column vectors above.

If we choose the coding matrix

$$A = \begin{bmatrix} 1 & 3 & 4 \\ 2 & 1 & 3 \\ 4 & 2 & 1 \end{bmatrix},$$

then the products of A with each of the column vectors above produce a new set of vectors

$$\begin{bmatrix} 96 \\ 87 \\ 74 \end{bmatrix}, \quad \begin{bmatrix} 125 \\ 70 \\ 95 \end{bmatrix}, \quad \begin{bmatrix} 112 \\ 74 \\ 133 \end{bmatrix}, \quad \begin{bmatrix} 108 \\ 81 \\ 102 \end{bmatrix}.$$

This set of vectors represents our coded message and it will be transmitted as 96, 87, 74, 125 and so on.

When the intended person receives the message, it is divided into groups of three numbers, and each group is formed into a column matrix. The message is easily decoded if the receiver knows the inverse of the original matrix. The inverse of matrix A is

$$A^{-1} = \begin{bmatrix} -0.2 & 0.2 & 0.2 \\ 0.4 & -0.6 & 0.2 \\ 0 & 0.4 & -0.2 \end{bmatrix}.$$

Thus, the message is decoded by taking the product of the inverse matrix with each column vector of the received message. For example,

$$A^{-1} \begin{bmatrix} 96 \\ 87 \\ 74 \end{bmatrix} = \begin{bmatrix} 13 \\ 1 \\ 20 \end{bmatrix}.$$

Unless the original matrix or its inverse is known, this type of code can be difficult to break. In fact, very large matrices can be used to encrypt data. It is interesting to note that many mathematicians are employed by the National Security Agency to develop encryption methods that are virtually unbreakable.

➤ 2.5 Exercises

Decide whether the given matrices are inverses of each other. (Check to see if their product is the identity matrix I.)

1. $\begin{bmatrix} 2 & 1 \\ 5 & 3 \end{bmatrix}$ and $\begin{bmatrix} 3 & -1 \\ -5 & 2 \end{bmatrix}$

2. $\begin{bmatrix} 1 & -4 \\ 2 & -7 \end{bmatrix}$ and $\begin{bmatrix} -7 & 4 \\ -2 & 1 \end{bmatrix}$

3. $\begin{bmatrix} 2 & 6 \\ 2 & 4 \end{bmatrix}$ and $\begin{bmatrix} -1 & 2 \\ 2 & -4 \end{bmatrix}$

4. $\begin{bmatrix} -1 & 2 \\ 3 & -5 \end{bmatrix}$ and $\begin{bmatrix} -5 & -2 \\ -3 & -1 \end{bmatrix}$

5. $\begin{bmatrix} 2 & 0 & 1 \\ 1 & 1 & 2 \\ 0 & 1 & 0 \end{bmatrix}$ and $\begin{bmatrix} 1 & 1 & -1 \\ 0 & 1 & 0 \\ -1 & -2 & 2 \end{bmatrix}$

6. $\begin{bmatrix} 0 & 1 & 0 \\ 0 & 0 & -2 \\ 1 & -1 & 0 \end{bmatrix}$ and $\begin{bmatrix} 1 & 0 & 1 \\ 1 & 0 & 0 \\ 0 & -1 & 0 \end{bmatrix}$

7. $\begin{bmatrix} 1 & 3 & 3 \\ 1 & 4 & 3 \\ 1 & 3 & 4 \end{bmatrix}$ and $\begin{bmatrix} 7 & -3 & -3 \\ -1 & 1 & 0 \\ -1 & 0 & 1 \end{bmatrix}$

8. $\begin{bmatrix} 1 & 0 & 0 \\ -1 & -2 & 3 \\ 0 & 1 & 0 \end{bmatrix}$ and $\begin{bmatrix} 1 & 0 & 0 \\ 0 & 0 & 1 \\ \frac{1}{3} & \frac{1}{3} & \frac{2}{3} \end{bmatrix}$

9. Does a matrix with a row of all zeros have an inverse? Why?

10. Matrix A has A^{-1} as its inverse. What does $(A^{-1})^{-1}$ equal? (*Hint:* Experiment with a few matrices to see what you get.)

Find the inverse, if it exists, for each matrix.

11. $\begin{bmatrix} 1 & -1 \\ 2 & 0 \end{bmatrix}$

12. $\begin{bmatrix} 1 & 1 \\ 2 & 3 \end{bmatrix}$

13. $\begin{bmatrix} 3 & -1 \\ -5 & 2 \end{bmatrix}$

14. $\begin{bmatrix} -3 & -8 \\ 1 & 3 \end{bmatrix}$

15. $\begin{bmatrix} 1 & -3 \\ -2 & 6 \end{bmatrix}$

16. $\begin{bmatrix} 5 & 10 \\ -3 & -6 \end{bmatrix}$

17. $\begin{bmatrix} 1 & 0 & 0 \\ 0 & -1 & 0 \\ 1 & 0 & 1 \end{bmatrix}$

18. $\begin{bmatrix} 1 & 3 & 0 \\ 0 & 2 & -1 \\ 1 & 0 & 2 \end{bmatrix}$

19. $\begin{bmatrix} -1 & -1 & -1 \\ 4 & 5 & 0 \\ 0 & 1 & -3 \end{bmatrix}$

20. $\begin{bmatrix} 2 & 1 & 0 \\ 0 & 3 & 1 \\ 4 & -1 & -3 \end{bmatrix}$

21. $\begin{bmatrix} 1 & 2 & 3 \\ -3 & -2 & -1 \\ -1 & 0 & 1 \end{bmatrix}$

22. $\begin{bmatrix} 2 & 0 & 4 \\ 1 & 0 & -1 \\ 3 & 0 & -2 \end{bmatrix}$

23. $\begin{bmatrix} 1 & 3 & -2 \\ 2 & 7 & -3 \\ 3 & 8 & -5 \end{bmatrix}$

24. $\begin{bmatrix} 4 & 1 & -4 \\ 2 & 1 & -1 \\ -2 & -4 & 5 \end{bmatrix}$

25. $\begin{bmatrix} 1 & -2 & 3 & 0 \\ 0 & 1 & -1 & 1 \\ -2 & 2 & -2 & 4 \\ 0 & 2 & -3 & 1 \end{bmatrix}$

26. $\begin{bmatrix} 1 & 1 & 0 & 2 \\ 2 & -1 & 1 & -1 \\ 3 & 3 & 2 & -2 \\ 1 & 2 & 1 & 0 \end{bmatrix}$

Solve each system of equations by using the inverse of the coefficient matrix.

27. $2x + 5y = 15$
$\quad x + 4y = 9$

28. $-x + 2y = 15$
$\quad -2x - y = 20$

29. $2x + y = 5$
$\quad 5x + 3y = 13$

30. $-x - 2y = 8$
$\quad 3x + 4y = 24$

31. $3x - 2y = 3$
$\quad 7x - 5y = 0$

32. $3x - 6y = 1$
$\quad -5x + 9y = -1$

33. $-x - 8y = 12$
$\quad 3x + 24y = -36$

34. $2x + 7y = 14$
$\quad 3x + 4y = 8$

Solve each system of equations by using the inverse of the coefficient matrix. (The inverses for the first four problems were found in Exercises 19, 20, 23, and 24.)

35. $-x - y - z = 1$
$4x + 5y = -2$
$y - 3z = 3$

36. $2x + y = 1$
$3y + z = 8$
$4x - y - 3z = 8$

37. $x + 3y - 2z = 4$
$2x + 7y - 3z = 8$
$3x + 8y - 5z = -4$

38. $4x + y - 4z = 17$
$2x + y - z = 12$
$-2x - 4y + 5z = 17$

39. $2x - 2y = 5$
$4y + 8z = 7$
$x + 2z = 1$

40. $x + 2z = -1$
$y - z = 5$
$-x - y = -8$

Solve each system of equations by using the inverse of the coefficient matrix. (The inverses were found in Exercises 25 and 26.)

41. $x - 2y + 3z = 4$
$y - z + w = -8$
$-2x + 2y - 2z + 4w = 12$
$2y - 3z + w = -4$

42. $x + y + 2w = 3$
$2x - y + z - w = 3$
$3x + 3y + 2z - 2w = 5$
$x + 2y + z = 3$

Let $A = \begin{bmatrix} a & b \\ c & d \end{bmatrix}$ in Exercises 43–48.

43. Show that $IA = A$.

44. Show that $AI = A$.

45. Show that $A \cdot O = O$.

46. Find A^{-1}.
(Assume $ad - bc \neq 0$.)

47. Show that $A^{-1}A = I$.

48. Show that $AA^{-1} = I$.

49. Using the definition and properties listed in this section, show that for square matrices A and B of the same size, if $AB = O$ and if A^{-1} exists, then $B = O$.

50. Prove that, if it exists, the inverse of a matrix is unique. (*Hint:* Assume there are two inverses B and C for some matrix A, so that $AB = BA = I$ and $AC = CA = I$. Multiply the first equation by C and the second by B.)

Use matrices C and D in Exercises 51–55.

$$C = \begin{bmatrix} -6 & 8 & 2 & 4 & -3 \\ 1 & 9 & 7 & -12 & 5 \\ 15 & 2 & -8 & 10 & 11 \\ 4 & 7 & 9 & 6 & -2 \\ 1 & 3 & 8 & 23 & 4 \end{bmatrix}, \quad D = \begin{bmatrix} 5 & -3 & 7 & 9 & 2 \\ 6 & 8 & -5 & 2 & 1 \\ 3 & 7 & -4 & 2 & 11 \\ 5 & -3 & 9 & 4 & -1 \\ 0 & 3 & 2 & 5 & 1 \end{bmatrix}$$

51. Find C^{-1}.   **52.** Find $(CD)^{-1}$.   **53.** Find D^{-1}.   **54.** Is $C^{-1}D^{-1} = (CD)^{-1}$?   **55.** Is $D^{-1}C^{-1} = (CD)^{-1}$?

Solve the matrix equation $AX = B$ for X by finding A^{-1}, given A and B as follows.

56. $A = \begin{bmatrix} 2 & -5 & 7 \\ 4 & -3 & 2 \\ 15 & 2 & 6 \end{bmatrix}$, $B = \begin{bmatrix} -2 \\ 5 \\ 8 \end{bmatrix}$

57. $A = \begin{bmatrix} 2 & 5 & 7 & 9 \\ 1 & 3 & -4 & 6 \\ -1 & 0 & 5 & 8 \\ 2 & -2 & 4 & 10 \end{bmatrix}$, $B = \begin{bmatrix} 3 \\ 7 \\ -1 \\ 5 \end{bmatrix}$

58. $A = \begin{bmatrix} 3 & 2 & -1 & -2 & 6 \\ -5 & 17 & 4 & 3 & 15 \\ 7 & 9 & -3 & -7 & 12 \\ 9 & -2 & 1 & 4 & 8 \\ 1 & 21 & 9 & -7 & 25 \end{bmatrix}$, $B = \begin{bmatrix} -2 \\ 5 \\ 3 \\ -8 \\ 25 \end{bmatrix}$

➤ Applications

Solve each exercise by using the inverse of the coefficient matrix to solve a system of equations.

59. *Analysis of Orders* The Bread Box Bakery sells three types of cakes, each requiring the amounts of the basic ingredients shown in the following matrix.

		Type of Cake		
		I	II	III
	Flour (in cups)	2	4	2
Ingredient	Sugar (in cups)	2	1	2
	Eggs	2	1	3

To fill its daily orders for these three kinds of cake, the bakery uses 72 cups of flour, 48 cups of sugar, and 60 eggs.

a. Write a 3×1 matrix for the amounts used daily.

b. Let the number of daily orders for cakes be a 3×1 matrix X with entries x_1, x_2, and x_3. Write a matrix equation that can be solved for X, using the given matrix and the matrix from part a.

c. Solve the equation from part b to find the number of daily orders for each type of cake.

60. *Production Requirements* An electronics company produces transistors, resistors, and computer chips. Each transistor requires 3 units of copper, 1 unit of zinc, and 2 units of glass. Each resistor requires 3, 2, and 1 units of the three materials, and each computer chip requires 2, 1, and 2 units of these materials, respectively. How many of each product can be made with the following amounts of materials?

a. 810 units of copper, 410 units of zinc, and 490 units of glass

b. 765 units of copper, 385 units of zinc, and 470 units of glass

c. 1010 units of copper, 500 units of zinc, and 610 units of glass

61. *Investments* An investment firm recommends that a client invest in AAA-, A-, and B-rated bonds. The average yield on AAA bonds is 6%, on A bonds 6.5%, and on B bonds 8%. The client wants to invest twice as much in AAA bonds as in B bonds. How much should be invested in each type of bond under the following conditions?

a. The total investment is $25,000, and the investor wants an annual return of $1650 on the three investments.

b. The values in part a are changed to $30,000 and $1985, respectively.

c. The values in part a are changed to $40,000 and $2660, respectively.

62. *Production* Pretzels cost $4 per lb, dried fruit $5 per lb, and nuts $9 per lb. The three ingredients are to be combined in a trail mix containing twice the weight of pretzels as dried fruit. How many pounds of each should be used to produce the following amounts at the given cost?

a. 140 lb at $6 per lb

b. 100 lb at $7.60 per lb

c. 125 lb at $6.20 per lb

63. *Vitamins* Greg Tobin mixes together three types of vitamin tablets. Each Super Vim tablet contains, among other things, 15 mg of niacin and 12 I.U. of vitamin E. The figures for a Multitab tablet are 20 mg and 15 I.U., and for a Mighty Mix are 25 mg and 35 I.U. How many of each tablet are there if the total number of tablets, total amount of niacin, and total amount of vitamin E are as follows?

a. 225 tablets, 4750 mg of niacin, and 5225 I.U. of vitamin E

b. 185 tablets, 3625 mg of niacin, and 3750 I.U. of vitamin E

c. 230 tablets, 4450 mg of niacin, and 4210 I.U. of vitamin E

64. *Encryption* Use the matrices presented in Example 6 of this section to do the following:

a. Encode the message, "All is fair in love and war."

b. Decode the message 138, 81, 102, 101, 67, 109, 162, 124, 173, 210, 150, 165.

65. *Encryption* Use the methods presented in Example 6 along with the given matrix B to do the following.

$$B = \begin{bmatrix} 2 & 4 & 6 \\ -1 & -4 & -3 \\ 0 & 1 & -1 \end{bmatrix}$$

a. Encode the message, "To be or not to be."

b. Find the inverse of B.

c. Use the inverse of B to decode the message 116, -60, -15, 294, -197, -2, 148, -92, -9, 96, -64, 4, 264, -182, -2.

66. *Music* During a marching band's half-time show, the band members generally line up in such a way that a common shape is recognized by the fans. For example, as illustrated in the figure, a band might form a letter T, where an X represents a member of the band. As the music is played, the band will either create a new shape or rotate the original shape. In doing this, each member of the band will need to move from one point on the field to another. For larger bands, keeping track of who goes where can be a daunting task. However, it is possible to use matrix inverses to make the process a bit easier.* The entire process is calculated by knowing how three band members, all of whom cannot be in a straight line, will move from the current position to a new position. For example, in the figure, we can see that there are band members at $(50, 0)$, $(50, 15)$, and $(45, 20)$. We will assume that these three band members move to $(40, 10)$, $(55, 10)$, and $(60, 15)$, respectively.

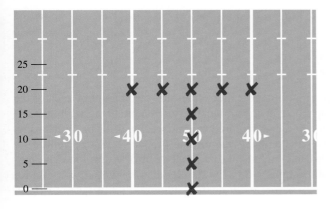

a. Find the inverse of $B = \begin{bmatrix} 50 & 50 & 45 \\ 0 & 15 & 20 \\ 1 & 1 & 1 \end{bmatrix}$.

b. Find $A = \begin{bmatrix} 40 & 55 & 60 \\ 10 & 10 & 15 \\ 1 & 1 & 1 \end{bmatrix} B^{-1}$.

c. Use the result of part b to find the new position of the other band members. What is the shape of the new position? (*Hint:* Multiply the matrix A by a 3×1 column vector with the first two components equal to the original position of each band member and the third component equal to 1. The new position of the band member is in the first two components of the product.)

2.6 Input-Output Models

? THINK ABOUT IT **What production levels are needed to keep an economy going and to supply demands from outside the economy?**

A method for solving such questions is developed in this section.

Wassily Leontief (1906–1999) developed an interesting and powerful application of matrix theory to economics and was recognized for this contribution with the Nobel prize in economics in 1973. His matrix models for studying the interdependencies in an economy are called *input-output* models. In practice these models are very complicated, with many variables. Only simple examples with a few variables are discussed here.

Input-output models are concerned with the production and flow of goods (and perhaps services). In an economy with n basic commodities, or sectors, the production of each commodity uses some (perhaps all) of the commodities in the economy as inputs. The amounts of each commodity used in the production of one unit of each commodity can be written as an $n \times n$ matrix A, called the **technological matrix** or **input-output matrix** of the economy.

EXAMPLE 1 Input-Output Matrix

Suppose a simplified economy involves just three commodity categories: agriculture, manufacturing, and transportation, all in appropriate units. Production of 1 unit of agriculture requires $1/2$ unit of manufacturing and $1/4$ unit of transportation; production of 1 unit of manufacturing requires $1/4$ unit of agriculture and $1/4$ unit of transportation; and production of 1 unit of transportation requires $1/3$ unit of agriculture and $1/4$ unit of manufacturing. Give the input-output matrix for this economy.

▶Solution

$$
\begin{array}{cc}
 & \begin{array}{ccc} \text{Agriculture} & \text{Manufacturing} & \text{Transportation} \end{array} \\
\begin{array}{c} \text{Agriculture} \\ \text{Manufacturing} \\ \text{Transportation} \end{array} &
\begin{bmatrix} 0 & \frac{1}{4} & \frac{1}{3} \\ \frac{1}{2} & 0 & \frac{1}{4} \\ \frac{1}{4} & \frac{1}{4} & 0 \end{bmatrix} = A
\end{array}
$$

The first column of the input-output matrix represents the amount of each of the three commodities consumed in the production of 1 unit of agriculture. The second column gives the amounts required to produce 1 unit of manufacturing, and the last column gives the amounts required to produce 1 unit of transportation. (Although it is perhaps unrealistic that production of a unit of each commodity requires none of that commodity, the simpler matrix involved is useful for our purposes.)

> **NOTE** Notice that for each commodity produced, the various units needed are put in a column. Each column corresponds to a commodity produced, and the rows correspond to what is needed to produce the commodity. ■

Another matrix used with the input-output matrix is the matrix giving the amount of each commodity produced, called the **production matrix**, or the matrix of gross output. In an economy producing n commodities, the production matrix can be represented by a column matrix X with entries $x_1, x_2, x_3, \ldots, x_n$.

EXAMPLE 2 Production Matrix

In Example 1, suppose the production matrix is

$$
X = \begin{bmatrix} 60 \\ 52 \\ 48 \end{bmatrix}.
$$

Then 60 units of agriculture, 52 units of manufacturing, and 48 units of transportation are produced. Because $1/4$ unit of agriculture is used for each unit of manufacturing produced, $1/4 \times 52 = 13$ units of agriculture must be used in the "production" of manufacturing. Similarly, $1/3 \times 48 = 16$ units of agriculture will be used in the "production" of transportation. Thus, $13 + 16 = 29$ units of agriculture are used for production in the economy. Look again at the matrices A and X. Since X gives the number of units of each commodity produced and A gives the amount (in units) of each commodity used to produce 1 unit of each of the various commodities, the matrix product AX gives the amount of each commodity used in the production process.

$$AX = \begin{bmatrix} 0 & \frac{1}{4} & \frac{1}{3} \\ \frac{1}{2} & 0 & \frac{1}{4} \\ \frac{1}{4} & \frac{1}{4} & 0 \end{bmatrix} \begin{bmatrix} 60 \\ 52 \\ 48 \end{bmatrix} = \begin{bmatrix} 29 \\ 42 \\ 28 \end{bmatrix}$$

From this result, 29 units of agriculture, 42 units of manufacturing, and 28 units of transportation are used to produce 60 units of agriculture, 52 units of manufacturing, and 48 units of transportation.

The matrix product AX represents the amount of each commodity used in the production process. The remainder (if any) must be enough to satisfy the demand for the various commodities from outside the production system. In an n-commodity economy, this demand can be represented by a **demand matrix** D with entries $d_1, d_2, \ldots, d_n$. If no production is to remain unused, the difference between the production matrix X and the amount AX used in the production process must equal the demand D, or

$$D = X - AX.$$

In Example 2,

$$D = \begin{bmatrix} 60 \\ 52 \\ 48 \end{bmatrix} - \begin{bmatrix} 29 \\ 42 \\ 28 \end{bmatrix} = \begin{bmatrix} 31 \\ 10 \\ 20 \end{bmatrix},$$

so production of 60 units of agriculture, 52 units of manufacturing, and 48 units of transportation would satisfy a demand of 31, 10, and 20 units of each commodity, respectively.

In practice, A and D usually are known and X must be found. That is, we need to decide what amounts of production are needed to satisfy the required demands. Matrix algebra can be used to solve the equation $D = X - AX$ for X.

$$D = X - AX$$
$$D = IX - AX \qquad \text{Identity property}$$
$$D = (I - A)X \qquad \text{Distributive property}$$

If the matrix $I - A$ has an inverse, then

$$X = (I - A)^{-1}D.$$

If the production matrix is large or complicated, we could use a graphing calculator. On the TI-83/84 Plus, for example, we would enter the command (identity(3) − [A])$^{-1}$* [D] for a 3 × 3 matrix A. It is also practical to do these calculations on a spreadsheet.

> ➤**FOR REVIEW**
> Recall that I is the identity matrix, a square matrix in which each element on the main diagonal is 1 and all other elements are 0.

EXAMPLE 3 **Demand Matrix**
Suppose, in the three-commodity economy from Examples 1 and 2, there is a demand for 516 units of agriculture, 258 units of manufacturing, and 129 units of transportation. What should production of each commodity be?

?

➤**Solution** The demand matrix is

$$D = \begin{bmatrix} 516 \\ 258 \\ 129 \end{bmatrix}.$$

To find the production matrix X, first calculate $I - A$.

$$I - A = \begin{bmatrix} 1 & 0 & 0 \\ 0 & 1 & 0 \\ 0 & 0 & 1 \end{bmatrix} - \begin{bmatrix} 0 & \frac{1}{4} & \frac{1}{3} \\ \frac{1}{2} & 0 & \frac{1}{4} \\ \frac{1}{4} & \frac{1}{4} & 0 \end{bmatrix} = \begin{bmatrix} 1 & -\frac{1}{4} & -\frac{1}{3} \\ -\frac{1}{2} & 1 & -\frac{1}{4} \\ -\frac{1}{4} & -\frac{1}{4} & 1 \end{bmatrix}$$

Use row operations to find the inverse of $I - A$ (the entries are rounded to two decimal places).

$$(I - A)^{-1} = \begin{bmatrix} 1.40 & 0.50 & 0.59 \\ 0.84 & 1.36 & 0.62 \\ 0.56 & 0.47 & 1.30 \end{bmatrix}$$

Since $X = (I - A)^{-1}D$,

$$X = \begin{bmatrix} 1.40 & 0.50 & 0.59 \\ 0.84 & 1.36 & 0.62 \\ 0.56 & 0.47 & 1.30 \end{bmatrix} \begin{bmatrix} 516 \\ 258 \\ 129 \end{bmatrix} = \begin{bmatrix} 928 \\ 864 \\ 578 \end{bmatrix}.$$

(Each entry in X has been rounded to the nearest whole number.)

The last result shows that production of 928 units of agriculture, 864 units of manufacturing, and 578 units of transportation are required to satisfy demands of 516, 258, and 129 units, respectively.

The entries in the matrix $(I - A)^{-1}$ are often called *multipliers*, and they have important economic interpretations. For example, every $1 increase in total agricultural demand will result in an increase in agricultural production by $1.40, an increase in manufacturing production by $0.84, and an increase in transportation production by $0.56. Similarly, every $3 increase in total manufacturing demand will result in an increase of $3(0.50) = 1.50$, $3(1.36) = 4.08$, and $3(0.47) = 1.41$ dollars in agricultural production, manufacturing production, and transportation production, respectively.

EXAMPLE 4 **Wheat and Oil Production**

An economy depends on two basic products, wheat and oil. To produce 1 metric ton of wheat requires 0.25 metric tons of wheat and 0.33 metric tons of oil. Production of 1 metric ton of oil consumes 0.08 metric tons of wheat and 0.11 metric tons of oil.

(a) Find the production that will satisfy a demand for 500 metric tons of wheat and 1000 metric tons of oil.

▶**Solution** The input-output matrix is

$$A = \begin{bmatrix} 0.25 & 0.08 \\ 0.33 & 0.11 \end{bmatrix}.$$

Also,

$$I - A = \begin{bmatrix} 0.75 & -0.08 \\ -0.33 & 0.89 \end{bmatrix}.$$

Next, calculate $(I - A)^{-1}$.

$$(I - A)^{-1} = \begin{bmatrix} 1.3882 & 0.1248 \\ 0.5147 & 1.1699 \end{bmatrix} \quad \text{(rounded)}$$

To find the production matrix X, use the equation $X = (I - A)^{-1}D$, with

$$D = \begin{bmatrix} 500 \\ 1000 \end{bmatrix}.$$

The production matrix is

$$X = \begin{bmatrix} 1.3882 & 0.1248 \\ 0.5147 & 1.1699 \end{bmatrix} \begin{bmatrix} 500 \\ 1000 \end{bmatrix} \approx \begin{bmatrix} 819 \\ 1427 \end{bmatrix}.$$

Production of 819 metric tons of wheat and 1427 metric tons of oil is required to satisfy the indicated demand.

(b) Suppose the demand for wheat goes up from 500 to 600 metric tons. Find the increased production in wheat and oil that will be required to meet the new demand.

▶**Solution** One way to solve this problem is using the multipliers for wheat, found in the first column of $(I - A)^{-1}$ from part (a). The element in the first row, 1.3882, is used to find the increased production in wheat, while the item in the second row, 0.5147, is used to find the increased production in oil. Since the increase in demand for wheat is 100 metric tons, the increased production in wheat must be $100(1.3882) \approx 139$ metric tons. Similarly, the increased production in oil is $100(0.5147) \approx 51$ metric tons.

Alternatively, we could have found the new production in wheat and oil with the equation $X = (I - A)^{-1}D$, giving

$$X = \begin{bmatrix} 1.3882 & 0.1248 \\ 0.5147 & 1.1699 \end{bmatrix} \begin{bmatrix} 600 \\ 1000 \end{bmatrix} \approx \begin{bmatrix} 958 \\ 1479 \end{bmatrix}.$$

We find the increased production by subtracting the answers found in part (a) from these answers. The increased production in wheat is $958 - 819 = 139$ metric tons, and the increased production in oil is $1479 - 1427 = 52$ metric tons. The slight difference here from the previous answer of 51 metric tons is due to rounding.

Closed Models

The input-output model discussed above is referred to as an **open model**, since it allows for a surplus from the production equal to D. In the **closed model**, all the production is consumed internally in the production process, so that $X = AX$. There is nothing left over to satisfy any outside demands from other parts of the economy or from other economies. In this case, the sum of each column in the input-output matrix equals 1.

To solve the closed model, set $D = O$ in the equation derived earlier.

$$(I - A)X = D = O$$

The system of equations that corresponds to $(I - A)X = O$ does not have a single unique solution, but it can be solved in terms of a parameter. (It can be shown that if the columns of a matrix A sum to 1, then the equation $(I - A)X = O$ has an infinite number of solutions.)

➤**FOR REVIEW**

Parameters were discussed in the first section of this chapter. As mentioned there, parameters are required when a system has infinitely many solutions.

EXAMPLE 5   **Closed Input-Output Model**

Use matrix A below to find the production of each commodity in a closed model.

$$A = \begin{bmatrix} \frac{1}{2} & \frac{1}{4} & \frac{1}{3} \\ 0 & \frac{1}{4} & \frac{1}{3} \\ \frac{1}{2} & \frac{1}{2} & \frac{1}{3} \end{bmatrix}$$

▶**Solution** Find the value of $I - A$, then set $(I - A)X = O$ to find X.

$$I - A = \begin{bmatrix} \frac{1}{2} & -\frac{1}{4} & -\frac{1}{3} \\ 0 & \frac{3}{4} & -\frac{1}{3} \\ -\frac{1}{2} & -\frac{1}{2} & \frac{2}{3} \end{bmatrix}$$

$$(I - A)X = \begin{bmatrix} \frac{1}{2} & -\frac{1}{4} & -\frac{1}{3} \\ 0 & \frac{3}{4} & -\frac{1}{3} \\ -\frac{1}{2} & -\frac{1}{2} & \frac{2}{3} \end{bmatrix} \begin{bmatrix} x_1 \\ x_2 \\ x_3 \end{bmatrix} = \begin{bmatrix} 0 \\ 0 \\ 0 \end{bmatrix}$$

Multiply to get

$$\begin{bmatrix} \frac{1}{2}x_1 - \frac{1}{4}x_2 - \frac{1}{3}x_3 \\ 0x_1 + \frac{3}{4}x_2 - \frac{1}{3}x_3 \\ -\frac{1}{2}x_1 - \frac{1}{2}x_2 + \frac{2}{3}x_3 \end{bmatrix} = \begin{bmatrix} 0 \\ 0 \\ 0 \end{bmatrix}.$$

The last matrix equation corresponds to the following system.

$$\frac{1}{2}x_1 - \frac{1}{4}x_2 - \frac{1}{3}x_3 = 0$$
$$\frac{3}{4}x_2 - \frac{1}{3}x_3 = 0$$
$$-\frac{1}{2}x_1 - \frac{1}{2}x_2 + \frac{2}{3}x_3 = 0$$

Solving the system with x_3 as the parameter gives the solution of the system

$$\left(\tfrac{8}{9}x_3, \tfrac{4}{9}x_3, x_3\right).$$

For example, if $x_3 = 9$ (a choice that eliminates fractions in the answer), then $x_1 = 8$ and $x_2 = 4$, so the production of the three commodities should be in the ratio 8:4:9.

Production matrices for actual economies are much larger than those shown in this section. An analysis of the U.S. economy in 1997 has close to 500 commodity categories.* Such matrices require large human and computer resources for their analysis. Some of the exercises at the end of this section use actual data in which categories have been combined to simplify the work.

*U.S. Bureau of Economic Analysis, http://www.bea.gov/bea/an2.htm.

> ### FINDING A PRODUCTION MATRIX
>
> To obtain the production matrix, X, for an open input-output model, follow these steps:
>
> **1.** Form the $n \times n$ input-output matrix, A, by placing in each column the amount of the various commodities required to produce 1 unit of a particular commodity.
>
> **2.** Calculate $I - A$, where I is the $n \times n$ identity matrix.
>
> **3.** Find the inverse, $(I - A)^{-1}$.
>
> **4.** Multiply the inverse on the right by the demand matrix, D, to obtain $X = (I - A)^{-1}D$.
>
> To obtain a production matrix, X, for a closed input-output model, solve the system $(I - A)X = O$.

2.6 Exercises

Find the production matrix for the following input-output and demand matrices using the open model.

1. $A = \begin{bmatrix} 0.8 & 0.2 \\ 0.2 & 0.7 \end{bmatrix}$, $D = \begin{bmatrix} 2 \\ 3 \end{bmatrix}$

2. $A = \begin{bmatrix} 0.2 & 0.04 \\ 0.6 & 0.05 \end{bmatrix}$, $D = \begin{bmatrix} 3 \\ 10 \end{bmatrix}$

3. $A = \begin{bmatrix} 0.1 & 0.03 \\ 0.07 & 0.6 \end{bmatrix}$, $D = \begin{bmatrix} 5 \\ 10 \end{bmatrix}$

4. $A = \begin{bmatrix} 0.02 & 0.03 \\ 0.06 & 0.08 \end{bmatrix}$, $D = \begin{bmatrix} 100 \\ 200 \end{bmatrix}$

5. $A = \begin{bmatrix} 0.8 & 0 & 0.1 \\ 0.1 & 0.5 & 0.2 \\ 0 & 0 & 0.7 \end{bmatrix}$, $D = \begin{bmatrix} 1 \\ 6 \\ 3 \end{bmatrix}$

6. $A = \begin{bmatrix} 0.1 & 0.5 & 0 \\ 0 & 0.3 & 0.4 \\ 0.1 & 0.2 & 0.1 \end{bmatrix}$, $D = \begin{bmatrix} 10 \\ 4 \\ 2 \end{bmatrix}$

Find the ratios of products A, B, *and* C *using a closed model.*

7.
	A	B	C
A	0.3	0.1	0.8
B	0.5	0.6	0.1
C	0.2	0.3	0.1

8.
	A	B	C
A	0.3	0.2	0.3
B	0.1	0.5	0.4
C	0.6	0.3	0.3

Use a graphing calculator or computer to find the production matrix X, given the following input-output and demand matrices.

9. $A = \begin{bmatrix} 0.25 & 0.25 & 0.25 & 0.05 \\ 0.01 & 0.02 & 0.01 & 0.1 \\ 0.3 & 0.3 & 0.01 & 0.1 \\ 0.2 & 0.01 & 0.3 & 0.01 \end{bmatrix}$, $D = \begin{bmatrix} 2930 \\ 3570 \\ 2300 \\ 580 \end{bmatrix}$

10. $A = \begin{bmatrix} 0.01 & 0.2 & 0.01 & 0.2 \\ 0.5 & 0.02 & 0.03 & 0.02 \\ 0.09 & 0.05 & 0.02 & 0.03 \\ 0.3 & 0.2 & 0.2 & 0.01 \end{bmatrix}$, $D = \begin{bmatrix} 5000 \\ 1000 \\ 4000 \\ 500 \end{bmatrix}$

▶ **Applications**

| BUSINESS AND ECONOMICS |

Input-Output Open Model In Exercises 11 and 12, refer to Example 4.

11. If the demand is changed to 925 metric tons of wheat and 1250 metric tons of oil, how many units of each commodity should be produced?

12. Change the technological matrix so that production of 1 metric ton of wheat requires 1/5 metric ton of oil (and no wheat), and production of 1 metric ton of oil requires 1/3 metric ton of wheat (and no oil). To satisfy the same demand matrix, how many units of each commodity should be produced?

Input-Output Open Model In Exercises 13–16, refer to Example 3.

13. If the demand is changed to 607 units of each commodity, how many units of each commodity should be produced?

14. Suppose 1/3 unit of manufacturing (no agriculture or transportation) is required to produce 1 unit of agriculture, 1/4 unit of transportation is required to produce 1 unit of manufacturing, and 1/2 unit of agriculture is required to produce 1 unit of transportation. How many units of each commodity should be produced to satisfy a demand of 1000 units of each commodity?

15. Suppose 1/4 unit of manufacturing and 1/2 unit of transportation are required to produce 1 unit of agriculture, 1/2 unit of agriculture and 1/4 unit of transportation to produce 1 unit of manufacturing, and 1/4 unit of agriculture and 1/4 unit of manufacturing to produce 1 unit of transportation. How many units of each commodity should be produced to satisfy a demand of 1000 units for each commodity?

16. If the input-output matrix is changed so that 1/4 unit of manufacturing and 1/2 unit of transportation are required to produce 1 unit of agriculture, 1/2 unit of agriculture and 1/4 unit of transportation are required to produce 1 unit of manufacturing, and 1/4 unit each of agriculture and manufacturing are required to produce 1 unit of transportation, find the number of units of each commodity that should be produced to satisfy a demand for 500 units of each commodity.

Input-Output Open Model

17. A primitive economy depends on two basic goods, yams and pork. Production of 1 bushel of yams requires 1/4 bushel of

yams and 1/2 of a pig. To produce 1 pig requires 1/6 bushel of yams. Find the amount of each commodity that should be produced to get the following.

a. 1 bushel of yams and 1 pig

b. 100 bushels of yams and 70 pigs

18. A simple economy depends on three commodities: oil, corn, and coffee. Production of 1 unit of oil requires 0.2 unit of oil, 0.4 unit of corn, and no units of coffee. To produce 1 unit of corn requires 0.4 unit of oil, 0.2 unit of corn, and 0.1 unit of coffee. To produce 1 unit of coffee requires 0.2 unit of oil, 0.1 unit of corn, and 0.2 unit of coffee. Find the production required to meet a demand of 1000 units each of oil, corn, and coffee.

19. In his work *Input-Output Economics*, Leontief provides an example of a simplified economy with just three sectors: agriculture, manufacturing, and households (i.e., the sector of the economy that produces labor).* It has the following input-output matrix:

	Agriculture	Manufacturing	Households
Agriculture	0.25	0.40	0.133
Manufacturing	0.14	0.12	0.100
Households	0.80	3.60	0.133

He also gives the demand matrix

$$D = \begin{bmatrix} 35 \\ 38 \\ 40 \end{bmatrix}.$$

Find the amount of each commodity that should be produced.

20. A much-simplified version of Leontief's 42-sector analysis of the 1947 American economy has the following input-output matrix.[†]

	Agriculture	Manufacturing	Households
Agriculture	0.245	0.102	0.051
Manufacturing	0.099	0.291	0.279
Households	0.433	0.372	0.011

The demand matrix (in billions of dollars) is

$$D = \begin{bmatrix} 2.88 \\ 31.45 \\ 30.91 \end{bmatrix}.$$

Find the amount of each commodity that should be produced.

*Leontief, Wassily, *Input-Output Economics*, 2nd ed., Oxford University Press, 1966, pp. 20–27.
[†]Ibid, pp. 6–9.

21. An analysis of the 1958 Israeli economy is simplified here by grouping the economy into three sectors, with the following input-output matrix:*

	Agriculture	Manufacturing	Energy
Agriculture	0.293	0	0
Manufacturing	0.014	0.207	0.017
Energy	0.044	0.010	0.216

The demand (in thousands of Israeli pounds) as measured by exports is

$$D = \begin{bmatrix} 138,213 \\ 17,597 \\ 1786 \end{bmatrix}.$$

Find the amount of each commodity that should be produced.

22. The 1981 Chinese economy can be simplified to three sectors: agriculture, industry and construction, and transportation and commerce.[†] The input-output matrix is given below.

	Agriculture	Industry/ Constr.	Trans./ Commerce
Agriculture	0.158	0.156	0.009
Industry/Constr.	0.136	0.432	0.071
Trans./Commerce	0.013	0.041	0.011

The demand (in 100,000 RMB, the unit of money in China) is

$$D = \begin{bmatrix} 106,674 \\ 144,739 \\ 26,725 \end{bmatrix}.$$

a. Find the amount of each commodity that should be produced.

b. Interpret the economic value of an increase in demand of 1 RMB in agricultural exports.

23. *Washington* The 1987 economy of the state of Washington has been simplified to four sectors: natural resources, manufacturing, trade and services, and personal consumption. The input-output matrix is given below.[‡]

	Natural Resources	Manufacturing	Trade & Services	Personal Consumption
Natural Resources	0.1045	0.0428	0.0029	0.0031
Manufacturing	0.0826	0.1087	0.0584	0.0321
Trade & Services	0.0867	0.1019	0.2032	0.3555
Personal Consumption	0.6253	0.3448	0.6106	0.0798

Suppose the demand (in millions of dollars) is

$$D = \begin{bmatrix} 450 \\ 300 \\ 125 \\ 100 \end{bmatrix}.$$

Find the amount of each commodity that should be produced.

24. *Washington* In addition to solving the previous input-output model, most models of this nature also include an employment equation. For the previous model, the employment equation is added and a new system of equations is obtained as follows.[‡]

$$\begin{bmatrix} x_1 \\ x_2 \\ x_3 \\ x_4 \\ N \end{bmatrix} = (I - B)^{-1}C,$$

where x_1, x_2, x_3, x_4 represent the amount, in millions of dollars, that must be produced to satisfy internal and external demands of the four sectors; N is the total workforce required for a particular set of demands; and

$$B = \begin{bmatrix} 0.1045 & 0.0428 & 0.0029 & 0.0031 & 0 \\ 0.0826 & 0.1087 & 0.0584 & 0.0321 & 0 \\ 0.0867 & 0.1019 & 0.2032 & 0.3555 & 0 \\ 0.6253 & 0.3448 & 0.6106 & 0.0798 & 0 \\ 21.6 & 6.6 & 20.2 & 0 & 0 \end{bmatrix}.$$

a. Suppose that a \$50 million change in manufacturing occurs. How will this increase in demand affect the economy? (*Hint:* Find $(I - B)^{-1}C$, where $C = \begin{bmatrix} 0 \\ 50 \\ 0 \\ 0 \\ 0 \end{bmatrix}$.)

b. Interpret the meaning of the bottom row in the matrix $(I - B)^{-1}$.

25. *Community Links* The use of input-output analysis can also be used to model how changes in one city can affect cities that are connected with it in some way.[§] For example, if a large manufacturing company shuts down in one city, it is very likely that the economic welfare of all of

*Ibid, pp. 174–177.

[†]*Input-Output Tables of China, 1981*, China Statistical Information and Consultancy Service Centre, 1987, pp. 17–19.

[‡]Chase, Robert, Philip Bourque, and Richard Conway Jr., "The 1987 Washington State Input-Output Study," Report to the Graduate School of Business Administration, University of Washington, Sept. 1993.

[§]The idea for this problem came from an example created by Thayer Watkins, Department of Economics, San Jose State University, www.sjsu/faculty/watkins/inputoutput.htm.

the cities around it will suffer. Consider three Pennsylvania communities: Sharon, Farrell, and Hermitage. Due to their proximity to each other, residents of these three communities regularly spend time and money in the other communities. Suppose that we have gathered information in the form of an input-output matrix.

$$A = \begin{array}{c} \\ S \\ F \\ H \end{array} \begin{array}{ccc} S & F & H \\ \left[\begin{array}{ccc} 0.2 & 0.1 & 0.1 \\ 0.1 & 0.1 & 0 \\ 0.5 & 0.6 & 0.7 \end{array} \right] \end{array}$$

This matrix can be thought of as the likelihood that a person from a particular community will spend money in each of the communities.

a. Treat this matrix like an input-output matrix and calculate $(I - A)^{-1}$.

b. Interpret the entries of this inverse matrix.

Input-Output Closed Model

26. Use the input-output matrix

$$\begin{array}{c} \\ \text{Yams} \\ \text{Pigs} \end{array} \begin{array}{cc} \text{Yams} & \text{Pigs} \\ \left[\begin{array}{cc} \frac{1}{4} & \frac{1}{2} \\ \frac{3}{4} & \frac{1}{2} \end{array} \right] \end{array}$$

and the closed model to find the ratio of yams to pigs produced.

27. Use the input-output matrix

$$\begin{array}{c} \\ \text{Steel} \\ \text{Coal} \end{array} \begin{array}{cc} \text{Steel} & \text{Coal} \\ \left[\begin{array}{cc} \frac{3}{4} & \frac{1}{3} \\ \frac{1}{4} & \frac{2}{3} \end{array} \right] \end{array}$$

and the closed model to find the ratio of coal to steel produced.

28. Suppose that production of 1 unit of agriculture requires 1/3 unit of agriculture, 1/3 unit of manufacturing, and 1/3 unit of transportation. To produce 1 unit of manufacturing requires 1/2 unit of agriculture, 1/4 unit of manufacturing, and 1/4 unit of transportation. To produce 1 unit of transportation requires 0 units of agriculture, 1/4 unit of manufacturing, and 3/4 unit of transportation. Find the ratio of the three commodities in the closed model.

29. Suppose that production of 1 unit of mining requires 1/5 unit of mining, 2/5 unit of manufacturing, and 2/5 unit of communication. To produce 1 unit of manufacturing requires 3/5 unit of mining, 1/5 unit of manufacturing, and 1/5 unit of communication. To produce 1 unit of communication requires 0 units of mining, 4/5 unit of manufacturing, and 1/5 unit of communication. Find the ratio of the three commodities in the closed model.

Chapter 2 Review

▶ Chapter Summary

In this chapter we extended our study of linear functions to include finding solutions of systems of linear equations. Techniques such as the echelon method and the Gauss-Jordan method were developed and used to solve systems of linear equations. We introduced matrices, which are used to store mathematical information. We saw that matrices can be combined using addition, subtraction, scalar multiplication, and matrix multiplication. Two special matrices, the zero matrix and the identity matrix, were also introduced.

- The zero matrix O is a matrix whose elements are all zero.
- The identity matrix I is an $n \times n$ matrix consisting of 1's along the diagonal and 0's elsewhere.

We then developed the concept of a multiplicative inverse of a matrix and used such inverses to solve systems of equations. We concluded the chapter by introducing the Leontief input-output models, which are used to study interdependencies in an economy.

SYSTEMS OF LINEAR EQUATIONS AND MATRICES SUMMARY

Row Operations For any augmented matrix of a system of equations, the following operations produce the augmented matrix of an equivalent system:

1. interchanging any two rows;
2. multiplying the elements of a row by a nonzero real number;
3. adding a nonzero multiple of the elements of one row to the corresponding elements of a nonzero multiple of some other row.

The Gauss-Jordan Method
1. Write each equation so that variable terms are in the same order on the left side of the equals sign and constants are on the right.
2. Write the augmented matrix that corresponds to the system.
3. Use row operations to transform the first column so that all elements except the element in the first row are zero.
4. Use row operations to transform the second column so that all elements except the element in the second row are zero.
5. Use row operations to transform the third column so that all elements except the element in the third row are zero.
6. Continue in this way, when possible, until the last row is written in the form

$$[0\ 0\ 0\ \cdots\ 0\,j\,|k],$$

where j and k are constants with $j \neq 0$. When this is not possible, continue until every row has more zeros on the left than the previous row (except possibly for any rows of all zero at the bottom of the matrix), and the first nonzero entry in each row is the only nonzero entry in its column.
7. Multiply each row by the reciprocal of the nonzero element in that row.

Adding Matrices The sum of two $m \times n$ matrices X and Y is the $m \times n$ matrix $X + Y$ in which each element is the sum of the corresponding elements of X and Y.

Subtracting Matrices For two $m \times n$ matrices X and Y, the difference $X - Y$ is the $m \times n$ matrix defined by

$$X - Y = X + (-Y).$$

Product of a Matrix and a Scalar The product of a scalar k and a matrix X is the matrix kX, each of whose elements is k times the corresponding element of X.

Product of Two Matrices Let A be an $m \times n$ matrix and let B be an $n \times k$ matrix. To find the element in the ith row and jth column of the product AB, multiply each element in the ith row of A by the corresponding element in the jth column of B, and then add these products. The product matrix AB is an $m \times k$ matrix.

Solving a System $AX = B$ Using Matrix Inverses To solve a system of equations $AX = B$, where A is a square matrix of coefficients, X is the matrix of variables, and B is the matrix of constants, first find A^{-1}. Then, $X = A^{-1}B$.

Finding a Production Matrix
1. Form the input-output matrix, A.
2. Calculate $I - A$, where I is the $n \times n$ identity matrix.
3. Find the inverse, $(I - A)^{-1}$.
4. Multiply the inverse on the right by the demand matrix, D, to obtain
   $X = (I - A)^{-1}D.$

To obtain a production matrix, X, for a closed input-output model, solve the system $(I - A)X = O$.

► Key Terms

To understand the concepts presented in this chapter, you should know the meaning and use of the following terms. For easy reference, the section in the chapter where a word (or expression) was first used is provided.

system of equations	parameter	column matrix (column	multiplicative inverse
2.1 first-degree equation in	**2.2** matrix (matrices)	vector)	matrix
n unknowns	element (entry)	additive inverse	coefficient matrix
unique solution	augmented matrix	(negative) of a matrix	**2.6** input-output
inconsistent system	row operations	zero matrix	(technological) matrix
dependent equations	Gauss-Jordan method	additive identity	production matrix
equivalent system	**2.3** size	**2.4** scalar	demand matrix
echelon method	square matrix	product matrix	open model
back-substitution	row matrix (row vector)	**2.5** identity matrix	closed model

► Concept Check

Determine whether each of the following statements is true or false, and explain why.

1. If a system of equations has three equations and four unknowns, then it could have a unique solution.

2. If $A = \begin{bmatrix} 2 & 3 \\ 1 & -1 \end{bmatrix}$ and $B = \begin{bmatrix} 3 & 4 \\ 7 & 4 \\ 1 & 0 \end{bmatrix}$, then $A + B = \begin{bmatrix} 5 & 7 \\ 8 & 3 \\ 1 & 0 \end{bmatrix}$.

3. If a system of equations has three equations and three unknowns, then it may have a unique solution, an infinite number of solutions, or no solutions.

4. The only solution to the system of equations

$$2x + 3y = 7$$
$$5x - 4y = 6$$

is $x = 2$ and $y = 1$.

5. If A is a 2×3 matrix and B is a 3×4 matrix, then $A + B$ is a 2×4 matrix.

6. If A is an $n \times k$ matrix and B is a $k \times m$ matrix, then AB is an $n \times m$ matrix.

7. If A is a 4×4 matrix and B is a 4×4 matrix, then $AB = BA$.

8. A 3×4 matrix could have an inverse.

9. It is not possible to find a matrix A such that $OA = AO = I$, where O is a 5×5 zero matrix and I is a 5×5 identity matrix.

10. When solving a system of equations by the Gauss-Jordan method, we can add a nonzero multiple of the elements of one column to the corresponding elements of some nonzero multiple of some other column.

11. Every square matrix has an inverse.

12. If A, B, and C are matrices such that $AB = C$, then $B = \dfrac{C}{A}$.

13. A system of three equations in three unknowns might have exactly five positive integer solutions.

14. If A and B are matrices such that $A = B^{-1}$, then $AB = BA$.

15. If A, B, and C are matrices such that $AB = CB$, then $A = C$.

16. The difference between an open and a closed input-output model is that in a closed model, the demand matrix D is a zero matrix.

Chapter 2 Review Exercises

1. What is true about the number of solutions to a system of m linear equations in n unknowns if $m = n$? If $m < n$? If $m > n$?

2. Suppose someone says that a more reasonable way to multiply two matrices than the method presented in the text is to multiply corresponding elements. For example, the result of

$$\begin{bmatrix} 1 & 2 \\ 3 & 4 \end{bmatrix} \cdot \begin{bmatrix} 3 & 5 \\ 7 & 11 \end{bmatrix} \quad \text{should be} \quad \begin{bmatrix} 3 & 10 \\ 21 & 44 \end{bmatrix},$$

according to this person. How would you respond?

Solve each system by the echelon method.

3. $2x - 3y = 14$
$3x + 2y = -5$

4. $\dfrac{x}{2} + \dfrac{y}{4} = 3$
$\dfrac{x}{4} - \dfrac{y}{2} = 4$

5. $2x - 3y + z = -5$
$x + 4y + 2z = 13$
$5x + 5y + 3z = 14$

6. $x + 2y + 3z = 9$
$x - 2y = 4$
$3x + 2z = 12$

Solve each system by the Gauss-Jordan method.

7. $2x + 4y = -6$
$-3x - 5y = 12$

8. $x - 4y = 10$
$5x + 3y = 119$

9. $x - y + 3z = 13$
$4x + y + 2z = 17$
$3x + 2y + 2z = 1$

10. $x - 2z = 5$
$3x + 2y = 8$
$-x + 2z = 10$

11. $3x - 6y + 9z = 12$
$-x + 2y - 3z = -4$
$x + y + 2z = 7$

Find the size of each matrix, find the values of any variables, and identify any square, row, or column matrices.

12. $\begin{bmatrix} 2 & 3 \\ 5 & q \end{bmatrix} = \begin{bmatrix} a & b \\ c & 9 \end{bmatrix}$

13. $\begin{bmatrix} 2 & x \\ y & 6 \\ 5 & z \end{bmatrix} = \begin{bmatrix} a & -1 \\ 4 & 6 \\ p & 7 \end{bmatrix}$

14. $\begin{bmatrix} 2m & 4 & 3z & -12 \end{bmatrix} = \begin{bmatrix} 12 & k+1 & -9 & r-3 \end{bmatrix}$

15. $\begin{bmatrix} a+5 & 3b & 6 \\ 4c & 2+d & -3 \\ -1 & 4p & q-1 \end{bmatrix} = \begin{bmatrix} -7 & b+2 & 2k-3 \\ 3 & 2d-1 & 4l \\ m & 12 & 8 \end{bmatrix}$

Given the matrices

$$A = \begin{bmatrix} 4 & 10 \\ -2 & -3 \\ 6 & 9 \end{bmatrix}, \quad B = \begin{bmatrix} 2 & 3 & -2 \\ 2 & 4 & 0 \\ 0 & 1 & 2 \end{bmatrix}, \quad C = \begin{bmatrix} 5 & 0 \\ -1 & 3 \\ 4 & 7 \end{bmatrix},$$

$$D = \begin{bmatrix} 6 \\ 1 \\ 0 \end{bmatrix}, \quad E = \begin{bmatrix} 1 & 3 & -4 \end{bmatrix}, \quad F = \begin{bmatrix} -1 & 4 \\ 3 & 7 \end{bmatrix}, \quad G = \begin{bmatrix} -2 & 0 \\ 1 & 5 \end{bmatrix},$$

find each of the following, if it exists.

16. $A + C$

17. $2G - 4F$

18. $3C + 2A$

19. $B - C$

20. $2A - 5C$

21. AG

22. AC

23. DE

24. ED

25. BD

26. EC

27. F^{-1}

28. B^{-1}

29. $(A + C)^{-1}$

Find the inverse of each matrix that has an inverse.

30. $\begin{bmatrix} 1 & 3 \\ 2 & 7 \end{bmatrix}$

31. $\begin{bmatrix} -4 & 2 \\ 0 & 3 \end{bmatrix}$

32. $\begin{bmatrix} 3 & -6 \\ -4 & 8 \end{bmatrix}$

33. $\begin{bmatrix} 6 & 4 \\ 3 & 2 \end{bmatrix}$

34. $\begin{bmatrix} 2 & -1 & 0 \\ 1 & 0 & 1 \\ 1 & -2 & 0 \end{bmatrix}$

35. $\begin{bmatrix} 2 & 0 & 4 \\ 1 & -1 & 0 \\ 0 & 1 & -2 \end{bmatrix}$

36. $\begin{bmatrix} 1 & 3 & 6 \\ 4 & 0 & 9 \\ 5 & 15 & 30 \end{bmatrix}$

37. $\begin{bmatrix} 2 & -3 & 4 \\ 1 & 5 & 7 \\ -4 & 6 & -8 \end{bmatrix}$

Solve the matrix equation $AX = B$ for X using the given matrices.

38. $A = \begin{bmatrix} 5 & 1 \\ -2 & -2 \end{bmatrix}$, $B = \begin{bmatrix} -8 \\ 24 \end{bmatrix}$

39. $A = \begin{bmatrix} 1 & 2 \\ 2 & 4 \end{bmatrix}$, $B = \begin{bmatrix} 5 \\ 10 \end{bmatrix}$

40. $A = \begin{bmatrix} 1 & 0 & 2 \\ -1 & 1 & 0 \\ 3 & 0 & 4 \end{bmatrix}$, $B = \begin{bmatrix} 8 \\ 4 \\ -6 \end{bmatrix}$

41. $A = \begin{bmatrix} 2 & 4 & 0 \\ 1 & -2 & 0 \\ 0 & 0 & 3 \end{bmatrix}$, $B = \begin{bmatrix} 72 \\ -24 \\ 48 \end{bmatrix}$

Solve each system of equations by inverses.

42. $x + 2y = 4$
$2x - 3y = 1$

43. $5x + 10y = 80$
$3x - 2y = 120$

44. $x + y + z = 1$
$2x + y = -2$
$3y + z = 2$

45. $x - 4y + 2z = -1$
$-2x + y - 3z = -9$
$3x + 5y - 2z = 7$

Find each production matrix, given the following input-output and demand matrices.

46. $A = \begin{bmatrix} 0.01 & 0.05 \\ 0.04 & 0.03 \end{bmatrix}$, $D = \begin{bmatrix} 200 \\ 300 \end{bmatrix}$

47. $A = \begin{bmatrix} 0.2 & 0.1 & 0.3 \\ 0.1 & 0 & 0.2 \\ 0 & 0 & 0.4 \end{bmatrix}$, $D = \begin{bmatrix} 500 \\ 200 \\ 100 \end{bmatrix}$

48. The following system of equations is given.

$$x + 2y + z = 7$$
$$2x - y - z = 2$$
$$3x - 3y + 2z = -5$$

a. Solve by the echelon method.

b. Solve by the Gauss-Jordan method. Compare with the echelon method.

c. Write the system as a matrix equation, $AX = B$.

d. Find the inverse of matrix A from part c.

e. Solve the system using A^{-1} from part d.

→ Applications

In Exercises 49–52, write a system of equations and solve.

49. *Scheduling Production* An office supply manufacturer makes two kinds of paper clips, standard and extra large. To make 1000 standard paper clips requires 1/4 hour on a cutting machine and 1/2 hour on a machine that shapes the clips. One thousand extra large paper clips require 1/3 hour on each machine. The manager of paper clip production has 4 hours per day available on the cutting machine and 6 hours per day on the shaping machine. How many of each kind of clip can he make?

50. *Production Requirements* The Waputi Indians make woven blankets, rugs, and skirts. Each blanket requires 24 hours for spinning the yarn, 4 hours for dyeing the yarn, and 15 hours for weaving. Rugs require 30, 5, and 18 hours and skirts 12, 3, and 9 hours, respectively. If there are 306, 59, and 201 hours available for spinning, dyeing, and weaving, respectively, how many of each item can be made? (*Hint:* Simplify the equations you write, if possible, before solving the system.)

51. *Distribution* An oil refinery in Tulsa sells 50% of its production to a Chicago distributor, 20% to a Dallas distributor, and 30% to an Atlanta distributor. Another refinery in New Orleans sells 40% of its production to the Chicago distributor, 40% to the Dallas distributor, and 20% to the Atlanta distributor. A third refinery in Ardmore sells the same distributors 30%, 40%, and 30% of its production. The three distributors received 219,000, 192,000, and 144,000 gal of oil, respectively. How many gallons of oil were produced at each of the three plants?

52. *Stock Reports* The New York Stock Exchange reports in daily newspapers give the dividend, price-to-earnings ratio, sales (in hundreds of shares), last price, and change in price for each company. Write the following stock reports as a 4 × 5 matrix: American Telephone & Telegraph: 1.33, 17.6, 152,000, 26.75, +1.88; General Electric: 1.00, 20.0, 238,200, 32.36, −1.50; Sara Lee: 0.79, 25.4, 39,110, 16.51, −0.89; Walt Disney Company: 0.27, 21.2, 122,500, 28.60, +0.75.

53. *Filling Orders* A printer has three orders for pamphlets that require three kinds of paper, as shown in the following matrix.

		Order		
		I	II	III
	High-grade	10	5	8
Paper	Medium-grade	12	0	4
	Coated	0	10	5

The printer has on hand 3170 sheets of high-grade paper, 2360 sheets of medium-grade paper, and 1800 sheets of coated paper. All the paper must be used in preparing the order.

a. Write a 3 × 1 matrix for the amounts of paper on hand.

b. Write a matrix of variables to represent the number of pamphlets that must be printed in each of the three orders.

c. Write a matrix equation using the given matrix and your matrices from parts a and b.

d. Solve the equation from part c.

54. *Input-Output* An economy depends on two commodities, goats and cheese. It takes 2/3 of a unit of goats to produce 1 unit of cheese and 1/2 unit of cheese to produce 1 unit of goats.

a. Write the input-output matrix for this economy.

b. Find the production required to satisfy a demand of 400 units of cheese and 800 units of goats.

55. *Nebraska* The 1970 economy of the state of Nebraska has been condensed to six sectors: livestock, crops, food products, mining and manufacturing, households, and other. The input-output matrix is given below.*

$$
\begin{bmatrix}
0.178 & 0.018 & 0.411 & 0 & 0.005 & 0 \\
0.143 & 0.018 & 0.088 & 0 & 0.001 & 0 \\
0.089 & 0 & 0.035 & 0 & 0.060 & 0.003 \\
0.001 & 0.010 & 0.012 & 0.063 & 0.007 & 0.014 \\
0.141 & 0.252 & 0.088 & 0.089 & 0.402 & 0.124 \\
0.188 & 0.156 & 0.103 & 0.255 & 0.008 & 0.474
\end{bmatrix}
$$

a. Find the matrix $(I - A)^{-1}$ and interpret the value in row 2, column 1 of this matrix.

b. Suppose the demand (in millions of dollars) is

$$
D = \begin{bmatrix}
1980 \\
650 \\
1750 \\
1000 \\
2500 \\
3750
\end{bmatrix}.
$$

Find the dollar amount of each commodity that should be produced.

*Lamphear, F. Charles and Theodore Roesler, "1970 Nebraska Input-Output Tables," *Nebraska Economic and Business Report No. 10*, Bureau of Business Research, University of Nebraska-Lincoln, 1971.

LIFE SCIENCES

56. *Animal Activity* The activities of a grazing animal can be classified roughly into three categories: grazing, moving, and resting. Suppose horses spend 8 hours grazing, 8 moving, and 8 resting; cattle spend 10 grazing, 5 moving, and 9 resting; sheep spend 7 grazing, 10 moving, and 7 resting; and goats spend 8 grazing, 9 moving, and 7 resting. Write this information as a 4 × 3 matrix.

57. *CAT Scans* Computer Aided Tomography (CAT) scanners take X-rays of a part of the body from different directions, and put the information together to create a picture of a cross section of the body.* The amount by which the energy of the X-ray decreases, measured in linear-attenuation units, tells whether the X-ray has passed through healthy tissue, tumorous tissue, or bone, based on the following table.

Type of Tissue	Linear-Attenuation Values
Healthy tissue	0.1625–0.2977
Tumorous tissue	0.2679–0.3930
Bone	0.3857–0.5108

The part of the body to be scanned is divided into cells. If an X-ray passes through more than one cell, the total linear-attenuation value is the sum of the values for the cells. For example, in the figure, let a, b, and c be the values for cells A, B, and C. The attenuation value for beam 1 is $a + b$ and for beam 2 is $a + c$.

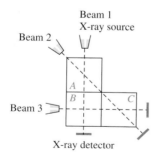

a. Find the attenuation value for beam 3.

b. Suppose that the attenuation values are 0.8, 0.55, and 0.65 for beams 1, 2, and 3, respectively. Set up and solve the system of three equations for a, b, and c. What can you conclude about cells A, B, and C?

c. Find the inverse of the coefficient matrix from part b to find a, b, and c for the following three cases, and make conclusions about cells A, B, and C for each.

	Linear-Attenuation Values		
Patient	Beam 1	Beam 2	Beam 3
X	0.54	0.40	0.52
Y	0.65	0.80	0.75
Z	0.51	0.49	0.44

58. *CAT Scans* (Refer to Exercise 57.)* Four X-ray beams are aimed at four cells, as shown in the following figure.

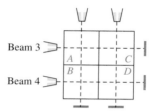

a. Suppose the attenuation values for beams 1, 2, 3, and 4 are 0.60, 0.75, 0.65, and 0.70, respectively. Do we have enough information to determine the values of a, b, c, and d? Explain.

b. Suppose we have the data from part a, as well as the following values for d. Find the values for a, b, and c, and draw conclusions about cells A, B, C, and D in each case.

(i) 0.33   **(ii)** 0.43

c. Two X-ray beams are added, as shown in the figure. In addition to the data in part a, we now have attenuation values for beams 5 and 6 of 0.85 and 0.50. Find the values for a, b, c, and d, and make conclusions about cells A, B, C, and D.

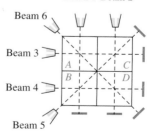

*Exercises 57 and 58 are based on the article "Medical Applications of Linear Equations" by David Jabon, Gail Nord, Bryce W. Wilson, and Penny Coffman, *The Mathematics Teacher*, Vol. 89, No. 5, May 1996, p. 398.

d. Six X-ray beams are not necessary because four appropriately chosen beams are sufficient. Give two examples of four beams (chosen from beams 1–6 in part c) that will give the solution. (*Note:* There are 12 possible solutions.)

e. Discuss what properties the four beams selected in part d must have in order to provide a unique solution.

59. *Hockey* In a recent study, the number of head and neck injuries among hockey players wearing full face shields and half face shields were compared. The following table provides the rates per 1000 athlete-exposures for specific injuries that caused a player wearing either shield to miss one or more events.*

	Half Shield	**Full Shield**
Head and Face Injuries *(Excluding Concussions)*	3.54	1.41
Concussions	1.53	1.57
Neck Injuries	0.34	0.29
Other	7.53	6.21

If an equal number of players in a large league wear each type of shield and the total number of athlete-exposures for the league in a season is 8000, use matrix operations to estimate the total number of injuries of each type.

PHYSICAL SCIENCES

60. *Roof Trusses* Linear systems occur in the design of roof trusses for new homes and buildings. The simplest type of roof truss is a triangle. The truss shown in the figure below is used to frame roofs of small buildings. If a 100-lb force is applied at the peak of the truss, then the forces or weights W_1 and W_2 exerted parallel to each rafter of the truss are determined by the following linear system of equations.

$$\frac{\sqrt{3}}{2}(W_1 + W_2) = 100$$

$$W_1 - W_2 = 0$$

Solve the system to find W_1 and W_2.[†]

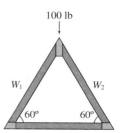

61. *Roof Trusses* (Refer to Exercise 60.) Use the following system of equations to determine the force or weights W_1 and W_2 exerted on each rafter for the truss shown in the figure.

$$\frac{1}{2}W_1 + \frac{\sqrt{2}}{2}W_2 = 150$$

$$\frac{\sqrt{3}}{2}W_1 - \frac{\sqrt{2}}{2}W_2 = 0$$

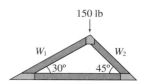

*Benson, Brian, Nicholas Nohtadi, Sarah Rose, and Willem Meeuwisse, "Head and Neck Injuries Among Ice Hockey Players Wearing Full Face Shields vs. Half Face Shields," *JAMA*, Vol. 282, No. 24, Dec. 22/29, 1999, pp. 2328–2332.
†Hibbeler, R., *Structural Analysis*, Prentice-Hall, 1995.

62. *Carbon Dioxide* Determining the amount of carbon dioxide in the atmosphere is important because carbon dioxide is known to be a greenhouse gas. Carbon dioxide concentrations (in parts per million) have been measured at Mauna Loa, Hawaii, for more than 40 years. The concentrations have increased quadratically.* The table lists readings for 3 years.

Year	CO_2
1960	317
1980	339
2004	377

a. If the relationship between the carbon dioxide concentration C and the year t is expressed as $C = at^2 + bt + c$, where $t = 0$ corresponds to 1960, use a linear system of equations to determine the constants a, b, and c.

b. Predict the year when the amount of carbon dioxide in the atmosphere will double from its 1960 level. (*Hint:* This requires solving a quadratic equation. For review on how to do this, see Section R.4.)

63. *Chemistry* When carbon monoxide (CO) reacts with oxygen (O_2), carbon dioxide (CO_2) is formed. This can be written as $CO + (1/2)O_2 = CO_2$ and as a matrix equation.[†] If we form a 2×1 column matrix by letting the first element be the number of carbon atoms and the second element be the number of oxygen atoms, then CO would have the column matrix

$$\begin{bmatrix} 1 \\ 1 \end{bmatrix}.$$

Similarly, O_2 and CO_2 would have the column matrices $\begin{bmatrix} 0 \\ 2 \end{bmatrix}$ and $\begin{bmatrix} 1 \\ 2 \end{bmatrix}$, respectively.

a. Use the Gauss-Jordan method to find numbers x and y (known as *stoichiometric numbers*) that solve the system of equations

$$\begin{bmatrix} 1 \\ 1 \end{bmatrix} x + \begin{bmatrix} 0 \\ 2 \end{bmatrix} y = \begin{bmatrix} 1 \\ 2 \end{bmatrix}.$$

Compare your answers to the equation written above.

b. Repeat the process for $xCO_2 + yH_2 + zCO = H_2O$, where H_2 is hydrogen, and H_2O is water. In words, what does this mean?

GENERAL INTEREST

64. *Students* Suppose 20% of the boys and 30% of the girls in a high school like tennis, and 60% of the boys and 90% of the girls like math. If 500 students like tennis and 1500 like math, how many boys and girls are in the school? Find all possible solutions.

65. *Baseball* In the 2004 Major League Baseball season, slugger Barry Bonds had a total of 135 hits. Bonds hit 15 times as many home runs as triples, and he hit 50% more home runs than doubles and triples. He also hit twice as many singles as doubles and triples.[‡] Find the number of singles, doubles, triples, and home runs that Bonds hit during the season.

66. *Cookies* Regular Nabisco Oreo cookies are made of two chocolate cookie wafers surrounding a single layer of vanilla cream. The claim on the package states that a single serving is 34 g, which is three cookies. Nabisco Double Stuf cookies are made of the same two chocolate cookie wafers surrounding a double layer of vanilla cream. The claim on this package states that a single serving is 29 g, which is two Double Stuf cookies. If the Double Stuf cookies truly have a double layer of vanilla cream, find the weight of a single chocolate wafer and the weight of a single layer of vanilla cream.

---

*Atmospheric Carbon Dioxide Record from Mauna Loa, University of California, La Jolla, http://cdiac.esd.ornl.gov/ftp/trends/co2/maunaloa.co2.
[†]Alberty, Robert, "Chemical Equations Are Actually Matrix Equations," *Journal of Chemical Education*, Vol. 68, No. 12, Dec. 1991, p. 984.
[‡]http://www.baseball-reference.com.

Contagion

Suppose that three people have contracted a contagious disease.* A second group of five people may have been in contact with the three infected persons. A third group of six people may have been in contact with the second group. We can form a 3×5 matrix P with rows representing the first group of three and columns representing the second group of five. We enter a one in the corresponding position if a person in the first group has contact with a person in the second group. These direct contacts are called *first-order contacts*. Similarly, we form a 5×6 matrix Q representing the first-order contacts between the second and third group. For example, suppose

$$P = \begin{bmatrix} 1 & 0 & 0 & 1 & 0 \\ 0 & 0 & 1 & 1 & 0 \\ 1 & 1 & 0 & 0 & 0 \end{bmatrix} \text{ and}$$

$$Q = \begin{bmatrix} 1 & 1 & 0 & 1 & 1 & 1 \\ 0 & 0 & 0 & 0 & 1 & 0 \\ 0 & 0 & 0 & 0 & 0 & 0 \\ 0 & 1 & 0 & 1 & 0 & 0 \\ 1 & 0 & 0 & 0 & 1 & 0 \end{bmatrix}.$$

From matrix P we see that the first person in the first group had contact with the first and fourth persons in the second group. Also, none of the first group had contact with the last person in the second group.

A *second-order contact* is an indirect contact between persons in the first and third groups through some person in the second group. The product matrix PQ indicates these contacts. Verify that the second-row, fourth-column entry of PQ is 1. That is, there is one second-order contact between the second person in group one and the fourth person in group three. Let a_{ij} denote the element in the ith row and jth column of the matrix PQ. By looking at the products that form a_{24} below, we see that the common contact was with the fourth individual in group two. (The p_{ij} are entries in P, and the q_{ij} are entries in Q.)

$$a_{24} = p_{21}q_{14} + p_{22}q_{24} + p_{23}q_{34} + p_{24}q_{44} + p_{25}q_{54}$$
$$= 0 \cdot 1 + 0 \cdot 0 + 1 \cdot 0 + 1 \cdot 1 + 0 \cdot 0$$
$$= 1$$

The second person in group 1 and the fourth person in group 3 both had contact with the fourth person in group 2.

This idea could be extended to third-, fourth-, and larger-order contacts. It indicates a way to use matrices to trace the spread of a contagious disease. It could also pertain to the dispersal of ideas or anything that might pass from one individual to another.

EXERCISES

1. Find the second-order contact matrix PQ mentioned in the text.

2. How many second-order contacts were there between the second contagious person and the third person in the third group?

3. Is there anyone in the third group who has had no contacts at all with the first group?

4. The totals of the columns in PQ give the total number of second-order contacts per person, while the column totals in P and Q give the total number of first-order contacts per person. Which person(s) in the third group had the most contacts, counting first- and second-order contacts?

DIRECTIONS FOR GROUP PROJECT

Assume that your group (3–5 students) is trying to map the spread of a new disease. Suppose also that the information given above has been obtained from interviews with the first three people that were hospitalized with symptoms of the disease and their contacts. Using the questions above as a guide, prepare a presentation for a public meeting that describes the method of obtaining the data, the data itself, and addresses the spirit of each question. Formulate a strategy for how to handle the spread of this disease to other people. The presentation should be mathematically sound, grammatically correct, and professionally crafted. Use presentation software, such as Microsoft PowerPoint, to present your findings.

---

*Grossman, Stanley, "First and Second Order Contact to a Contagious Disease." *Finite Mathematics with Applications to Business, Life Sciences, and Social Sciences*, WCB/McGraw-Hill, 1993.

3

Linear Programming: The Graphical Method

▶ An oil refinery turns crude oil into many different products, including gasoline and fuel oil. Efficient management requires matching the output of each product to the demand and the available shipping capacity. In an exercise in Section 3, we explore the use of linear programming to allocate refinery production for maximum profit.

Many realistic problems involve inequalities—a factory can manufacture *no more* than 12 items on a shift, or a medical researcher must interview *at least* a hundred patients to be sure that a new treatment for a disease is better than the old treatment. *Linear inequalities* of the form $ax + by \leq c$ (or with $\geq$, $<$, or $>$ instead of $\leq$) can be used in a process called *linear programming* to *optimize* (find the maximum or minimum value of a quantity) for a given situation.

In this chapter we introduce some *linear programming* problems that can be solved by graphical methods. Then, in Chapter 4, we discuss the simplex method, a general method for solving linear programming problems with many variables.

3.1 Graphing Linear Inequalities

? THINK ABOUT IT

How can a company determine the feasible number of units of each product to manufacture in order to meet all production requirements?

We can answer this question by graphing a set of inequalities.

As mentioned above, a linear inequality is defined as follows.

LINEAR INEQUALITY

A **linear inequality** in two variables has the form

$$ax + by \leq c$$
$$ax + by < c,$$
$$ax + by \geq c,$$
or
$$ax + by > c,$$

for real numbers a, b, and c, with a and b not both 0.

EXAMPLE 1 Graphing an Inequality

Graph the linear inequality $2x - 3y \leq 12$.

►FOR REVIEW

Recall from Chapter 1 that one way to sketch a line is to first let $x = 0$ to find the y-intercept, then let $y = 0$ to find the x-intercept. For example, given $2x - 3y = 12$, letting $x = 0$ yields $-3y = 12$, so $y = -4$, and the corresponding point is $(0, -4)$. Letting $y = 0$ yields $2x = 12$, so $x = 6$ and the point is $(6, 0)$. Plot these two points, as in Figure 1, then use a straightedge to draw a line through them.

►Solution Because of the "=" portion of $\leq$, the points of the line $2x - 3y = 12$ satisfy the linear inequality $2x - 3y \leq 12$ and are part of its graph. As in Chapter 1, find the intercepts by first letting $x = 0$ and then letting $y = 0$; use these points to get the graph of $2x - 3y = 12$ shown in Figure 1.

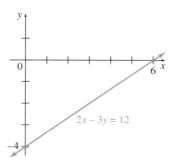

FIGURE 1

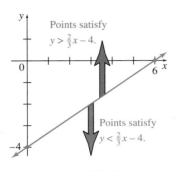

FIGURE 2

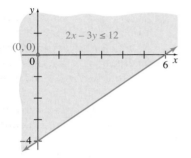

FIGURE 3

The points on the line satisfy "$2x - 3y$ *equals* 12." To locate the points satisfying "$2x - 3y$ *is less than* or equal to 12," first solve $2x - 3y \leq 12$ for y.

$$2x - 3y \leq 12$$
$$-3y \leq -2x + 12 \qquad \text{Subtract } 2x.$$
$$y \geq \frac{2}{3}x - 4 \qquad \text{Multiply by } -\frac{1}{3}.$$

(Recall that multiplying both sides of an inequality by a negative number reverses the direction of the inequality symbol.)

As shown in Figure 2, the points *above* the line $2x - 3y = 12$ satisfy

$$y > \frac{2}{3}x - 4,$$

while those below the line satisfy

$$y < \frac{2}{3}x - 4.$$

In summary, the inequality $2x - 3y \leq 12$ is satisfied by all points *on or above* the line $2x - 3y = 12$. Indicate the points above the line by shading, as in Figure 3. The line and shaded region in Figure 3 make up the graph of the linear inequality $2x - 3y \leq 12$.

CAUTION In this chapter, be sure to use a straightedge to draw lines, and to plot the points with care. A sloppily drawn line could give a deceptive picture of the region being considered. ∎

In Example 1, the line $2x - 3y = 12$, which separates the points in the solution from the points that are not in the solution, is called the **boundary**.

There is an alternative way to find the correct region to shade, or to check the method shown above. Choose as a test point any point not on the boundary line. For example, in Example 1 we could choose the point $(0, 0)$, which is not on the line $2x - 3y = 12$. Substitute 0 for x and 0 for y in the given inequality.

$$2x - 3y \leq 12$$
$$2(0) - 3(0) \leq 12$$
$$0 \leq 12 \qquad \text{True}$$

Since the result $0 \leq 12$ is true, the test point $(0, 0)$ belongs on the side of the boundary where all points satisfy $2x - 3y < 12$. For this reason, we shade the side containing $(0, 0)$, as in Figure 3. Choosing a point on the other side of the line, such as $(4, -3)$, would produce a false result when the values $x = 4$ and $y = -3$ were substituted into the given inequality. In such a case, we would shade the side of the line *not including* the test point.

EXAMPLE 2 **Graphing an Inequality**
Graph $x - 4y > 4$.

▶**Solution** The boundary here is the line $x - 4y = 4$. Since the points on this line do not satisfy $x - 4y > 4$, the line is drawn dashed, as in Figure 4. To

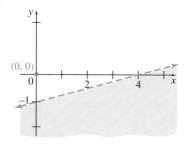

FIGURE 4

decide whether to shade the region above the line or the region below the line, we will choose a test point not on the boundary line. Choosing (0, 0), we replace x with 0 and y with 0:

$$x - 4y > 4$$
$$0 - 4(0) > 4$$
$$0 > 4. \quad \text{False}$$

The correct half-plane is the one that does *not* contain (0, 0); the region below the boundary line is shaded, as shown in Figure 4.

CAUTION Be careful. If the point $(0, 0)$ is on the boundary line, it cannot be used as a test point. ■

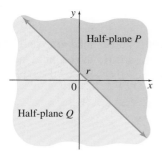

FIGURE 5

As the examples above suggest, the graph of a linear inequality is represented by a shaded region in the plane, perhaps including the line that is the boundary of the region. Each shaded region is an example of a **half-plane**, a region on one side of a line. For example, in Figure 5 line r divides the plane into half-planes P and Q. The points on r belong neither to P nor to Q. Line r is the boundary of each half-plane.

Graphing calculators can shade regions on the plane. Casio has an inequality mode that offers options for $y >$, $y <$, $y \geq$, or $y \leq$. Refer to your instruction book for details.

TI calculators have a DRAW menu that includes an option to shade above or below a line. For instance, to graph the inequality in Example 2, first solve the equation for y, then use your calculator to graph the line $y = (1/4)x - 1$. Select the DRAW feature, then the Shade option, which requires an upper and a lower boundary for the region to be shaded. To match Figure 5, choose for the lower boundary a horizontal line that lies below the bottom of the graphing calculator screen. We will use a standard window with $-10 \leq y \leq 10$, and so we let $y = -20$ be the lower boundary. For the upper boundary, use $y = (1/4)x - 1$. Then the command Shade(−20, (1/4)X − 1) produces Figure 6(a).

The TI-83/84 Plus calculator offers another way to graph the region above or below a line. Press the y= key. Note the slanted line to the right of Y_1, Y_2, and so on. Use the left arrow key to move the cursor to that position for Y_1. Press ENTER until you see the symbol ◤. This indicates that the calculator will shade below the line whose equation is entered in Y_1. (The symbol ◥ operates similarly to shade above a line.) We used this method to get the graph in Figure 6(b).

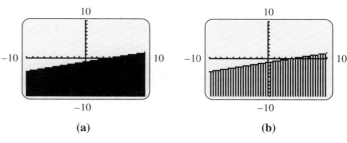

(a)   (b)

FIGURE 6

Notice that you cannot tell from the calculator graph whether the boundary line is solid or dashed. It is important to understand the concepts in order to interpret the graph correctly. In this case, the points on the line are not part of the solution, because of the strict inequality, $<$.

See *The Spreadsheet Manual* available with this book for information on graphing linear inequalities with a spreadsheet.

The steps in graphing a linear inequality are summarized below.

GRAPHING A LINEAR INEQUALITY

1. Draw the graph of the boundary line. Make the line solid if the inequality involves $\leq$ or $\geq$; make the line dashed if the inequality involves $<$ or $>$.

2. Decide which half-plane to shade. Use either of the following methods.

   a. Solve the inequality for y; shade the region above the line if the inequality is of the form $y >$ or $y \geq$; shade the region below the line if the inequality is of the form $y <$ or $y \leq$.

   b. Choose any point not on the line as a test point. Shade the half-plane that includes the test point if the test point satisfies the original inequality; otherwise, shade the half-plane on the other side of the boundary line.

Systems of Inequalities   Realistic problems often involve many inequalities. For example, a manufacturing problem might produce inequalities resulting from production requirements as well as inequalities about cost requirements. A collection of at least two inequalities is called a **system of inequalities**. The solution of a system of inequalities is made up of all those points that satisfy all the inequalities of the system at the same time. To graph the solution of a system of inequalities, graph all the inequalities on the same axes and identify, by heavy shading, the region common to all graphs. The next example shows how this is done.

NOTE   When shading regions by hand, it may be difficult to tell what is shaded heavily and what is shaded only lightly, particularly when more than two inequalities are involved. In such cases, an alternative technique is to shade the region *opposite* that of the inequality. In other words, the region that is *not* wanted can be shaded. Then, when the various regions are shaded, whatever is not shaded is the desired region. We will not use this technique in this text, but you may wish to try it on your own.   ■

EXAMPLE 3   **Graphing a System of Inequalities**
Graph the system

$$y < -3x + 12$$

$$x < 2y.$$

▶**Solution**   The graph of the first inequality has the line $y = -3x + 12$ as its boundary. Because of the $<$ symbol, we use a dotted line and shade *below* the line. The second inequality should first be solved for y to get $y > (1/2)x$ to see that the graph is the region *above* the dotted boundary line $y = (1/2)x$.

The heavily shaded region in Figure 7(a) shows all the points that satisfy both inequalities of the system. Since the points on the boundary lines are not in the solution, the boundary lines are dashed.

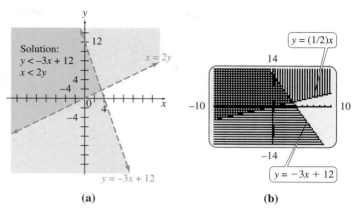

FIGURE 7

A calculator graph of the system in Example 3 is shown in Figure 7(b). You can also graph this system on your calculator using $\text{Shade}(Y_2, Y_1)$.

A region consisting of the overlapping parts of two or more graphs of inequalities in a system, such as the heavily shaded region in Figure 7, is sometimes called the **region of feasible solutions** or the **feasible region**, since it is made up of all the points that satisfy (are feasible for) all inequalities of the system.

EXAMPLE 4 **Graphing a Feasible Region**
Graph the feasible region for the system

$$y \leq -2x + 8$$
$$-2 \leq x \leq 1.$$

▶**Solution** The boundary line of the first inequality is $y = -2x + 8$. Because of the $\leq$ symbol, we use a solid line and shade *below* the line.

The second inequality is a compound inequality, indicating $-2 \leq x$ *and* $x \leq 1$. Recall that the graph $x = -2$ is the vertical line through $(-2, 0)$, and the graph $x = 1$ is the vertical line through $(1, 0)$. For $-2 \leq x$ we draw a vertical line and shade the region to the right. For $x \leq 1$, we draw a vertical line and shade the region to the left.

The shaded region in Figure 8 shows all the points that satisfy the system of inequalities.

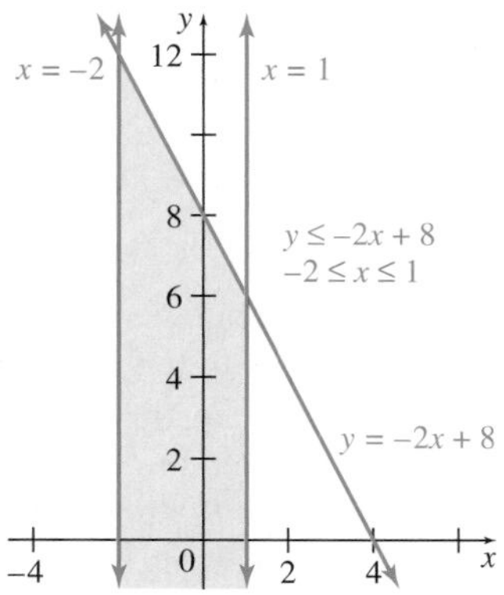

FIGURE 8

EXAMPLE 5 **Graphing a Feasible Region**
Graph the feasible region for the system

$$2x - 5y \leq 10$$
$$x + 2y \leq 8$$
$$x \geq 0$$
$$y \geq 0.$$

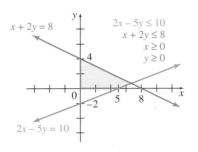

$x + 2y = 8$

$2x - 5y \leq 10$
$x + 2y \leq 8$
$x \geq 0$
$y \geq 0$

$2x - 5y = 10$

FIGURE 9

►**Solution** On the same axes, graph each inequality by graphing the boundary and choosing the appropriate half-plane. Then find the feasible region by locating the overlap of all the half-planes. This feasible region is shaded in Figure 9.

NOTE The inequalities $x \geq 0$ and $y \geq 0$ restrict the feasible region to the first quadrant. ■

Applications As shown in the rest of this chapter, many realistic problems lead to systems of linear inequalities. The next example is typical of such problems.

EXAMPLE 6 **Manufacturing**

Happy Ice Cream Cone Company makes cake cones and sugar cones, both of which must be processed in the mixing department and the baking department. Manufacturing one batch of cake cones requires 1 hour in the mixing department and 2 hours in the baking department, and producing one batch of sugar cones requires 2 hours in the mixing department and 1 hour in the baking department. Each department is operated for at most 12 hours per day.

(a) Write a system of inequalities that expresses these restrictions.

►**Solution** Let x represent the number of batches of cake cones made and y represent the number of batches of sugar cones made. Then, make a table that summarizes the given information.

	Cake	Sugar		Total
Number of Units Made	x	y		
Hours in Mixing Dept.	1	2	$\leq$	12
Hours in Baking Dept.	2	1	$\leq$	12

Since the departments operate at most 12 hours per day, we put the total number of hours as ≤ 12. Putting the inequality ($\leq$ or $\geq$) next to the number in the chart may help you remember which way to write the inequality.

In the mixing department, x batches of cake cones require a total of $1 \cdot x = x$ hours, and y batches of sugar cones require $2 \cdot y = 2y$ hours. Since the mixing department can operate no more than 12 hours per day,

$$x + 2y \leq 12. \quad \text{Mixing department}$$

We translated "no more than" as "less than or equal to." Notice how this inequality corresponds to the row in the table for the mixing department. Similarly, the row corresponding to the baking department gives

$$2x + y \leq 12. \quad \text{Baking department}$$

Since it is not possible to produce a negative number of cake cones or sugar cones,

$$x \geq 0 \quad \text{and} \quad y \geq 0.$$

(b) Graph the feasible region.

▶**Solution** The feasible region for this system of inequalities is shown in Figure 10.

(c) Using the graph from part (b), can 3 batches of cake cones and 2 batches of sugar cones be manufactured in one day? Can 4 batches of cake cones and 6 batches of sugar cones be manufactured in one day?

▶**Solution** Three batches of cake cones and two batches of sugar cones correspond to the point $(3, 2)$. Since $(3, 2)$ is in the feasible region in Figure 10, it is possible to manufacture these quantities in one day. However, since $(4, 6)$ is *not* in the feasible region in Figure 10, it is *not* possible to manufacture 4 batches of cake cones and 6 batches of sugar cones in one day.

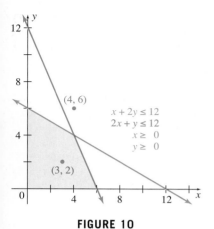

FIGURE 10

The following steps summarize the process of finding the feasible region.

1. Form a table that summarizes the information.

2. Convert the table into a set of linear inequalities.

3. Graph each linear inequality.

4. Graph the region that is common to all the regions graphed in step 3.

➤ 3.1 Exercises

Graph each linear inequality.

1. $x + y \leq 2$

2. $y \leq x + 1$

3. $x \geq 2 - y$

4. $y \geq x - 3$

5. $4x - y < 6$

6. $4y + x > 6$

7. $4x + y < 8$

8. $2x - y > 2$

9. $x + 3y \geq -2$

10. $2x + 3y \leq 6$

11. $x \leq 3y$

12. $2x \geq y$

13. $x + y \leq 0$

14. $3x + 2y \geq 0$

15. $y < x$

16. $y > 5x$

17. $x < 4$

18. $y > 5$

19. $y \leq -2$

20. $x \geq -4$

Graph the feasible region for each system of inequalities.

21. $x + y \leq 1$
  $x - y \geq 2$

22. $4x - y < 6$
  $3x + y < 9$

23. $x + 3y \leq 6$
  $2x + 4y \geq 7$

24. $-x - y < 5$
  $2x - y < 4$

25. $x + y \leq \ \ 7$
  $x - y \leq -4$
  $4x + y \geq \ \ 0$

26. $3x - 2y \geq \ \ 6$
  $x + \ \ y \leq -5$
  $y \leq \ \ 4$

27. $-2 < x < 3$
  $-1 \leq y \leq 5$
  $2x + y < 6$

28. $1 < x < 4$
  $y > 2$
  $x > y$

29. $y - 2x \leq 4$
  $y \geq 2 - x$
  $x \geq 0$
  $y \geq 0$

30. $2x + 3y \leq \ \ 12$
  $2x + 3y > -6$
  $3x + y < \ \ 4$
  $x \geq \ \ 0$
  $y \geq \ \ 0$

31. $3x + 4y > 12$
  $2x - 3y < \ \ 6$
  $0 \leq y \leq \ \ 2$
  $x \geq \ \ 0$

32. $0 \leq x \leq \ \ 9$
  $x - 2y \geq \ \ 4$
  $3x + 5y \leq 30$
  $y \geq 0$

Use a graphing calculator to graph the following.

33. $2x - 6y > 12$

34. $4x - 3y < 12$

35. $3x - 4y < \ \ 6$
  $2x + 5y > 15$

36. $6x - 4y > 8$
  $2x + 5y < 5$

37. The regions A through G in the figure can be described by the inequalities

$$x + 3y \;?\; 6$$
$$x + y \;?\; 3$$
$$x - 2y \;?\; 2$$
$$x \geq 0$$
$$y \geq 0,$$

where ? can be either $\leq$ or $\geq$. For each region, tell what the ? should be in the three inequalities. For example, for region A, the ? should be $\geq$, $\leq$, and $\leq$, because region A is described by the inequalities

$$x + 3y \geq 6$$
$$x + y \leq 3$$
$$x - 2y \leq 2$$
$$x \geq 0$$
$$y \geq 0.$$

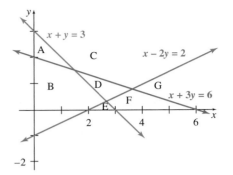

▶ Applications

38. *Production Scheduling* A small pottery shop makes two kinds of planters, glazed and unglazed. The glazed type requires 1/2 hour to throw on the wheel and 1 hour in the kiln. The unglazed type takes 1 hour to throw on the wheel and 6 hours in the kiln. The wheel is available for at most 8 hours per day, and the kiln for at most 20 hours per day.

a. Complete the following table.

	Glazed	Unglazed	Total
Number Made	x	y	
Time on Wheel			
Time in Kiln			

b. Set up a system of inequalities and graph the feasible region.

c. Using your graph from part b, can 5 glazed and 2 unglazed planters be made? Can 10 glazed and 2 unglazed planters be made?

39. *Time Management* Carmella and Walt produce handmade shawls and afghans. They spin the yarn, dye it, and then weave it. A shawl requires 1 hour of spinning, 1 hour of dyeing, and 1 hour of weaving. An afghan needs 2 hours of spinning, 1 hour of dyeing, and 4 hours of weaving. Together, they spend at most 8 hours spinning, 6 hours dyeing, and 14 hours weaving.

a. Complete the following table.

	Shawls	Afghans	Total
Number Made	x	y	
Spinning Time			
Dyeing Time			
Weaving Time			

b. Set up a system of inequalities and graph the feasible region.

c. Using your graph from part b, can 3 shawls and 2 afghans be made? Can 4 shawls and 3 afghans be made?

For Exercises 40–45, perform the following steps.

a. *Write a system of inequalities to express the conditions of the problem.*

b. *Graph the feasible region of the system.*

40. *Transportation* Southwestern Oil supplies two distributors located in the Northwest. One distributor needs at least 3000 barrels of oil, and the other needs at least 5000 barrels. Southwestern can send out at most 10,000 barrels. Let x = the number of barrels of oil sent to distributor 1 and y = the number sent to distributor 2.

41. *Finance* The loan department in a bank will use at most $30 million for commercial and home loans. The bank's policy is to allocate at least four times as much money to home loans as to commercial loans. The bank's return is 6% on a home loan and 8% on a commercial loan. The manager of the loan department wants to earn a return of at least $1.6 million on these loans. Let x = the amount (in millions) for home loans and y = the amount (in millions) for commercial loans.

42. *Transportation* The California Almond Growers have at most 2400 boxes of almonds to be shipped from their plant in Sacramento to Des Moines and San Antonio. The Des Moines market needs at least 1000 boxes, while the San Antonio market must have at least 800 boxes. Let x = the number of boxes to be shipped to Des Moines and y = the number of boxes to be shipped to San Antonio.

43. *Management* The Gillette Company produces two popular battery-operated razors, the M3Power™ and the Fusion Power™. Because of demand, the number of M3Power™ razors is never more than one-half the number of Fusion Power™ razors. The factory's production cannot exceed 800 razors per day. Let x = the number of M3Power™ razors and y = the number of Fusion Power™ razors produced per day.

44. *Production Scheduling* A cement manufacturer produces at least 3.2 million barrels of cement annually. He is told by the Environmental Protection Agency (EPA) that his operation emits 2.5 lb of dust for each barrel produced. The EPA has ruled that annual emissions must be reduced to no more than 1.8 million lb. To do this, the manufacturer plans to replace the present dust collectors with two types of electronic precipitators. One type would reduce emissions to 0.5 lb per barrel and operating costs would be 16¢ per barrel. The other would reduce the dust to 0.3 lb per barrel and operating costs would be 20¢ per barrel. The manufacturer does not want to spend more than 0.8 million dollars in operating costs on the precipitators. He needs to know how many barrels he could produce with each type. Let x = the number of barrels (in millions) produced with the first type and y = the number of barrels (in millions) produced with the second type.

LIFE SCIENCES

45. *Nutrition* A dietician is planning a snack package of fruit and nuts. Each ounce of fruit will supply 1 unit of protein, 2 units of carbohydrates, and 1 unit of fat. Each ounce of nuts will supply 1 unit of protein, 1 unit of carbohydrates, and 1 unit of fat. Every package must provide at least 7 units of protein, at least 10 units of carbohydrates, and no more than 9 units of fat. Let x = the ounces of fruit and y = the ounces of nuts to be used in each package.

3.2 Solving Linear Programming Problems Graphically

Many mathematical models designed to solve problems in business, biology, and economics involve finding an optimum value (maximum or minimum) of a function, subject to certain restrictions. In a **linear programming** problem, we must find the maximum or minimum value of a function, called the **objective function**, and also satisfy a set of restrictions, or **constraints**, given by linear inequalities. When only two variables are involved, the solution to a linear programming problem can be found by first graphing the set of constraints, then finding the feasible region as discussed in the previous section. This method is explained in the following example.

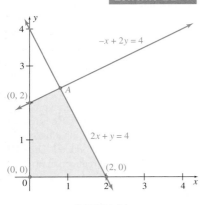

FIGURE 11

EXAMPLE 1 **Maximization**

Find the maximum value of the objective function $z = 3x + 4y$, subject to the following constraints.

$$2x + y \leq 4$$
$$-x + 2y \leq 4$$
$$x \geq 0$$
$$y \geq 0$$

▶**Solution** The feasible region is graphed in Figure 11. We can find the coordinates of point A, $(4/5, 12/5)$, by solving the system

$$2x + y = 4$$
$$-x + 2y = 4.$$

Every point in the feasible region satisfies all the constraints; however, we want to find those points that produce the maximum possible value of the objective function. To see how to find this maximum value, change the graph of Figure 11 by adding lines that represent the objective function $z = 3x + 4y$ for various sample values of z. By choosing the values 0, 5, 10, and 15 for z, the objective function becomes (in turn)

$$0 = 3x + 4y, \quad 5 = 3x + 4y, \quad 10 = 3x + 4y, \quad \text{and} \quad 15 = 3x + 4y.$$

These four lines are graphed in Figure 12. (Why are the lines parallel?) The figure shows that z cannot take on the value 15 because the graph for $z = 15$ is entirely outside the feasible region. The maximum possible value of z will be obtained from a line parallel to the others and between the lines representing the objective function when $z = 10$ and $z = 15$. The value of z will be as large as possible and all constraints will be satisfied if this line just touches the feasible region. This occurs at point A. We find that A has coordinates $(4/5, 12/5)$. (See the review in the margin.) The value of z at this point is

$$z = 3x + 4y = 3\left(\frac{4}{5}\right) + 4\left(\frac{12}{5}\right) = \frac{60}{5} = 12.$$

▶**FOR REVIEW**

Recall from Chapter 2 that two equations in two unknowns can be solved by using row operations to eliminate one variable. For example, to solve the system

$$2x + y = 4$$
$$-x + 2y = 4,$$

we could take the first equation plus 2 times the second to eliminate x. (This is equivalent to $R_1 + 2R_2 \rightarrow R_2$ in the Gauss-Jordan method.) The result is $5y = 12$, so $y = 12/5$. We can then substitute this value of y into either equation and solve for x. For example, substitution into the first equation yields

$$2x + \frac{12}{5} = 4$$
$$2x = \frac{8}{5}$$
$$x = \frac{4}{5}.$$

We instead could have subtracted the two original equations to eliminate y, yielding $5x = 4$, or $x = 4/5$.

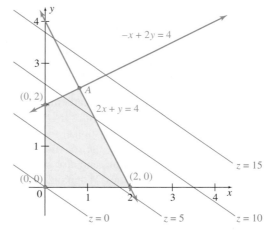

FIGURE 12

The maximum possible value of z is 12. Of all the points in the feasible region, A leads to the largest possible value of z.

A graphing calculator is particularly useful for finding the coordinates of intersection points such as point A. We do this by solving each equation for y, graphing each line, and then using the capability of the calculator to find the coordinates of the point of intersection.

Points such as A in Example 1 are called corner points. A **corner point** is a point in the feasible region where the boundary lines of two constraints cross. Since corner points occur where two straight lines cross, the coordinates of a corner point are the solution of a system of two linear equations. As we saw in Example 1, corner points play a key role in the solution of linear programming problems. We will make this explicit after the following example.

EXAMPLE 2 **Minimization**

Solve the following linear programming problem.

$$\text{Minimize} \quad z = 2x + 4y$$
$$\text{subject to:} \quad x + 2y \geq 10$$
$$3x + y \geq 10$$
$$x \geq 0$$
$$y \geq 0.$$

▶**Solution** Figure 13 shows the feasible region and the lines that result when z in the objective function is replaced by 0, 10, 20, 40, and 50. The line representing the objective function touches the region of feasible solutions when $z = 20$. Two corner points, $(2, 4)$ and $(10, 0)$, lie on this line; both $(2, 4)$ and $(10, 0)$, as well as all the points on the boundary line between them, give the same optimum value of z. There are infinitely many equally good values of x and y that will give the same minimum value of the objective function $z = 2x + 4y$. This minimum value is 20.

The feasible region in Example 1 is **bounded**, since the region is enclosed by boundary lines on all sides. Linear programming problems with bounded regions

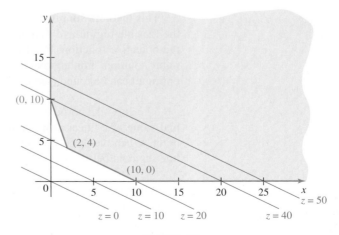

FIGURE 13

always have solutions. On the other hand, the feasible region in Example 2 is **unbounded**, and no solution will *maximize* the value of the objective function.

Some general conclusions can be drawn from the method of solution used in Examples 1 and 2. Figure 14 shows various feasible regions and the lines that result from various values of z. (We assume the lines are in order from left to right as z increases.) In Figure 14(a), the objective function takes on its minimum value at corner point Q and its maximum value at P. The minimum is again at Q in part (b), but the maximum occurs at P_1 or P_2, or any point on the line segment connecting them. Finally, in part (c), the minimum value occurs at Q, but the objective function has no maximum value because the feasible region is unbounded. As long as the objective function increases as x and y increase, the objective function will have no maximum over an unbounded region.

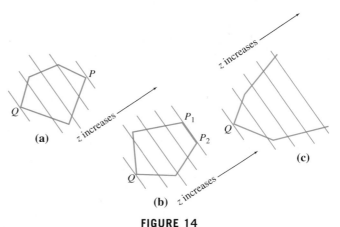

FIGURE 14

The preceding discussion suggests the truth of the **corner point theorem**.

CORNER POINT THEOREM

If an optimum value (either a maximum or a minimum) of the objective function exists, it will occur at one or more of the corner points of the feasible region.

This theorem simplifies the job of finding an optimum value. First, we graph the feasible region and find all corner points. Then we test each corner point in the objective function. Finally, we identify the corner point producing the optimum solution. For unbounded regions, we must decide whether the required optimum can be found (see Example 2).

NOTE As the corner point theorem states and Example 2 illustrates, the optimal value of a linear programming problem may occur at more than one corner point. When the optimal solution occurs at two corner points, every point on the line segment between the two points is also an optimal solution. ∎

With the theorem, we can solve the problem in Example 1 by first identifying the four corner points in Figure 11: $(0, 0)$, $(0, 2)$, $(4/5, 12/5)$, and $(2, 0)$. Then we substitute each of the four points into the objective function $z = 3x + 4y$ to identify the corner point that produces the maximum value of z.

Corner Point	Value of $z = 3x + 4y$	
$(0, 0)$	$3(0) + 4(0) = 0$	
$(0, 2)$	$3(0) + 4(2) = 8$	
$\left(\frac{4}{5}, \frac{12}{5}\right)$	$3\left(\frac{4}{5}\right) + 4\left(\frac{12}{5}\right) = 12$	Maximum
$(2, 0)$	$3(2) + 4(0) = 6$	

From these results, the corner point $(4/5, 12/5)$ yields the maximum value of 12. This is the same as the result found earlier.

The following summary gives the steps to use in solving a linear programming problem by the graphical method.

SOLVING A LINEAR PROGRAMMING PROBLEM

1. Write the objective function and all necessary constraints.
2. Graph the feasible region.
3. Identify all corner points.
4. Find the value of the objective function at each corner point.
5. For a bounded region, the solution is given by the corner point producing the optimum value of the objective function.
6. For an unbounded region, check that a solution actually exists. If it does, it will occur at a corner point.

EXAMPLE 3   **Maximization and Minimization**

Sketch the feasible region for the following set of constraints, and then find the maximum and minimum values of the objective function $z = x + 10y$.

$$x + 4y \geq 12$$
$$x - 2y \leq 0$$
$$2y - x \leq 6$$
$$x \leq 6$$

▶**Solution** The graph in Figure 15 shows that the feasible region is bounded. Use the corner points from the graph to find the maximum and minimum values of the objective function.

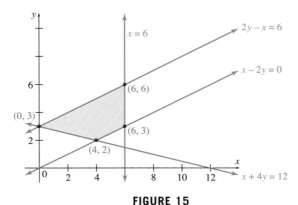

FIGURE 15

Corner Point	Value of $z = x + 10y$	
$(0, 3)$	$0 + 10(3) = 30$	
$(4, 2)$	$4 + 10(2) = 24$	Minimum
$(6, 3)$	$6 + 10(3) = 36$	
$(6, 6)$	$6 + 10(6) = 66$	Maximum

The minimum value of $z = x + 10y$ is 24 at the corner point $(4, 2)$. The maximum value is 66 at $(6, 6)$.

To verify that the minimum or maximum is correct in a linear programming problem, you might want to add the graph of the line $z = 0$ to the graph of the feasible region. For instance, in Example 3, the result of adding the line $x + 10y = 0$ is shown in Figure 16. Now imagine moving a straightedge through the feasible region parallel to this line. It appears that the first place the line touches the feasible region is at $(4, 2)$, where we found the minimum. Similarly, the last place the line touches is at $(6, 6)$, where we found the maximum. In Figure 16, these parallel lines, labeled $z = 24$ and $z = 66$, are also shown.

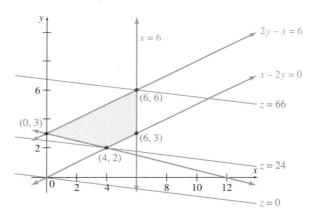

FIGURE 16

▶ 3.2 Exercises

The following graphs show regions of feasible solutions. Use these regions to find maximum and minimum values of the given objective functions.

1. a. $z = 3x + 2y$
   b. $z = x + 4y$

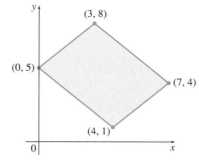

2. a. $z = x + 4y$
   b. $z = 5x + 2y$

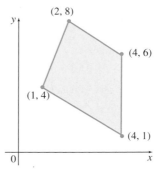

3. a. $z = 0.40x + 0.75y$

b. $z = 1.50x + 0.25y$

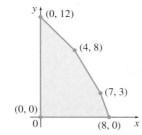

4. a. $z = 0.35x + 1.25y$

b. $z = 1.5x + 0.5y$

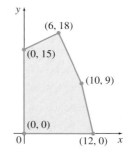

5. a. $z = 4x + 2y$

b. $z = 2x + 3y$

c. $z = 2x + 4y$

d. $z = x + 4y$

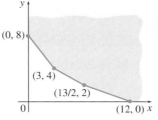

6. a. $z = 4x + y$

b. $z = 5x + 6y$

c. $z = x + 2y$

d. $z = x + 6y$

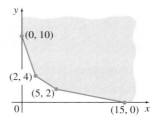

Use graphical methods to solve each linear programming problem.

7. Minimize $z = 4x + 7y$
subject to:
$$x - y \geq 1$$
$$3x + 2y \geq 18$$
$$x \geq 0$$
$$y \geq 0.$$

8. Minimize $z = x + 3y$
subject to:
$$x + y \leq 10$$
$$5x + 2y \geq 20$$
$$-x + 2y \geq 0$$
$$x \geq 0$$
$$y \geq 0.$$

9. Maximize $z = 5x + 2y$
subject to:
$$4x - y \leq 16$$
$$2x + y \geq 11$$
$$x \geq 3$$
$$y \leq 8.$$

10. Maximize $z = 10x + 8y$
subject to:
$$2x + 3y \leq 100$$
$$5x + 4y \leq 200$$
$$x \geq 10$$
$$0 \leq y \leq 20.$$

11. Maximize $z = 10x + 10y$
subject to:
$$5x + 8y \geq 200$$
$$25x - 10y \geq 250$$
$$x + y \leq 150$$
$$x \geq 0$$
$$y \geq 0.$$

12. Maximize $z = 4x + 5y$
subject to:
$$10x - 5y \leq 100$$
$$20x + 10y \geq 150$$
$$x + y \geq 12$$
$$x \geq 0$$
$$y \geq 0.$$

13. Maximize $z = 3x + 6y$
subject to:
$$2x - 3y \leq 12$$
$$x + y \leq 5$$
$$3x + 4y \geq 24$$
$$x \geq 0$$
$$y \geq 0.$$

14. Maximize $z = 4x + 6y$
subject to:
$$3 \leq x + y \leq 10$$
$$x - y \geq 3$$
$$x \geq 0$$
$$y \geq 0.$$

15. Find values of $x \geq 0$ and $y \geq 0$ that maximize $z = 10x + 12y$ subject to each set of constraints.

a. $x + y \leq 20$
$-x + 3y \leq 24$

b. $3x + y \leq 15$
$x + 2y \leq 18$

c. $2x + 5y \geq 22$
$4x + 3y \leq 28$
$2x + 2y \leq 17$

16. Find values of $x \geq 0$ and $y \geq 0$ that minimize $z = 3x + 2y$ subject to each set of constraints.

a. $10x + 7y \leq 42$
$4x + 10y \geq 35$

b. $6x + 5y \geq 25$
$2x + 6y \geq 15$

c. $x + 2y \geq 10$
$2x + y \geq 12$
$x - y \leq 8$

17. You are given the following linear programming problem:*

Maximize $\quad z = c_1x_1 + c_2x_2$

subject to: $\quad 2x_1 + x_2 \leq 11$

$$-x_1 + 2x_2 \leq 2$$

$$x_1 \geq 0, x_2 \geq 0.$$

If $c_2 > 0$, determine the range of c_1/c_2 for which $(x_1, x_2) = (4, 3)$ is an optimal solution. (Choose one of the following.)

a. $[-2, 1/2]$ **b.** $[-1/2, 2]$ **c.** $[-11, -1]$ **d.** $[1, 11]$ **e.** $[-11, 11]$

 Applications of Linear Programming

? THINK ABOUT IT   **How many canoes and kayaks should a business purchase, given a limited budget and limited storage?**

We will use linear programming to answer this question in Example 1.

EXAMPLE 1   **Canoe Rentals**

Mr. Trenga plans to start a new business called River Explorers, which will rent canoes and kayaks to people to travel 10 miles down the Clarion River in Cook Forest State Park. He has $45,000 to purchase new boats. He can buy the canoes for $600 each and the kayaks for $750 each. His facility can hold up to 65 boats. The canoes will rent for $25 a day, and the kayaks will rent for $30 a day. How many canoes and how many kayaks should he buy to earn the most revenue?

 ▶**Solution**   Let x represent the number of canoes and let y represent the number of kayaks. Summarize the given information in a table.

	Canoes	Kayaks		Total
Number of Boats	x	y	$\leq$	65
Cost of Each	$600	$750	$\leq$	$45,000
Revenue	$25	$30		

The constraints, imposed by the number of boats and the cost, correspond to the rows in the table as follows.

$$x + y \leq 65$$

$$600x + 750y \leq 45,000$$

Dividing both sides of the second constraint by 150 gives the equivalent inequality

$$4x + 5y \leq 300.$$

Since the number of boats cannot be negative, $x \geq 0$ and $y \geq 0$. The objective function to be maximized gives the amount of revenue. If the variable z represents

---

*Problem 5 from "November 1989 Course 130 Examination Operations Research" of the *Education and Examination Committee of The Society of Actuaries*. Reprinted by permission of The Society of Actuaries.

the total revenue, the objective function is

$$z = 25x + 30y.$$

In summary, the mathematical model for the given linear programming problem is as follows:

Maximize	$z = 25x + 30y$		**(1)**
subject to:	$x + y \leq 65$		**(2)**
	$4x + 5y \leq 300$		**(3)**
	$x \geq 0$		**(4)**
	$y \geq 0.$		**(5)**

   Using the methods described in the previous section, graph the feasible region for the system of inequalities (2)–(5), as in Figure 17. Three of the corner points can be identified from the graph as (0, 0), (65, 0), and (0, 60). The fourth corner point, labeled Q in the figure, can be found by solving the system of equations

$$x + y = 65$$
$$4x + 5y = 300.$$

Solve this system to find that Q is the point (25, 40). Now test these four points in the objective function to determine the maximum value of z. The results are shown in the table.

Corner Point	Value of $z = 25x + 30y$	
$(0, 0)$	$25(0) + 30(0) = 0$	
$(65, 0)$	$25(65) + 30(0) = 1625$	
$(0, 60)$	$25(0) + 30(60) = 1800$	
$(25, 40)$	$25(25) + 30(40) = 1825$	Maximum

The objective function, which represents revenue, is maximized when $x = 25$ and $y = 40$. He should buy 25 canoes and 40 kayaks.

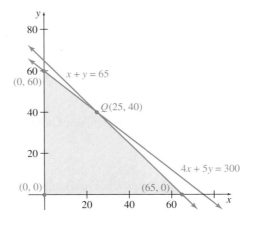

FIGURE 17

Fortunately, the answer to the linear programming problem in Example 1 is a point with integer coordinates, as the number of each type of boat must be an integer. Unfortunately, there is no guarantee that this will always happen. When the solution to a linear programming problem is restricted to integers, it is an *integer programming* problem, which is more difficult to solve than a linear programming problem. In this text, all problems in which fractional solutions are meaningless are contrived to have integer solutions.

EXAMPLE 2   **Farm Animals**

A 4-H member raises only goats and pigs. She wants to raise no more than 16 animals, including no more than 10 goats. She spends $25 to raise a goat and $75 to raise a pig, and she has $900 available for this project. The 4-H member wishes to maximize her profits. Each goat produces $12 in profit and each pig $40 in profit.

▶**Solution**   First, set up a table that shows the information given in the problem.

	Goats	Pigs		Total
Number Raised	x	y	$\leq$	16
Goat Limit	x		$\leq$	10
Cost to Raise	$25	$75	$\leq$	$900
Profit (each)	$12	$40		

Use the table to write the necessary constraints. Since the total number of animals cannot exceed 16, the first constraint is

$$x + y \leq 16.$$

"No more than 10 goats" means

$$x \leq 10.$$

The cost to raise x goats at $25 per goat is $25x$ dollars, while the cost for y pigs at $75 each is $75y$ dollars. Since only $900 is available,

$$25x + 75y \leq 900.$$

Dividing both sides by 25 gives the equivalent inequality

$$x + 3y \leq 36.$$

The number of goats and pigs cannot be negative, so

$$x \geq 0 \quad \text{and} \quad y \geq 0.$$

The 4-H member wants to know how many goats and pigs to raise in order to produce maximum profit. Each goat yields $12 profit and each pig $40. If z represents total profit, then

$$z = 12x + 40y.$$

In summary, we have the following linear programming problem:

$$\text{Maximize} \quad z = 12x + 40y$$
$$\text{subject to:} \quad x + y \leq 16$$
$$x + 3y \leq 36$$
$$x \leq 10$$
$$x \geq 0$$
$$y \geq 0.$$

A graph of the feasible region is shown in Figure 18. The corner points $(0, 12)$, $(0, 0)$, and $(10, 0)$ can be read directly from the graph. The coordinates of each of the other corner points can be found by solving a system of linear equations.

Test each corner point in the objective function to find the maximum profit.

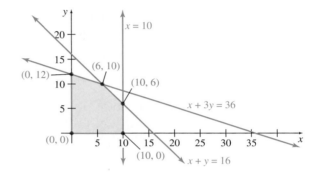

FIGURE 18

Corner Point	Value of $z = 12x + 40y$	
$(0, 12)$	$12(0) + 40(12) = 480$	Maximum
$(6, 10)$	$12(6) + 40(10) = 472$	
$(10, 6)$	$12(10) + 40(6) = 360$	
$(10, 0)$	$12(10) + 40(0) = 120$	
$(0, 0)$	$12(0) + 40(0) = 0$	

The maximum of 480 occurs at $(0, 12)$. Thus, 12 pigs and no goats will produce a maximum profit of $480.

In the maximization problem in Example 2, since the profit for a single pig is $40 and the profit for a single goat is only $12, it is more profitable to raise only pigs and no goats. However, if the profit from raising pigs begins to decrease (or the profit from goats begins to increase), it will eventually be more profitable to raise both goats and pigs. In fact, if the profit from raising pigs decreases to a number below $36, then the previous solution is no longer optimal.

To see why this is true, in Figure 19 we have graphed the original objective function ($z = 12x + 40y$) for various values of z, as we did in Example 1 of the previous section. Notice that each of these objective lines has slope

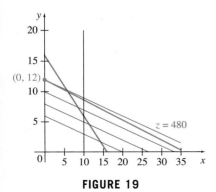

FIGURE 19

$m = -12/40 = -3/10$. When $z = 480$, the line touches only one feasible point, $(0, 12)$, which is where the maximum profit occurs.

If the profit from raising pigs decreases from \$40 to \$$p$, where p is a value slightly below 40, the objective function lines will have the equation $z = 12x + py$ for various values of z, and the slope of the lines becomes $m = -12/p$. Eventually, as p becomes smaller, the slope of these objective lines will be equal to the slope of the line $x + 3y = 36$ (that is, $-1/3$), corresponding to the second constraint. This occurs when $-12/p = -1/3$, or $p = 36$, as illustrated by the overlapping blue and dotted lines in Figure 20. In this case, the optimal solution occurs at every point on the line segment that joins $(0, 12)$ and $(6, 10)$.

Once the profit from raising pigs decreases to below \$36, the slopes of the sample objective function lines become more negative (steeper) and the optimal solution changes, as indicated in Figure 21. As z increases, the last feasible point that the lines touch is $(6, 10)$. For profits from raising pigs that are slightly below \$36, the optimal solution will occur when $x = 6$ and $y = 10$. In other words, the maximum profit will occur when she raises both goats and pigs.

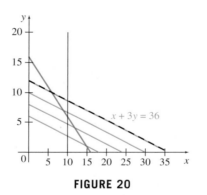

FIGURE 20

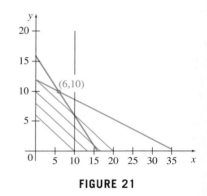

FIGURE 21

EXAMPLE 3 **Nutrition**

Certain animals in a rescue shelter must have at least 30 g of protein and at least 20 g of fat per feeding period. These nutrients come from food A, which costs 18 cents per unit and supplies 2 g of protein and 4 g of fat; and food B, which costs 12 cents per unit and has 6 g of protein and 2 g of fat. Food B is bought under a long-term contract requiring that at least 2 units of B be used per serving.

(a) How much of each food must be bought to produce the minimum cost per serving?

▶**Solution** Let x represent the required amount of food A and y the amount of food B. Use the given information to prepare the following table.

	Food A	Food B	Total
Number of Units	x	y	
Grams of Protein	2	6	$\geq$ 30
Grams of Fat	4	2	$\geq$ 20
Long-Term Contract		y	$\geq$ 2
Cost	18¢	12¢	

Since the animals must have *at least* 30 g of protein and 20 g of fat, we use $\geq$ in the inequality. If the animals needed *at most* a certain amount of some nutrient, we would use $\leq$. The long-term contract requires that $y \geq 2$.

The linear programming problem can be stated as follows.

$$\text{Minimize} \qquad z = 0.18x + 0.12y$$

$$\text{subject to:} \qquad 2x + 6y \geq 30 \qquad \text{Protein}$$

$$4x + 2y \geq 20 \qquad \text{Fat}$$

$$y \geq 2$$

$$x \geq 0.$$

(The usual constraint $y \geq 0$ is redundant because of the constraint $y \geq 2$.) A graph of the feasible region is shown in Figure 22. The corner points are $(0, 10)$, $(3, 4)$, and $(9, 2)$.

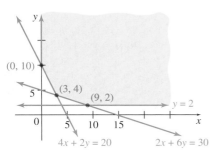

FIGURE 22

Test each corner point in the objective function to find the minimum cost.

Corner Point	Value of $z = 0.18x + 0.12y$	
$(0, 10)$	$0.18(0) + 0.12(10) = 1.20$	
$(3, 4)$	$0.18(3) + 0.12(4) = 1.02$	Minimum
$(9, 2)$	$0.18(9) + 0.12(2) = 1.86$	

The minimum of 1.02 occurs at $(3, 4)$. Thus, 3 units of food A and 4 units of food B will produce a minimum cost of $1.02 per serving.

(b) The rescue shelter manager notices that although the long-term contract states that at least 2 units of food B be used per serving, the solution uses 4 units of food B, which is 2 units more than the minimum amount required. Can a more economical solution be found that only uses 2 units of food B?

▶**Solution** The solution found in part (a) is the most economical solution, even though it exceeds the requirement for using at least 2 units of food B. Notice from Figure 22 that the three lines representing the three constraints do not meet at a single point, so any solution in the feasible region will have to exceed at least one constraint. The rescue shelter manager might use this information to negotiate a better deal with the distributor of food B by making a guarantee to use at least 4 units of food B per serving in the future.

The notion that some constraints are not met exactly is related to the concepts of *surplus* and *slack variables*, which will be explored in the next chapter.

The feasible region in Figure 22 is an *unbounded* feasible region—the region extends indefinitely to the upper right. With this region it would not be possible to *maximize* the objective function, because the total cost of the food could always be increased by encouraging the animals to eat more.

▶ 3.3 Exercises

Write Exercises 1–6 as linear inequalities. Identify all variables used. (Note: Not all of the given information is used in Exercises 5 and 6.)

1. Product A requires 3 hours on machine I, while product B needs 5 hours on the same machine. The machine is available for at most 60 hours per week.

2. A cow requires a third of an acre of pasture and a sheep needs a quarter acre. A rancher wants to use at least 120 acres of pasture.

3. Jessica Corpo needs at least 1500 units of calcium supplements per day. Her calcium carbonate supplement provides 600 units, and her calcium citrate supplement supplies 250 units.

4. Pauline Wong spends 3 hours selling a small computer and 5 hours selling a larger model. She works no more than 45 hours per week.

5. Coffee costing $8 per lb is to be mixed with coffee costing $10 per lb to get at least 40 lb of a blended coffee.

6. A tank in an oil refinery holds 120 gal. The tank contains a mixture of light oil worth $1.25 per gal and heavy oil worth $0.80 per gal.

▶ Applications

BUSINESS AND ECONOMICS

7. *Transportation* The Miers Company produces small engines for several manufacturers. The company receives orders from two assembly plants for their Top-flight engine. Plant I needs at least 45 engines, and plant II needs at least 32 engines. The company can send at most 90 engines to these two assembly plants. It costs $30 per engine to ship to plant I and $40 per engine to ship to plant II. Plant I gives Miers $20 in rebates toward its products for each engine they buy, while plant II gives similar $15 rebates. Miers estimates that they need at least $1200 in rebates to cover products they plan to buy from the two plants. How many engines should be shipped to each plant to minimize shipping costs? What is the minimum cost?

8. *Transportation* A manufacturer of refrigerators must ship at least 100 refrigerators to its two West Coast warehouses. Each warehouse holds a maximum of 100 refrigerators. Warehouse A holds 25 refrigerators already, and warehouse B has 20 on hand. It costs $12 to ship a refrigerator to warehouse A and $10 to ship one to warehouse B. Union rules require that at least 300 workers be hired. Shipping a refrigerator to warehouse A requires 4 workers, while shipping a refrigerator to warehouse B requires 2 workers. How many refrigerators should be shipped to each warehouse to minimize costs? What is the minimum cost?

9. *Insurance Premiums* A company is considering two insurance plans with the types of coverage and premiums shown in the following table.

	Policy A	Policy B
Fire/Theft	$10,000	$15,000
Liability	$180,000	$120,000
Premium	$50	$40

(For example, this means that $50 buys one unit of plan A, consisting of $10,000 fire and theft insurance and $180,000 of liability insurance.)

a. The company wants at least $300,000 fire/theft insurance and at least $3,000,000 liability insurance from these plans. How many units should be purchased from each plan to minimize the cost of the premiums? What is the minimum premium?

b. Suppose the premium for policy A is reduced to $25. Now how many units should be purchased from each plan to minimize the cost of the premiums? What is the minimum premium?

10. *Profit* The Muro Manufacturing Company makes two kinds of plasma screen television sets. It produces the Flexscan set that sells for $350 profit and the Panoramic I that sells for $500 profit. On the assembly line, the Flexscan requires 5 hours, and the Panoramic I takes 7 hours. The cabinet shop spends 1 hour on the cabinet for the Flexscan and 2 hours on the cabinet for the Panoramic I. Both sets require 4 hours for testing and packing. On a particular production run, the Muro Company has available 3600 work-hours on the

assembly line, 900 work-hours in the cabinet shop, and 2600 work-hours in the testing and packing department.

a. How many sets of each type should it produce to make a maximum profit? What is the maximum profit?

b. Suppose the profit on the Flexscan goes up to $450. Now how many sets of each type should it produce to make a maximum profit. What is the maximum profit?

c. The solutions from parts a and b leave some unused time in either the assembly line, the cabinet shop, or the testing and packing department. Identify any unused time in each solution. Is it possible to have a solution that leaves no excess time? Explain.

11. *Revenue* A machine shop manufactures two types of bolts. The bolts require time on each of the three groups of machines, but the time required on each group differs, as shown in the table below.

	Type I	Type II
Machine 1	0.2 min	0.2 min
Machine 2	0.6 min	0.2 min
Machine 3	0.04 min	0.08 min

Production schedules are made up one day at a time. In a day, 300, 720, and 100 minutes are available, respectively, on these machines. Type I bolts sell for 15¢ and type II bolts for 20¢.

a. How many of each type of bolt should be manufactured per day to maximize revenue?

b. What is the maximum revenue?

c. Suppose the selling price of type I bolts began to increase. How much would this price have to increase before a different number of each type of bolts should be produced to maximize revenue?

12. *Revenue* The manufacturing process requires that oil refineries must manufacture at least 2 gal of gasoline for every gallon of fuel oil. To meet the winter demand for fuel oil, at least 3 million gal a day must be produced. The demand for gasoline is no more than 6.4 million gal per day. It takes 0.25 hour to ship each million gal of gasoline and 1 hour to ship each million gal of fuel oil out of the warehouse. No more than 4.65 hours are available for shipping. If the refinery sells gasoline for $2.50 per gal and fuel oil for $2 per gal, how much of each should be produced to maximize revenue? Find the maximum revenue.

13. *Revenue* A candy company has 150 kg of chocolate-covered nuts and 90 kg of chocolate-covered raisins to be sold as two different mixes. One mix will contain half nuts and half raisins and will sell for $7 per kg. The other mix

will contain 3/4 nuts and 1/4 raisins and will sell for $9.50 per kg.

a. How many kilograms of each mix should the company prepare for the maximum revenue? Find the maximum revenue.

b. The company raises the price of the second mix to $11 per kg. Now how many kilograms of each mix should the company prepare for the maximum revenue? Find the maximum revenue.

14. *Profit* A small country can grow only two crops for export, coffee and cocoa. The country has 500,000 hectares of land available for the crops. Long-term contracts require that at least 100,000 hectares be devoted to coffee and at least 200,000 hectares to cocoa. Cocoa must be processed locally, and production bottlenecks limit cocoa to 270,000 hectares. Coffee requires two workers per hectare, with cocoa requiring five. No more than 1,750,000 people are available for working with these crops. Coffee produces a profit of $220 per hectare and cocoa a profit of $550 per hectare. How many hectares should the country devote to each crop in order to maximize profit? Find the maximum profit.

15. *Blending* The Mostpure Milk Company gets milk from two dairies and then blends the milk to get the desired amount of butterfat for the company's premier product. Milk from dairy I costs $2.40 per gal, and milk from dairy II costs $0.80 per gal. At most $144 is available for purchasing milk. Dairy I can supply at most 50 gal of milk averaging 3.7% butterfat. Dairy II can supply at most 80 gal of milk averaging 3.2% butterfat.

a. How much milk from each supplier should Mostpure use to get at most 100 gal of milk with the maximum total percent of butterfat? What is the maximum percent of butterfat?

b. The solution from part a leaves both dairy I and dairy II with excess capacity. Calculate the amount of additional milk each dairy could produce. Is there any way all this capacity could be used while still meeting the other constraints? Explain.

16. *Transportation* A greeting card manufacturer has 370 boxes of a particular card in warehouse I and 290 boxes of the same card in warehouse II. A greeting card shop in San Jose orders 350 boxes of the card, and another shop in Memphis orders 300 boxes. The shipping costs per box to these shops from the two warehouses are shown in the following table.

		Destination	
		San Jose	*Memphis*
Warehouse	I	$0.25	$0.22
	II	$0.23	$0.21

How many boxes should be shipped to each city from each warehouse to minimize shipping costs? What is the minimum cost? (*Hint:* Use x, $350 - x$, y, and $300 - y$ as the variables.)

17. *Finance* A pension fund manager decides to invest a total of at most $30 million in U.S. Treasury bonds paying 4% annual interest and in mutual funds paying 8% annual interest. He plans to invest at least $5 million in bonds and at least $10 million in mutual funds. Bonds have an initial fee of $100 per million dollars, while the fee for mutual funds is $200 per million. The fund manager is allowed to spend no more than $5000 on fees. How much should be invested in each to maximize annual interest? What is the maximum annual interest?

Manufacturing (*Note: Exercises 18–20 are from qualification examinations for Certified Public Accountants.**) *The Random Company manufactures two products, Zeta and Beta. Each product must pass through two processing operations. All materials are introduced at the start of Process No. 1. There are no work-in-process inventories. Random may produce either one product exclusively or various combinations of both products subject to the following constraints:*

	Process No. 1	Process No. 2	Contribution Margin (per unit)
Hours Required to Produce One Unit:			
Zeta	1 hr	1 hr	$4.00
Beta	2 hr	3 hr	$5.25
Total Capacity (in hours per day)	1000 hr	1275 hr	

A shortage of technical labor has limited Beta production to 400 units per day. There are no constraints on the production of Zeta other than the hour constraints in the above schedule. Assume that all relationships between capacity and production are linear.

18. Given the objective to maximize total contribution margin, what is the production constraint for Process No. 1? (Choose one of the following.)

a. Zeta + Beta $\leq$ 1000   **b.** Zeta + 2 Beta $\leq$ 1000

c. Zeta + Beta $\geq$ 1000   **d.** Zeta + 2 Beta $\geq$ 1000

19. Given the objective to maximize total contribution margin, what is the labor constraint for production of Beta? (Choose one of the following.)

a. Beta $\leq$ 400   **b.** Beta $\geq$ 400

c. Beta $\leq$ 425   **d.** Beta $\geq$ 425

20. What is the objective function of the data presented? (Choose one of the following.)

a. Zeta + 2 Beta = $9.25

b. $4.00 Zeta + 3($5.25)Beta = Total Contribution Margin

c. $4.00 Zeta + $5.25 Beta = Total Contribution Margin

d. 2($4.00) Zeta + 3($5.25) Beta = Total Contribution Margin

LIFE SCIENCES

21. *Health Care* Mark, who is ill, takes vitamin pills. Each day he must have at least 16 units of vitamin A, 5 units of vitamin B_1, and 20 units of vitamin C. He can choose between pill 1, which contains 8 units of A, 1 of B_1, and 2 of C; and pill 2, which contains 2 units of A, 1 of B_1, and 7 of C. Pill 1 costs 15¢, and pill 2 costs 30¢.

a. How many of each pill should he buy in order to minimize his cost? What is the minimum cost?

b. For the solution in part a, Mark is receiving more than he needs of at least one vitamin. Identify that vitamin, and tell how much surplus he is receiving. Is there any way he can avoid receiving that surplus while still meeting the other constraints and minimizing the cost? Explain.

22. *Predator Food Requirements* A certain predator requires at least 10 units of protein and 8 units of fat per day. One prey of species I provides 5 units of protein and 2 units of fat; one prey of species II provides 3 units of protein and 4 units of fat. Capturing and digesting each species-II prey requires 3 units of energy, and capturing and digesting each species-I prey requires 2 units of energy. How many of each prey would meet the predator's daily food requirements with the least expenditure of energy? Are the answers reasonable? How could they be interpreted?

23. *Nutrition* A dietician is planning a snack package of fruit and nuts. Each ounce of fruit will supply zero units of protein, 2 units of carbohydrates, and 1 unit of fat, and will contain 20 calories. Each ounce of nuts will supply 3 units of protein, 1 unit of carbohydrate, and 2 units of fat, and will contain 30 calories. Every package must provide at least 6 units of protein, at least 10 units of carbohydrates, and no more than 9 units of fat. Find the number of ounces of fruit and number of ounces of nuts that will meet the requirement with the least number of calories. What is the least number of calories?

24. *Health Care* Ms. Oliveras was given the following advice. She should supplement her daily diet with at least 6000 USP units of vitamin A, at least 195 mg of vitamin C, and at least 600 USP units of vitamin D. Ms. Oliveras finds that

---

*Material from *Uniform CPA Examinations and Unofficial Answers*, copyright © 1973, 1974, 1975 by the American Institute of Certified Public Accountants, Inc., is reprinted with permission.

Mason's Pharmacy carries Brand X vitamin pills at 5¢ each and Brand Y vitamins at 4¢ each. Each Brand X pill contains 3000 USP units of A, 45 mg of C, and 75 USP units of D, while Brand Y pills contain 1000 USP units of A, 50 mg of C, and 200 USP units of D.

a. What combination of vitamin pills should she buy to obtain the least possible cost? What is the least possible cost per day?

b. For the solution in part a, Ms. Oliveras is receiving more than she needs of at least one vitamin. Identify that vitamin, and tell how much surplus she is receiving. Is there any way she can avoid receiving that surplus while still meeting the other constraints and minimizing the cost? Explain.

SOCIAL SCIENCES

25. *Anthropology* An anthropology article presents a hypothetical situation that could be described by a linear programming model.* Suppose a population gathers plants and animals for survival. They need at least 360 units of energy, 300 units of protein, and 8 hides during some time period. One unit of plants provides 30 units of energy, 10 units of protein, and no hides. One animal provides 20 units of energy, 25 units of protein, and 1 hide.

Only 25 units of plants and 25 animals are available. It costs the population 30 hours of labor to gather one unit of a plant and 15 hours for an animal. Find how many units of plants and how many animals should be gathered to meet the requirements with a minimum number of hours of labor.

GENERAL INTEREST

 26. *Construction* In a small town in South Carolina, zoning rules require that the window space (in square feet) in a house be at least one-sixth of the space used up by solid walls. The cost to build windows is $10 per ft^2, while the cost to build solid walls is $20 per ft^2. The total amount available for building walls and windows is no more than $12,000. The estimated monthly cost to heat the house is $0.32 for each square foot of windows and $0.20 for each square foot of solid walls. Find the maximum total area (windows plus walls) if no more than $160 per month is available to pay for heat.

27. *Farming* An agricultural advisor looks at the results of Example 2 and claims that it cannot possibly be correct. After all, the 4-H member is able to raise 16 animals, and she is only raising 12 animals. Surely she can earn more profit by raising all 16 animals. How would you respond?

Chapter 3 Review

→ Chapter Summary

In this chapter, we introduced linear programming, which attempts to solve maximization and minimization problems with linear constraints. Linear programming models can be used to analyze a wide range of applications from many disciplines. The corner point theorem assures us that the optimal solution to a linear program, if it exists, must occur at one or more of the corner points of the feasible region. Linear programs can be solved using the graphical method, which graphs the region described by the linear constraints and then locates the corner point corresponding to the optimal solution value. The graphical method, however, is restricted to problems with two or three variables. In the next chapter, we will study a method that does not have this restriction.

LINEAR PROGRAMMING: THE GRAPHICAL METHOD SUMMARY

Graphing a Linear Inequality   **1.** Draw the graph of the boundary line. Make the line solid if the inequality involves ≤ or ≥; make the line dashed if the inequality involves < or >.

---

*Reidhead, Van A., "Linear Programming Models in Archaeology," *Annual Review of Anthropology,* Vol. 8, 1979, pp. 543–578.

2. Decide which half-plane to shade. Use either of the following methods.

   a. Solve the inequality for y; shade the region above the line if the inequality is of the form of $y >$ or $y \geq$; shade the region below the line if the inequality is of the form of $y <$ or $y \leq$.

   b. Choose any point not on the line as a test point. Shade the half-plane that includes the test point if the test point satisfies the original inequality; otherwise, shade the half-plane on the other side of the boundary line.

Corner Point Theorem   If an optimum value (either a maximum or a minimum) of the objective function exists, it will occur at one or more of the corner points of the feasible region.

Solving a Linear Programming Problem

1. Write the objective function and all necessary constraints.

2. Graph the feasible region.

3. Identify all corner points.

4. Find the value of the objective function at each corner point.

5. For a bounded region, the solution is given by the corner point(s) producing the optimum value of the objective function.

6. For an unbounded region, check that a solution actually exists. If it does, it will occur at one or more corner points.

▶ Key Terms

To understand the concepts presented in this chapter, you should know the meaning and use of the following terms.

3.1 **linear inequality**
boundary
half-plane

system of inequalities
region of feasible
solutions

3.2 **linear programming**
objective function
constraints

corner point
bounded
unbounded

▶ Concept Check

Determine whether each of the following statements is true or false, and explain why.

1. The graphical method can be used to solve a linear programming problem with four variables.

2. For the inequality $5x + 4y \geq 20$, the test point $(3, 4)$ suggests that the correct half-plane to shade includes this point.

3. Let x represent the number of acres of wheat planted and y represent the number of acres of corn planted. The inequality $x \leq 2y$ implies that the number of acres of wheat planted will be at least twice the number of acres of corn planted.

4. For the variables in Exercise 3, assume that we have a total of 60 hours to plant the wheat and corn and that it takes 2 hours per acre to prepare a wheat field and 1 hour per acre to prepare a corn field. The inequality $2x + y \geq 60$ represents the constraint on the amount of time available for planting.

5. For the variables in Exercise 3, assume that we make a profit of $14 for each acre of corn and $10 for each acre of wheat. The objective function that can be used to maximize profit is $14x + 10y$.

6. The point $(2, 3)$ is a corner point of the linear programming problem

$$\text{Maximize} \quad z = 7x + 4y$$
$$\text{subject to:} \quad 3x + 8y \leq 30$$
$$4x + 2y \leq 15$$
$$x \geq 0, y \geq 0.$$

7. The point (2, 3) is a feasible point of the linear programming problem in Exercise 6.

8. The optimal solution to the linear programming problem in Exercise 6 occurs at point (2, 3).

9. It is possible to find a point that lies on both sides of a linear inequality.

10. Every linear programming problem either has a solution or is unbounded.

11. Solutions to linear programming problems may include fractions.

12. The inequality $4^2x + 5^2y \leq 7^2$ is a linear constraint.

13. The optimal solution to a linear programming problem can occur at a point that is not a corner point.

➤ *Chapter 3 Review Exercises*

1. Why doesn't the graphical method work for more than three variables?

2. How many constraints are we limited to in the graphical method?

Graph each linear inequality.

3. $y \geq 2x + 3$

4. $5x - 2y \leq 10$

5. $2x + 6y \leq 8$

6. $2x - 6y \geq 18$

7. $y \geq x$

8. $y \geq -2$

Graph the solution of each system of inequalities. Find all corner points.

9. $x + y \leq 6$
   $2x - y \geq 3$

10. $3x + 2y \geq 12$
   $4x - 5y \leq 20$

11. $-4 \leq x \leq 2$
   $-1 \leq y \leq 3$
   $x + y \leq 4$

12. $2 \leq x \leq 5$
   $1 \leq y \leq 7$
   $x - y \leq 3$

13. $x + 2y \leq 4$
   $5x - 6y \leq 12$
   $x \geq 0$
   $y \geq 0$

14. $x + 2y \leq 4$
   $2x - 3y \leq 6$
   $x \geq 0$
   $y \geq 0$

Use the given regions to find the maximum and minimum values of the objective function $z = 2x + 4y$.

15.

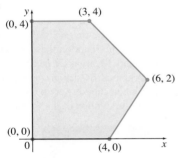

16.

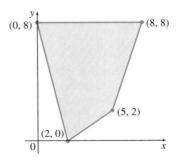

Use the graphical method to solve each linear programming problem.

17. Maximize $z = 2x + 4y$
   subject to: $3x + 2y \leq 12$
               $5x + y \geq 5$
               $x \geq 0$
               $y \geq 0.$

18. Minimize $z = 5x + 3y$
   subject to: $8x + 5y \geq 40$
               $4x + 10y \geq 40$
               $x \geq 0$
               $y \geq 0.$

19. Minimize $z = 4x + 2y$

subject to: $x + y \le 50$

$2x + y \ge 20$

$x + 2y \ge 30$

$x \ge 0$

$y \ge 0.$

20. Maximize $z = 8x + 4y$

subject to: $3x + 12y \le 36$

$x + y \le 4$

$x \ge 0$

$y \ge 0.$

21. Why must the solution to a linear programming problem always occur at a corner point of the feasible region?

22. Is there necessarily a unique point in the feasible region where the maximum or minimum occurs? Why or why not?

23. It is not necessary to check all corner points in a linear programming problem. This exercise illustrates an alternative procedure, which is essentially an expansion of the ideas illustrated in Example 1 of Section 3.2.

Maximize $z = 3x + 4y$

subject to: $2x + y \le 4$

$-x + 2y \le 4$

$x \ge 0$

$y \ge 0.$

a. Sketch the feasible region, and add the line $z = 8$. (*Note:* 8 is chosen because the numbers work out simply, but the chosen value of z is arbitrary.)

b. Draw a line parallel to the line $z = 8$ that is as far from the origin as possible but still touches the feasible region.

c. The line you drew in part b should go through the point $(4/5, 12/5)$. Explain how you know the maximum must be located at this point.

24. Use the method described in the previous exercise to solve Exercise 20.

▶ Applications

BUSINESS AND ECONOMICS

25. *Time Management* A bakery makes both cakes and cookies. Each batch of cakes requires 2 hours in the oven and 3 hours in the decorating room. Each batch of cookies needs $1\frac{1}{2}$ hours in the oven and $\frac{2}{3}$ hour in the decorating room. The oven is available no more than 15 hours per day, and the decorating room can be used no more than 13 hours per day. Set up a system of inequalities, and then graph the solution of the system.

26. *Cost Analysis* DeMarco's pizza shop makes two specialty pizzas, the Mighty Meaty and the Very Veggie. The Mighty Meaty is topped with 5 different meat toppings and 2 different cheeses. The Very Veggie has 6 different vegetable toppings and 4 different cheeses. The shop sells at least 4 Mighty Meaty and 6 Very Veggie pizzas every day. The cost of the toppings for each Mighty Meaty is $3, and the

cost of the vegetable toppings is $2 for each Very Veggie. No more than $60 per day can be spent on these toppings. The cheese used for the Mighty Meaty is $2 per pizza, and the cheese for the Very Veggie is $4 per pizza. No more than $80 per day can be spent on cheese. Set up a system of inequalities, and then graph the solution of the system.

27. *Profit* Refer to Exercise 25.

    a. How many batches of cakes and cookies should the bakery in Exercise 25 make in order to maximize profits if cookies produce a profit of $20 per batch and cakes produce a profit of $30 per batch?

    b. How much would the profit from selling cookies have to increase before it becomes more profitable to sell only cookies?

28. *Revenue* How many pizzas of each kind should the pizza shop in Exercise 26 make in order to maximize revenue if the Mighty Meaty sells for $15 and the Very Veggie sells for $12?

29. *Planting* In Karla's garden shop, she makes two kinds of mixtures for planting. A package of gardening mixture requires 2 lb of soil, 1 lb of peat moss, and 1 lb of fertilizer. A package of potting mixture requires 1 lb of soil, 2 lb of peat moss, and 3 lb of fertilizer. She has 16 lb of soil, 11 lb of peat moss, and 15 lb of fertilizer. If a package of gardening mixture sells for $3 and a package of potting mixture for $5, how many of each should she make in order to maximize her income? What is the maximum income?

30. *Construction* A contractor builds boathouses in two basic models, the Atlantic and the Pacific. Each Atlantic model requires 1000 ft of framing lumber, 3000 ft^3 of concrete, and $2000 for advertising. Each Pacific model requires 2000 ft of framing lumber, 3000 ft^3 of concrete, and $3000 for advertising. Contracts call for using at least 8000 ft of framing lumber, 18,000 ft^3 of concrete, and $15,000 worth of advertising. If the construction cost for each Atlantic model is $30,000 and the construction cost for each Pacific model is $40,000, how many of each model should be built to minimize construction costs?

31. *Steel* A steel company produces two types of alloys. A run of type I requires 3000 lb of molybdenum and 2000 tons of iron ore pellets as well as $2000 in advertising. A run of

type II requires 3000 lb of molybdenum and 1000 tons of iron ore pellets as well as $3000 in advertising. Total costs are $15,000 on a run of type I and $6000 on a run of type II. Because of various contracts, the company must use at least 18,000 lb of molybdenum and 7000 tons of iron ore pellets and spend at least $14,000 on advertising. How much of each type should be produced to minimize costs?

32. *Nutrition* A dietician in a hospital is to arrange a special diet containing two foods, Health Trough and Power Gunk. Each ounce of Health Trough contains 30 mg of calcium, 10 mg of iron, 10 IU of vitamin A, and 8 mg of cholesterol. Each ounce of Power Gunk contains 10 mg of calcium, 10 mg of iron, 30 IU of vitamin A, and 4 mg of cholesterol. If the minimum daily requirements are 360 mg of calcium, 160 mg of iron, and 240 IU of vitamin A, how many ounces of each food should be used to meet the minimum requirements and at the same time minimize the cholesterol intake? Also, what is the minimum cholesterol intake?

33. *Anthropology* A simplified model of the Mountain Fur economy of central Africa has been proposed.* In this model, two crops can be grown, millet and wheat, which produce 400 lb and 800 lb per acre, respectively. Millet requires 36 days to harvest one acre, while wheat requires only 8 days. There are 2 acres of land and 48 days of harvest labor available. How many acres should be devoted to each crop to maximize the pounds of grain harvested?

34. *Studying* Ron Hampton is trying to allocate his study time this weekend. He can spend time working with either his math tutor or his accounting tutor to prepare for exams in both classes the following Monday. His math tutor charges $20 per hour, and his accounting tutor charges $40 per hour. He has $220 to spend on tutoring. Each hour that he spends working with his math tutor requires 1 aspirin and 1 hour of sleep to recover, while each hour he spends with his accounting tutor requires 1/2 aspirin and 3 hours of sleep. The maximum dosage of aspirin that he can safely take during his study time is 8 tablets, and he can only afford 15 hours of sleep this weekend. He expects that each hour with his math tutor will increase his score on the math exam by 3 points, while each hour with his accounting tutor will increase his score on the accounting exam by 5 points. How many hours should he spend with each tutor in order to maximize the number of points he will get on the two tests combined?

*Joy, Leonard, "Barth's Presentation of Economic Spheres in Darfur," in *Themes in Economic Anthropology*, edited by Raymond Firth, Tavistock Publications, 1967, pp. 175–189.

4

Linear Programming: The Simplex Method

▶ Each type of beer has its own recipe and an associated cost per unit, and brings in a specific revenue per unit. The brewery manager must meet a revenue target with minimum production costs. An exercise in Section 3 formulates the manager's goal as a linear programming problem and solves for the optimum production schedule when there are two beer varieties.

EXERCISES

1. Suppose you plan to build a raised flower bed using landscape timbers, which come in 8-ft lengths. You want the bed's outer dimensions to be 6 ft by 4 ft, and you will use three layers of timbers. The timbers are 6 in. by 6 in. in cross section, so if you make the bottom and top layers with 6 ft lengths on the sides and 3 ft lengths on the ends, and the middle layer with 5 ft lengths on the sides and 4 ft lengths on the ends, you could build the bed out of the following lengths.

Plan A	
Length	Number Needed
3 ft	4
4 ft	2
5 ft	2
6 ft	4

  a. What is the smallest number of timbers you can buy to build your bed? How will you lay out the cuts? How much wood will you waste?

  b. If you overlap the corners in a different way, you can build the bed with this plan:

Plan B	
Length	Number Needed
3 ft	2
4 ft	4
5 ft	4
6 ft	2

  Does plan B allow you to build the bed with fewer 8-ft timbers?

  c. What is the smallest length for the uncut timbers that would allow you to build the bed with no waste?

2. For the list of standard paper roll widths given earlier, write down four more possible cutting patterns that use at most four cuts and leave less than 14 in. of waste on the end. See if you can find ones that aren't in the list of patterns returned by the optimizer.

3. Four of the 33 possible patterns use up the raw roll with no waste, that is, the widths add up to exactly 100 in. Find these four patterns.

4. For the computer solution of the cutting problem, figure out the percent of the 356 rolls used that is wasted.

5. In our cutting plan, we elected to use up as much as possible of each 100-in. roll with standard widths. Why might it be a better idea to allow leftover rolls that are *wider* than 14 in.?

6. The following table shows the weights of six objects and their values.

Weight	2	2.5	3	3.5	4	4.5
Value	12	11	7	13	10	11

If your knapsack holds a maximum weight of 9, what is the highest value you can pack in?

DIRECTIONS FOR GROUP PROJECT

Suppose you and three of the students from class have met at your house to study and your father questions each of you on what you are learning in college. While this is happening, your mother is busy planning a new raised-bed garden and your sister is attempting to choose which items she will put in a backpack for a field trip. Using the data in Exercises 1 and 6, prepare a presentation for your family on the value of what you're learning in college.

5

Mathematics of Finance

Buying a car usually requires both some savings for a down payment and a loan for the balance. An exercise in Section 2 calculates the regular deposits that would be needed to save up the full purchase price, and other exercises and examples in this chapter compute the payments required to amortize a loan.

Everybody uses money. Sometimes you work for your money and other times your money works for you. For example, unless you are attending college on a full scholarship, it is very likely that you and your family have either saved money or borrowed money, or both, to pay for your education. When we borrow money, we normally have to pay interest for that privilege. When we save money, for a future purchase or retirement, we are lending money to a financial institution and we expect to earn interest on our investment. We will develop the mathematics in this chapter to better understand the principles of borrowing and saving. These ideas will then be used to compare different financial opportunities and make informed decisions.

5.1 Simple and Compound Interest

? THINK ABOUT IT

If you can borrow money at 8% interest compounded annually or at 7.9% compounded monthly, which loan would cost less?

We shall see how to make such comparisons in this section.

Simple Interest Interest on loans of a year or less is frequently calculated as **simple interest**, a type of interest that is charged (or paid) only on the amount borrowed (or invested), and not on past interest. The amount borrowed is called the **principal**. The **rate** of interest is given as a percentage per year, expressed as a decimal. For example, $6\% = 0.06$ and $11\frac{1}{2}\% = 0.115$. The **time** the money is earning interest is calculated in years. Simple interest is the product of the principal, rate, and time.

SIMPLE INTEREST

$$I = Prt$$

where

P is the principal;

r is the annual interest rate;

t is the time in years.

EXAMPLE 1 Simple Interest

To buy furniture for a new apartment, Jennifer Wall borrowed $5000 at 8% simple interest for 11 months. How much interest will she pay?

▶**Solution** From the formula, $I = Prt$, with $P = 5000$, $r = 0.08$, and $t = 11/12$ (in years). The total interest she will pay is

$$I = 5000(0.08)(11/12) \approx 366.67,$$

or $366.67.

A deposit of P dollars today at a rate of interest r for t years produces interest of $I = Prt$. The interest, added to the original principal P, gives

$$P + Prt = P(1 + rt).$$

This amount is called the *future value* of P dollars at an interest rate r for time t in years. When loans are involved, the future value is often called the *maturity value* of the loan. This idea is summarized as follows.

FUTURE OR MATURITY VALUE FOR SIMPLE INTEREST

The **future** or **maturity value** A of P dollars at a simple interest rate r for t years is

$$A = P(1 + rt).$$

EXAMPLE 2 **Maturity Values**

Find the maturity value for each loan at simple interest.

(a) A loan of $2500 to be repaid in 8 months with interest of 9.2%

▶**Solution** The loan is for 8 months, or $8/12 = 2/3$ of a year. The maturity value is

$$A = P(1 + rt)$$

$$A = 2500\left[1 + 0.092\left(\frac{2}{3}\right)\right]$$

$$A \approx 2500(1 + 0.06133) \approx 2653.33,$$

or $2653.33. (The answer is rounded to the nearest cent, as is customary in financial problems.) Of this maturity value,

$$\$2653.33 - \$2500 = \$153.33$$

represents interest.

(b) A loan of $11,280 for 85 days at 11% interest

▶**Solution** It is common to assume 360 days in a year when working with simple interest. We shall usually make such an assumption in this book. The maturity value in this example is

$$A = 11,280\left[1 + 0.11\left(\frac{85}{360}\right)\right] \approx 11,572.97,$$

or $11,572.97.

CAUTION When using the formula for future value, as well as all other formulas in this chapter, we neglect the fact that in real life, money amounts are rounded to the nearest penny. As a consequence, when the amounts are rounded, their values may differ by a few cents from the amounts given by these formulas. For instance, in Example 2(a), the interest in each monthly payment would be $2500(0.092/12) \approx \$19.17$, rounded to the nearest penny.

After 8 months, the total is $8(\$19.17) = \$153.36$, which is 3¢ more than we computed in the example. ∎

In part (b) of Example 2 we assumed 360 days in a year. Historically, to simplify calculations, it was often assumed that each year had twelve 30-day months, making a year 360 days long. Treasury bills sold by the U.S. government assume a 360-day year in calculating interest. Interest found using a 360-day year is called *ordinary interest* and interest found using a 365-day year is called *exact interest*.

The formula for future value has four variables, P, r, t, and A. We can use the formula to find any of the quantities that these variables represent, as illustrated in the next example.

EXAMPLE 3 **Simple Interest**

Becky Anderson wants to borrow $8000 from Christine O'Brien. She is willing to pay back $8380 in 6 months. What interest rate will she pay?

▶**Solution**   Use the formula for future value, with $A = 8380$, $P = 8000$, $t = 6/12 = 0.5$, and solve for r.

$$A = P(1 + rt)$$
$$8380 = 8000(1 + 0.5r)$$
$$8380 = 8000 + 4000r \qquad \text{Distributive property}$$
$$380 = 4000r \qquad \text{Subtract 8000.}$$
$$r = 0.095 \qquad \text{Divide by 4000.}$$

Thus, the interest rate is 9.5%. ▬

Compound Interest   As mentioned earlier, simple interest is normally used for loans or investments of a year or less. For longer periods compound interest is used. With **compound interest**, interest is charged (or paid) on interest as well as on principal. For example, if $1000 is deposited at 5% interest for 1 year, at the end of the year the interest is $\$1000(0.05)(1) = \$50$. The balance in the account is $\$1000 + \$50 = \$1050$. If this amount is left at 5% interest for another year, the interest is calculated on $1050 instead of the original $1000, so the amount in the account at the end of the second year is $\$1050 + \$1050(0.05)(1) = \$1102.50$. Note that simple interest would produce a total amount of only

$$\$1000[1 + (0.05)(2)] = \$1100.$$

To find a formula for compound interest, first suppose that P dollars is deposited at a rate of interest r per year. The amount on deposit at the end of the first year is found by the simple interest formula, with $t = 1$.

$$A = P(1 + r \cdot 1) = P(1 + r)$$

If the deposit earns compound interest, the interest earned during the second year is paid on the total amount on deposit at the end of the first year. Using the formula $A = P(1 + rt)$ again, with P replaced by $P(1 + r)$ and $t = 1$, gives the total amount on deposit at the end of the second year.

$$A = [P(1 + r)](1 + r \cdot 1) = P(1 + r)^2$$

In the same way, the total amount on deposit at the end of the third year is

$$P(1 + r)^3.$$

Generalizing, in t years the total amount on deposit is

$$A = P(1 + r)^t,$$

called the **compound amount**.

NOTE Compare this formula for compound interest with the formula for simple interest.

Compound interest $\quad A = P(1 + r)^t$

Simple interest $\qquad A = P(1 + rt)$

The important distinction between the two formulas is that in the compound interest formula, the number of years, t, is an *exponent*, so that money grows much more rapidly when interest is compounded. ∎

Interest can be compounded more than once per year. Common compounding periods include *semiannually* (two periods per year), *quarterly* (four periods per year), *monthly* (twelve periods per year), or *daily* (usually 365 periods per year). The *interest rate per period*, i, is found by dividing the annual interest rate, r, by the number of compounding periods, m, per year. To find the total number of compounding periods, n, we multiply the number of years, t, by the number of compounding periods per year, m. The following formula can be derived in the same way as the previous formula.

COMPOUND AMOUNT

$$A = P(1 + i)^n$$

where $i = \dfrac{r}{m}$ and $n = mt$,

$A \quad$ is the future (maturity) value;

$P \quad$ is the principal;

$r \quad$ is the annual interest rate;

$m \quad$ is the number of compounding periods per year;

$t \quad$ is the number of years;

$n \quad$ is the number of compounding periods;

$i \quad$ is the interest rate per period.

EXAMPLE 4 **Compound Interest**

Suppose $1000 is deposited for 6 years in an account paying 4.25% per year compounded annually.

(a) Find the compound amount.

▶**Solution** In the formula for the compound amount, $P = 1000$, $i = 0.0425/1$, and $n = 6(1) = 6$. The compound amount is

$$A = P(1 + i)^n$$
$$A = 1000(1.0425)^6.$$

Using a calculator, we get

$$A \approx \$1283.68,$$

the compound amount.

(b) Find the amount of interest earned.

▶**Solution** Subtract the initial deposit from the compound amount.

$$\text{Amount of interest} = \$1283.68 - \$1000 = \$283.68$$

EXAMPLE 5 **Compound Interest**

Find the amount of interest earned by a deposit of $2450 for 6.5 years at 5.25% compounded quarterly.

▶**Solution** Interest compounded quarterly is compounded 4 times a year. In 6.5 years, there are $6.5(4) = 26$ periods. Thus, $n = 26$. Interest of 5.25% per year is 5.25%/4 per quarter, so $i = 0.0525/4$. Now use the formula for compound amount.

$$A = P(1 + i)^n$$
$$A = 2450(1 + 0.0525/4)^{26} \approx 3438.78$$

Rounded to the nearest cent, the compound amount is $3438.78, so the interest is $3438.78 - $2450 = $988.78.

$\boxed{\text{CAUTION}}$ As shown in Example 5, compound interest problems involve two rates—the annual rate r and the rate per compounding period i. Be sure you understand the distinction between them. When interest is compounded annually, these rates are the same. In all other cases, $i \neq r$. ∎

It is interesting to compare loans at the same rate when simple or compound interest is used. Figure 1 shows the graphs of the simple interest and compound interest formulas with $P = 1000$ at an annual rate of 10% from 0 to 20 years. The future value after 15 years is shown for each graph. After 15 years at compound

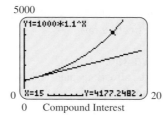

Compound Interest

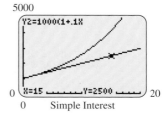

Simple Interest

FIGURE 1

interest, $1000 grows to $4177.25, whereas with simple interest, it amounts to $2500.00, a difference of $1677.25.

Spreadsheets are ideal for performing financial calculations. Figure 2 shows a Microsoft Excel spreadsheet with the formulas for compound and simple interest used to create columns B and C, respectively, when $1000 is invested at an annual rate of 10%. Compare row 16 with the calculator results in Figure 1. For more details on the use of spreadsheets in the mathematics of finance, see *The Spreadsheet Manual* available with this book.

	A	B	C
1	period	compound	simple
2	1	1100	1100
3	2	1210	1200
4	3	1331	1300
5	4	1464.1	1400
6	5	1610.51	1500
7	6	1771.561	1600
8	7	1948.7171	1700
9	8	2143.58881	1800
10	9	2357.947691	1900
11	10	2593.74246	2000
12	11	2853.116706	2100
13	12	3138.428377	2200
14	13	3452.271214	2300
15	14	3797.498336	2400
16	15	4177.248169	2500
17	16	4594.972986	2600
18	17	5054.470285	2700
19	18	5559.917313	2800
20	19	6115.909045	2900
21	20	6727.499949	3000

FIGURE 2

Effective Rate

Effective Rate   If $1 is deposited at 4% compounded quarterly, a calculator can be used to find that at the end of one year, the compound amount is $1.0406, an increase of 4.06% over the original $1. The actual increase of 4.06% in the money is somewhat higher than the stated increase of 4%. To differentiate between these two numbers, 4% is called the **nominal** or **stated rate** of interest, while 4.06% is called the *effective rate*.* To avoid confusion between stated rates and effective rates, we shall continue to use r for the stated rate and we will use r_e for the effective rate.

EXAMPLE 6   **Effective Rate**

Find the effective rate corresponding to a stated rate of 6% compounded semiannually.

---

*When applied to consumer finance, the effective rate is called the annual percentage rate, APR, or annual percentage yield, APY.

▶**Solution** Here, $i = r/m = 6\%/2 = 3\%$ for $m = 2$ periods. Use a calculator to find that $(1.03)^2 \approx 1.06090$, which shows that $1 will increase to $1.06090, an actual increase of 6.09%. The effective rate is $r_e = 6.09\%$.

Generalizing from this example, the effective rate of interest is given by the following formula.

EFFECTIVE RATE

The **effective rate** corresponding to a stated rate of interest r compounded m times per year is

$$r_e = \left(1 + \frac{r}{m}\right)^m - 1.$$

EXAMPLE 7 **Effective Rate**

A bank pays interest of 4.9% compounded monthly. Find the effective rate.

▶**Solution** Use the formula given above with $r = 0.049$ and $m = 12$. The effective rate is

$$r_e = \left(1 + \frac{0.049}{12}\right)^{12} - 1 = 0.050115575,$$

or 5.01%.

EXAMPLE 8 **Effective Rate**

Joe Vetere needs to borrow money. His neighborhood bank charges 8% interest compounded semiannually. A downtown bank charges 7.9% interest compounded monthly. At which bank will Joe pay the lesser amount of interest?

?

▶**Solution** Compare the effective rates.

Neighborhood bank: $\quad r_e = \left(1 + \dfrac{0.08}{2}\right)^2 - 1 = 0.0816 = 8.16\%$

Downtown bank: $\quad r_e = \left(1 + \dfrac{0.079}{12}\right)^{12} - 1 = 0.081924 \approx 8.19\%$

The neighborhood bank has the lower effective rate, although it has a higher stated rate.

Present Value The formula for compound interest, $A = P(1 + i)^n$, has four variables: A, P, i, and n. Given the values of any three of these variables, the value of the fourth can be found. In particular, if A (the future amount), i, and n are known, then P can be found. Here P is the amount that should be deposited today to produce A dollars in n periods.

EXAMPLE 9

Present Value

Rachel Reeve must pay a lump sum of $6000 in 5 years. What amount deposited today at 6.2% compounded annually will amount to $6000 in 5 years?

▶**Solution** Here $A = 6000$, $i = 0.062$, $n = 5$, and P is unknown. Substituting these values into the formula for the compound amount gives

$$6000 = P(1.062)^5$$

$$P = \frac{6000}{(1.062)^5} \approx 4441.49,$$

or $4441.49. If Rachel leaves $4441.49 for 5 years in an account paying 6.2% compounded annually, she will have $6000 when she needs it. To check your work, use the compound interest formula with $P = \$4441.49$, $i = 0.062$, and $n = 5$. You should get $A = \$6000.00$.

As Example 9 shows, $6000 in 5 years is approximately the same as $4441.49 today (if money can be deposited at 6.2% compounded annually). An amount that can be deposited today to yield a given sum in the future is called the *present value* of the future sum. Generalizing from Example 9, by solving $A = P(1 + i)^n$ for P, we get the following formula for present value.

PRESENT VALUE FOR COMPOUND INTEREST

The **present value** of A dollars compounded at an interest rate i per period for n periods is

$$P = \frac{A}{(1 + i)^n} \quad \text{or} \quad P = A(1 + i)^{-n}.$$

EXAMPLE 10

Present Value

Find the present value of $16,000 in 9 years if money can be deposited at 6% compounded semiannually.

▶**Solution** In 9 years there are $2 \cdot 9 = 18$ semiannual periods. A rate of 6% per year is 3% in each semiannual period. Apply the formula with $A = 16,000$, $i = 0.03$, and $n = 18$.

$$P = \frac{A}{(1 + i)^n} = \frac{16,000}{(1.03)^{18}} \approx 9398.31$$

A deposit of $9398.31 today, at 6% compounded semiannually, will produce a total of $16,000 in 9 years.

We can solve the compound amount formula for n also, as the following example shows.

EXAMPLE 11

Price Doubling

Suppose the general level of inflation in the economy averages 8% per year. Find the number of years it would take for the overall level of prices to double.

▶**Solution** To find the number of years it will take for \$1 worth of goods or services to cost \$2, find n in the equation

$$2 = 1(1 + 0.08)^n,$$

where $A = 2$, $P = 1$, and $i = 0.08$. This equation simplifies to

$$2 = (1.08)^n.$$

By trying various values of n, we find that $n = 9$ is approximately correct, because $1.08^9 = 1.99900 \approx 2$. The exact value of n can be found quickly by using logarithms, but that is beyond the scope of this chapter. Thus, the overall level of prices will double in about 9 years.

The doubling time for an amount being compounded can be estimated quickly using the rule of 72. Simply divide 72 by the rate (expressed as a percentage) to approximate the time it takes an amount to double. In Example 11, the inflation rate is 8%, so the doubling time is approximately $72/8 = 9$ years. The rule of 72 is fairly accurate for rates between 4% and 20%. For smaller rates or for daily compounding, the rule of 70, in which we divide 70 by the rate (expressed as a percentage) to approximate the time it takes an amount to double, is more accurate.

At this point, it seems helpful to summarize the notation and the most important formulas for simple and compound interest. We use the following variables.

P = principal or present value

A = future or maturity value

r = annual (stated or nominal) interest rate

t = number of years

m = number of compounding periods per year

i = interest rate per period $i = r/m$

n = total number of compounding periods $n = tm$

r_e = effective rate

Simple Interest	Compound Interest
$A = P(1 + rt)$	$A = P(1 + i)^n$
$P = \dfrac{A}{1 + rt}$	$P = \dfrac{A}{(1 + i)^n} = A(1 + i)^{-n}$
	$r_e = \left(1 + \dfrac{r}{m}\right)^m - 1$

▶ 5.1 Exercises

1. What factors determine the amount of interest earned on a fixed principal?

2. In your own words, describe the *maturity value* of a loan.

3. What is meant by the *present value* of money?

4. We calculated the loan in Example 2(b) assuming 360 days in a year. Find the maturity value using 365 days in a year. Which is more advantageous to the borrower?

Find the simple interest.

5. $25,000 at 3% for 9 months

6. $4289 at 4.5% for 35 weeks

7. $1974 at 6.3% for 25 weeks

8. $6125 at 1.25% for 6 months

Find the simple interest. Assume a 360-day year.

9. $8192.17 at 3.1% for 72 days

10. $7236.15 at 4.25% for 30 days

Find the maturity value and the amount of simple interest earned.

11. $3125 at 2.85% for 7 months

12. $12,000 at 5.3% for 11 months

13. If $1500 earned simple interest of $56.25 in 6 months, what was the simple interest rate?

14. If $23,500 earned simple interest of $1057.50 in 9 months, what was the simple interest rate?

15. Explain the difference between simple interest and compound interest.

16. What is the difference between r and i?

17. What is the difference between t and n?

18. In Figure 1, one graph is a straight line and the other is curved. Explain why this is, and which represents each type of interest.

Find the compound amount for each deposit and the amount of interest earned.

19. $1000 at 6% compounded annually for 8 years

20. $1000 at 4.5% compounded annually for 6 years

21. $470 at 5.4% compounded semiannually for 12 years

22. $15,000 at 6% compounded monthly for 10 years

23. $8500 at 8% compounded quarterly for 5 years

24. $9100 at 6.4% compounded quarterly for 9 years

Find the present value (the amount that should be invested now to accumulate the following amount) if the money is compounded as indicated.

25. $12,820.77 at 4.8% compounded annually for 6 years

26. $36,527.13 at 5.3% compounded annually for 10 years

27. $2000 at 6% compounded semiannually for 8 years

28. $2000 at 7% compounded semiannually for 8 years

29. $8800 at 5% compounded quarterly for 5 years

30. $7500 at 5.5% compounded quarterly for 9 years

31. How do the nominal or stated interest rate and the effective interest rate differ?

32. If interest is compounded more than once per year, which rate is higher, the stated rate or the effective rate?

Find the effective rate corresponding to each nominal rate.

33. 4% compounded quarterly

34. 6% compounded quarterly

35. 7.25% compounded semiannually

36. 6.25% compounded semiannually

▶ Applications

BUSINESS AND ECONOMICS

37. *Loan Repayment* Amy Bastide borrowed $7200 from her father to buy a used car. She repaid him after 9 months, at an annual interest rate of 6.2%. Find the total amount she repaid. How much of this amount is interest?

38. *Delinquent Taxes* An accountant for a corporation forgot to pay the firm's income tax of $321,812.85 on time. The government charged a penalty based on an annual interest rate of 13.4% for the 29 days the money was late. Find the total amount (tax and penalty) that was paid. (Use a 365-day year.)

39. *Savings* A $1500 certificate of deposit held for 75 days was worth $1521.25. To the nearest tenth of a percent, what interest rate was earned? Assume a 360-day year.

40. *Bond Interest* A bond with a face value of $10,000 in 10 years can be purchased now for $5988.02. What is the simple interest rate?

41. *Savings* A department has ordered 8 new Dell computers at a cost of $2309 each. The order will not be delivered for 6 months. What amount could the department deposit in a special 6-month CD paying 4.79% compounded monthly to have enough to pay for the machines at time of delivery?

42. *Stock Growth* A stock that sold for $22 at the beginning of the year was selling for $24 at the end of the year. If the stock paid a dividend of $0.50 per share, what is the simple interest rate on an investment in this stock? (*Hint:* Consider the interest to be the increase in value plus the dividend.)

43. *Loan Interest* A small business borrows $50,000 for expansion at 8% interest compounded monthly. The loan is due in 6 years. How much interest will the business pay?

44. *Wealth* A 1997 article in *The New York Times* discussed how long it would take for Bill Gates, the world's second richest person at the time (behind the Sultan of Brunei), to become the world's first trillionaire.* His birthday is October 28, 1955, and on July 16, 1997, he was worth $42 billion. (*Note:* A trillion dollars is 1000 billion dollars.)

a. Assume that Bill Gates's fortune grows at an annual rate of 58%, the historical growth rate through 1997 of Microsoft stock, which made up most of his wealth in 1997. Find the age at which he becomes a trillionaire. (*Hint:* Use the formula for interest compounded annually, $A = P(1 + i)^n$, with $P = 42$. Graph the future value as a function of n on a graphing calculator, and find where the graph crosses the line $y = 1000$.)

b. Repeat part a using 10.5% growth, the average return on all stocks since 1926.[†]

c. What rate of growth would be necessary for Bill Gates to become a trillionaire by the time he is eligible for Social Security on January 1, 2022, after he has turned 66?

d. *Forbes* magazine's listings of billionaires for 2003 and 2006 have given Bill Gates's worth as roughly $40.7 billion and $50 billion, respectively.[‡] What was the rate of growth of his wealth between 2003 and 2006?

45. *Rule of 72* On the day of their first grandchild's birth, a new set of grandparents invested $10,000 in a trust fund earning 4.5% compounded monthly.

a. Use the rule of 72 to estimate how old the grandchild will be when the trust fund is worth $20,000.

b. Use your answer to part a to determine the actual amount that will be in the trust fund at that time. How close was your estimate in part a?

The New York Times, July 20, 1997, Sec. 4, p. 2.
[†]http://money.cnn.com.
[‡]http://www.forbes.com/2004/02/25/bill04land.html and http://www.forbes.com/lists/2006/10/BH69.html.
To find the current net worth of Bill Gates, see www.quuxuum.org/~evan/bgnw.html.

46. *Student Loan* Upon graduation from college, Kelly was able to defer payment on his $40,000 subsidized Stafford student loan for 6 months. Since the interest will no longer be paid on his behalf, it will be added to the principal until payments begin.* If the interest is 6.54% compounded monthly, what will the principal amount be when he must begin repaying his loan?

47. *Buying a House* Robert Herbert wants to have $30,000 available in 5 years for a down payment on a house. He has inherited $25,000. How much of the inheritance should he invest now to accumulate $30,000, if he can get an interest rate of 5.5% compounded quarterly?

48. *Comparing Investments* Two partners agree to invest equal amounts in their business. One will contribute $10,000 immediately. The other plans to contribute an equivalent amount in 3 years, when she expects to acquire a large sum of money. How much should she contribute at that time to match her partner's investment now, assuming an interest rate of 6% compounded semiannually?

49. *Comparing Investments* As the prize in a contest, you are offered $1000 now or $1210 in 5 years. If money can be invested at 6% compounded annually, which is larger?

50. *Comparing CD Rates* Marine Bank offered the following CD (Certificates of Deposit) rates.† The rates are annual percentage yields, or effective rates, which are higher than the corresponding nominal rates. Assume quarterly compounding. Solve for *r* to approximate the corresponding nominal rates to the nearest hundredth.

Term	6 mo	Special! 9 mo	1 yr	2 yr	3 yr
APY%	2.50	5.10	4.25	4.50	5.25

51. *Effective Rate* A Web site for E*TRADE Financial claims that they have "one of the highest yields in the nation" on a 6-month CD. The stated yield was 5.46%; the actual rate was not stated.‡ Assuming monthly compounding, find the actual rate.

52. *Effective Rate* According to a financial Web site, on August 18, 2006, Centennial Bank of Fountain Valley, California, paid 5.5% interest, compounded monthly, on a 1-year CD, while First Source Bank of South Bend, Indiana, paid 5.63% compounded annually.§ What are the effective rates for the two CDs, and which bank pays a higher effective rate?

53. *Retirement Savings* The pie graph below shows the percent of baby boomers aged 46–49 who said they had investments with a total value as shown in each category.‖

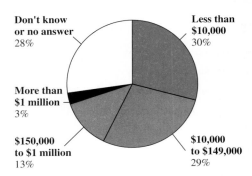

Figures add to more than 100% because of rounding.

Note that 30% have saved less than $10,000. Assume the money is invested at an average rate of 8% compounded quarterly. What will the top numbers in each category amount to in 20 years, when this age group will be ready for retirement?

Doubling Time Use the ideas from Example 11 to find the time it would take for the general level of prices in the economy to double at each average annual inflation rate.

54. 4%   **55.** 5%

56. *Doubling Time* The consumption of electricity has increased historically at 6% per year. If it continues to increase at this rate indefinitely, find the number of years before the electric utilities will need to double their generating capacity.

57. *Doubling Time* Suppose a conservation campaign coupled with higher rates causes the demand for electricity to increase at only 2% per year, as it has recently. Find the number of years before the utilities will need to double generating capacity.

Negative Interest Under certain conditions, Swiss banks pay negative interest: they charge you. (You didn't think all that secrecy was free?) Suppose a bank "pays" −2.4% interest compounded annually. Find the compound amount for a deposit of $150,000 after each period.

58. 4 years   **59.** 8 years

60. *Interest Rate* In 1995, O. G. McClain of Houston, Texas mailed a $100 check to a descendant of Texas indepen-

*SallieMae: http://www.salliemae.com/get_student_loan/find_student_loan/undergrad_student_loan/federal_student_loans/.
†http://www.ibankmarine.com.
‡http://us.etrade.com.
§https://www.bankrate.com.
‖*The New York Times*, Dec. 31, 1995, Sec. 3. p. 5.

dence hero Sam Houston to repay a $100 debt of McClain's great-great-grandfather, who died in 1835, to Sam Houston.* A bank estimated the interest on the loan to be $420 million for the 160 years it was due. Find the interest rate the bank was using, assuming interest is compounded annually.

61. *Investment* In the New Testament, Jesus commends a widow who contributed 2 mites to the temple treasury (Mark 12:42–44). A mite was worth roughly 1/8 of a cent. Suppose the temple invested those 2 mites at 4% interest compounded quarterly. How much would the money be worth 2000 years later?

62. *Investments* Sun Kang borrowed $5200 from his friend Hop Fong Yee to pay for remodeling work on his house. He repaid the loan 10 months later with simple interest at 7%. Yee then invested the proceeds in a 5-year certificate of deposit paying 6.3% compounded quarterly. How much will he have at the end of 5 years? (*Hint:* You need to use both simple and compound interest.)

63. *Investments* Suppose $10,000 is invested at an annual rate of 5% for 10 years. Find the future value if interest is compounded as follows.

a. Annually **b.** Quarterly

c. Monthly **d.** Daily (365 days)

64. *Investments* In Exercise 63, notice that as the money is compounded more often, the compound amount becomes larger and larger. Is it possible to compound often enough so that the compound amount is $17,000 after 10 years? Explain.

The following exercise is from an actuarial examination.†

65. *Savings* On January 1, 2000, Jack deposited $1000 into bank X to earn interest at a rate of j per annum compounded semiannually. On January 1, 2005, he transferred his account to bank Y to earn interest at the rate of k per annum compounded quarterly. On January 1, 2008, the balance of bank Y is $1990.76. If Jack could have earned interest at the rate of k per annum compounded quarterly from January 1, 2000, through January 1, 2008, his balance would have been $2203.76. Calculate the ratio k/j.

 Future Value of an Annuity

> **?** **THINK ABOUT IT**
>
> If you deposit $1500 each year for 6 years in an account paying 8% interest compounded annually, how much will be in your account at the end of this period?

In this section and the next, we develop future value and present value formulas for such periodic payments. To develop these formulas, we must first discuss *sequences*.

Geometric Sequences

If a and r are nonzero real numbers, the infinite list of numbers a, ar, ar^2, ar^3, $ar^4, \ldots, ar^n, \ldots$ is called a **geometric sequence**. For example, if $a = 3$ and $r = -2$, we have the sequence

$$3, 3(-2), 3(-2)^2, 3(-2)^3, 3(-2)^4, \ldots,$$

or

$$3, -6, 12, -24, 48, \ldots.$$

The New York Times, March 30, 1995.
†Adapted from Problem 5 from "Course 140 Examination, Mathematics of Compound Interest" of the *Education and Examination Committee of The Society of Actuaries*. Reprinted by permission of The Society of Actuaries.

In the sequence $a, ar, ar^2, ar^3, ar^4, \ldots$, the number a is called the **first term** of the sequence, ar is the **second term**, ar^2 is the **third term**, and so on. Thus, for any $n \geq 1$,

$$ar^{n-1} \text{ is the nth term of the sequence.}$$

Each term in the sequence is r times the preceding term. The number r is called the **common ratio** of the sequence.

EXAMPLE 1   **Geometric Sequence**

Find the seventh term of the geometric sequence $5, 20, 80, 320, \ldots$.

▶**Solution** The first term in the sequence is 5, so $a = 5$. The common ratio, found by dividing the second term by the first, is $r = 20/5 = 4$. We want the seventh term, so $n = 7$. Use ar^{n-1}, with $a = 5$, $r = 4$, and $n = 7$.

$$ar^{n-1} = (5)(4)^{7-1} = 5(4)^6 = 20{,}480$$

EXAMPLE 2   **Geometric Sequence**

Find the first five terms of the geometric sequence with $a = 10$ and $r = 2$.

▶**Solution** The first five terms are

$$10, 10(2), 10(2)^2, 10(2)^3, 10(2)^4,$$

or

$$10, 20, 40, 80, 160.$$

Next, we need to find the sum S_n of the first n terms of a geometric sequence, where

$$S_n = a + ar + ar^2 + ar^3 + ar^4 + \cdots + ar^{n-1}. \tag{1}$$

If $r = 1$, then

$$S_n = \underbrace{a + a + a + a + \cdots + a}_{n \text{ terms}} = na.$$

If $r \neq 1$, multiply both sides of equation (1) by r to get

$$rS_n = ar + ar^2 + ar^3 + ar^4 + \cdots + ar^n. \tag{2}$$

Now subtract corresponding sides of equation (1) from equation (2).

$$
\begin{aligned}
rS_n &= \quad\;\; ar + ar^2 + ar^3 + ar^4 + \cdots + ar^{n-1} + ar^n \\
-S_n &= -(a + ar + ar^2 + ar^3 + ar^4 + \cdots + ar^{n-1}) \\
\hline
rS_n - S_n &= -a + ar^n \\
S_n(r-1) &= a(r^n - 1) \qquad \text{Factor.} \\
S_n &= \frac{a(r^n - 1)}{r - 1} \qquad \text{Divide both sides by } r - 1.
\end{aligned}
$$

This result is summarized on the next page.

> ### SUM OF TERMS
>
> If a geometric sequence has first term a and common ratio r, then the sum S_n of the first n terms is given by
>
> $$S_n = \frac{a(r^n - 1)}{r - 1}, \quad r \neq 1.$$

EXAMPLE 3

Sum of a Geometric Sequence

Find the sum of the first six terms of the geometric sequence $3, 12, 48, \ldots$.

▶ **Solution** Here $a = 3$, $r = 4$, and $n = 6$. Find S_6 by the formula above.

$$S_6 = \frac{3(4^6 - 1)}{4 - 1} \qquad n = 6, a = 3, r = 4.$$

$$= \frac{3(4096 - 1)}{3}$$

$$= 4095$$

Ordinary Annuities

A sequence of equal payments made at equal periods of time is called an **annuity**. If the payments are made at the end of the time period, and if the frequency of payments is the same as the frequency of compounding, the annuity is called an **ordinary annuity**. The time between payments is the **payment period**, and the time from the beginning of the first payment period to the end of the last period is called the **term** of the annuity. The **future value of the annuity**, the final sum on deposit, is defined as the sum of the compound amounts of all the payments, compounded to the end of the term.

Two common uses of annuities are to accumulate funds for some goal or to withdraw funds from an account. For example, an annuity may be used to save money for a large purchase, such as an automobile, a college education, or a down payment on a home. An annuity also may be used to provide monthly payments for retirement. We explore these options in this and the next section.

For example, suppose $1500 is deposited at the end of each year for the next 6 years in an account paying 8% per year compounded annually. Figure 3 shows this annuity. To find the future value of the annuity, look separately at each of the $1500 payments. The first of these payments will produce a compound amount of

$$1500(1 + 0.08)^5 = 1500(1.08)^5.$$

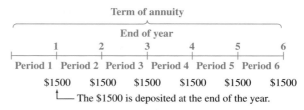

FIGURE 3

Use 5 as the exponent instead of 6, since the money is deposited at the *end* of the first year and earns interest for only 5 years. The second payment of $1500 will produce a compound amount of $1500(1.08)^4$. As shown in Figure 4, the future value of the annuity is

$$1500(1.08)^5 + 1500(1.08)^4 + 1500(1.08)^3 + 1500(1.08)^2$$
$$+ 1500(1.08)^1 + 1500.$$

(The last payment earns no interest at all.)

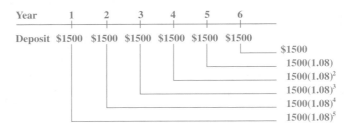

FIGURE 4

Reading this sum in reverse order, we see that it is the sum of the first six terms of a geometric sequence, with $a = 1500$, $r = 1.08$, and $n = 6$. Thus, the sum equals

$$\frac{a(r^n - 1)}{r - 1} = \frac{1500[(1.08)^6 - 1]}{1.08 - 1} \approx \$11{,}003.89.$$

To generalize this result, suppose that payments of R dollars each are deposited into an account at the end of each period for n periods, at a rate of interest i per period. The first payment of R dollars will produce a compound amount of $R(1 + i)^{n-1}$ dollars, the second payment will produce $R(1 + i)^{n-2}$ dollars, and so on; the final payment earns no interest and contributes just R dollars to the total. If S represents the future value (or sum) of the annuity, then (as shown in Figure 5 below),

$$S = R(1 + i)^{n-1} + R(1 + i)^{n-2} + R(1 + i)^{n-3} + \cdots + R(1 + i) + R,$$

or, written in reverse order,

$$S = R + R(1 + i)^1 + R(1 + i)^2 + \cdots + R(1 + i)^{n-1}.$$

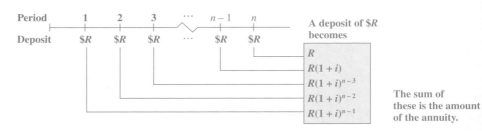

FIGURE 5

This result is the sum of the first n terms of the geometric sequence having first term R and common ratio $1 + i$. Using the formula for the sum of the first n

terms of a geometric sequence,

$$S = \frac{R[(1 + i)^n - 1]}{(1 + i) - 1} = \frac{R[(1 + i)^n - 1]}{i} = R\left[\frac{(1 + i)^n - 1}{i}\right].$$

The quantity in brackets is commonly written $s_{\overline{n}|i}$ (read "*s*-angle-*n* at *i*"), so that

$$S = R \cdot s_{\overline{n}|i}.$$

Values of $s_{\overline{n}|i}$ can be found with a calculator.

A formula for the future value of an annuity S of n payments of R dollars each at the end of each consecutive interest period, with interest compounded at a rate i per period, follows.* Recall that this type of annuity, with payments at the *end* of each time period, is called an ordinary annuity.

FUTURE VALUE OF AN ORDINARY ANNUITY

$$S = R\left[\frac{(1 + i)^n - 1}{i}\right] \qquad \text{or} \qquad S = Rs_{\overline{n}|i}$$

where

S is the future value;

R is the payment;

i is the interest rate per period;

n is the number of periods.

A calculator will be very helpful in computations with annuities. The TI-83/84 Plus graphing calculator has a special FINANCE menu that is designed to give any desired result after entering the basic information. If your calculator does not have this feature, many calculators can easily be programmed to evaluate the formulas introduced in this section and the next. We include these programs in *The Graphing Calculator Manual* available for this text.

EXAMPLE 4 **Ordinary Annuity**

Karen Scott is an athlete who believes that her playing career will last 7 years. To prepare for her future, she deposits $22,000 at the end of each year for 7 years in an account paying 6% compounded annually. How much will she have on deposit after 7 years?

▶**Solution** Her payments form an ordinary annuity, with $r = 22,000$, $n = 7$, and $i = 0.06$. The future value of this annuity (by the formula above) is

$$S = 22,000\left[\frac{(1.06)^7 - 1}{0.06}\right] \approx 184,664.43,$$

or $184,664.43. Note that she made 7 payments of $22,000, or $154,000. The interest that she earned is $184,664.43 − $154,000 = $30,664.43.   ▬

*We use S for the future value here, instead of A as in the compound interest formula, to help avoid confusing the two formulas.

Sinking Funds A fund set up to receive periodic payments as in Example 4 is called a **sinking fund**. The periodic payments, together with the interest earned by the payments, are designed to produce a given sum at some time in the future. For example, a sinking fund might be set up to receive money that will be needed to pay off the principal on a loan at some future time. If the payments are all the same amount and are made at the end of a regular time period, they form an ordinary annuity.

EXAMPLE 5

Sinking Fund

Experts say that the baby boom generation (Americans born between 1946 and 1960) cannot count on a company pension or Social Security to provide a comfortable retirement, as their parents did. It is recommended that they start to save early and regularly. Sarah Santora, a baby boomer, has decided to deposit $200 each month for 20 years in an account that pays interest of 7.2% compounded monthly.

(a) How much will be in the account at the end of 20 years?

▶**Solution** This savings plan is an annuity with $R = 200$, $i = 0.072/12$, and $n = 12(20)$. The future value is

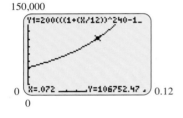

$$S = 200\left[\frac{(1 + (0.072/12))^{12(20)} - 1}{0.072/12}\right] \approx 106{,}752.47,$$

or $106,752.47. Figure 6 shows a calculator graph of the function

$$S = 200\left[\frac{(1 + (x/12))^{12(20)} - 1}{x/12}\right]$$

where r, the annual interest rate, is designated x. The value of the function at $x = 0.072$, shown at the bottom of the window, agrees with our result above.

FIGURE 6

(b) Sarah believes she needs to accumulate $130,000 in the 20-year period to have enough for retirement. What interest rate would provide that amount?

▶**Solution**

METHOD 1
Graphing Calculator

One way to answer this question is to solve the equation for S in terms of x with $S = 130{,}000$. This is a difficult equation to solve. Although trial and error could be used, it would be easier to use the graphing calculator graph in Figure 6. Adding the line $y = 130{,}000$ to the graph and then using the capability of the calculator to find the intersection point with the curve shows the annual interest rate must be at least 8.79% to the nearest hundredth. See Figure 7 below.

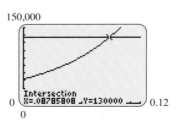

FIGURE 7

METHOD 2
TVM Solver

FIGURE 8

Using the TVM Solver under the FINANCE menu on the TI-83/84 Plus calculator, enter 240 for N (the number of periods), 0 for PV (present value), −200 for PMT (negative because the money is being paid out), 130000 for FV (future value), and 12 for P/Y (payments per year). Put the cursor next to I% (payment) and press SOLVE. The result, shown in Figure 8, indicates that an interest rate of 8.79% is needed.

In Example 5 we used sinking fund calculations to determine the amount of money that accumulates over time through monthly payments and interest. We can also use this formula to determine the amount of money necessary to periodically invest at a given interest rate to reach a particular goal. Start with the annuity formula

$$S = R\left[\frac{(1 + i)^n - 1}{i}\right],$$

and multiply both sides by $i/[(1 + i)^n - 1]$ to derive the following formula.

SINKING FUND PAYMENT

$$R = \frac{Si}{(1 + i)^n - 1}$$

where

R is the payment;

S is the future value;

i is the interest rate per period;

n is the number of periods.

EXAMPLE 6 **Sinking Fund Payment**

Suppose Sarah, in Example 5, cannot get the higher interest rate to produce $130,000 in 20 years. To meet that goal, she must increase her monthly payment. What payment should she make each month?

▶Solution   Sarah's goal is to accumulate $130,000 in 20 years at 7.2% compounded monthly. Therefore, the future value is $S = 130,000$, the monthly interest rate is $i = 0.072/12$, and the number of periods is $n = 12(20)$. Use the sinking fund payment formula to find the payment R.

$$R = \frac{(130,000)(0.072/12)}{(1 + (0.072/12))^{12(20)} - 1} \approx 243.5540887$$

Sarah will need payments of $243.56 each month for 20 years to accumulate at least $130,000. Notice that $243.55 is not quite enough, so round up here. Figure 9 shows the point of intersection of the graphs of

$$Y_1 = X\left[\frac{(1 + 0.072/12)^{12(20)} - 1}{0.072/12}\right]$$

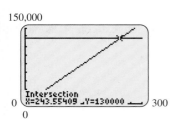

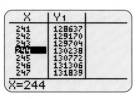

FIGURE 9

and $Y_2 = 130,000$. The result agrees with the answer we found above analytically. The table shown in Figure 9 confirms that the payment should be between $243 and $244.

We can also use a graphing calculator or spreadsheet to make a table of the amount in a sinking fund. In the formula for future value of an annuity, simply let n be a variable with values from 1 to the total number of payments. Figure 10(a) shows the beginning of such a table generated on a TI-83/84 Plus for Example 6. Figure 10(b) shows the beginning of the same table using Microsoft Excel.

n	Amount in Fund
1	243.55
2	488.56
3	735.04
4	983.00
5	1232.45
6	1483.40
7	1735.85
8	1989.81
9	2245.30
10	2502.32
11	2760.89
12	3021.00

X	Y₁
1	243.55
2	488.56
3	735.04
4	983
5	1232.5
6	1483.4
7	1735.8

X=1

(a)   (b)

FIGURE 10

Annuities Due   The formula developed above is for *ordinary annuities*—those with payments made at the *end* of each time period. These results can be modified slightly to apply to **annuities due**—annuities in which payments are made at the *beginning* of each time period. To find the future value of an annuity due, treat each payment as if it were made at the *end* of the *preceding* period. That is, find $s_{\overline{n}|i}$ for *one additional period*; to compensate for this, subtract the amount of one payment.

Thus, the **future value of an annuity due** of n payments of R dollars each at the beginning of consecutive interest periods, with interest compounded at the rate of i per period, is

$$S = R\left[\frac{(1 + i)^{n+1} - 1}{i}\right] - R \qquad \text{or} \qquad S = Rs_{\overline{n+1}|i} - R.$$

The finance feature of the TI-83/84 Plus can be used to find the future value of an annuity due as well as an ordinary annuity. If this feature is not built in, you may wish to program your calculator to evaluate this formula, too.

EXAMPLE 7   **Future Value of an Annuity Due**
Find the future value of an annuity due if payments of $500 are made at the beginning of each quarter for 7 years, in an account paying 6% compounded quarterly.

▶**Solution** In 7 years, there are $n = 28$ quarterly periods. Add one period to get $n + 1 = 29$, and use the formula with $i = 6\%/4 = 1.5\%$.

$$S = 500\left[\frac{(1.015)^{29} - 1}{0.015}\right] - 500 \approx 17{,}499.35$$

The account will have a total of $17,499.35 after 7 years.

▶ 5.2 Exercises

Find the fifth term of each geometric sequence.

1. $a = 3;\quad r = 2$ **2.** $a = 7;\quad r = 5$ **3.** $a = -8;\quad r = 3$ **4.** $a = -6;\quad r = 2$

5. $a = 1;\quad r = -3$ **6.** $a = 12;\quad r = -2$ **7.** $a = 256;\quad r = \dfrac{1}{4}$ **8.** $a = 729;\quad r = \dfrac{1}{3}$

Find the sum of the first four terms for each geometric sequence.

9. $a = 1;\quad r = 2$ **10.** $a = 4;\quad r = 4$ **11.** $a = 5;\quad r = \dfrac{1}{5}$

12. $a = 6;\quad r = \dfrac{1}{2}$ **13.** $a = 128;\quad r = -\dfrac{3}{2}$ **14.** $a = 64;\quad r = -\dfrac{3}{4}$

Find each value.

15. $s_{\overline{12}|0.05}$ **16.** $s_{\overline{15}|0.04}$ **17.** $s_{\overline{10}|0.052}$ **18.** $s_{\overline{18}|0.015}$

19. List some reasons for establishing a sinking fund.

20. Explain the difference between an ordinary annuity and an annuity due.

Find the future value of each ordinary annuity. Interest is compounded annually.

21. $R = 100;\quad i = 0.06;\quad n = 4$ **22.** $R = 1000;\quad i = 0.06;\quad n = 5$

23. $R = 25{,}000;\quad i = 0.045;\quad n = 36$ **24.** $R = 29{,}500;\quad i = 0.058;\quad n = 15$

Find the future value of each ordinary annuity, if payments are made and interest is compounded as given. Then determine how much of this value is from contributions and how much is from interest.

25. $R = 9200$; 10% interest compounded semiannually for 7 years

26. $R = 1250$; 5% interest compounded semiannually for 18 years

27. $R = 800$; 6.51% interest compounded semiannually for 12 years

28. $R = 4600$; 8.73% interest compounded quarterly for 9 years

29. $R = 12{,}000$; 4.8% interest compounded quarterly for 16 years

30. $R = 42{,}000$; 10.05% interest compounded semiannually for 12 years

Find the future value of each annuity due. Assume that interest is compounded annually.

31. $R = 600;\quad i = 0.06;\quad n = 8$ **32.** $R = 1700;\quad i = 0.04;\quad n = 15$

33. $R = 16{,}000;\quad i = 0.05;\quad n = 7$ **34.** $R = 4000;\quad i = 0.06;\quad n = 11$

Find the future value of each annuity due. Then determine how much of this value is from contributions and how much is from interest.

35. Payments of $1000 made at the beginning of each semiannual period for 9 years at 8.15% compounded semiannually

36. $750 deposited at the beginning of each month for 15 years at 5.9% compounded monthly

37. $250 deposited at the beginning of each quarter for 12 years at 4.2% compounded quarterly

38. $1500 deposited at the beginning of each semiannual period for 11 years at 5.6% compounded semiannually

Find the periodic payment that will amount to each given sum under the given conditions.

39. $S = \$10,000$; interest is 5% compounded annually; payments are made at the end of each year for 12 years.

40. $S = \$150,000$; interest is 6% compounded semiannually; payments are made at the end of each semiannual period for 11 years.

41. What is meant by a sinking fund? Give an example of a sinking fund.

Find the amount of each payment to be made into a sinking fund so that enough will be present to accumulate the following amounts. Payments are made at the end of each period.

42. $8500; money earns 8% compounded annually; there are 7 annual payments.

43. $2750; money earns 5% compounded annually; there are 5 annual payments.

44. $75,000; money earns 6% compounded semiannually for $4\frac{1}{2}$ years.

45. $25,000; money earns 5.7% compounded quarterly for $3\frac{1}{2}$ years.

46. $65,000; money earns 7.5% compounded quarterly for $2\frac{1}{2}$ years.

47. $9000; money earns 4.8% compounded monthly for $2\frac{1}{2}$ years.

► Applications

BUSINESS AND ECONOMICS

48. *Comparing Accounts* Alex Levering deposits $12,000 at the end of each year for 9 years in an account paying 8% interest compounded annually.

   a. Find the final amount she will have on deposit.

   b. Alex's brother-in-law works in a bank that pays 6% compounded annually. If she deposits money in this bank instead of the one above, how much will she have in her account?

   c. How much would Alex lose over 9 years by using her brother-in-law's bank?

49. *Savings* Tom DeMarco is saving for a Plasma HDTV. At the end of each month he puts $100 in a savings account that pays 2.25% interest compounded monthly. How much is in the account after 2 years? How much did Tom deposit? How much interest did he earn?

50. *Savings* Hassi is paid on the first day of the month and $80 is automatically deducted from his pay and deposited in a savings account. If the account pays 2.5% interest compounded monthly, how much will be in the account after 3 years and 9 months?

51. *Savings* A typical pack-a-day smoker spends about $130.50 per month on cigarettes.* Suppose the smoker invests that amount each month in a savings account at 4.8% interest compounded monthly. What would the account be worth after 40 years?

52. *Savings* A father opened a savings account for his daughter on the day she was born, depositing $1000. Each year on her birthday he deposits another $1000, making the last deposit on her 21st birthday. If the account pays 5.25% interest compounded annually, how much is in the account at the end of the day on his daughter's 21st birthday? How much interest has been earned?

*Campaign for Tobacco-Free Kids, July 1, 2006, at http://tobaccofreekids.org/reports/prices.

53. *Retirement Planning* A 45-year-old man puts $2500 in a retirement account at the end of each quarter until he reaches the age of 60, then makes no further deposits. If the account pays 6% interest compounded quarterly, how much will be in the account when the man retires at age 65?

54. *Retirement Planning* At the end of each quarter, a 50-year-old woman puts $3000 in a retirement account that pays 5% interest compounded quarterly. When she reaches 60, she withdraws the entire amount and places it in a mutual fund that pays 6.9% interest compounded monthly. From then on she deposits $300 in the mutual fund at the end of each month. How much is in the account when she reaches age 65?

55. *Savings* Jasspreet Kaur deposits $2435 at the beginning of each semiannual period for 8 years in an account paying 6% compounded semiannually. She then leaves that money alone, with no further deposits, for an additional 5 years. Find the final amount on deposit after the entire 13-year period.

56. *Savings* Chuck Hickman deposits $10,000 at the beginning of each year for 12 years in an account paying 5% compounded annually. He then puts the total amount on deposit in another account paying 6% compounded semiannually for another 9 years. Find the final amount on deposit after the entire 21-year period.

57. *Savings* Greg Tobin needs $10,000 in 8 years.

   a. What amount should he deposit at the end of each quarter at 8% compounded quarterly so that he will have his $10,000?

   b. Find Greg's quarterly deposit if the money is deposited at 6% compounded quarterly.

58. *Buying Equipment* Harv, the owner of Harv's Meats, knows that he must buy a new deboner machine in 4 years. The machine costs $12,000. In order to accumulate enough money to pay for the machine, Harv decides to deposit a sum of money at the end of each 6 months in an account paying 6% compounded semiannually. How much should each payment be?

59. *Buying a Car* Marie Flynn wants to have a $20,000 down payment when she buys a new car in 6 years. How much money must she deposit at the end of each quarter in an account paying 3.2% compounded quarterly so that she will have the down payment she desires?

Individual Retirement Accounts Suppose a 40-year-old person deposits $4000 per year in an Individual Retirement Account until age 65. Find the total in the account with the following assumptions of interest rates. (Assume quarterly compounding, with payments of $1000 made at the end of each quarter period.) Find the total amount of interest earned.

60. 6%   **61.** 8%   **62.** 4%   **63.** 10%

In Exercises 64 and 65, use a graphing calculator to find the value of i that produces the given value of S. (See Example 5(b).)

64. *Retirement* To save for retirement, Karla Harby put $300 each month into an ordinary annuity for 20 years. Interest was compounded monthly. At the end of the 20 years, the annuity was worth $147,126. What annual interest rate did she receive?

65. *Rate of Return* Jennifer Wall made payments of $250 per month at the end of each month to purchase a piece of property. At the end of 30 years, she completely owned the property, which she sold for $330,000. What annual interest rate would she need to earn on an annuity for a comparable rate of return?

66. *Lottery* In a 1992 Virginia lottery, the jackpot was $27 million. An Australian investment firm tried to buy all possible combinations of numbers, which would have cost $7 million. In fact, the firm ran out of time and was unable to buy all combinations, but ended up with the only winning ticket anyway. The firm received the jackpot in 20 equal annual payments of $1.35 million.* Assume these payments meet the conditions of an ordinary annuity.

   a. Suppose the firm can invest money at 8% interest compounded annually. How many years would it take until the investors would be further ahead than if they had simply invested the $7 million at the same rate? (*Hint:* Experiment with different values of *n*, the number of years, or use a graphing calculator to plot the value of both investments as a function of the number of years.)

   b. How many years would it take in part a at an interest rate of 12%?

67. *Buying Real Estate* Marisa Raffaele sells some land in Nevada. She will be paid a lump sum of $60,000 in 7 years. Until then, the buyer pays 8% simple interest quarterly.

   a. Find the amount of each quarterly interest payment on the $60,000.

   b. The buyer sets up a sinking fund so that enough money will be present to pay off the $60,000. The buyer will make semiannual payments into the sinking fund; the account pays 6% compounded semiannually. Find the amount of each payment into the fund.

68. *Buying Rare Stamps* Paul Altier bought a rare stamp for his collection. He agreed to pay a lump sum of $4000 after 5 years. Until then, he pays 6% simple interest semiannually on the $4000.

   a. Find the amount of each semiannual interest payment.

   b. Paul sets up a sinking fund so that enough money will be present to pay off the $4000. He will make annual payments into the fund. The account pays 8% compounded annually. Find the amount of each payment.

69. *Down Payment* A conventional loan, such as for a car or a house, is similar to an annuity, but usually includes a down payment. Show that if a down payment of D dollars is made at the beginning of the loan period, the future value of all the payments, including the down payment, is

$$S = D(1 + i)^n + R\left[\frac{(1 + i)^n - 1}{i}\right].$$

5.3 Present Value of an Annuity; Amortization

? THINK ABOUT IT

What monthly payment will pay off a $10,000 car loan in 36 monthly payments at 6% annual interest?

The answer to this question is given later in this section. We shall see that it involves finding the present value of an annuity.

Suppose that at the end of each year, for the next 10 years, $500 is deposited in a savings account paying 7% interest compounded annually. This is an example of an ordinary annuity. The **present value of an annuity** is the amount that would have to be deposited in one lump sum today (at the same compound interest rate) in order to produce exactly the same balance at the end of 10 years. We can find a formula for the present value of an annuity as follows.

Suppose deposits of R dollars are made at the end of each period for n periods at interest rate i per period. Then the amount in the account after n periods is the future value of this annuity:

$$S = R \cdot s_{\overline{n}|i} = R\left[\frac{(1 + i)^n - 1}{i}\right].$$

On the other hand, if P dollars are deposited today at the same compound interest rate i, then at the end of n periods, the amount in the account is $P(1 + i)^n$. If P is the present value of the annuity, this amount must be the same as the amount S in the formula above; that is,

$$P(1 + i)^n = R\left[\frac{(1 + i)^n - 1}{i}\right].$$

To solve this equation for P, multiply both sides by $(1 + i)^{-n}$.

$$P = R(1 + i)^{-n}\left[\frac{(1 + i)^n - 1}{i}\right]$$

FOR REVIEW

Recall that for any nonzero number a, $a^0 = 1$. Also, by the product rule for exponents, $a^x \cdot a^y = a^{x+y}$. In particular, for any nonzero number a, $a^n \cdot a^{-n} = a^{n+(-n)} = a^0 = 1$.

Use the distributive property; also recall that $(1 + i)^{-n}(1 + i)^n = 1$.

$$P = R\left[\frac{(1 + i)^{-n}(1 + i)^n - (1 + i)^{-n}}{i}\right] = R\left[\frac{1 - (1 + i)^{-n}}{i}\right]$$

The amount P is the *present value of the annuity*. The quantity in brackets is abbreviated as $a_{\overline{n}|i}$, so

$$a_{\overline{n}|i} = \frac{1 - (1 + i)^{-n}}{i}.$$

(The symbol $a_{\overline{n}|i}$ is read "*a*-angle-*n* at *i*." Compare this quantity with $s_{\overline{n}|i}$ in the previous section.) The formula for the present value of an annuity is summarized below.

PRESENT VALUE OF AN ANNUITY

The present value P of an annuity of n payments of R dollars each at the end of consecutive interest periods with interest compounded at a rate of interest i per period is

$$P = R\left[\frac{1-(1+i)^{-n}}{i}\right] \qquad \text{or} \qquad P = Ra_{\overline{n}|i}.$$

CAUTION   Don't confuse the formula for the present value of an annuity with the one for the future value of an annuity. Notice the difference: the numerator of the fraction in the present value formula is $1-(1+i)^{-n}$, but in the future value formula, it is $(1+i)^n - 1$. ∎

The financial feature of the TI-83/84 Plus calculator can be used to find the present value of an annuity by choosing that option from the menu and entering the required information. If your calculator does not have this built-in feature, it will be useful to store a program to calculate present value of an annuity in your calculator. A program is given in *The Graphing Calculator Manual* available with this book.

EXAMPLE 1   **Present Value of an Annuity**
Mr. Bryer and Ms. Gonsalez are both graduates of the Brisbane Institute of Technology. They both agree to contribute to the endowment fund of BIT. Mr. Bryer says that he will give $500 at the end of each year for 9 years. Ms. Gonsalez prefers to give a lump sum today. What lump sum can she give that will equal the present value of Mr. Bryer's annual gifts, if the endowment fund earns 7.5% compounded annually?

▶**Solution** Here, $R = 500$, $n = 9$, and $i = 0.075$, and we have

$$P = R \cdot a_{\overline{9}|0.075} = 500\left[\frac{1-(1.075)^{-9}}{0.075}\right] \approx 3189.44.$$

Therefore, Ms. Gonsalez must donate a lump sum of $3189.44 today.

One of the most important uses of annuities is in determining the equal monthly payments needed to pay off a loan, as illustrated in the next example.

EXAMPLE 2   **Car Payments**
A car costs $12,000. After a down payment of $2000, the balance will be paid off in 36 equal monthly payments with interest of 6% per year on the unpaid balance. Find the amount of each payment.

?

▶**Solution** A single lump sum payment of $10,000 today would pay off the loan. So, $10,000 is the present value of an annuity of 36 monthly payments with interest of $6\%/12 = 0.5\%$ per month. Thus, $P = 10{,}000$, $n = 36$, $i = 0.005$, and we must find the monthly payment R in the formula

$$P = R\left[\frac{1 - (1 + i)^{-n}}{i}\right]$$

$$10{,}000 = R\left[\frac{1 - (1.005)^{-36}}{0.005}\right]$$

$$R \approx 304.22.$$

A monthly payment of $304.22 will be needed.

Each payment in Example 2 includes interest on the unpaid balance, with the remainder going to reduce the loan. For example, the first payment of $304.22 includes interest of $0.005(\$10{,}000) = \$50$ and is divided as follows.

monthly payment	interest due	to reduce the balance

$$\$304.22 - \$50 = \$254.22$$

At the end of this section, amortization schedules show that this procedure does reduce the loan to $0 after all payments are made (the final payment may be slightly different).

Amortization

A loan is **amortized** if both the principal and interest are paid by a sequence of equal periodic payments. In Example 2, a loan of $10,000 at 6% interest compounded monthly could be amortized by paying $304.22 per month for 36 months.

The periodic payment needed to amortize a loan may be found, as in Example 2, by solving the present value equation for R.

AMORTIZATION PAYMENTS

A loan of P dollars at interest rate i per period may be amortized in n equal periodic payments of R dollars made at the end of each period, where

$$R = \frac{P}{a_{\overline{n}|i}} = \frac{P}{\left[\dfrac{1 - (1 + i)^{-n}}{i}\right]} = \frac{Pi}{1 - (1 + i)^{-n}}.$$

EXAMPLE 3   **Home Mortgage**

The Perez family buys a house for $275,000, with a down payment of $55,000. They take out a 30-year mortgage for $220,000 at an annual interest rate of 6%.

(a) Find the amount of the monthly payment needed to amortize this loan.

▶**Solution** Here $P = 220,000$ and the monthly interest rate is $6\%/12 = 0.06/12 = 0.005.$* The number of monthly payments is $12(30) = 360$. Therefore,

$$R = \frac{220,000}{a\,\overline{_{360}}|_{0.005}} = \frac{220,000}{\left[\dfrac{1 - (1.005)^{-360}}{0.005}\right]} = 1319.01.$$

Monthly payments of $1319.01 are required to amortize the loan.

(b) Find the total amount of interest paid when the loan is amortized over 30 years.

▶**Solution** The Perez family makes 360 payments of $1319.01 each, for a total of $474,843.60. Since the amount of the loan was $220,000, the total interest paid is

$$\$474,843.60 - \$220,000 = \$254,843.60.$$

This large amount of interest is typical of what happens with a long mortgage. A 15-year mortgage would have higher payments but would involve significantly less interest.

(c) Find the part of the first payment that is interest and the part that is applied to reducing the debt.

▶**Solution** During the first month, the entire $220,000 is owed. Interest on this amount for 1 month is found by the formula for simple interest, with r = annual interest rate and t = time in years.

$$I = Prt = 220,000(0.06)\frac{1}{12} = \$1100$$

At the end of the month, a payment of $1319.01 is made; since $1100 of this is interest, a total of

$$\$1319.01 - \$1100 = \$219.01$$

is applied to the reduction of the original debt.

It can be shown that the unpaid balance after x payments is approximately given by the function

$$y = R\left[\frac{1 - (1 + i)^{-(n-x)}}{i}\right].$$

For example, the unpaid balance in Example 3 after 1 payment is approximately

$$y = 1319.01\left[\frac{1 - (1.005)^{-359}}{0.005}\right] \approx 219,780.80.$$

This is very close to the amount left after deducting the $219.01 applied to the loan in part (c):

$$\$220,000 - \$219.01 = \$219,780.99.$$

A calculator graph of this function is shown in Figure 11.

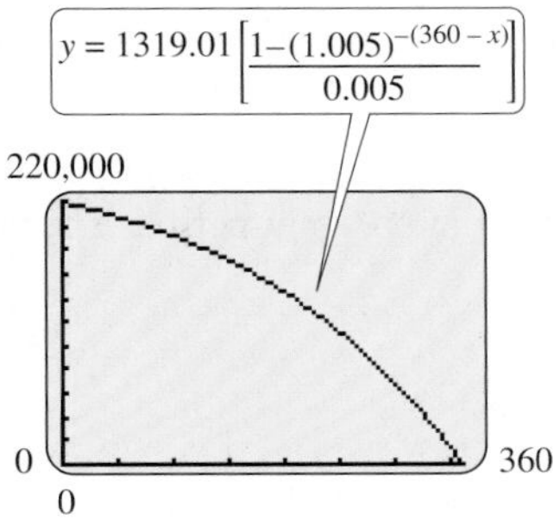

$$y = 1319.01\left[\frac{1-(1.005)^{-(360-x)}}{0.005}\right]$$

FIGURE 11

*Mortgage rates are quoted in terms of annual interest, but it is always understood that the monthly rate is 1/12 of the annual rate and that interest is compounded monthly.

We can find the unpaid balance after any number of payments, x, by finding the y-value that corresponds to x. For example, the remaining balance after 5 years or 60 payments is shown at the bottom of the window in Figure 12(a). You may be surprised that the remaining balance on a $220,000 loan is as large as $204,719.41. This is because most of the early payments on a loan go toward interest, as we saw in Example 3(c).

By adding the graph of $y = (1/2)220,000 = 110,000$ to the figure, we can find when half the loan has been repaid. From Figure 12(b) we see that 252 payments are required. Note that only 108 payments remain at that point, which again emphasizes the fact that the earlier payments do little to reduce the loan.

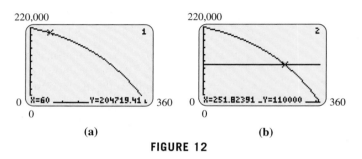

(a)   (b)

FIGURE 12

Amortization Schedules   In the preceding example, 360 payments are made to amortize a $220,000 loan. The loan balance after the first payment is reduced by only $219.01, which is much less than $(1/360)(220,000) \approx \$611.11$. Therefore, even though equal *payments* are made to amortize a loan, the loan *balance* does not decrease in equal steps. This fact is very important if a loan is paid off early.

EXAMPLE 4   **Early Payment**
Susan Stewart borrows $1000 for 1 year at 12% annual interest compounded monthly. Verify that her monthly loan payment is $88.85. After making three payments, she decides to pay off the remaining balance all at once. How much must she pay?

▶**Solution** Since nine payments remain to be paid, they can be thought of as an annuity consisting of nine payments of $88.85 at 1% interest per period. The present value of this annuity is

$$88.85\left[\frac{1 - (1.01)^{-9}}{0.01}\right] \approx 761.09.$$

So Susan's remaining balance, computed by this method, is $761.09.

An alternative method of figuring the balance is to consider the payments already made as an annuity of three payments. At the beginning, the present value of this annuity was

$$88.85\left[\frac{1 - (1.01)^{-3}}{0.01}\right] \approx 261.31.$$

So she still owes the difference $1000 - $261.31 = $738.69. Furthermore, she owes the interest on this amount for 3 months, for a total of

$$(738.69)(1.01)^3 \approx \$761.07.$$

This balance due differs from the one obtained by the first method by 2 cents because the monthly payment and the other calculations were rounded to the nearest penny.

Although most people would not quibble about a difference of 2 cents in the balance due in Example 4, the difference in other cases (larger amounts or longer terms) might be more than that. A bank or business must keep its books accurately to the nearest penny, so it must determine the balance due in such cases unambiguously and exactly. This is done by means of an **amortization schedule**, which lists how much of each payment is interest and how much goes to reduce the balance, as well as how much is owed after *each* payment.

EXAMPLE 5

Amortization Table

Determine the exact amount Susan Stewart in Example 4 owes after three monthly payments.

▶**Solution** An amortization table for the loan is shown below. It is obtained as follows. The annual interest rate is 12% compounded monthly, so the interest rate per month is 12%/12 = 1% = 0.01. When the first payment is made, 1 month's interest—namely 0.01(1000) = $10—is owed. Subtracting this from the $88.85 payment leaves $78.85 to be applied to repayment. Hence, the principal at the end of the first payment period is $1000 - $78.85 = $921.15, as shown in the "payment 1" line of the chart.

When payment 2 is made, 1 month's interest on $921.15 is owed, namely 0.01(921.15) = $9.21. Subtracting this from the $88.85 payment leaves $79.64 to reduce the principal. Hence, the principal at the end of payment 2 is $921.15 - $79.64 = $841.51. The interest portion of payment 3 is based on this amount, and the remaining lines of the table are found in a similar fashion.

The schedule shows that after three payments, she still owes $761.08, an amount that differs slightly from that obtained by either method in Example 4.

Payment Number	Amount of Payment	Interest for Period	Portion to Principal	Principal at End of Period
0	—	—	—	$1000.00
1	$88.85	$10.00	$78.85	$921.15
2	$88.85	$9.21	$79.64	$841.51
3	$88.85	$8.42	$80.43	$761.08
4	$88.85	$7.61	$81.24	$679.84
5	$88.85	$6.80	$82.05	$597.79
6	$88.85	$5.98	$82.87	$514.92
7	$88.85	$5.15	$83.70	$431.22
8	$88.85	$4.31	$84.54	$346.68
9	$88.85	$3.47	$85.38	$261.30
10	$88.85	$2.61	$86.24	$175.06
11	$88.85	$1.75	$87.10	$87.96
12	$88.84	$0.88	$87.96	$0.00

The amortization schedule in Example 5 is typical. In particular, note that all payments are the same except the last one. It is often necessary to adjust the amount of the final payment to account for rounding off earlier, and to ensure that the final balance is exactly 0.

An amortization schedule also shows how the periodic payments are applied to interest and principal. The amount going to interest decreases with each payment, while the amount going to reduce the principal increases with each payment.

A graphing calculator program to produce an amortization schedule is available in *The Graphing Calculator Manual* available with this book. The TI-83/84 Plus includes a built-in program to find the amortization payment. Spreadsheets are another useful tool for creating amortization tables. Microsoft Excel has a built-in feature for calculating monthly payments. Figure 13 shows an Excel amortization table for Example 5. For more details, see *The Spreadsheet Manual*, also available with this book.

	A	B	C	D	E	F
1	Pmt #	Payment	Interest	Principal	End Prncpl	
2	0				1000	
3	1	88.85	10.00	78.85	921.15	
4	2	88.85	9.21	79.64	841.51	
5	3	88.85	8.42	80.43	761.08	
6	4	88.85	7.61	81.24	679.84	
7	5	88.85	6.80	82.05	597.79	
8	6	88.85	5.98	82.87	514.92	
9	7	88.85	5.15	83.70	431.22	
10	8	88.85	4.31	84.54	346.68	
11	9	88.85	3.47	85.38	261.30	
12	10	88.85	2.61	86.24	175.06	
13	11	88.85	1.75	87.10	87.96	
14	12	88.85	0.88	87.97	-0.01	

FIGURE 13

5.3 Exercises

1. Which of the following is represented by $a_{\overline{n}|i}$?

a. $\dfrac{(1 + i)^{-n} - 1}{i}$

b. $\dfrac{(1 + i)^n - 1}{i}$

c. $\dfrac{1 - (1 + i)^{-n}}{i}$

d. $\dfrac{1 - (1 + i)^n}{i}$

2. Which of the choices in Exercise 1 represents $s_{\overline{n}|i}$?

Find each value.

3. $a_{\overline{15}|0.065}$

4. $a_{\overline{10}|0.041}$

5. $a_{\overline{18}|0.055}$

6. $a_{\overline{32}|0.039}$

7. Explain the difference between the present value of an annuity and the future value of an annuity. For a given annuity, which is larger? Why?

8. What does it mean to amortize a loan?

Find the present value of each ordinary annuity.

 9. Payments of $890 each year for 16 years at 6% compounded annually

10. Payments of $1400 each year for 8 years at 6% compounded annually

11. Payments of $10,000 semiannually for 15 years at 5% compounded semiannually

12. Payments of $50,000 quarterly for 10 years at 4% compounded quarterly

13. Payments of $15,806 quarterly for 3 years at 6.8% compounded quarterly

14. Payments of $18,579 every 6 months for 8 years at 5.4% compounded semiannually

Find the lump sum deposited today that will yield the same total amount as payments of $10,000 at the end of each year for 15 years at each of the given interest rates.

15. 4% compounded annually

16. 6% compounded annually

Find the payment necessary to amortize each loan. Then calculate the total payments and the total amount of interest paid.

17. $2500; 6% compounded quarterly; 6 quarterly payments

18. $41,000; 8% compounded semiannually; 10 semiannual payments

19. $90,000; 6% compounded annually; 12 annual payments

20. $140,000; 8% compounded quarterly; 15 quarterly payments

21. $7400; 6.2% compounded semiannually; 18 semiannual payments

22. $5500; 10% compounded monthly; 24 monthly payments

Use the amortization table in Example 5 to answer the questions in Exercises 23–26.

23. How much of the fourth payment is interest?

24. How much of the eleventh payment is used to reduce the debt?

25. How much interest is paid in the first 4 months of the loan?

26. How much interest is paid in the last 4 months of the loan?

27. What sum deposited today at 5% compounded annually for 8 years will provide the same amount as $1000 deposited at the end of each year for 8 years at 6% compounded annually?

28. What lump sum deposited today at 8% compounded quarterly for 10 years will yield the same final amount as deposits of $4000 at the end of each 6-month period for 10 years at 6% compounded semiannually?

Find the monthly house payments necessary to amortize each loan. Then calculate the total payments and the total amount of interest paid.

29. $199,000 at 7.01% for 25 years

30. $175,000 at 6.24% for 30 years

31. $253,000 at 6.45% for 30 years

32. $310,000 at 5.96% for 25 years

➡ Applications

---

33. *House Payments* Calculate the monthly payment and total amount of interest paid in Example 3 with a 15-year loan, and then compare with the results of Example 3.

34. *Installment Buying* Stereo Shack sells a stereo system for $600 down and monthly payments of $30 for the next 3 years. If the interest rate is 1.25% per month on the unpaid balance, find

 a. the cost of the stereo system;

 b. the total amount of interest paid.

35. *Car Payments* Hong Le buys a car costing $14,000. He agrees to make payments at the end of each monthly period for 4 years. He pays 7% interest, compounded monthly.

 a. What is the amount of each payment?

 b. Find the total amount of interest Le will pay.

36. *Credit Card Debt* Tom Shaffer charged $8430 on his credit card to relocate for his first job. When he realized that the interest rate for the unpaid balance was 27% compounded monthly, he decided not to charge any more on that account. He wants to have this account paid off by the end of 3 years, so he arranges to have automatic payments sent at the end of each month.

 a. What monthly payment must he make to have the account paid off by the end of 3 years?

 b. How much total interest will he have paid?

37. *New Car* "Saab's Final Summer Clearance" campaign offered a cash-back allowance of $5000 or 1.9% financing for 36 months for a 2006 Saab 9-2X car.*

 a. Determine the payments on a Saab 9-2X if a person chooses the 1.9% financing option and needs to finance $20,000 for 36 months, compounded monthly. Find the total amount he or she will pay for this option.

 b. Determine the payments on a Saab 9-2X if a person chooses the cash-back option and now needs to finance only $15,000. Assume that the buyer is able to find financing from a local bank at 6.93% for 4 years, compounded monthly. Find the total amount he or she will pay for this option.

 c. Discuss which deal is best and why.

38. *New Hummer* As an incentive to buy a Hummer H3 SUV, the company is offering a cash-back allowance of $2000 or 0% financing for 36 months.*

 a. Determine the payments on the H3 SUV if a person chooses the 0% financing and needs to finance $28,000 for 36 months.

 b. If a person purchases an H3 SUV and chooses the cash-back option, she will need to finance $26,000. Assume that she is able to choose between two options. At her local bank she is able to find financing at 6.93% for 4 years, compounded monthly. From the Internet, she is able to finance from Capital One at 6.35% for 5 years, compounded monthly. Find the monthly payment and the total amount she will pay back on each option.

 c. Of the three deals, discuss which is best and why.

39. *Lottery Winnings* In most states, the winnings of million-dollar lottery jackpots are divided into equal payments given annually for 20 years. (In Colorado, the results are distributed over 25 years.)[†] This means that the present value of the jackpot is worth less than the stated prize, with the actual value determined by the interest rate at which the money could be invested.

 a. Find the present value of a $1 million lottery jackpot distributed in equal annual payments over 20 years, using an interest rate of 5%.

 b. Find the present value of a $1 million lottery jackpot distributed in equal annual payments over 20 years, using an interest rate of 9%.

 c. Calculate the answer for part a using the 25-year distribution time in Colorado.

 d. Calculate the answer for part b using the 25-year distribution time in Colorado.

---

*http://www.cars.com.
[†]Gould, Lois, "Ticket to Trouble," *The New York Times Magazine*, April 23, 1995, p. 39.

Student Loans *Student borrowers now have more options to choose from when selecting repayment plans.* The standard plan repays the loan in 10 years with equal monthly payments. The extended plan allows from 12 to 30 years to repay the loan. A student borrows $35,000 at 7.43% compounded monthly.*

40. Find the monthly payment and total interest paid under the standard plan.

41. Find the monthly payment and total interest paid under the extended plan with 20 years to pay off the loan.

Installment Buying *In Exercises 42–44, prepare an amortization schedule showing the first four payments for each loan.*

42. An insurance firm pays $4000 for a new printer for its computer. It amortizes the loan for the printer in 4 annual payments at 8% compounded annually.

43. Large semitrailer trucks cost $110,000 each. Ace Trucking buys such a truck and agrees to pay for it by a loan that will be amortized with 9 semiannual payments at 8% compounded semiannually.

44. One retailer charges $1048 for a laptop computer. A firm of tax accountants buys 8 of these laptops. They make a down payment of $1200 and agree to amortize the balance with monthly payments at 6% compounded monthly for 4 years.

45. *Investment* In 1995, Oseola McCarty donated $150,000 to the University of Southern Mississippi to establish a scholarship fund.[†] What is unusual about her is that the entire amount came from what she was able to save each month from her work as a washer woman, a job she began in 1916 at the age of 8, when she dropped out of school.

a. How much would Ms. McCarty have to put into her savings account at the end of every 3 months to accumulate $150,000 over 79 years? Assume she received an interest rate of 5.25% compounded quarterly.

b. Answer part a using a 2% and a 7% interest rate.

46. *Loan Payments* When Nancy Hart opened her law office, she bought $14,000 worth of law books and $7200 worth of office furniture. She paid $1200 down and agreed to amortize the balance with semiannual payments for 5 years, at 8% compounded semiannually.

a. Find the amount of each payment.

b. Refer to the text and Figures 11 and 12. When her loan had been reduced below $5000, Nancy received a large tax refund and decided to pay off the loan. How many payments were left at this time?

47. *House Payments* Kareem Adiagbo buys a house for $285,000. He pays $60,000 down and takes out a mortgage at 6.5% on the balance. Find his monthly payment and the total amount of interest he will pay if the length of the mortgage is

a. 15 years;

b. 20 years;

c. 25 years.

d. Refer to the text and Figures 11 and 12. When will half the 20-year loan in part b be paid off?

48. *House Payments* The Chavara family buys a house for $225,000. They pay $50,000 down and take out a 30-year mortgage on the balance. Find their monthly payment and the total amount of interest they will pay if the interest rate is

a. 6%;

b. 6.5%;

c. 7%.

d. Refer to the text and Figures 11 and 12. When will half the 7% loan in part c be paid off?

49. *Refinancing a Mortgage* Fifteen years ago, the Budai family bought a home and financed $150,000 with a 30-year mortgage at 8.2%.

a. Find their monthly payment, the total amount of their payments, and the total amount of interest they will pay over the life of this loan.

*Hansell, Saul, "Money and College," *The New York Times*, April 2, 1995, p. 28.
†*The New York Times,* Nov. 12, 1996, pp. A1, A22.

b. The Budais made payments for 15 years. Estimate the unpaid balance using the formula

$$y = R\left[\frac{1 - (1 + i)^{-(n - x)}}{i}\right],$$

and then calculate the total of their remaining payments.

c. Suppose interest rates have dropped since the Budai family took out their original loan. One local bank now offers a 30-year mortgage at 6.5%. The bank fees for refinancing are $3400. If the Budais pay this fee up front and refinance the balance of their loan, find their monthly payment. Including the refinancing fee, what is the total amount of their payments? Discuss whether or not the family should refinance with this option.

d. A different bank offers the same 6.5% rate but on a 15-year mortgage. Their fee for financing is $4500. If the Budais pay this fee up front and refinance the balance of their loan, find their monthly payment. Including the refinancing fee, what is the total amount of their payments? Discuss whether or not the family should refinance with this option.

50. *Inheritance* Sandy Glover has inherited $25,000 from her grandfather's estate. She deposits the money in an account offering 6% interest compounded annually. She wants to make equal annual withdrawals from the account so that the money (principal and interest) lasts exactly 8 years.

a. Find the amount of each withdrawal.

b. Find the amount of each withdrawal if the money must last 12 years.

51. *Charitable Trust* The trustees of a college have accepted a gift of $150,000. The donor has directed the trustees to deposit the money in an account paying 6% per year, compounded semiannually. The trustees may make equal withdrawals at the end of each 6-month period; the money must last 5 years.

a. Find the amount of each withdrawal.

b. Find the amount of each withdrawal if the money must last 6 years.

Amortization Prepare an amortization schedule for each loan.

52. A loan of $37,948 with interest at 6.5% compounded annually, to be paid with equal annual payments over 10 years.

53. A loan of $4836 at 7.25% interest compounded semi-annually, to be repaid in 5 years in equal semiannual payments.

54. *Perpetuity* A *perpetuity* is an annuity in which the payments go on forever. We can derive a formula for the present value of a perpetuity by taking the formula for the present value of an annuity and looking at what happens when n gets larger and larger. Explain why the present value of an annuity is given by

$$P = \frac{R}{i}.$$

55. *Perpetuity* Using the result of Exercise 54, find the present value of perpetuities for each of the following.

a. Payments of $1000 a year with 4% interest compounded annually

b. Payments of $600 every 3 months with 6% interest compounded quarterly

Chapter 5 Review

Chapter Summary

In this chapter we introduced the mathematics of finance. We first extended simple interest calculations to compound interest, which is interest earned on interest previously earned. We then developed the mathematics associated with the following financial concepts.

- In an annuity, money continues to be deposited at regular intervals, and compound interest is earned on that money as well.

- In an ordinary annuity, the compounding period is the same as the time between payments, which simplifies the calculations.

- An annuity due is slightly different, in that the payments are made at the beginning of each time period.

- A sinking fund is like an ordinary annuity; a fund is set up to receive periodic payments. The payments plus the compound interest will produce a desired sum by a certain date.

- The present value of an annuity is the amount that would have to be deposited today to produce the same amount as the annuity at the end of a specified time.

- An amortization table shows how a loan is paid back after a specified time. It shows the payments broken down into interest and principal.

MATHEMATICS OF FINANCE SUMMARY

We have presented a lot of new formulas in this chapter. By answering the following questions, you can decide which formula to use for a particular problem.

1. Is simple or compound interest involved?

   Simple interest is normally used for investments or loans of a year or less; compound interest is normally used in all other cases.

2. If simple interest is being used, what is being sought: interest amount, future value, present value, or interest rate?

3. If compound interest is being used, does it involve a lump sum (single payment) or an annuity (sequence of payments)?

   a. For a lump sum, what is being sought: present value, future value, number of periods at interest, or effective rate?

   b. For an annuity,

      i. Is it an ordinary annuity (payment at the end of each period) or an annuity due (payment at the beginning of each period)?

      ii. What is being sought: present value, future value, or payment amount?

Once you have answered these questions, choose the appropriate formula and work the problem. As a final step, consider whether the answer you get makes sense. For instance, present value should always be less than future value. The amount of interest or the payments in an annuity should be fairly small compared to the total future value.

List of Variables

r is the annual interest rate.

i is the interest rate per period.

t is the number of years.

n is the number of periods.

m is the number of periods per year.

P is the principal or present value.

A is the future value of a lump sum.

S is the future value of an annuity.

R is the periodic payment in an annuity.

$$i = \frac{r}{m} \qquad n = tm$$

	Simple Interest	Compound Interest
Interest	$I = Prt$	$I = A - P$
Future Value	$A = P(1 + rt)$	$A = P(1 + i)^n$
Present Value	$P = \dfrac{A}{1 + rt}$	$P = \dfrac{A}{(1 + i)^n} = A(1 + i)^{-n}$
Effective Rate		$r_e = \left(1 + \dfrac{r}{m}\right)^m - 1$

Ordinary Annuity   Future Value $S = R\left[\dfrac{(1 + i)^n - 1}{i}\right] = R \cdot s_{\overline{n}|i}$

Present Value $P = R\left[\dfrac{1 - (1 + i)^{-n}}{i}\right] = R \cdot a_{\overline{n}|i}$

Annuity Due   Future Value $S = R\left[\dfrac{(1 + i)^{n+1} - 1}{i}\right] - R$

Sinking Fund Payment $R = \dfrac{Si}{(1 + i)^n - 1}$

Amortization Payments $R = \dfrac{Pi}{1 - (1 + i)^{-n}} = \dfrac{P}{a_{\overline{n}|i}}$

Key Terms

5.1 simple interest	nominal (stated) rate	ordinary annuity	annuity due
principal	effective rate	payment period	future value of an
rate	present value	future value of an	annuity due
time	**5.2** geometric sequence	annuity	**5.3** present value of an
future value	terms	future value of an	annuity
maturity value	common ratio	ordinary annuity	amortize a loan
compound interest	annuity	sinking fund	amortization schedule
compound amount			

Concept Check

Determine whether each of the following statements is true or false, and explain why.

1. For a particular interest rate, compound interest is always better than simple interest.

2. The sequence 1, 2, 4, 6, 8, . . . is a geometric sequence.

3. If a geometric sequence has first term 3 and common ratio 2, then the sum of the first 5 terms is $S_5 = 93$.

4. The value of a sinking fund should decrease over time.

5. For payments made on a mortgage, the (noninterest) portion of the payment applied on the principal increases over time.

6. On a 30-year conventional home mortgage, at recent interest rates, it is common to pay more money on the interest on the loan than the actual loan itself.

7. One can use the amortization payments formula to calculate the monthly payment of a car loan.

8. The effective rate formula can be used to calculate the present value of a loan.

9. The following calculation gives the monthly payment on a $25,000 loan, compounded monthly at a rate of 5% for a period of six years:

$$25,000\left[\frac{(1 + 0.05/12)^{72} - 1}{0.05/12}\right].$$

10. The following calculation gives the present value of an annuity of $5,000 payments at the end of each year for 10 years. The fund earns 4.5% compounded annually.

$$5000\left[\frac{11 - (1.045)^{-10}}{0.045}\right]$$

➤ *Chapter 5 Review Exercises*

Find the simple interest for each loan.

1. $15,903 at 6% for 8 months

2. $4902 at 5.4% for 11 months

3. $42,368 at 5.22% for 7 months

4. $3478 at 6.8% for 88 days
   (assume a 360-day year)

5. For a given amount of money at a given interest rate for a given time period, does simple interest or compound interest produce more interest?

Find the compound amount in each loan.

6. $2800 at 7% compounded annually for 10 years

7. $19,456.11 at 8% compounded semiannually for 7 years

8. $312.45 at 5.6% compounded semiannually for 16 years

9. $57,809.34 at 6% compounded quarterly for 5 years

Find the amount of interest earned by each deposit.

10. $3954 at 8% compounded annually for 10 years

11. $12,699.36 at 5% compounded semiannually for 7 years

12. $12,903.45 at 6.4% compounded quarterly for 29 quarters

13. $34,677.23 at 4.8% compounded monthly for 32 months

14. What is meant by the present value of an amount A?

Find the present value of each amount.

15. $42,000 in 7 years, 6% compounded monthly

16. $17,650 in 4 years, 4% compounded quarterly

17. $1347.89 in 3.5 years, 6.77% compounded semiannually

18. $2388.90 in 44 months, 5.93% compounded monthly

19. Write the first five terms of the geometric sequence with $a = 2$ and $r = 3$.

20. Write the first four terms of the geometric sequence with $a = 4$ and $r = 1/2$.

21. Find the sixth term of the geometric sequence with $a = -3$ and $r = 2$.

22. Find the fifth term of the geometric sequence with $a = -2$ and $r = -2$.

23. Find the sum of the first four terms of the geometric sequence with $a = -3$ and $r = 3$.

24. Find the sum of the first five terms of the geometric sequence with $a = 8000$ and $r = -1/2$.

25. Find $s\,\overline{_{30}}|_{0.02}$.

26. Find $s\,\overline{_{20}}|_{0.06}$.

27. What is meant by the future value of an annuity?

Find the future value of each annuity and the amount of interest earned.

28. $500 deposited at the end of each 6-month period for 10 years; money earns 6% compounded semiannually.

29. $1288 deposited at the end of each year for 14 years; money earns 4% compounded annually.

30. $4000 deposited at the end of each quarter for 7 years; money earns 5% compounded quarterly.

31. $233 deposited at the end of each month for 4 years; money earns 4.8% compounded monthly.

32. $672 deposited at the beginning of each quarter for 7 years; money earns 4.4% compounded quarterly.

33. $11,900 deposited at the beginning of each month for 13 months; money earns 6% compounded monthly.

34. What is the purpose of a sinking fund?

Find the amount of each payment that must be made into a sinking fund to accumulate each amount.

35. $6500; money earns 5% compounded annually for 6 years.

36. $57,000; money earns 4% compounded semiannually for $8\frac{1}{2}$ years.

37. $233,188; money earns 5.2% compounded quarterly for $7\frac{3}{4}$ years.

38. $1,056,788; money earns 7.2% compounded monthly for $4\frac{1}{2}$ years.

Find the present value of each ordinary annuity.

39. Deposits of $850 annually for 4 years at 6% compounded annually

40. Deposits of $1500 quarterly for 7 years at 5% compounded quarterly

41. Payments of $4210 semiannually for 8 years at 4.2% compounded semiannually

42. Payments of $877.34 monthly for 17 months at 6.4% compounded monthly

43. Give two examples of the types of loans that are commonly amortized.

Find the amount of the payment necessary to amortize each loan. Calculate the total interest paid.

44. $80,000; 5% compounded annually; 9 annual payments

45. $3200; 8% compounded quarterly; 12 quarterly payments

46. $32,000; 6.4% compounded quarterly; 17 quarterly payments

47. $51,607; 8% compounded monthly; 32 monthly payments

Find the monthly house payments for each mortgage. Calculate the total payments and interest.

48. $256,890 at 5.96% for 25 years

49. $177,110 at 6.68% for 30 years

A portion of an amortization table is given below for a $127,000 loan at 8.5% interest compounded monthly for 25 years.

Payment Number	Amount of Payment	Interest for Period	Portion to Principal	Principal at End of Period
1	$1022.64	$899.58	$123.06	$126,876.94
2	$1022.64	$898.71	$123.93	$126,753.01
3	$1022.64	$897.83	$124.81	$126,628.20
4	$1022.64	$896.95	$125.69	$126,502.51
5	$1022.64	$896.06	$126.58	$126,375.93
6	$1022.64	$895.16	$127.48	$126,248.45
7	$1022.64	$894.26	$128.38	$126,120.07
8	$1022.64	$893.35	$129.29	$125,990.78
9	$1022.64	$892.43	$130.21	$125,860.57
10	$1022.64	$891.51	$131.13	$125,729.44
11	$1022.64	$890.58	$132.06	$125,597.38
12	$1022.64	$889.65	$132.99	$125,464.39

Use the table to answer the following questions.

50. How much of the fifth payment is interest?

51. How much of the twelfth payment is used to reduce the debt?

52. How much interest is paid in the first 3 months of the loan?

53. How much has the debt been reduced at the end of the first year?

➤ Applications

BUSINESS AND ECONOMICS

54. *Personal Finance* Peter Silvia owes $5800 to his mother. He has agreed to repay the money in 10 months at an interest rate of 5.3%. How much will he owe in 10 months? How much interest will he pay?

55. *Business Financing* Eric Saulnier needs to borrow $9820 to buy new equipment for his business. The bank charges him 6.7% for a 7-month loan. How much interest will he be charged? What amount must he pay in 7 months?

56. *Business Financing* An accountant loans $28,000 at simple interest to her business. The loan is at 6.5% and earns $1365 interest. Find the time of the loan in months.

57. *Business Investment* A developer deposits $84,720 for 7 months and earns $4055.46 in simple interest. Find the interest rate.

58. *Personal Finance* In 3 years Amanda Abramovich must pay a pledge of $7500 to her college's building fund. What lump sum can she deposit today, at 5% compounded semi-annually, so that she will have enough to pay the pledge?

59. *Personal Finance* Tom, a graduate student, is considering investing $500 now, when he is 23, or waiting until he is 40 to invest $500. How much more money will he have at the age of 65 if he invests now, given that he can earn 5% interest compounded quarterly?

60. *Pensions* Pension experts recommend that you start drawing at least 40% of your full pension as early as possible.* Suppose you have built up a pension of $12,000-annual payments by working 10 years for a company. When you leave to accept a better job, the company gives you the option of collecting half of the full pension when you reach age 55 or the full pension at age 65. Assume an interest rate

*"Pocket That Pension," *Smart Money,* Oct. 1994, p. 33.

of 8% compounded annually. By age 75, how much will each plan produce? Which plan would produce the larger amount?

61. *Business Investment* A firm of attorneys deposits $5000 of profit-sharing money at the end of each semiannual period for $7\frac{1}{2}$ years. Find the final amount in the account if the deposits earn 10% compounded semiannually. Find the amount of interest earned.

62. *Business Financing* A small resort must add a swimming pool to compete with a new resort built nearby. The pool will cost $28,000. The resort borrows the money and agrees to repay it with equal payments at the end of each quarter for $6\frac{1}{2}$ years at an interest rate of 8% compounded quarterly. Find the amount of each payment.

63. *Business Financing* The owner of Eastside Hallmark borrows $48,000 to expand the business. The money will be repaid in equal payments at the end of each year for 7 years. Interest is 6.5%. Find the amount of each payment and the total amount of interest paid.

64. *Personal Finance* To buy a new computer, Mark Nguyen borrows $3250 from a friend at 4.2% interest compounded annually for 4 years. Find the compound amount he must pay back at the end of the 4 years.

65. *Effective Rate* According to a financial Web site, on September 1, 2006, First Community Bank of Columbus, Ohio, paid 5.15% interest, compounded quarterly, on a 1-year CD, while UFB Direct.com of Irvine, California, paid 5.13% compounded monthly.* What are the effective rates for the two CDs and which bank pays a higher effective rate?

66. *Home Financing* When the Lee family bought their home, they borrowed $315,700 at 7.5% compounded monthly for 25 years. If they make all 300 payments, repaying the loan on schedule, how much interest will they pay? (Assume the last payment is the same as the previous ones.)

67. *New Car* Toyota offered the following financing options for its 2006 Toyota 4Runner: a cash-back allowance of $2000, 0% financing for 36 months, 1.9% financing for 48 months, or 2.9% financing for 60 months.†

  a. Determine the payments on a Toyota 4Runner if a person chooses the 0% financing option and needs to finance $20,000 for 36 months, compounded monthly. Find the total amount of payments.

  b. Repeat part a for the 1.9% financing option for 48 months and for the 2.9% financing option for 60 months, compounded monthly.

  c. Determine the payments on a Toyota 4Runner if a person chooses the cash-back option and now needs to finance

only $18,000. Assume that the buyer is able to find financing from a local bank for 6.35% for 48 months, compounded monthly. Find the total amount of payments.

  d. Discuss which deal is best and why.

68. *New Car* Pontiac offered a cash-back allowance of $1000 or 0% financing for 36 months for a 2006 Pontiac G6.†

  a. Determine the payments on a Pontiac G6 car if a person chooses the 0% financing option and needs to finance $16,000 for 36 months.

  b. Determine the payments on a Pontiac G6 car if a person chooses the cash-back option and now needs to finance only $15,000. Assume that the buyer is able to find financing from a local bank at 6.94% for 48 months, compounded monthly.

  c. Discuss which deal is best and why.

  d. Find the interest rate at the bank that would make the total amount of payments for the two options equal.

69. *Buying and Selling a House* The Zambrano family bought a house for $191,000. They paid $40,000 down and took out a 30-year mortgage for the balance at 6.5%.

  a. Find their monthly payment.

  b. How much of the first payment is interest?

After 180 payments, the family sells its house for $238,000. They must pay closing costs of $3700 plus 2.5% of the sale price.

  c. Estimate the current mortgage balance at the time of the sale using one of the methods from Example 4 in Section 3.

  d. Find the total closing costs.

  e. Find the amount of money they receive from the sale after paying off the mortgage.

*http://www.bankrate.com.
†http://www.cars.com.

The following exercise is from an actuarial examination.*

70. *Death Benefit* The proceeds of a $10,000 death benefit are left on deposit with an insurance company for 7 years at an annual effective interest rate of 5%. The balance at the end of 7 years is paid to the beneficiary in 120 equal monthly payments of X, with the first payment made immediately. During the payout period, interest is credited at an annual effective interest rate of 3%. Calculate X. (Choose one of the following.)

  a. 117   **b.** 118   **c.** 129   **d.** 135   **e.** 158

71. *Investment* *The New York Times* posed a scenario with two individuals, Sue and Joe, who each have $1200 a month to spend on housing and investing. Each takes out a mortgage for $140,000. Sue gets a 30-year mortgage at a rate of 6.625%. Joe gets a 15-year mortgage at a rate of 6.25%. Whatever money is left after the mortgage payment is invested in a mutual fund with a return of 10% annually.†

  a. What annual interest rate, when compounded monthly, gives an effective annual rate of 10%?

  b. What is Sue's monthly payment?

  c. If Sue invests the remainder of her $1200 each month, after the payment in part b, in a mutual fund with the interest rate in part a, how much money will she have in the fund at the end of 30 years?

  d. What is Joe's monthly payment?

  e. You found in part d that Joe has nothing left to invest until his mortgage is paid off. If he then invests the entire $1200 monthly in a mutual fund with the interest rate in part a, how much money will he have at the end of 30 years (that is, after 15 years of paying the mortgage and 15 years of investing)?

  f. Who is ahead at the end of the 30 years, and by how much?

  g. Discuss to what extent the difference found in part f is due to the different interest rates or to the different amounts of time.

*Problem 16 from "Course 140 Examination, Mathematics of Compound Interest" of the *Education and Examination Committee of The Society of Actuaries*. Reprinted by permission of The Society of Actuaries.
†*The New York Times,* Sept. 27, 1998, p. BU 10.

Time, Money, and Polynomials*

A *time line* is often helpful for evaluating complex investments. For example, suppose you buy a $1000 CD at time t_0. After one year $2500 is added to the CD at t_1. By time t_2, after another year, your money has grown to $3851 with interest. What rate of interest, called *yield to maturity* (YTM), did your money earn? A time line for this situation is shown in Figure 14.

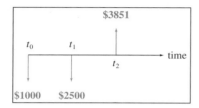

FIGURE 14

Assuming interest is compounded annually at a rate i, and using the compound interest formula, gives the following description of the YTM.

$$1000(1 + i)^2 + 2500(1 + i) = 3851$$

To determine the yield to maturity, we must solve this equation for i. Since the quantity $1 + i$ is repeated, let $x = 1 + i$ and first solve the second-degree (quadratic) polynomial equation for x.

$$1000x^2 + 2500x - 3851 = 0$$

We can use the quadratic formula with $a = 1000$, $b = 2500$, and $c = -3851$.

$$x = \frac{-2500 \pm \sqrt{2500^2 - 4(1000)(-3851)}}{2(1000)}$$

We get $x = 1.0767$ and $x = -3.5767$. Since $x = 1 + i$, the two values for i are $0.0767 = 7.67\%$ and $-4.5767 = -457.67\%$. We reject the negative value because the final accumulation is greater than the sum of the deposits. In some applications, however, negative rates may be meaningful. By checking in the first equation, we see that the yield to maturity for the CD is 7.67%.

Now let us consider a more complex but realistic problem. Suppose Bill Poole has contributed for 4 years to a retirement fund. He contributed $6000 at the beginning of the first year. At the beginning of the next 3 years, he contributed $5840, $4000, and $5200, respectively. At the end of the fourth year, he had $29,912.38 in his fund. The interest rate earned by the fund varied between 21% and −3%, so Poole would like to know the YTM $= i$ for his hard-earned retirement dollars. From a time line (see Figure 15), we set up the following equation in $1 + i$ for Poole's savings program.

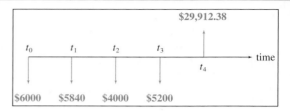

FIGURE 15

$$6000(1 + i)^4 + 5840(1 + i)^3 + 4000(1 + i)^2$$
$$+5200(1 + i) = 29,912.38$$

Let $x = 1 + i$. We need to solve the fourth-degree polynomial equation

$$f(x) = 6000x^4 + 5840x^3 + 4000x^2 + 5200x$$
$$-29,912.38 = 0.$$

There is no simple way to solve a fourth-degree polynomial equation, so we will use a graphing calculator.

We expect that $0 < i < 1$, so that $1 < x < 2$. Let us calculate $f(1)$ and $f(2)$. If there is a change of sign, we will know that there is a solution to $f(x) = 0$ between 1 and 2. We find that

$$f(1) = -8872.38 \quad \text{and} \quad f(2) = 139{,}207.62.$$

Using a graphing calculator, we find that there is one positive solution to this equation, $x = 1.14$, so $i = \text{YTM} = 0.14 = 14\%$.

EXERCISES

1. Dianne Dietrich received $50 on her 16th birthday, and $70 on her 17th birthday, both of which she immediately invested in the bank, with interest compounded annually. On her 18th birthday, she had $127.40 in her account. Draw a time line, set up a polynomial equation, and calculate the YTM.

2. At the beginning of the year, Jay Beckenstein invested $10,000 at 5% for the first year. At the beginning of the second year, he added $12,000 to the account. The total account earned 4.5% for the second year.

   a. Draw a time line for this investment.

   b. How much was in the fund at the end of the second year?

   c. Set up and solve a polynomial equation and determine the YTM. What do you notice about the YTM?

3. On January 2 each year for 3 years, Neil Wijentunga deposited bonuses of $1025, $2200, and $1850, respec-

*Copyright COMAP "Consortium" 1991. COMAP, Inc. 57 Bedford Street #210, Lexington, MA 02420.

tively, in an account. He received no bonus the following year, so he made no deposit. At the end of the fourth year, there was $5864.17 in the account.

    a. Draw a time line for these investments.

    b. Write a polynomial equation in x ($x = 1 + i$) and use a graphing calculator to find the YTM for these investments.

4. Erik Thomas invested yearly in a fund for his children's college education. At the beginning of the first year, he invested $1000; at the beginning of the second year, $2000; at the third through the sixth, $2500 each year, and at the beginning of the seventh, he invested $5000. At the beginning of the eighth year, there was $21,259 in the fund.

    a. Draw a time line for this investment program.

    b. Write a seventh-degree polynomial equation in $1 + i$ that gives the YTM for this investment program.

    c. Use a graphing calculator to show that the YTM is less than 5.07% and greater than 5.05%.

    d. Use a graphing calculator to calculate the solution for $1 + i$ and find the YTM.

5. People often lose money on investments. Jeremy Quist invested $50 at the beginning of each of 2 years in a mutual fund, and at the end of 2 years his investment was worth $90.

    a. Draw a time line and set up a polynomial equation in $1 + i$. Solve for i.

    b. Examine each negative solution (rate of return on the investment) to see if it has a reasonable interpretation in the context of the problem. To do this, use the compound interest formula on each value of i to trace each $50 payment to maturity.

DIRECTIONS FOR GROUP PROJECT

Assume that you are in charge of a group of financial analysts and that you have been asked by the broker at your firm to develop a time line for each of the people listed in the exercises above. Prepare a report for each client that presents the YTM for each investment strategy. Make sure that you describe the methods used to determine the YTM in a manner that the average client should understand.

6

Logic

▶ The rules of a game often include complex conditional statements, such as "if you roll doubles, you can roll again, but if you roll doubles twice in a row, you lose a turn." As exercises in this chapter illustrate, logical analysis of complex statements helps us clarify not only the rules of games but any precise use of language, from legal codes to medical diagnoses.

7

Sets and Probability

▶ The study of probability begins with counting. An exercise in Section 2 of this chapter counts trucks carrying different combinations of early, late, and extra late peaches from the orchard to canning facilities. You'll see trees in another context in Section 5, where we use branching tree diagrams to calculate conditional probabilities.

In this chapter and the next, we introduce the basic ideas of probability theory, a branch of mathematics that has become increasingly important in management and in the biological and social sciences. Probability theory is valuable because it provides a way to deal with uncertainty. Since the language of sets and set operations is used in the study of probability, we begin there.

7.1 Sets

THINK ABOUT IT

In how many ways can two candidates win the 50 states plus the District of Columbia in a U.S. presidential election?

Using knowledge of sets, we will answer this question in one of the exercises.

Think of a **set** as a well-defined collection of objects in which it is possible to determine if a given object is included in the collection. A set of coins might include one of each type of coin now put out by the U.S. government. Another set might be made up of all the students in your English class. By contrast, a collection of young adults does not constitute a set unless the designation "young adult" is clearly defined. For example, this set might be defined as those aged 18 to 29.

In mathematics, sets are often made up of numbers. The set consisting of the numbers 3, 4, and 5 is written

$$\{3, 4, 5\},$$

with set braces, { }, enclosing the numbers belonging to the set. The numbers 3, 4, and 5 are called the **elements** or **members** of this set. To show that 4 is an element of the set $\{3, 4, 5\}$, we use the symbol $\in$ and write

$$4 \in \{3, 4, 5\},$$

read "4 is an element of the set containing 3, 4, and 5." Also, $5 \in \{3, 4, 5\}$.

To show that 8 is *not* an element of this set, place a slash through the symbol:

$$8 \notin \{3, 4, 5\}.$$

Sets often are named with capital letters, so that if

$$B = \{5, 6, 7\},$$

then, for example, $6 \in B$ and $10 \notin B$.

It is possible to have a set with no elements. Some examples are the set of counting numbers less than one, the set of foreign-born presidents of the United States, and the set of men more than 10 feet tall. A set with no elements is called the **empty set** and is written $\emptyset$.

CAUTION Be careful to distinguish between the symbols 0, $\emptyset$, {0}, and $\{\emptyset\}$. The symbol 0 represents a *number*; $\emptyset$ represents a *set* with 0 elements; {0} represents a set with one element, 0; and $\{\emptyset\}$ represents a set with one element, $\emptyset$. ∎

We use the symbol $n(A)$ to indicate the *number* of elements in a finite set A. For example, if $A = \{a, b, c, d, e\}$, then $n(A) = 5$. Using this notation, we can write the information in the Caution on the previous page as $n(\emptyset) = 0$ and $n(\{0\}) = n(\{\emptyset\}) = 1$.

Two sets are *equal* if they contain the same elements. The sets $\{5, 6, 7\}$, $\{7, 6, 5\}$, and $\{6, 5, 7\}$ all contain exactly the same elements and are equal. In symbols,

$$\{5, 6, 7\} = \{7, 6, 5\} = \{6, 5, 7\}.$$

This means that the ordering of the elements in a set is unimportant. Note that each element of the set is only listed once. Sets that do not contain exactly the same elements are *not equal*. For example, the sets $\{5, 6, 7\}$ and $\{7, 8, 9\}$ do not contain exactly the same elements and thus are not equal. To indicate that these sets are not equal, we write

$$\{5, 6, 7\} \neq \{7, 8, 9\}.$$

Sometimes we are interested in a common property of the elements in a set, rather than a list of the elements. This common property can be expressed by using **set-builder notation**, for example,

$$\{x \mid x \text{ has property } P\}$$

(read "the set of all elements x such that x has property P") represents the set of all elements x having some stated property P.

| EXAMPLE 1 | **Sets** |

Write the elements belonging to each set.

(a) $\{x \mid x \text{ is a natural number less than 5}\}$

▶**Solution** The natural numbers less than 5 make up the set $\{1, 2, 3, 4\}$.

(b) $\{x \mid x \text{ is a state that borders Florida}\}$

▶**Solution** The states that border Florida make up the set $\{$Alabama, Georgia$\}$.

The **universal set** for a particular discussion is a set that includes all the objects being discussed. In elementary school arithmetic, for instance, the set of whole numbers might be the universal set, while in a college algebra class the universal set might be the set of real numbers. The universal set will be specified when necessary, or it will be clearly understandable from the context of the problem.

Subsets   Sometimes every element of one set also belongs to another set. For example, if

$$A = \{3, 4, 5, 6\}$$

and

$$B = \{2, 3, 4, 5, 6, 7, 8\},$$

then every element of A is also an element of B. This is an example of the following definition.

SUBSET

Set A is a **subset** of set B (written $A \subseteq B$) if every element of A is also an element of B. Set A is a *proper subset* (written $A \subset B$) if $A \subseteq B$ and $A \neq B$.

To indicate that A is *not* a subset of B, we write $A \nsubseteq B$.

EXAMPLE 2   **Sets**

Decide whether the following statements are *true* or *false*.

(a) $\{3, 4, 5, 6\} = \{4, 6, 3, 5\}$

▶**Solution** Both sets contain exactly the same elements, so the sets are equal and the given statement is true. (The fact that the elements are listed in a different order does not matter.)

(b) $\{5, 6, 9, 12\} \subseteq \{5, 6, 7, 8, 9, 10, 11\}$

▶**Solution** The first set is not a subset of the second because it contains an element, 12, that does not belong to the second set. Therefore, the statement is false.

By the definition of subset, the empty set (which contains no elements) is a subset of every set. That is, if A is any set, and the symbol $\emptyset$ represents the empty set, then $\emptyset \subseteq A$. Also, the definition of subset can be used to show that every set is a subset of itself; that is, if A is any set, then $A \subseteq A$.

For any set A,

$$\emptyset \subseteq A \qquad \text{and} \qquad A \subseteq A.$$

EXAMPLE 3   **Subsets**

List all possible subsets for each set.

(a) $\{7, 8\}$

▶**Solution** There are 4 subsets of $\{7, 8\}$:

$$\emptyset, \quad \{7\}, \quad \{8\}, \quad \text{and} \quad \{7, 8\}.$$

(b) $\{a, b, c\}$

▶**Solution** There are 8 subsets of $\{a, b, c\}$:

$$\emptyset, \quad \{a\}, \quad \{b\}, \quad \{c\}, \quad \{a, b\}, \quad \{a, c\}, \quad \{b, c\}, \quad \text{and} \quad \{a, b, c\}.$$

A good way to find the subsets of $\{7, 8\}$ and the subsets of $\{a, b, c\}$ in Example 3 is to use a **tree diagram**—a systematic way of listing all the subsets of a given set. Figure 1 shows tree diagrams for finding the subsets of $\{7, 8\}$ and $\{a, b, c\}$.

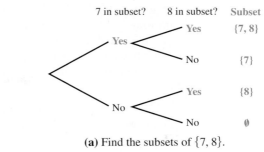

(a) Find the subsets of $\{7, 8\}$.

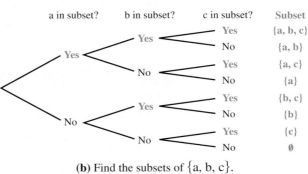

(b) Find the subsets of $\{a, b, c\}$.

FIGURE 1

As Figure 1 shows, there are two possibilities for each element (either it's in the subset or it's not), so a set with 2 elements has $2 \cdot 2 = 2^2 = 4$ subsets, and a set with 3 elements has $2^3 = 8$ subsets. This idea can be extended to a set with any finite number of elements, which leads to the following conclusion.

A set of k distinct elements has 2^k subsets.

In other words, if $n(A) = k$, then $n(\text{the set of all subsets of } A) = 2^k$.

EXAMPLE 4

Subsets
Find the number of subsets for each set.

(a) $\{3, 4, 5, 6, 7\}$

▶**Solution** This set has 5 elements; thus, it has 2^5 or 32 subsets.

(b) $\{x \mid x \text{ is a day of the week}\}$

▶**Solution** This set has 7 elements and therefore has $2^7 = 128$ subsets.

(c) $\emptyset$

▶**Solution** Since the empty set has 0 elements, it has $2^0 = 1$ subset—itself.

$A \subseteq B$

FIGURE 2

Figure 2 shows a set A that is a subset of set B. The rectangle represents the universal set, U. Such diagrams, called **Venn diagrams**—after the English logician John Venn (1834–1923), who invented them in 1876—are used to help illustrate relationships among sets. Venn diagrams are very similar to Euler diagrams, described in Section 6.6. Euler diagrams are used in logic to denote variables having a certain property or not, while Venn diagrams are used in the context of sets to denote something being an element of a set or not.

Set Operations

It is possible to form new sets by combining or manipulating one or more existing sets. Given a set A and a universal set U, the set of all elements of U that do *not* belong to A is called the *complement* of set A. For example, if set A is the set of all the female students in a class, and U is the set of all students in the class, then the complement of A would be the set of all male students in the class. The complement of set A is written A', read "A-prime."

COMPLEMENT OF A SET

Let A be any set, with U representing the universal set. Then the **complement** of A, colored pink in the figure, is

$$A' = \{x \mid x \notin A \text{ and } x \in U\}.$$

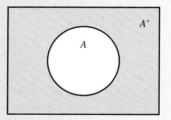

EXAMPLE 5 **Set Operations**

Let $U = \{1, 2, 3, 4, 5, 6, 7, 8, 9, 10, 11\}$, $A = \{1, 2, 4, 5, 7\}$, and $B = \{2, 4, 5, 7, 9, 11\}$. Find each set.

(a) A'

▶**Solution** Set A' contains the elements of U that are not in A.

$$A' = \{3, 6, 8, 9, 10, 11\}$$

(b) $B' = \{1, 3, 6, 8, 10\}$

(c) $\emptyset' = U$ and $U' = \emptyset$

(d) $(A')' = A$

Given two sets A and B, the set of all elements belonging to *both* set A and set B is called the *intersection* of the two sets, written $A \cap B$. For example, the elements that belong to both set $A = \{1, 2, 4, 5, 7\}$ and set $B = \{2, 4, 5, 7, 9, 11\}$ are 2, 4, 5, and 7, so that

$$A \cap B = \{1, 2, 4, 5, 7\} \cap \{2, 4, 5, 7, 9, 11\} = \{2, 4, 5, 7\}.$$

INTERSECTION OF TWO SETS

The **intersection** of sets A and B, shown in green in the figure, is

$$A \cap B = \{x \mid x \in A \text{ and } x \in B\}.$$

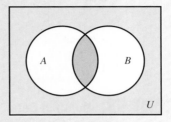

EXAMPLE 6   **Set Operations**

Let $A = \{3, 6, 9\}$, $B = \{2, 4, 6, 8\}$, and the universal set $U = \{0, 1, 2, \ldots, 10\}$. Find each set.

(a) $A \cap B$

▶Solution

$$A \cap B = \{3, 6, 9\} \cap \{2, 4, 6, 8\} = \{6\}$$

(b) $A \cap B'$

▶Solution

$$A \cap B' = \{3, 6, 9\} \cap \{0, 1, 3, 5, 7, 9, 10\} = \{3, 9\}$$

Two sets that have no elements in common are called *disjoint sets*. For example, there are no elements common to both $\{50, 51, 54\}$ and $\{52, 53, 55, 56\}$, so these two sets are disjoint, and

$$\{50, 51, 54\} \cap \{52, 53, 55, 56\} = \emptyset.$$

This result can be generalized as follows.

DISJOINT SETS

For any sets A and B, if A and B are **disjoint sets**, then $A \cap B = \emptyset$.

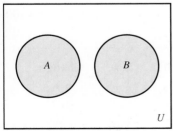

A and *B* are disjoint sets.

FIGURE 3

Figure 3 shows a pair of disjoint sets.

The set of all elements belonging to set A, to set B, or to both sets is called the *union* of the two sets, written $A \cup B$. For example,

$$\{1, 3, 5\} \cup \{3, 5, 7, 9\} = \{1, 3, 5, 7, 9\}.$$

UNION OF TWO SETS

The **union** of sets A and B, shown in blue in the figure, is

$$A \cup B = \{x \mid x \in A \text{ or } x \in B\}.$$

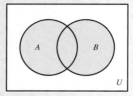

EXAMPLE 7 **Union of Sets**

Let $A = \{1, 3, 5, 7, 9, 11\}$, $B = \{3, 6, 9, 12\}$, $C = \{1, 2, 3, 4, 5\}$, and the universal set $U = \{0, 1, 2, \ldots, 12\}$. Find each set.

(a) $A \cup B$

▶**Solution** Begin by listing the elements of the first set, $\{1, 3, 5, 7, 9, 11\}$. Then include any elements from the second set *that are not already listed*. Doing this gives

$$A \cup B = \{1, 3, 5, 7, 9, 11\} \cup \{3, 6, 9, 12\} = \{1, 3, 5, 7, 9, 11, 6, 12\}$$
$$= \{1, 3, 5, 6, 7, 9, 11, 12\}.$$

(b) $(A \cup B) \cap C'$

▶**Solution** Begin with the expression in parentheses, which we calculated in part (a), and then intersect this with C'.

$$(A \cup B) \cap C' = \{1, 3, 5, 6, 7, 9, 11, 12\} \cap \{0, 6, 7, 8, 9, 10, 11, 12\}$$
$$= \{6, 7, 9, 11, 12\}$$

NOTE **1.** As Example 7 shows, when forming sets, do not list the same element more than once. In our final answer, we listed the elements in numerical order to make it easier to see what elements are in the set, but the set is the same, regardless of the order of the elements.

2. As shown in the definitions, an element is in the *intersection* of sets A and B if it is in A *and* B. On the other hand, an element is in the *union* of sets A and B if it is in A *or* B (or both). ■

EXAMPLE 8 **Stocks**

The following table gives the 52-week high and low prices, the closing price, and the change from the previous day for six stocks in the Standard & Poor's 100 on April 11, 2006.*

Stock	Low	High	Close	Change
AT&T	21.75	28.82	25.78	−0.25
CocaCola	39.36	45.26	41.29	−0.74
Dell Inc.	28.60	41.99	29.66	−0.06
Disney	22.89	28.85	27.77	−0.02
Office Max Inc.	24.20	33.95	32.09	+0.02
Texas Instruments	22.51	34.95	32.89	+0.13

*The New York Times, April 12, 2006, p. C8.

Let the universal set U consist of the six stocks listed in the table. Let A contain all stocks with a high price greater than \$34, B all stocks with a closing price between \$26 and \$30, and C all stocks with a positive price change. Find the following.

(a) A'

▶**Solution** Set A' contains all the listed stocks that are not in set A, or those with a high price less than or equal to \$34, so

$$A' = \{\text{AT\&T, Disney, Office Max Inc.}\}.$$

(b) $A \cap C$

▶**Solution** The intersection of A and C will contain those stocks that are in both sets A and C, or those with a high price greater than \$34 and a positive price change.

$$A \cap C = \{\text{Texas Instruments}\}$$

(c) $A \cup B$

▶**Solution** The union of A and B contains all stocks with a high price greater than \$34 and a closing price between \$26 and \$30.

$$A \cup B = \{\text{CocaCola, Dell Inc., Disney, Texas Instruments}\}$$

EXAMPLE 9 **Employment**

A department store classifies credit applicants by gender, marital status, and employment status. Let the universal set be the set of all applicants, M be the set of male applicants, S be the set of single applicants, and E be the set of employed applicants. Describe each set in words.

(a) $M \cap E$

▶**Solution** The set $M \cap E$ includes all applicants who are both male *and* employed; that is, employed male applicants.

(b) $M' \cup S$

▶**Solution** This set includes all applicants who are female (not male) *or* single. *All* female applicants and *all* single applicants are in this set.

(c) $M' \cap S'$

▶**Solution** These applicants are female *and* married (not single); thus, $M' \cap S'$ is the set of all married female applicants.

(d) $M \cup E'$

▶**Solution** $M \cup E'$ is the set of applicants that are male *or* unemployed. The set includes *all* male applicants and *all* unemployed applicants.

→ 7.1 Exercises

In Exercises 1–9, write true or false for each statement.

1. $3 \in \{2, 5, 7, 9, 10\}$

2. $6 \in \{-2, 6, 9, 5\}$

3. $9 \notin \{2, 1, 5, 8\}$

4. $3 \notin \{7, 6, 5, 4\}$

5. $\{2, 5, 8, 9\} = \{2, 5, 9, 8\}$

6. $\{3, 7, 12, 14\} = \{3, 7, 12, 14, 0\}$

7. $\{\text{all whole numbers greater than 7 and less than 10}\} = \{8, 9\}$

8. $\{x \,|\, x \text{ is an odd integer}; 6 \le x \le 18\} = \{7, 9, 11, 15, 17\}$

9. $0 \in \emptyset$

10. What is set-builder notation? Give an example.

Let $A = \{2, 4, 6, 8, 10, 12\}$, $B = \{2, 4, 8, 10\}$, $C = \{4, 8, 12\}$, $D = \{2, 10\}$, $E = \{6\}$, and $U = \{2, 4, 6, 8, 10, 12, 14\}$. Insert $\subseteq$ or $\nsubseteq$ to make the statement true.

11. $A \underline{\quad} U$

12. $E \underline{\quad} A$

13. $A \underline{\quad} E$

14. $B \underline{\quad} C$

15. $\emptyset \underline{\quad} A$

16. $\{0, 2\} \underline{\quad} D$

17. $D \underline{\quad} B$

18. $A \underline{\quad} C$

19. Repeat Exercises 11–18 except insert $\subset$ or $\not\subset$ to make the statement true.

Insert a number in each blank to make the statement true, using the sets for Exercises 11–18.

20. There are exactly $\underline{\quad}$ subsets of A.

21. There are exactly $\underline{\quad}$ subsets of B.

22. There are exactly $\underline{\quad}$ subsets of C.

23. There are exactly $\underline{\quad}$ subsets of D.

24. Describe the intersection and union of sets. How do they differ?

Insert $\cap$ or $\cup$ to make each statement true.

25. $\{5, 7, 9, 19\} \underline{\quad} \{7, 9, 11, 15\} = \{7, 9\}$

26. $\{8, 11, 15\} \underline{\quad} \{8, 11, 19, 20\} = \{8, 11\}$

27. $\{2, 1, 7\} \underline{\quad} \{1, 5, 9\} = \{1\}$

28. $\{6, 12, 14, 16\} \underline{\quad} \{6, 14, 19\} = \{6, 14\}$

29. $\{3, 5, 9, 10\} \underline{\quad} \emptyset = \emptyset$

30. $\{3, 5, 9, 10\} \underline{\quad} \emptyset = \{3, 5, 9, 10\}$

31. $\{1, 2, 4\} \underline{\quad} \{1, 2, 4\} = \{1, 2, 4\}$

32. Is it possible for two nonempty sets to have the same intersection and union? If so, give an example.

Let $U = \{1, 2, 3, 4, 5, 6, 7, 8, 9\}$, $X = \{2, 4, 6, 8\}$, $Y = \{2, 3, 4, 5, 6\}$, and $Z = \{1, 2, 3, 8, 9\}$. List the members of each set, using set braces.

33. $X \cap Y$

34. $X \cup Y$

35. X'

36. Y'

37. $X' \cap Y'$

38. $X' \cap Z$

39. $Y \cap (X \cup Z)$

40. $X' \cap (Y' \cup Z)$

41. $(X \cap Y') \cup Z'$

42. a. In Example 6, what set do you get when you calculate $(A \cap B) \cup (A \cap B')$?

   b. Explain in words why $(A \cap B) \cup (A \cap B') = A$.

Let $U = \{\text{all students in this school}\}$, $M = \{\text{all students taking this course}\}$, $N = \{\text{all students taking accounting}\}$, and $P = \{\text{all students taking zoology}\}$. Describe each set in words.

43. M'

44. $M \cup N$

45. $N \cap P$

46. $N' \cap P'$

47. Refer to the sets listed for Exercises 11–18. Which pairs of sets are disjoint?

48. Refer to the sets listed for Exercises 33–41. Which pairs are disjoint?

Refer to Example 8 in the text. Describe each set in Exercises 49–52 in words; then list the elements of each set.

49. B'

50. $A \cap B$

51. $(A \cap B)'$

52. $(A \cup C)'$

53. Let $A = \{1, 2, 3, \{3\}, \{1, 4, 7\}\}$. Answer each of the following as *true* or *false*.

   a. $1 \in A$ **b.** $\{3\} \in A$ **c.** $\{2\} \in A$ **d.** $4 \in A$

   e. $\{\{3\}\} \subset A$ **f.** $\{1, 4, 7\} \in A$ **g.** $\{1, 4, 7\} \subseteq A$

54. Let $B = \{a, b, c, \{d\}, \{e, f\}\}$. Answer each of the following as *true* or *false*.

   a. $a \in B$ **b.** $\{b, c, d\} \subset B$ **c.** $\{d\} \in B$ **d.** $\{d\} \subseteq B$

   e. $\{e, f\} \in B$ **f.** $\{a, \{e, f\}\} \subset B$ **g.** $\{e, f\} \subset B$

➡ Applications

BUSINESS AND ECONOMICS

Mutual Funds The table below shows the top five holdings of four major mutual funds on January 27, 2006.*

Vanguard 500	Janus Fund	Fidelity Magellan	T. Rowe Price Blue Chip Growth Fund
General Electric Co.	Boeing Co.	Nokia Corp.	UnitedHealth Group
ExxonMobil Corp.	Procter & Gamble	UnitedHealth Group	General Electric Co.
Citigroup, Inc.	Yahoo!, Inc.	Schlumberger Ltd.	Microsoft Corp.
Microsoft Corp.	UnitedHealth Group	Google Inc.	Citigroup, Inc.
Procter & Gamble	Microsoft Corp.	General Electric Co.	American International Group

Let U be the smallest possible set that includes all the corporations listed, and V, J, F, and T be the set of top-five holdings for each mutual fund, respectively. Find each set.

55. $V \cap J$

56. $V \cap (F \cup T)$

57. $(J \cup F)'$

58. $J' \cap T'$

LIFE SCIENCES

Health The following table shows some symptoms of an overactive thyroid and an underactive thyroid.[†]

Underactive Thyroid	Overactive Thyroid
Sleepiness, s	Insomnia, i
Dry hands, d	Moist hands, m
Intolerance of cold, c	Intolerance of heat, h
Goiter, g	Goiter, g

Let U be the smallest possible set that includes all the symptoms listed, N be the set of symptoms for an underactive thyroid, and O be the set of symptoms for an overactive thyroid. Find each set.

59. O'

60. N'

61. $N \cap O$

62. $N \cup O$

63. $N \cap O'$

SOCIAL SCIENCES

64. *Electoral College* U.S. presidential elections are decided by the Electoral College, in which each of the 50 states, plus the District of Columbia, gives all of its votes to a candidate.[‡] Ignoring the number of votes each state has in the Electoral College, but including all possible combinations of states that could be won by either candidate, how many outcomes are possible in the Electoral College if there are two candidates? (*Hint:* The states that can be won by a candidate form a subset of all the states.)

GENERAL INTEREST

65. *Musicians* A concert featured a cellist, a flutist, a harpist, and a vocalist. Throughout the concert, different subsets of

*Top five holdings found for each fund at www.vanguard.com, ww4.janus.com, www.fidelity.com, www.troweprice.com, respectively.
[†]*The Merck Manual of Diagnosis and Therapy,* 16th ed., Merck Research Laboratories, 1992, pp. 1075 and 1080.
[‡]The exceptions are Maine and Nebraska, which allocate their electoral college votes according to the winner in each congressional district.

the four musicians performed together, with at least two musicians playing each piece. How many subsets of at least two are possible?

66. Cat Food Suppose 9 flavors of cat food are available in a store. Euclid, the mathematical cat, could like all 9 flavors, or none, or any combination of selected flavors. How many possibilities are there for the set of flavors that Euclid likes? (*Hint:* Each set of flavors is a subset of the original 9 flavors.)

Pay-Cable Services *The following table lists the top five pay-cable services for 2004–2005.* Use this information for Exercises 67–72.*

Network	Subscribers (millions)	Content
The Disney Channel	85.0	Movies, cartoons
Showtime	39.5	Movies, variety, comedy, sports
HBO	39.0	Movies, variety, sports, documentaries
Encore	24.5	Movies
Starz	14.0	Movies

List the elements of the following sets.

67. *F*, the set of networks with more than 20 million subscribers

68. *G*, the set of networks that feature sports

69. *H*, the set of networks that feature only movies

70. $F \cap H$ **71.** $G \cup H$ **72.** G'

73. Games In David Gale's game of Subset Takeaway, the object is for each player, at his or her turn, to pick a non-empty proper subset of a given set subject to the condition that no subset chosen earlier by either player can be a subset of the newly chosen set.[†] The winner is the last person who can make a legal move. Consider the set $A = \{1, 2, 3\}$. Suppose Joe and Dorothy are playing the game and Dorothy goes first. If she chooses the proper subset $\{1\}$, then Joe cannot choose any subset that includes the element 1. Joe can, however, choose $\{2\}$ or $\{3\}$ or $\{2, 3\}$. Develop a strategy for Joe so that he can always win the game if Dorothy goes first.

States *In the following list of states, let A* = {states whose name contains the letter *e*}, *let B* = {states with a population of more than 4,000,000}, *and C* = {states with an area greater than 40,000 square miles}.[‡]

State	Population (1000s)	Area (sq. mi.)
Alabama	4447	52,419
Alaska	627	663,267
Colorado	4301	104,094
Florida	15,982	65,755
Hawaii	1212	10,931
Indiana	6080	36,418
Kentucky	4042	40,409
Maine	1275	35,385
Nebraska	1711	77,354
New Jersey	8414	8721

74. a. Describe in words the set $A \cup (B \cap C)'$.

    b. List all elements in the set $A \cup (B \cap C)'$.

75. a. Describe in words the set $(A \cup B)' \cap C$.

    b. List all elements in the set $(A \cup B)' \cap C$.

**The New York Times 2006 Almanac,* p. 401.
[†]Stewart, Ian, "Mathematical Recreations: A Strategy for Subsets," *Scientific American,* Mar. 2000, pp. 96–98.
[‡]*The New York Times 2006 Almanac,* pp. 177–211.

7.2 Applications of Venn Diagrams

? *THINK ABOUT IT*

The responses to a survey of 100 households show that 21 have a DVD player, 56 have a videocassette recorder, and 12 have both. How many have neither a DVD player nor a videocassette recorder?

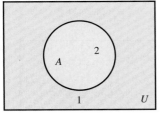

One set leads to 2 regions
(numbering is arbitrary).

FIGURE 4

It is difficult to answer this question from the given information. In this section we show how a Venn diagram can be used to sort out such information, and later in this section, we are able to answer this question.

Venn diagrams were used in the previous section to illustrate set union and intersection. The rectangular region of a Venn diagram represents the universal set U. Including only a single set A inside the universal set, as in Figure 4, divides U into two regions. Region 1 represents those elements of U outside set A (that is, the elements in A'), and region 2 represents those elements belonging to set A. (The numbering of these regions is arbitrary.)

The Venn diagram in Figure 5(a) shows two sets inside U. These two sets divide the universal set into four regions. As labeled in Figure 5(a), region 1 represents the set whose elements are outside both set A and set B. Region 2 shows the set whose elements belong to A and not to B. Region 3 represents the set whose elements belong to both A and B. Which set is represented by region 4? (Again, the labeling is arbitrary.)

Two other situations can arise when representing sets by Venn diagrams. If it is known that $A \cap B = \emptyset$, then the Venn diagram is drawn as in Figure 5(b). If it is known that $A \subseteq B$, then the Venn diagram is drawn as in Figure 5(c). For the material presented throughout this chapter we will only refer to Venn diagrams like the one in Figure 5(a), and note that some of the regions of the Venn diagram may be equal to the null set.

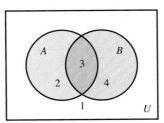

Two sets lead to 4 regions
(numbering is arbitrary).

(a)

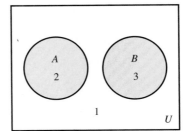

Two sets lead to 3 regions
(numbering is arbitrary).

(b)

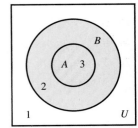

Two sets lead to 3 regions
(numbering is arbitrary).

(c)

FIGURE 5

EXAMPLE 1 **Venn Diagrams**
Draw Venn diagrams similar to Figure 5(a) and shade the regions representing each set.

(a) $A' \cap B$

►**Solution** Set A' contains all the elements outside set A. As labeled in Figure 5(a), A' is represented by regions 1 and 4. Set B is represented by regions 3 and 4. The intersection of sets A' and B, the set $A' \cap B$, is given by the region common to the combined regions 1 and 4 and the combined regions 3 and 4. The result is the set represented by region 4, which is blue in Figure 6. When looking for the intersection, remember to choose the area that is in one region *and* the other region.

In addition to the fact that region 4 in Figure 6 is $A' \cap B$, notice that region 1 is $A' \cap B'$, region 2 is $A \cap B'$, and region 3 is $A \cap B$.

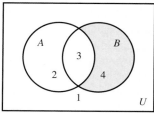

FIGURE 6

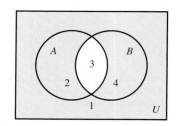

FIGURE 7

(b) $A' \cup B'$

►**Solution** Again, set A' is represented by regions 1 and 4, and set B' by regions 1 and 2. To find $A' \cup B'$, identify the region that represents the set of all elements in A', B', or both. The result, which is blue in Figure 7, includes regions 1, 2, and 4. When looking for the union, remember to choose the area that is in one region *or* the other region (or both). ——————

Venn diagrams also can be drawn with three sets inside U. These three sets divide the universal set into eight regions, which can be numbered (arbitrarily) as in Figure 8.

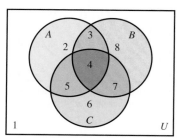

Three sets lead to 8 regions.

FIGURE 8

EXAMPLE 2 **Venn Diagram**
In a Venn diagram, shade the region that represents $A' \cup (B \cap C')$.

►**Solution** First find $B \cap C'$. Set B is represented by regions 3, 4, 7, and 8, and set C' by regions 1, 2, 3, and 8. The overlap of these regions (regions 3 and 8)

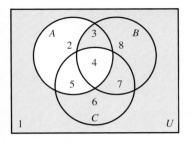

FIGURE 9

represents the set $B \cap C'$. Set A' is represented by regions 1, 6, 7, and 8. The union of the set represented by regions 3 and 8 and the set represented by regions 1, 6, 7, and 8 is the set represented by regions 1, 3, 6, 7, and 8, which are blue in Figure 9.

Applications

We can now use a Venn diagram to answer the question posed at the beginning of this section. A researcher collecting data on 100 households finds that

21 have a DVD player;

56 have a videocassette recorder (VCR); and

12 have both.

The researcher wants to answer the following questions.

(a) How many do not have a VCR?

(b) How many have neither a DVD player nor a VCR?

(c) How many have a DVD player but not a VCR?

▶**Solution** A Venn diagram like the one in Figure 10 will help sort out the information. In Figure 10(a), we put the number 12 in the region common to both a VCR and a DVD player, because 12 households have both. Of the 21 with a DVD player, $21 - 12 = 9$ have no VCR, so in Figure 10(b) we put 9 in the region for a DVD but no VCR. Similarly, $56 - 12 = 44$ households have a VCR but not a DVD player, so we put 44 in that region. Finally, the diagram shows that $100 - 44 - 12 - 9 = 35$ households have neither a VCR nor a DVD player. Now we can answer the questions:

(a) $35 + 9 = 44$ do not have a VCR.

(b) 35 have neither.

(c) 9 have a DVD player but not a VCR.

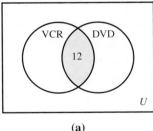

(a)   (b)

FIGURE 10

EXAMPLE 3   **Magazines**

A survey of 77 freshman business students at a large university produced the following results.

25 of the students read *Business Week*;

19 read *The Wall Street Journal*;

27 do not read *Fortune*;

11 read *Business Week* but not *The Wall Street Journal*;

11 read *The Wall Street Journal* and *Fortune*;

13 read *Business Week* and *Fortune*;

9 read all three.

Use this information to answer the following questions.

(a) How many students read none of the publications?

(b) How many read only *Fortune*?

(c) How many read *Business Week* and *The Wall Street Journal*, but not *Fortune*?

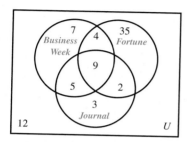

FIGURE 11

▶**Solution** Since 9 students read all three publications, begin by placing 9 in the area that belongs to all three regions, as shown in Figure 11. Of the 13 students who read *Business Week* and *Fortune*, 9 also read *The Wall Street Journal*. Therefore, only 13 − 9 = 4 read just *Business Week* and *Fortune*. Place the number 4 in the area of Figure 11 common only to *Business Week* and *Fortune* readers.

In the same way, place 11 − 9 = 2 in the region common only to *Fortune* and *The Wall Street Journal*. Of the 11 students who read *Business Week* but not *The Wall Street Journal*, 4 read *Fortune*, so place 11 − 4 = 7 in the region for those who read only *Business Week*.

The data show that 25 students read *Business Week*. However, 7 + 4 + 9 = 20 readers have already been placed in the region representing *Business Week*. The balance of this region will contain only 25 − 20 = 5 students. These students read *Business Week* and *The Wall Street Journal*, but not *Fortune*. In the same way, 19 − (5 + 9 + 2) = 3 students read only *The Wall Street Journal*.

Using the fact that 27 of the 77 students do not read *Fortune*, we know that 50 do read *Fortune*. We already have 4 + 9 + 2 = 15 students in the region representing *Fortune*, leaving 50 − 15 = 35 who read only *Fortune*.

A total of 7 + 4 + 35 + 5 + 9 + 2 + 3 = 65 students are placed in the three circles in Figure 11. Since 77 students were surveyed, 77 − 65 = 12 students read none of the three publications, and 12 is placed outside all three regions.

Now Figure 11 can be used to answer the questions asked above.

(a) There are 12 students who read none of the three publications.

(b) There are 35 students who read only *Fortune*.

(c) The overlap of the regions representing readers of *Business Week* and *The Wall Street Journal* shows that 5 students read *Business Week* and *The Wall Street Journal* but not *Fortune*.

CAUTION A common error in solving problems of this type is to make a circle represent one set and another circle represent its complement. In Example 3, with one circle representing those who read *Business Week*, we did not draw another for those who do not read *Business Week*. An additional circle is not only unnecessary (because those not in one set are automatically in the other) but very confusing, because the region outside or inside both circles must be empty. Similarly, if a problem involves men and women, do not draw one circle for men and another for women. Draw one circle; if you label it "women," for example, then men are automatically those outside the circle. ■

EXAMPLE 4 **Utility Maintenance**

Jeff Friedman is a section chief for an electric utility company. The employees in his section cut down trees, climb poles, and splice wire. Friedman reported the following information to the management of the utility.

"Of the 100 employees in my section,

45 can cut trees;

50 can climb poles;

57 can splice wire;

22 can climb poles but can't cut trees;

20 can climb poles and splice wire;

25 can cut trees and splice wire;

14 can cut trees and splice wire but can't climb poles;

9 can't do any of the three (management trainees)."

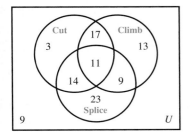

FIGURE 12

The data supplied by Friedman lead to the numbers shown in Figure 12. Add the numbers from all of the regions to get the total number of employees:

$$9 + 3 + 14 + 23 + 11 + 9 + 17 + 13 = 99.$$

Friedman claimed to have 100 employees, but his data indicate only 99. Management decided that Friedman didn't qualify as a section chief, and he was reassigned as a night-shift meter reader in Guam. (*Moral:* He should have taken this course.)

NOTE In all the examples above, we started with a piece of information specifying the relationship with all the categories. This is usually the best way to begin solving problems of this type.

As we saw in the previous section, we use the symbol $n(A)$ to indicate the *number* of elements in a finite set A. The following statement about the number of elements in the union of two sets will be used later in our study of probability.

UNION RULE FOR SETS

$$n(A \cup B) = n(A) + n(B) - n(A \cap B)$$

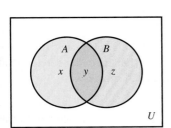

FIGURE 13

To prove this statement, let $x + y$ represent $n(A)$, y represent $n(A \cap B)$, and $y + z$ represent $n(B)$, as shown in Figure 13. Then

$$n(A \cup B) = x + y + z,$$

$$n(A) + n(B) - n(A \cap B) = (x + y) + (y + z) - y = x + y + z,$$

so $\qquad\qquad n(A \cup B) = n(A) + n(B) - n(A \cap B).$

EXAMPLE 5 **School Activities**

A group of 10 students meet to plan a school function. All are majoring in accounting or economics or both. Five of the students are economics majors and 7 are majors in accounting. How many major in both subjects?

▶**Solution** Let A represent the set of accounting majors and B represent the set of economics majors. Use the union rule, with $n(A) = 5$, $n(B) = 7$, and $n(A \cup B) = 10$. Find $n(A \cap B)$.

$$n(A \cup B) = n(A) + n(B) - n(A \cap B)$$
$$10 = 5 + 7 - n(A \cap B),$$

so
$$n(A \cap B) = 5 + 7 - 10 = 2.$$

When A and B are disjoint, then $n(A \cap B) = 0$, so the union rule simplifies to $n(A \cup B) = n(A) + n(B)$.

CAUTION The rule $n(A \cup B) = n(A) + n(B)$ is *only* valid when A and B are disjoint. When A and B are *not* disjoint, use the rule $n(A \cup B) = n(A) + n(B) - n(A \cap B)$. ∎

EXAMPLE 6 **Endangered Species**

The following table gives the number of threatened and endangered animal species in the world as of April 2006.*

	Endangered (E)	Threatened (T)	Totals
Amphibians and reptiles (A)	99	50	149
Arachnids and insects (I)	52	9	61
Birds (B)	252	21	273
Clams, crustaceans, and snails (C)	108	23	131
Fishes (F)	85	47	132
Mammals (M)	323	33	356
Totals	919	183	1102

Using the letters given in the table to denote each set, find the number of species in each of the following sets.

(a) $E \cap B$

▶**Solution** The set $E \cap B$ consists of all species that are endangered *and* are birds. From the table, we see that there are 252 such species.

(b) $E \cup B$

▶**Solution** The set $E \cup B$ consists of all species that are endangered *or* are birds. We include all 919 endangered species, plus the 21 bird species who are threatened but not endangered, for a total of 940. Alternatively, we could use the formula $n(E \cup B) = n(E) + n(B) - n(E \cap B) = 919 + 273 - 252 = 940$.

*U.S. Fish and Wildlife Service, http://ecos.fws.gov.

(c) $(F \cup M) \cap T'$

▶**Solution** Begin with the set $F \cup M$, which is all species that are fish or mammals. This consists of the four categories with 85, 47, 323, and 33 species. Of this set, take those that are *not* threatened, for a total of $85 + 323 = 408$ species. This is the number of species of fish and mammals that are not threatened.

EXAMPLE 7 **Chat Rooms**

Suppose that a group of 150 students have joined at least one of three chat rooms: one on auto-racing, one on bicycling, and one for college students. For simplicity, we will call these rooms A, B, and C. In addition,

90 students joined room A;

50 students joined room B;

70 students joined room C;

15 students joined rooms A and C;

12 students joined rooms B and C;

10 students joined all three rooms.

Determine how many students joined both chat rooms A and B.

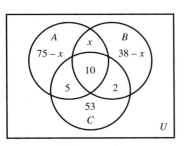

FIGURE 14

▶**Solution** Since 10 students joined all three rooms, begin by placing 10 in the area that belongs to all three regions, as shown in Figure 14. Of the 15 students who joined rooms A and C, 10 also joined room B. Thus, only $15 - 10 = 5$ students were in the area of Figure 14 common only to rooms A and C. Likewise, there are $12 - 10 = 2$ students who joined only rooms B and C. Since there are already $5 + 10 + 2 = 17$ students in room C, there are $70 - 17 = 53$ students who joined only room C.

We cannot use the information about room A, since there are two regions in A for which we have no information. Similarly, we cannot use the information about room B. In such cases, we label a region with the variable x. Here we place x in the region common only to A and B, as shown in Figure 14.

Of the 90 students in room A, the number who joined only room A must be $90 - x - 10 - 5 = 75 - x$, and this expression is placed in the appropriate region in Figure 14. Similarly, the number who only joined room B is $50 - x - 10 - 2 = 38 - x$. Notice that because all 150 students joined at least one room, there are no elements in the region outside the three circles.

Now that the diagram is filled out, we can determine the value of x by recalling that the total number of students who joined at least one chat room was 150. Thus,

$$(75 - x) + 5 + x + 10 + (38 - x) + 2 + 53 = 150.$$

Simplifying, we have $183 - x = 150$, implying that $x = 33$. The number of students who joined both chat rooms A and B is

$$33 + 10 = 43.$$

→7.2 Exercises

Sketch a Venn diagram like the one in the figure, and use shading to show each set.

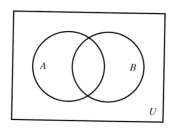

1. $B \cap A'$

2. $A \cup B'$

3. $A' \cup B$

4. $A' \cap B'$

5. $B' \cup (A' \cap B')$

6. $(A \cap B) \cup B'$

7. U'

8. $\emptyset'$

9. Three sets divide the universal set into at most _____ regions.

10. What does the notation $n(A)$ represent?

Sketch a Venn diagram like the one shown, and use shading to show each set.

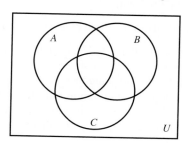

11. $(A \cap B) \cap C$

12. $(A \cap C') \cup B$

13. $A \cap (B \cup C')$

14. $A' \cap (B \cap C)$

15. $(A' \cap B') \cap C$

16. $(A \cap B') \cap C$

17. $(A \cap B') \cup C$

18. $A' \cap (B' \cup C)$

19. $(A \cup B') \cap C$

20. $A \cup (B' \cap C)$

Use the union rule to answer the following questions.

21. If $n(A) = 5$, $n(B) = 12$, and $n(A \cap B) = 4$, what is $n(A \cup B)$?

22. If $n(A) = 15$, $n(B) = 30$, and $n(A \cup B) = 33$, what is $n(A \cap B)$?

23. Suppose $n(B) = 9$, $n(A \cap B) = 5$, and $n(A \cup B) = 22$. What is $n(A)$?

24. Suppose $n(A \cap B) = 5$, $n(A \cup B) = 38$, and $n(A) = 13$. What is $n(B)$?

Draw a Venn diagram and use the given information to fill in the number of elements for each region.

25. $n(U) = 41$, $n(A) = 16$, $n(A \cap B) = 12$, $n(B') = 20$

26. $n(A) = 28$, $n(B) = 12$, $n(A \cup B) = 32$, $n(A') = 19$

27. $n(A \cup B) = 24$, $n(A \cap B) = 6$, $n(A) = 11$, $n(A' \cup B') = 25$

28. $n(A') = 31$, $n(B) = 25$, $n(A' \cup B') = 46$, $n(A \cap B) = 12$

29. $n(A) = 28$, $n(B) = 34$, $n(C) = 25$, $n(A \cap B) = 14$, $n(B \cap C) = 15$, $n(A \cap C) = 11$, $n(A \cap B \cap C) = 9$, $n(U) = 59$

30. $n(A) = 54, n(A \cap B) = 22, n(A \cup B) = 85, n(A \cap B \cap C) = 4,$
$n(A \cap C) = 15, n(B \cap C) = 16, n(C) = 44, n(B') = 63$

31. $n(A \cap B) = 6, n(A \cap B \cap C) = 4, n(A \cap C) = 7, n(B \cap C) = 4,$
$n(A \cap C') = 11, n(B \cap C') = 8, n(C) = 15, n(A' \cap B' \cap C') = 5$

32. $n(A) = 13, n(A \cap B \cap C) = 4, n(A \cap C) = 6, n(A \cap B') = 6, n(B \cap C) = 6,$
$n(B \cap C') = 11, n(B \cup C) = 22, n(A' \cap B' \cap C') = 5$

In Exercises 33–36, show that the statement is true by drawing Venn diagrams and shading the regions representing the sets on each side of the equals sign.*

33. $(A \cup B)' = A' \cap B'$

34. $(A \cap B)' = A' \cup B'$

35. $A \cap (B \cup C) = (A \cap B) \cup (A \cap C)$

36. $A \cup (B \cap C) = (A \cup B) \cap (A \cup C)$

37. Use the union rule of sets to prove that $n(A \cup B \cup C) = n(A) + n(B) + n(C) - n(A \cap B) - n(A \cap C) - n(B \cap C) + n(A \cap B \cap C)$. (*Hint:* Write $A \cup B \cup C$ as $A \cup (B \cup C)$ and use the formula from Exercise 35.)

➡ Applications

BUSINESS AND ECONOMICS

Use Venn diagrams to answer the following questions.

38. *Cooking Preferences* Jeff Friedman, of Example 4 in the text, was again reassigned, this time to the home economics department of the electric utility. He interviewed 140 people in a suburban shopping center to discover some of their cooking habits. He obtained the following results:

    58 use microwave ovens;
    63 use electric ranges;
    58 use gas ranges;
    19 use microwave ovens and electric ranges;
    17 use microwave ovens and gas ranges;
    4 use both gas and electric ranges;
    1 uses all three;
    2 use none of the three.

Should he be reassigned one more time? Why or why not?

39. *Harvesting Fruit* Toward the middle of the harvesting season, peaches for canning come in three types, early, late, and extra late, depending on the expected date of ripening. During a certain week, the following data were recorded at a fruit delivery station:

    34 trucks went out carrying early peaches;
    61 carried late peaches;
    50 carried extra late;

    25 carried early and late;
    30 carried late and extra late;
    8 carried early and extra late;
    6 carried all three;
    9 carried only figs (no peaches at all).

a. How many trucks carried only late variety peaches?

b. How many carried only extra late?

c. How many carried only one type of peach?

d. How many trucks (in all) went out during the week?

40. *Cola Consumption* Market research showed that the adult residents of a certain small town in Georgia fit the following categories of cola consumption. (We assume here that no one drinks both regular cola and diet cola.)

Age	Drink Regular Cola (R)	Drink Diet Cola (D)	Drink No Cola (N)	Totals
21–25 (Y)	40	15	15	70
26–35 (M)	30	30	20	80
Over 35 (O)	10	50	10	70
Totals	80	95	45	220

*The statements in Exercises 33 and 34 are known as De Morgan's Laws. They are named for the English mathematician Augustus De Morgan (1806–1871). They are analogous to De Morgan's Laws for logic seen in the previous chapter.

Using the letters given in the table, find the number of people in each set.

a. $Y \cap R$ **b.** $M \cap D$

c. $M \cup (D \cap Y)$ **d.** $Y' \cap (D \cup N)$

e. $O' \cup N$ **f.** $M' \cap (R' \cap N')$

g. Describe the set $M \cup (D \cap Y)$ in words.

41. *Investment Habits* The following table shows the results of a survey taken by a bank in a medium-sized town in Tennessee. The survey asked questions about the investment habits of bank customers. (We assume here that no one invests in more than one of type of investment.)

Age	Stocks (S)	Bonds (B)	Savings Accounts (A)	Totals
18–29 (Y)	6	2	15	23
30–49 (M)	14	5	14	33
50 or over (O)	32	20	12	64
Totals	52	27	41	120

Using the letters given in the table, find the number of people in each set.

a. $Y \cap B$ **b.** $M \cup A$ **c.** $Y \cap (S \cup B)$

d. $O' \cup (S \cup A)$ **e.** $(M' \cup O') \cap B$

f. Describe the set $Y \cap (S \cup B)$ in words.

42. *Investment Survey* Most mathematics professors love to invest their hard-earned money. A recent survey of 150 math professors revealed that

> 111 invested in stocks;
> 98 invested in bonds;
> 100 invested in certificates of deposit;
> 80 invested in stocks and bonds;
> 83 invested in bonds and certificates of deposit;
> 85 invested in stocks and certificates of deposit;
> 9 did not invest in any of the three.

How many mathematics professors invested in stocks and bonds and certificates of deposit?

LIFE SCIENCES

43. *Genetics* After a genetics experiment on 50 pea plants, the number of plants having certain characteristics was tallied, with the following results.

> 22 were tall;
> 25 had green peas;
> 39 had smooth peas;

> 9 were tall and had green peas;
> 20 had green peas and smooth peas;
> 6 had all three characteristics;
> 4 had none of the characteristics.

a. Find the number of plants that were tall and had smooth peas.

b. How many plants were tall and had peas that were neither smooth nor green?

c. How many plants were not tall but had peas that were smooth and green?

44. *Blood Antigens* Human blood can contain the A antigen, the B antigen, both the A and B antigens, or neither antigen. A third antigen, called the Rh antigen, is important in human reproduction, and again may or may not be present in an individual. Blood is called type A-positive if the individual has the A and Rh, but not the B antigen. A person having only the A and B antigens is said to have type AB-negative blood. A person having only the Rh antigen has type O-positive blood. Other blood types are defined in a similar manner. Identify the blood types of the individuals in regions (a)–(h) below.

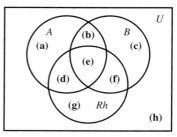

45. *Blood Antigens* (Use the diagram from Exercise 44.) In a certain hospital, the following data were recorded.

> 25 patients had the A antigen;
> 8 had the A and not the B antigen;
> 27 had the B antigen;
> 22 had the B and Rh antigens;
> 30 had the Rh antigen;
> 12 had none of the antigens;
> 16 had the A and Rh antigens;
> 15 had all three antigens.

How many patients

a. were represented?   **b.** had exactly one antigen?

c. had exactly two antigens?   **d.** had O-positive blood?

e. had AB-positive blood?   **f.** had B-negative blood?

g. had O-negative blood?   **h.** had A-positive blood?

46. *Mortality* The table on the next page lists the number of deaths in the United States during 2003 according to race and gender.* Use this information and the letters given to find the number of people in each set.

	White (W)	Black (B)	American Indian (I)	Asian or Pacific Islander (A)
Female (F)	1,078,064	143,278	6041	18,941
Male (M)	1,025,650	148,022	7106	21,186

a. F

b. $F \cap (I \cup A)$

c. $M \cup B$

d. $W' \cup I' \cup A'$

e. In words, describe the set in part b.

47. *Hockey* The table to the right lists the number of head and neck injuries for 319 ice hockey players wearing either a full shield or half shield in the Canadian Inter-University Athlet-

ics Union during one season.* Using the letters given in the table, find the number of injuries in each set.

	Half Shield (H)	Full Shield (F)
Head and Face Injuries (A)	95	34
Concussions (B)	41	38
Neck Injuries (C)	9	7
Other Injuries (D)	202	150

a. $A \cap F$

b. $C \cap (H \cup F)$

c. $D \cup F$

d. $B' \cap C'$

SOCIAL SCIENCES

48. *Military* The number of female military personnel in 2004 is given in the following table.[†] Use this information and the letters given to find the number of female military personnel in each set.

	Army (A)	Air Force (B)	Navy (C)	Marines (D)	Totals
Officers (O)	12,309	13,596	8111	1096	35,112
Enlisted (E)	60,395	59,436	45,415	9683	174,929
Cadets & Midshipmen (M)	639	754	722	0	2115
Totals	73,343	73,786	54,248	10,779	212,156

a. $A \cup B$

b. $E \cup (C \cup D)$

c. $O' \cap M'$

U.S. Population The projected U.S. population in 2020 (in millions) by age and race or ethnicity is given in the following table. Use this information in Exercises 49–54.[‡]

	Non-Hispanic White (A)	Hispanic (B)	Black (C)	Asian (D)	American Indian (E)	Totals
Under 45 (F)	110.6	37.6	30.2	13.1	2.2	193.7
45–64 (G)	55.3	10.3	9.9	4.3	0.6	80.4
65 and over (H)	41.4	4.7	5.0	2.2	0.3	53.6
Totals	207.3	52.6	45.1	19.6	3.1	327.7

*Benson, Brian, Nicholas Nohtaki, M. Sarah Rose, Willem Meeuwisse, "Head and Neck Injuries Among Ice Hockey Players Wearing Full Face Shields vs. Half Face Shields," *JAMA*, Vol. 282, No. 24, Dec. 22/29, 1999, pp. 2328–2332.
[†]*Selected Manpower Statistics, Fiscal Year 2004*, U.S. Department of Defense, p. 31.
[‡]*Population Projections of the United States by Age, Sex, Race, and Hispanic Origin: 1995 to 2050*, U.S. Bureau of the Census, Feb. 1996, pp. 16–17.

Using the letters given in the table on the previous page, find the number of people in each set.

49. $A \cap F$

50. $G \cup B$

51. $G \cup (C \cap H)$

52. $F \cap (B \cup H)$

53. $H \cup D$

54. $G' \cap (A' \cap C')$

Marital Status *The following table gives the population breakdown (in thousands) of the U.S. population in 2003 based on marital status and race or ethnic origin.**

	White (W)	Black (B)	Hispanic (H)	Asian or Pacific Islander (A)
Never married (N)	49,101	11,783	9862	3181
Married (M)	104,689	9279	14,239	5594
Widowed (I)	11,754	1730	918	418
Divorced/ separated (D)	21,372	4250	2917	607

Find the number of people in each set.

55. $N \cap (B \cup H)$

56. $(M \cup I) \cap A$

57. $(D \cup W) \cap A'$

58. $M' \cap (B \cup A)$

GENERAL INTEREST

59. *Chinese New Year* A survey of people attending a Lunar New Year celebration in Chinatown yielded the following results:

> 120 were women;
> 150 spoke Cantonese;
> 170 lit firecrackers;
> 108 of the men spoke Cantonese;
> 100 of the men did not light firecrackers;
> 18 of the non-Cantonese-speaking women lit firecrackers;
> 78 non-Cantonese-speaking men did not light firecrackers;
> 30 of the women who spoke Cantonese lit firecrackers.

a. How many attended?

b. How many of those who attended did not speak Cantonese?

c. How many women did not light firecrackers?

d. How many of those who lit firecrackers were Cantonese-speaking men?

60. *Native American Ceremonies* At a pow-wow in Arizona 75 Native American families from all over the Southwest came to participate in the ceremonies. A coordinator of the pow-wow took a survey and found that

> 15 families brought food, costumes, and crafts;
> 25 families brought food and crafts;
> 42 families brought food;
> 6 families brought costumes and crafts, but not food;
> 4 families brought crafts, but neither food nor costumes;
> 10 families brought none of the three items;
> 18 families brought costumes but not crafts.

a. How many families brought costumes and food?

b. How many families brought costumes?

c. How many families brought crafts, but not costumes?

d. How many families did not bring crafts?

e. How many families brought food or costumes?

61. *Poultry Analysis* A chicken farmer surveyed his flock with the following results. The farmer had

> 9 fat red roosters;
> 13 thin brown hens;
> 15 red roosters;
> 11 thin red chickens (hens and roosters);
> 17 red hens;
> 56 fat chickens (hens and roosters);
> 41 roosters;
> 48 hens.

Assume all chickens are thin or fat, red or brown, and hens (female) or roosters (male). How many chickens were

a. fat?   **b.** red?

c. fat roosters?   **d.** fat hens?

e. thin and brown?   **f.** red and fat?

7.3 Introduction to Probability

? *THINK ABOUT IT*

What is the probability that a randomly selected person in the United States is Hispanic or Black?

After introducing probability, we will answer this question in one of the exercises.

If you go to a supermarket and buy 5 pounds of peaches at 99 cents per pound, you can easily find the *exact* price of your purchase: $4.95. On the other hand, the produce manager of the market is faced with the problem of ordering peaches. The manager may have a good estimate of the number of pounds of peaches that will be sold during the day, but it is impossible to predict the *exact* amount. The number of pounds that customers will purchase during a day is *random*: the quantity cannot be predicted exactly. A great many problems that come up in applications of mathematics involve random phenomena—those for which exact prediction is impossible. The best that we can do is determine the *probability* of the possible outcomes.

Sample Spaces In probability, an **experiment** is an activity or occurrence with an observable result. Each repetition of an experiment is called a **trial**. The possible results of each trial are called **outcomes**. The set of all possible outcomes for an experiment is the **sample space** for that experiment. A sample space for the experiment of tossing a coin is made up of the outcomes heads (*h*) and tails (*t*). If *S* represents this sample space, then

$$S = \{h, t\}.$$

EXAMPLE 1 Sample Spaces

Give the sample space for each experiment.

(a) A spinner like the one in Figure 15 is spun.

▶**Solution** The three outcomes are 1, 2, or 3, so the sample space is

$$\{1, 2, 3\}.$$

(b) For the purposes of a public opinion poll, respondents are classified as young, middle-aged, or senior, and as male or female.

▶**Solution** A sample space for this poll could be written as a set of ordered pairs:

{(young, male), (young, female), (middle-aged, male),

(middle-aged, female), (senior, male), (senior, female)}.

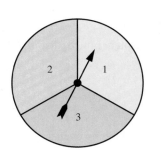

FIGURE 15

(c) An experiment consists of studying the numbers of boys and girls in families with exactly 3 children. Let *b* represent *boy* and *g* represent *girl*.

▶**Solution** A three-child family can have 3 boys, written *bbb*, 3 girls, *ggg*, or various combinations, such as *bgg*. A sample space with four outcomes (not equally likely) is

$$S_1 = \{3 \text{ boys, 2 boys and 1 girl, 1 boy and 2 girls, 3 girls}\}.$$

Notice that a family with 3 boys or 3 girls can occur in just one way, but a family of 2 boys and 1 girl or 1 boy and 2 girls can occur in more than one way. If the *order* of the births is considered, so that *bgg* is different from *gbg* or *ggb*, for example, another sample space is

$$S_2 = \{bbb, bbg, bgb, gbb, bgg, gbg, ggb, ggg\}.$$

The second sample space, S_2, has equally likely outcomes if we assume that boys and girls are equally likely. This assumption, while not quite true, is approximately true, so we will use it throughout this book. The outcomes in S_1 are not equally likely, since there is more than one way to get a family with 2 boys and 1 girl (*bbg, bgb,* or *gbb*) or a family with 2 girls and 1 boy (*ggb, gbg,* or *bgg*), but only one way to get 3 boys (*bbb*) or 3 girls (*ggg*).

CAUTION An experiment may have more than one sample space, as shown in Example 1(c). The most convenient sample spaces have equally likely outcomes, but it is not always possible to choose such a sample space. ∎

Events An **event** is a subset of a sample space. If the sample space for tossing a coin is $S = \{h, t\}$, then one event is $E = \{h\}$, which represents the outcome "heads."

An ordinary die is a cube whose six different faces show the following numbers of dots: 1, 2, 3, 4, 5, and 6. If the die is fair (not "loaded" to favor certain faces over others), then any one of the faces is equally likely to come up when the die is rolled. The sample space for the experiment of rolling a single fair die is $S = \{1, 2, 3, 4, 5, 6\}$. Some possible events are listed below.

The die shows an even number: $E_1 = \{2, 4, 6\}$.

The die shows a 1: $E_2 = \{1\}$.

The die shows a number less than 5: $E_3 = \{1, 2, 3, 4\}$.

The die shows a multiple of 3: $E_4 = \{3, 6\}$.

Using the notation introduced earlier in this chapter, notice that $n(S) = 6$, $n(E_1) = 3$, $n(E_2) = 1$, $n(E_3) = 4$, and $n(E_4) = 2$.

EXAMPLE 2 Events

For the sample space S_2 in Example 1(c), write the following events.

(a) Event *H*: the family has exactly two girls

▶**Solution** Families with three children can have exactly two girls with either *bgg, gbg,* or *ggb*, so event *H* is

$$H = \{bgg, gbg, ggb\}.$$

(b) Event *K*: the three children are the same sex

▶**Solution** Two outcomes satisfy this condition: all boys or all girls.

$$K = \{bbb, ggg\}$$

(c) Event *J*: the family has three girls

▶**Solution** Only *ggg* satisfies this condition, so

$$J = \{ggg\}.$$

In Example 2(c), event *J* had only one possible outcome, *ggg*. Such an event, with only one possible outcome, is a **simple event**. If event *E* equals the sample space *S*, then *E* is called a **certain event**. If event $E = \emptyset$, then *E* is called an **impossible event**.

EXAMPLE 3 Events

Suppose a coin is flipped until both a head and a tail appear, or until the coin has been flipped four times, whichever comes first. Write each of the following events in set notation.

(a) The coin is flipped exactly three times.

▶**Solution** This means that the first two flips of the coin did not include both a head and a tail, so they must both be heads or both be tails. Because the third flip is the last one, it must show the side of the coin not yet seen. Thus the event is

$$\{hht, tth\}.$$

(b) The coin is flipped at least three times.

▶**Solution** In addition to the outcomes listed in part a, there is also the possibility that the coin is flipped four times, which only happens when the first three flips are all heads or all tails. Thus the event is

$$\{hht, tth, hhhh, hhht, tttt, ttth\}.$$

(c) The coin is flipped at least two times.

▶**Solution** This event consists of the entire sample space:

$$S = \{ht, th, hht, tth, hhhh, hhht, tttt, ttth\}.$$

This is an example of a certain event.

(d) The coin is flipped fewer than two times.

▶**Solution** The coin cannot be flipped fewer than two times under the rules described, so the event is the empty set $\emptyset$. This is an example of an impossible event.

Since events are sets, we can use set operations to find unions, intersections, and complements of events. A summary of the set operations for events is given below.

SET OPERATIONS FOR EVENTS

Let *E* and *F* be events for a sample space *S*.

$E \cap F$ occurs when both *E* **and** *F* occur;

$E \cup F$ occurs when *E* **or** *F* **or both** occur;

E' occurs when *E* does **not** occur.

EXAMPLE 4 **Minimum-Wage Workers**

A study of workers earning the minimum wage grouped such workers into various categories, which can be interpreted as events when a worker is selected at random.* Consider the following events:

E: worker is under 20;

F: worker is white;

G: worker is female.

Describe the following events in words.

(a) E'

▶**Solution** E' is the event that the worker is 20 or over.

(b) $F \cap G'$

▶**Solution** $F \cap G'$ is the event that the worker is white and not a female, that is, the worker is a white male.

(c) $E \cup G$

▶**Solution** $E \cup G$ is the event that the worker is under 20 or is female. Note that this event includes all workers under 20, both male and female, and all female workers of any age.

Two events that cannot both occur at the same time, such as rolling an even number and an odd number with a single roll of a die, are called *mutually exclusive events*.

MUTUALLY EXCLUSIVE EVENTS

Events E and F are **mutually exclusive events** if $E \cap F = \emptyset$.

Any event E and its complement E' are mutually exclusive. By definition, mutually exclusive events are disjoint sets.

EXAMPLE 5 **Mutually Exclusive Events**

Let $S = \{1, 2, 3, 4, 5, 6\}$, the sample space for tossing a single die. Let $E = \{4, 5, 6\}$, and let $G = \{1, 2\}$. Then E and G are mutually exclusive events since they have no outcomes in common: $E \cap G = \emptyset$. See Figure 16.

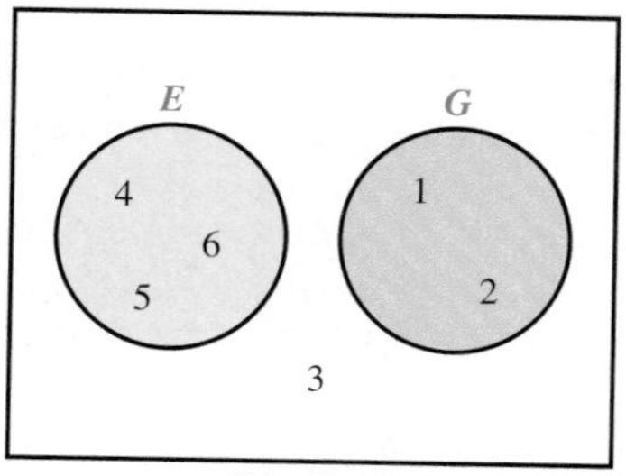

Probability For sample spaces with *equally likely* outcomes, the probability of an event is defined as follows.

$E \cap G = \emptyset$

FIGURE 16

*http://www.epinet.org/Issuebriefs/IB133.pdf.

> **BASIC PROBABILITY PRINCIPLE**
>
> Let S be a sample space of equally likely outcomes, and let event E be a subset of S. Then the **probability** that event E occurs is
>
> $$P(E) = \frac{n(E)}{n(S)}.$$

By this definition, the probability of an event is a number that indicates the relative likelihood of the event.

CAUTION The basic probability principle only applies when the outcomes are equally likely. ▪

EXAMPLE 6 **Basic Probabilities**

Suppose a single fair die is rolled. Use the sample space $S = \{1, 2, 3, 4, 5, 6\}$ and give the probability of each event.

(a) E: the die shows an even number

▶**Solution** Here, $E = \{2, 4, 6\}$, a set with three elements. Since S contains six elements,

$$P(E) = \frac{3}{6} = \frac{1}{2}.$$

(b) F: the die shows a number less than 10

▶**Solution** Event F is a certain event, with

$$F = \{1, 2, 3, 4, 5, 6\},$$

so that

$$P(F) = \frac{6}{6} = 1.$$

(c) G: the die shows an 8

▶**Solution** This event is impossible, so

$$P(G) = 0.$$

A standard deck of 52 cards has four suits: hearts (♥), clubs (♣), diamonds (♦), and spades (♠), with 13 cards in each suit. The hearts and diamonds are red, and the spades and clubs are black. Each suit has an ace (A), a king (K), a queen (Q), a jack (J), and cards numbered from 2 to 10. The jack, queen, and king are called *face cards* and for many purposes can be thought of as having values 11, 12, and 13, respectively. The ace can be thought of as the low card (value 1) or the high card (value 14). See Figure 17 on the next page. We will refer to this standard deck of cards often in our discussion of probability.

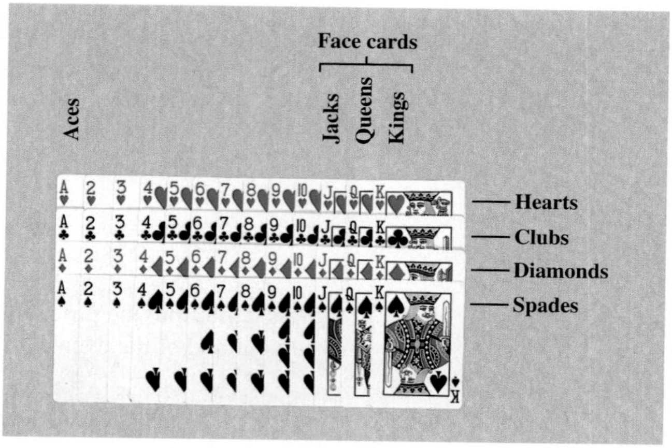

FIGURE 17

EXAMPLE 7 Playing Cards

If a single playing card is drawn at random from a standard 52-card deck, find the probability of each event.

(a) Drawing an ace

▶Solution There are 4 aces in the deck. The event "drawing an ace" is

{heart ace, diamond ace, club ace, spade ace}.

Therefore,

$$P(\text{ace}) = \frac{4}{52} = \frac{1}{13}.$$

(b) Drawing a face card

▶Solution Since there are 12 face cards (three in each of the four suits),

$$P(\text{face card}) = \frac{12}{52} = \frac{3}{13}.$$

(c) Drawing a spade

▶Solution The deck contains 13 spades, so

$$P(\text{spade}) = \frac{13}{52} = \frac{1}{4}.$$

(d) Drawing a spade or a heart

▶Solution Besides the 13 spades, the deck contains 13 hearts, so

$$P(\text{spade or heart}) = \frac{26}{52} = \frac{1}{2}.$$

In the preceding examples, the probability of each event was a number between 0 and 1. The same thing is true in general. Any event E is a subset of the sample space S, so $0 \leq n(E) \leq n(S)$. Since $P(E) = n(E)/n(S)$, it follows that $0 \leq P(E) \leq 1$.

For any event E, $\quad \mathbf{0 \leq P(E) \leq 1}$.

EXAMPLE 8 **Congressional Service**

The following table gives the number of years of service of senators in the 109th Congress of the United States of America, which convened on January 4, 2005.*

Years of Service	Number of Senators
0–9	50
10–19	28
20–29	15
30–39	4
40 or more	3

Find the probability that a randomly selected senator of the 109th Congress served 20–29 years when Congress convened.

▶**Solution** This probability is found by dividing the number of senators who served 20–29 years by the total number of senators. Thus,

$$P(\text{20–29 years}) = \frac{15}{100} = 0.15.$$

➤ 7.3 Exercises

1. What is meant by a "fair" coin or die?

2. What is the sample space for an experiment?

Write sample spaces for the experiments in Exercises 3–10.

3. A month of the year is chosen for a wedding.

4. A day in April is selected for a bicycle race.

5. A student is asked how many points she earned on a recent 80-point test.

6. A person is asked the number of hours (to the nearest hour) he watched television yesterday.

7. The management of an oil company must decide whether to go ahead with a new oil shale plant or to cancel it.

8. A record is kept each day for three days about whether a particular stock goes up or down.

9. A coin is tossed, and a die is rolled.

10. A box contains five balls, numbered 1, 2, 3, 4, and 5. A ball is drawn at random, the number on it recorded, and the ball replaced. The box is shaken, a second ball is drawn, and its number is recorded.

Time Almanac 2006, pp. 46–47.

11. Define an event.

12. What is a simple event?

For the experiments in Exercises 13–18, write out the sample space S and give the value of n(S). Then tell whether the outcomes in S are equally likely. Finally, write the indicated events in set notation.

13. A committee of 2 people is selected from 5 executives: Alam, Bartolini, Chinn, Dickson, and Ellsberg.

   a. Chinn is on the committee.

   b. Dickson and Ellsberg are not both on the committee.

   c. Both Alam and Chinn are on the committee.

14. Five states are being considered as the location for three new high-energy physics laboratories: California (CA), Colorado (CO), New Jersey (NJ), New York (NY), and Utah (UT). Three states will be chosen. Write elements of the sample space in the form (CA, CO, NJ).

   a. All three states border an ocean.

   b. Exactly two of the three states border an ocean.

   c. Exactly one of the three states is west of the Mississippi River.

15. Slips of paper marked with the numbers 1, 2, 3, 4, and 5 are placed in a box. After being mixed, two slips are drawn simultaneously.

   a. Both slips are marked with even numbers.

   b. One slip is marked with an odd number and the other is marked with an even number.

   c. Both slips are marked with the same number.

16. An unprepared student takes a three-question, true/false quiz in which he guesses the answers to all three questions, so each answer is equally likely to be correct or wrong.

   a. The student gets three answers wrong.

   b. The student gets exactly two answers correct.

   c. The student gets only the first answer correct.

17. A coin is flipped until two heads appear, up to a maximum of four flips. (If three tails are flipped, the coin is still tossed a fourth time to complete the experiment).

   a. The coin is tossed four times.

   b. Exactly two heads are tossed.

   c. No heads are tossed.

18. One jar contains four balls, labeled 1, 2, 3, and 4. A second jar contains five balls, labeled 1, 2, 3, 4, and 5. An experiment consists of taking one ball from the first jar, and then taking a ball from the second jar.

   a. The number on the first ball is even.

   b. The number on the second ball is even.

   c. The sum of the numbers on the two balls is 5.

   d. The sum of the numbers on the two balls is 1.

A single fair die is rolled. Find the probabilities of each event.

19. Getting a 2

20. Getting an odd number

21. Getting a number less than 5

22. Getting a number greater than 2

23. Getting a 3 or a 4

24. Getting any number except 3

A card is drawn from a well-shuffled deck of 52 cards. Find the probability of drawing the following.

25. A 9

26. A black card

27. A black 9

28. A heart

29. The 9 of hearts

30. A face card

31. A 2 or a queen

32. A black 7 or a red 8

33. A red card or a 10

34. A spade or a king

A jar contains 3 white, 4 orange, 5 yellow, and 8 black marbles. If a marble is drawn at random, find the probability that it is the following.

35. White

36. Orange

37. Yellow

38. Black

39. Not black

40. Orange or yellow

41. The student sitting next to you in class concludes that the probability of the ceiling falling down on both of you before class ends is 1/2, because there are two possible outcomes—the ceiling will fall or not fall. What is wrong with this reasoning?

42. The following puzzler was given on the *Car Talk* radio program on February 24, 2001.*

"Three different numbers are chosen at random, and one is written on each of three slips of paper. The slips are then placed face down on the table. The objective is to choose the slip upon which is written the largest number. Here are the rules: You can turn over any slip of paper and look at the amount written on it. If for any reason you think this is the largest, you're done; you keep it. Otherwise you discard it and turn over a second slip. Again, if you think this is the one with the biggest number, you keep that one and the game is over. If you don't, you discard that one too. . . . The chance of getting the highest number is one in three. Or is it? Is there a strategy by which you can improve the odds?"

The answer to the puzzler is that you can indeed improve the probability of getting the highest number by the following strategy. Pick one of the slips of paper, and after looking at the number, throw it away. Then pick a second slip; if it has a larger number than the first slip, stop. If not, pick the third slip. Find the probability of winning with this strategy.

→ Applications

BUSINESS AND ECONOMICS

43. *Survey of Workers* The management of a firm wishes to check on the opinions of its assembly line workers. Before the workers are interviewed, they are divided into various categories. Define events E, F, and G as follows.

E: worker is female
F: worker has worked less than 5 years
G: worker contributes to a voluntary retirement plan

Describe each event in words.

a. E' **b.** $E \cap F$ **c.** $E \cup G'$

d. F' **e.** $F \cup G$ **f.** $F' \cap G'$

*Source: Car Talk, Feb. 24, 2001. http://www.cartalk.com/content/puzzler/transcripts/200107/. Cartalk.com is a production of Dewey, Cheetham and Howe. Contents © 2007, Dewey, Cheetham and Howe. This is a special case of the famous Googol problem. For more details, see "Recognizing the Maximum of a Sequence" by John P. Gilbert and Frederick Mosteller, *Journal of the American Statistical Association*, Vol. 61, No. 313, March 1966, pp. 35–73.

44. *Research Funding* In 2001, funding for university research in the United States totaled $32.723 billion. Support came from various sources, as shown in the following table.*

Source	Amount (in billions of dollars)
Federal government	19.191
State and local government	2.315
Industry	2.234
Academic institutions	6.553
Other	2.430

Find the probability that funds for a particular project came from each source.

a. Federal government

b. Industry

c. Academic institutions

45. *Investment Survey* Exercise 42 of the previous section presented a survey of 150 mathematics professors. Use the information given in that exercise to find each probability.

a. A randomly chosen professor invested in stocks and bonds.

b. A randomly chosen professor invested in stocks and bonds and certificates of deposit.

LIFE SCIENCES

46. *Medical Survey* For a medical experiment, people are classified as to whether they smoke, have a family history of heart disease, or are overweight. Define events E, F, and G as follows.

> E: person smokes
> F: person has a family history of heart disease
> G: person is overweight

Describe each event in words.

a. G' **b.** $F \cap G$ **c.** $E \cup G'$

47. *Medical Survey* Refer to Exercise 46. Describe each event in words.

a. $E \cup F$ **b.** $E' \cap F$ **c.** $F' \cup G'$

48. *Causes of Death* There were 2,447,864 U.S. deaths in 2002. They are listed according to cause in the following table.† If a randomly selected person died in 2002, use this information to find the following probabilities.

Cause	Number of Deaths
Heart disease	695,754
Cancer	558,847
Cerebrovascular disease	163,010
Chronic lower respiratory disease	125,500
Accidents	102,303
Diabetes mellitus	73,119
Pneumonia and influenza	65,984
All other causes	663,347

a. The probability that the cause of death was heart disease

b. The probability that the cause of death was cancer or heart disease

c. The probability that the cause of death was not an accident and was not diabetes mellitus

SOCIAL SCIENCES

49. *U.S. Population* The projected U.S. population (in thousands) by race in 2020 and 2050 is given in the following table.‡

Race	2020	2050
White	207,393	207,901
Hispanic	52,652	96,508
Black	41,538	53,555
Asian and Pacific Islander	18,557	32,432
Other	2602	3535

Find the probability that a randomly selected person in the given year is of the race specified.

a. Hispanic in 2020   **b.** Hispanic in 2050

c. Black in 2020   **d.** Black in 2050

NSF Science and Engineering Indicators 2004, http://www.nsf.gov/statistics/seind04/c5/c5s1.htm#p4.
†*The New York Times 2006 Almanac*, p. 384.
‡*Population Projections of the United States by Age, Sex, Race, and Hispanic Origin: 1995 to 2050*, Bureau of the Census, Feb. 1996, p. 12.

50. *Civil War* Estimates of the Union Army's strength and losses for the battle of Gettysburg are given in the following table, where *strength* is the number of soldiers immediately preceding the battle and *loss* indicates a soldier who was killed, wounded, captured, or missing.*

Unit	Strength	Loss
I Corps (Reynolds)	12,222	6059
II Corps (Hancock)	11,347	4369
III Corps (Sickles)	10,675	4211
V Corps (Sykes)	10,907	2187
VI Corps (Sedgwick)	13,596	242
XI Corps (Howard)	9188	3801
XII Corps (Slocum)	9788	1082
Cavalry (Pleasonton)	11,851	610
Artillery (Tyler)	2376	242
Total	91,950	22,803

a. Find the probability that a randomly selected union soldier was from the XI Corps.

b. Find the probability that a soldier was lost in the battle.

c. Find the probability that a I Corps soldier was lost in the battle.

d. Which group had the highest probability of not being lost in the battle?

e. Which group had the highest probability of loss?

f. Explain why these probabilities vary.

51. *Civil War* Estimates of the Confederate Army's strength and losses for the battle of Gettysburg are given in the following table, where *strength* is the number of soldiers immediately preceding the battle and *loss* indicates a soldier who was killed, wounded, captured, or missing.*

Unit	Strength	Loss
I Corps (Longstreet)	20,706	7661
II Corps (Ewell)	20,666	6603
III Corps (Hill)	22,083	8007
Cavalry (Stuart)	6621	286
Total	70,076	22,557

a. Find the probability that a randomly selected confederate soldier was from the III Corps.

b. Find the probability that a confederate soldier was lost in the battle.

c. Find the probability that a I Corps soldier was lost in the battle.

d. Which group had the highest probability of not being lost in the battle?

e. Which group had the highest probability of loss?

GENERAL INTEREST

52. *Native American Ceremonies* Exercise 60 of the previous section presented a survey of families participating in a pow-wow in Arizona. Use the information given in that exercise to find each probability.

a. A randomly chosen family brought costumes and food.

b. A randomly chosen family brought crafts, but neither food nor costumes.

c. A randomly chosen family brought food or costumes.

53. *Chinese New Year* Exercise 59 of the previous section presented a survey of people attending a Lunar New Year celebration in Chinatown. Use the information given in that exercise to find each of the following probabilities.

a. A randomly chosen attendee speaks Cantonese.

b. A randomly chosen attendee does not speak Cantonese.

c. A randomly chosen attendee was a woman that did not light a firecracker.

*Busey, John and David Martin, *Regimental Strengths and Losses at Gettysburg*, Hightstown, N.J., Longstreet House, 1986, p. 270.

7.4 Basic Concepts of Probability

? *THINK ABOUT IT*

What is the probability that a dollar of advertising in the United States is spent on broadcast television or newspapers?

We determine the probability of this and other events in this section. But first we need to develop additional rules for calculating probability, beginning with the probability of a union of two events.

To determine the probability of the union of two events E and F in a sample space S, use the union rule for sets,

$$n(E \cup F) = n(E) + n(F) - n(E \cap F),$$

which was proved in Section 7.2. Assuming that the events in the sample space S are equally likely, divide both sides by $n(S)$, so that

$$\frac{n(E \cup F)}{n(S)} = \frac{n(E)}{n(S)} + \frac{n(F)}{n(S)} - \frac{n(E \cap F)}{n(S)}$$

$$P(E \cup F) = P(E) + P(F) - P(E \cap F).$$

Although our derivation is valid only for sample spaces with equally likely events, the result is valid for any events E and F from any sample space, and is called the **union rule for probability**.

UNION RULE FOR PROBABILITY

For any events E and F from a sample space S,

$$P(E \cup F) = P(E) + P(F) - P(E \cap F).$$

EXAMPLE 1 **Probabilities with Playing Cards**
If a single card is drawn from an ordinary deck of cards, find the probability that it will be a red or a face card.

▶Solution Let R represent the event "red card" and F the event "face card." There are 26 red cards in the deck, so $P(R) = 26/52$. There are 12 face cards in the deck, so $P(F) = 12/52$. Since there are 6 red face cards in the deck, $P(R \cap F) = 6/52$. By the union rule, the probability of the card being red or a face card is

$$P(R \cup F) = P(R) + P(F) - P(R \cap F)$$

$$= \frac{26}{52} + \frac{12}{52} - \frac{6}{52} = \frac{32}{52} = \frac{8}{13}.$$

EXAMPLE 2 **Probabilities with Dice**
Suppose two fair dice are rolled. Find each probability.

(a) The first die shows a 2, or the sum of the results is 6 or 7.

▶Solution The sample space for the throw of two dice is shown in Figure 18, where 1-1 represents the event "the first die shows a 1 and the second die shows a 1," 1-2 represents "the first die shows a 1 and the second die shows a 2," and so on. Let A represent the event "the first die shows a 2," and B represent the event "the sum of the results is 6 or 7." These events are indicated in Figure 18. From the diagram, event A has 6 elements, B has 11 elements, the intersection of A and B has 2 elements, and the sample space has 36 elements. Thus,

$$P(A) = \frac{6}{36}, \quad P(B) = \frac{11}{36}, \quad \text{and} \quad P(A \cap B) = \frac{2}{36}.$$

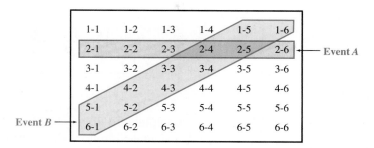

FIGURE 18

By the union rule,

$$P(A \cup B) = P(A) + P(B) - P(A \cap B)$$

$$P(A \cup B) = \frac{6}{36} + \frac{11}{36} - \frac{2}{36} = \frac{15}{36} = \frac{5}{12}.$$

(b) The sum of the results is 11, or the second die shows a 5.

▶**Solution** $P(\text{sum is } 11) = 2/36$, $P(\text{second die shows a } 5) = 6/36$, and $P(\text{sum is 11 and second die shows a } 5) = 1/36$, so

$$P(\text{sum is 11 or second die shows a } 5) = \frac{2}{36} + \frac{6}{36} - \frac{1}{36} = \frac{7}{36}.$$

CAUTION You may wonder why we did not use $S = \{2, 3, 4, 5, \ldots, 12\}$ as the sample space in Example 2. Remember, we prefer to use a sample space with equally likely outcomes. The outcomes in set S above are not equally likely—a sum of 2 can occur in just one way, a sum of 3 in two ways, a sum of 4 in three ways, and so on, as shown in Figure 18. ■

If events E and F are mutually exclusive, then $E \cap F = \emptyset$ by definition; hence, $P(E \cap F) = 0$. In this case the union rule simplifies to $P(E \cup F) = P(E) + P(F)$.

CAUTION The rule $P(E \cup F) = P(E) + P(F)$ is *only* valid when E and F are mutually exclusive. When E and F are *not* mutually exclusive, use the rule $P(E \cup F) = P(E) + P(F) - P(E \cap F)$. ■

By the definition of E', for any event E from a sample space S,

$$E \cup E' = S \quad \text{and} \quad E \cap E' = \emptyset.$$

Since $E \cap E' = \emptyset$, events E and E' are mutually exclusive, so that

$$P(E \cup E') = P(E) + P(E').$$

However, $E \cup E' = S$, the sample space, and $P(S) = 1$. Thus

$$P(E \cup E') = P(E) + P(E') = 1.$$

Rearranging these terms gives the following useful rule for complements.

COMPLEMENT RULE

$$P(E) = 1 - P(E') \qquad \text{and} \qquad P(E') = 1 - P(E).$$

EXAMPLE 3 **Complement Rule**

If a fair die is rolled, what is the probability that any number but 5 will come up?

▶**Solution** If E is the event that 5 comes up, then E' is the event that any number but 5 comes up. Since $P(E) = 1/6$, we have $P(E') = 1 - 1/6 = 5/6$. ▬▬▬

EXAMPLE 4 **Complement Rule**

In Example 2, find the probability that the sum of the numbers rolled is greater than 3.

▶**Solution** To calculate this probability directly, we must find the probabilities that the sum is 4, 5, 6, 7, 8, 9, 10, 11, or 12 and then add them. It is much simpler to first find the probability of the complement, the event that the sum is less than or equal to 3.

$$P(\text{sum} \leq 3) = P(\text{sum is } 2) + P(\text{sum is } 3)$$

$$= \frac{1}{36} + \frac{2}{36}$$

$$= \frac{3}{36} = \frac{1}{12}$$

Now use the fact that $P(E) = 1 - P(E')$ to get

$$P(\text{sum} > 3) = 1 - P(\text{sum} \leq 3)$$

$$= 1 - \frac{1}{12} = \frac{11}{12}.$$

Odds Sometimes probability statements are given in terms of **odds**, a comparison of $P(E)$ with $P(E')$. For example, suppose $P(E) = 4/5$. Then $P(E') = 1 - 4/5 = 1/5$. These probabilities predict that E will occur 4 out of 5 times and E' will occur 1 out of 5 times. Then we say the *odds in favor* of E are 4 to 1.

> **ODDS**
>
> The **odds in favor** of an event E are defined as the ratio of $P(E)$ to $P(E')$, or
>
> $$\frac{P(E)}{P(E')}, \quad P(E') \neq 0.$$

EXAMPLE 5 **Odds in Favor of Rain**

Suppose the weather forecaster says that the probability of rain tomorrow is $1/3$. Find the odds in favor of rain tomorrow.

▶**Solution** Let E be the event "rain tomorrow." Then E' is the event "no rain tomorrow." Since $P(E) = 1/3$, $P(E') = 2/3$. By the definition of odds, the odds in favor of rain are

$$\frac{1/3}{2/3} = \frac{1}{2}, \qquad \text{written} \qquad \text{1 to 2, or } 1:2.$$

On the other hand, the odds that it will *not* rain, or the *odds against* rain, are

$$\frac{2/3}{1/3} = \frac{2}{1}, \qquad \text{written} \qquad \text{2 to 1, or } 2:1.$$

If the odds in favor of an event are, say, 3 to 5, then the probability of the event is $3/8$, while the probability of the complement of the event is $5/8$. (Odds of 3 to 5 indicate 3 outcomes in favor of the event out of a total of 8 possible outcomes.) This example suggests the following generalization.

> If the odds favoring event E are m to n, then
>
> $$P(E) = \frac{m}{m+n} \qquad \text{and} \qquad P(E') = \frac{n}{m+n}.$$

EXAMPLE 6 **Winning Bids**

The odds that a particular bid will be the low bid are 4 to 5.

(a) Find the probability that the bid will be the low bid.

▶**Solution** Odds of 4 to 5 show 4 favorable chances out of $4 + 5 = 9$ chances altogether:

$$P(\text{bid will be low bid}) = \frac{4}{4+5} = \frac{4}{9}.$$

(b) Find the odds against that bid being the low bid.

▶**Solution** There is a $5/9$ chance that the bid will not be the low bid, so the odds against a low bid are

$$\frac{P(\text{bid will not be low})}{P(\text{bid will be low})} = \frac{5/9}{4/9} = \frac{5}{4},$$

or $5:4$.

EXAMPLE 7 **Odds in Horse Racing**

If the odds in favor of a particular horse's winning a race are 5 to 7, what is the probability that the horse will win the race?

▶**Solution** The odds indicate chances of 5 out of 12 (5 + 7 = 12) that the horse will win, so

$$P(\text{winning}) = \frac{5}{12}.$$

Race tracks generally give odds *against* a horse winning. In this case, the track would give the odds as 7 to 5. Of course, race tracks, casinos, and other gambling establishments need to give odds that are more favorable to the house than those representing the actual probabilities, because they need to make a profit. ▬▬▬

Empirical Probability   In many real-life problems, it is not possible to establish exact probabilities for events. Instead, useful approximations are often found by drawing on past experience. The next example shows one approach to such **empirical probabilities**.

EXAMPLE 8 **Advertising Volume**

The following table lists U.S. advertising volume in millions of dollars by medium in 2004.*

Medium	Expenditures
Direct mail	52,191
Newspapers	46,614
Broadcast TV	46,264
Cable TV	21,527
Radio	19,581
Yellow pages	14,002
Magazines	12,247
Other	51,340

Find the empirical probability that a dollar of advertising is spent on each medium.

▶**Solution** We could first find the total spent and then divide the amount spent on each medium by the total. Verify that the amounts in the table sum to 263,766. The probability that a dollar is spent on newspapers, for example, is $P(\text{newspapers}) = 46,614/263,766 \approx 0.1767$. Similarly, we could divide each amount by 263,766, with the results (rounded to four decimal places) shown in the following table.

*The New York Times 2006 Almanac, p. 357.

Medium	Probabilities
Direct mail	0.1979
Newspapers	0.1767
Broadcast TV	0.1754
Cable TV	0.0816
Radio	0.0742
Yellow pages	0.0531
Magazines	0.0464
Other	0.1946

The numbers in this table sum to 0.9999. In theory, they should total 1.0000, but this does not always occur when the individual numbers are rounded.

The categories in the table are mutually exclusive simple events. Thus, to find the probability that an advertising dollar is spent on newspapers or broadcast TV, we use the union rule to calculate

$$P(\text{newspapers or broadcast TV}) = 0.1767 + 0.1754 = 0.3521.$$

We could get this same result by summing the amount spent on newspapers and broadcast television, and dividing the total by 263,766.

Thus, more than a third of all advertising dollars are spent on these two media, a figure that should be of interest to both advertisers and the owners of the various media.

A table of probabilities, as in Example 8, sets up a **probability distribution**; that is, for each possible outcome of an experiment, a number, called the probability of that outcome, is assigned. This assignment may be done in any reasonable way (on an empirical basis, as in Example 8, or by theoretical reasoning, as in Section 7.3), provided that it satisfies the following conditions.

PROPERTIES OF PROBABILITY

Let S be a sample space consisting of n distinct outcomes, $s_1, s_2, \ldots, s_n$. An acceptable probability assignment consists of assigning to each outcome s_i a number p_i (the probability of s_i) according to these rules.

1. The probability of each outcome is a number between 0 and 1.

$$0 \leq p_1 \leq 1, \quad 0 \leq p_2 \leq 1, \ldots, \quad 0 \leq p_n \leq 1$$

2. The sum of the probabilities of all possible outcomes is 1.

$$p_1 + p_2 + p_3 + \cdots + p_n = 1$$

Probability distributions are discussed further in the next chapter.

EXAMPLE 9   **Clothing**

Susan is a college student who receives heavy sweaters from her aunt at the first sign of cold weather. Susan has determined that the probability that a sweater is

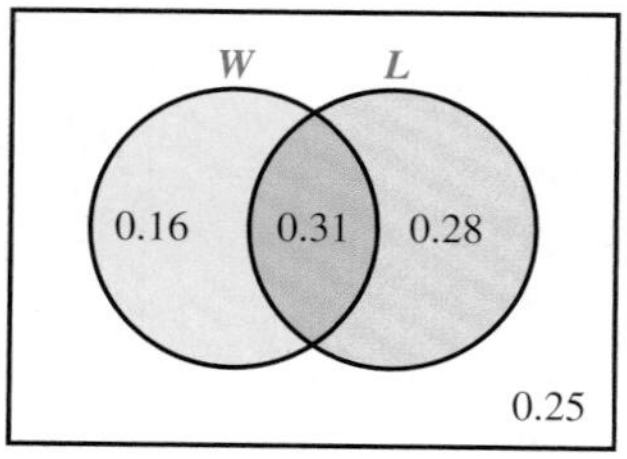

FIGURE 19

the wrong size is 0.47, the probability that it is a loud color is 0.59, and the probability that it is both the wrong size and a loud color is 0.31.

(a) Find the probability that the sweater is the correct size and not a loud color.

▶**Solution** Let W represent the event "wrong size," and L represent "loud color." Place the given information on a Venn diagram, starting with 0.31 in the intersection of the regions W and L (See Figure 19). As stated earlier, event W has probability 0.47. Since 0.31 has already been placed inside the intersection of W and L,

$$0.47 - 0.31 = 0.16$$

goes inside region W, but outside the intersection of W and L, that is, in the region $W \cap L'$. In the same way,

$$0.59 - 0.31 = 0.28$$

goes inside the region for L, and outside the overlap, that is, in the region $L \cap W'$.

Using regions W and L, the event we want is $W' \cap L'$. From the Venn diagram in Figure 19, the labeled regions have a total probability of

$$0.16 + 0.31 + 0.28 = 0.75.$$

Since the entire region of the Venn diagram must have probability 1, the region outside W and L, or $W' \cap L'$, has probability

$$1 - 0.75 = 0.25.$$

The probability is 0.25 that the sweater is the correct size and not a loud color.

(b) Find the probability that the sweater is the correct size or is not loud.

▶**Solution** The corresponding region, $W' \cup L'$, has probability

$$0.25 + 0.16 + 0.28 = 0.69.$$

▶ 7.4 Exercises

1. Define mutually exclusive events in your own words.

Decide whether the events in Exercises 2–7 are mutually exclusive.

2. Owning a dog and owning an MP3 player

3. Being a business major and being from Texas

4. Being retired and being 70 years old

5. Being a teenager and being 70 years old

6. Being one of the ten tallest people in the United States and being under 4 feet tall

7. Being male and being a nurse

Two dice are rolled. Find the probabilities of rolling the given sums.

8. **a.** 2 **b.** 4 **c.** 5 **d.** 6

9. **a.** 8 **b.** 9 **c.** 10 **d.** 13

10. a. 9 or more   **b.** Less than 7   **c.** Between 5 and 8 (exclusive)

11. a. Not more than 5   **b.** Not less than 8   **c.** Between 3 and 7 (exclusive)

Two dice are rolled. Find the probabilities of the following events.

12. The first die is 3 or the sum is 8.   **13.** The second die is 5 or the sum is 10.

14. Three unusual dice, A, B, and C, are constructed such that die A has the numbers 3, 3, 4, 4, 8, 8; die B has the numbers 1, 1, 5, 5, 9, 9; and die C has the numbers 2, 2, 6, 6, 7, 7.

    a. If dice A and B are rolled, find the probability that B beats A, that is, the number that appears on die B is greater than the number that appears on die A.

    b. If dice B and C are rolled, find the probability that C beats B.

    c. If dice A and C are rolled, find the probability that A beats C.

    d. Which die is better? Explain.

One card is drawn from an ordinary deck of 52 cards. Find the probabilities of drawing the following cards.

15 a. A 9 or 10

    b. A red card or a 3

    c. A 9 or a black 10

    d. A heart or a black card

    e. A face card or a diamond

16. a. Less than a 4 (count aces as ones)

    b. A diamond or a 7

    c. A black card or an ace

    d. A heart or a jack

    e. A red card or a face card

Pam Snow invites 13 relatives to a party: her mother, 2 aunts, 3 uncles, 2 brothers, 1 male cousin, and 4 female cousins. If the chances of any one guest arriving first are equally likely, find the probabilities that the first guest to arrive is as follows.

17. a. A brother or an uncle   **b.** A brother or a cousin   **c.** A brother or her mother

18. a. An uncle or a cousin   **b.** A male or a cousin   **c.** A female or a cousin

The numbers 1, 2, 3, 4, and 5 are written on slips of paper, and 2 slips are drawn at random one at a time without replacement. Find the probabilities in Exercises 19 and 20.

19. a. The sum of the numbers is 9.

    b. The sum of the numbers is 5 or less.

    c. The first number is 2 or the sum is 6.

20. a. Both numbers are even.

    b. One of the numbers is even or greater than 3.

    c. The sum is 5 or the second number is 2.

Use Venn diagrams to work Exercises 21 and 22.

21. Suppose $P(E) = 0.26$, $P(F) = 0.41$, and $P(E \cap F) = 0.16$. Find the following.

    a. $P(E \cup F)$ **b.** $P(E' \cap F)$ **c.** $P(E \cap F')$ **d.** $P(E' \cup F')$

22. Let $P(Z) = 0.42$, $P(Y) = 0.35$, and $P(Z \cup Y) = 0.59$. Find each probability.

    a. $P(Z' \cap Y')$ **b.** $P(Z' \cup Y')$ **c.** $P(Z' \cup Y)$ **d.** $P(Z \cap Y')$

23. Define what is meant by odds.

A single fair die is rolled. Find the odds in favor of getting the results in Exercises 24–27.

24. 3   **25.** 4, 5, or 6   **26.** 2, 3, 4, or 5   **27.** Some number less than 6

28. A marble is drawn from a box containing 3 yellow, 4 white, and 11 blue marbles. Find the odds in favor of drawing the following.

    a. A yellow marble   **b.** A blue marble   **c.** A white marble

29. Find the odds of *not* drawing a white marble in Exercise 28.

30. Two dice are rolled. Find the odds of rolling a 7 or 11.

31. In the "Ask Marilyn" column of *Parade* magazine, a reader wrote about the following game: You and I each roll a die. If your die is higher than mine, you win. Otherwise, I win. The reader thought that the probability that each player wins is 1/2. Is this correct? If not, what is the probability that each player wins?*

32. On page 134 of Roger Staubach's autobiography, *First Down, Lifetime to Go*, Staubach makes the following statement regarding his experience in Vietnam:[†]

> "Odds against a direct hit are very low but when your life is in danger, you don't worry too much about the odds."

Is this wording consistent with our definition of odds, for and against? How could it have been said so as to be technically correct?

33. The following table gives the odds that a particular event will occur.[‡] Convert each odd to the probability that the event will occur.

Event	Odds for the Event
You will eat out today.	1 to 2
The next bottled water you buy will be nothing more than tap water.	1 to 4
The Earth will be struck by a huge meteor during your lifetime.	1 to 9000
You will go to Disney World this year.	1 to 9
You'll regain weight you lost by dieting.	9 to 10

Which of Exercises 34–41 are examples of empirical probability?

34. The probability of heads on 5 consecutive tosses of a coin

35. The probability that a freshman entering college will graduate with a degree

36. The probability that a person is allergic to penicillin

37. The probability of drawing an ace from a standard deck of 52 cards

38. The probability that a person will get lung cancer from smoking cigarettes

39. A weather forecast that predicts a 70% chance of rain tomorrow

40. A gambler's claim that on a roll of a fair die, $P(\text{even}) = 1/2$

41. A surgeon's prediction that a patient has a 90% chance of a full recovery

42. What is a probability distribution?

An experiment is conducted for which the sample space is $S = \{s_1, s_2, s_3, s_4, s_5\}$. Which of the probability assignments in Exercises 43–48 is possible for this experiment? If an assignment is not possible, tell why.

43.

Outcomes	s_1	s_2	s_3	s_4	s_5
Probabilities	0.09	0.32	0.21	0.25	0.13

*Source: *Parade* magazine, Nov. 6, 1994, p. 11. © 1994 Marilyn vos Savant. Initially published in *Parade* magazine. All rights reserved.
[†]Staubach, Roger, *First Down, Lifetime to Go,* Word Incorporated, Dallas, 1976.
[‡]The Forum for Investor Advice; Krantz, Les, *What the Odds Are,* Harper Perennial, 1992; and Laudan, Larry, *Danger Ahead: The Risks You Really Face on Life's Highway,* John Wiley & Sons, New York, 1997.

44.

Outcomes	s_1	s_2	s_3	s_4	s_5
Probabilities	0.92	0.03	0	0.02	0.03

45.

Outcomes	s_1	s_2	s_3	s_4	s_5
Probabilities	1/3	1/4	1/6	1/8	1/10

46.

Outcomes	s_1	s_2	s_3	s_4	s_5
Probabilities	1/5	1/3	1/4	1/5	1/10

47.

Outcomes	s_1	s_2	s_3	s_4	s_5
Probabilities	0.64	−0.08	0.30	0.12	0.02

48.

Outcomes	s_1	s_2	s_3	s_4	s_5
Probabilities	0.05	0.35	0.5	0.2	−0.3

One way to solve a probability problem is to repeat the experiment many times, keeping track of the results. Then the probability can be approximated using the basic definition of the probability of an event E: $P(E) = n(E)/n(S)$, where E occurs $n(E)$ times out of $n(S)$ trials of an experiment. This is called the Monte Carlo method of finding probabilities. If physically repeating the experiment is too tedious, it may be simulated using a random-number generator, available on most computers and scientific or graphing calculators. To simulate a coin toss or the roll of a die on the TI-83/84 Plus, change the setting to fixed decimal mode with 0 digits displayed, and enter `rand` *or* `rand*6+.5`, *respectively. For a coin toss, interpret 0 as a head and 1 as a tail. In either case, the* `ENTER` *key can be pressed repeatedly to perform multiple simulations.*

49. Suppose two dice are rolled. Use the Monte Carlo method with at least 50 repetitions to approximate the following probabilities. Compare with the results of Exercise 11.

a. P(the sum is not more than 5) **b.** P(the sum is not less than 8)

50. Suppose two dice are rolled. Use the Monte Carlo method with at least 50 repetitions to approximate the following probabilities. Compare with the results of Exercise 10.

a. P(the sum is 9 or more) **b.** P(the sum is less than 7)

51. Suppose three dice are rolled. Use the Monte Carlo method with at least 100 repetitions to approximate the following probabilities.

a. P(the sum is 5 or less) **b.** P(neither a 1 nor a 6 is rolled)

52. Suppose a coin is tossed 5 times. Use the Monte Carlo method with at least 50 repetitions to approximate the following probabilities.

a. P(exactly 4 heads) **b.** P(2 heads and 3 tails)

53. The following description of the classic "Linda problem" appeared in the *New Yorker*[*]: "In this experiment, subjects are told, 'Linda is thirty-one years old, single, outspoken, and very bright. She majored in philosophy. As a student, she was deeply concerned with issues of discrimination and social justice and also participated in

*Menand, Louis, "Everybody's an Expert: Putting Predictions to the Test," *New Yorker*, Dec. 5, 2005, pp. 98–101.

antinuclear demonstrations.' They are then asked to rank the probability of several possible descriptions of Linda today. Two of them are 'bank teller' and 'bank teller and active in the feminist movement.'" Many people rank the second event as more likely. Explain why this violates basic concepts of probability.

54. You are given $P(A \cup B) = 0.7$ and $P(A \cup B') = 0.9$. Determine $P(A)$.* (Choose one of the following.)

   a. 0.2   **b.** 0.3   **c.** 0.4   **d.** 0.6   **e.** 0.8

▶ Applications

BUSINESS AND ECONOMICS

55. *Defective Merchandise* Suppose that 8% of a certain batch of calculators have a defective case, and that 11% have defective batteries. Also, 3% have both a defective case and defective batteries. A calculator is selected from the batch at random. Find the probability that the calculator has a good case and good batteries.

56. *Credit Charges* The table shows the probabilities of a person accumulating specific amounts of credit card charges over a 12-month period. Find the probabilities that a person's total charges during the period are the following.

   a. $500 or more   **b.** Less than $1000

   c. $500 to $2999   **d.** $3000 or more

Amount Spent	Probability
Below $10	0.02
$10–$24.99	0.05
$25–$49.99	0.11
$50–$74.99	0.13
$75–$99.99	0.14
$100–$199.99	0.22
$200–$349.99	0.18
$350–$499.99	0.12
$500 or more	0.03

Charges	Probability
Under $100	0.21
$100–$499	0.17
$500–$999	0.16
$1000–$1999	0.15
$2000–$2999	0.12
$3000–$4999	0.08
$5000–$9999	0.07
$10,000 or more	0.04

Customer Purchases The following table shows the probability that a customer of a department store will make a purchase in the indicated range.

Find the probabilities that a customer makes a purchase in the following ranges.

57. **a.** Less than $25   **b.** More than $24.99
   c. $50 to $199.99

58. **a.** Less than $350   **b.** $75 or more
   c. $200 or more

59. *Profit* The probability that a company will make a profit this year is 0.74. Find the odds against the company making a profit.

LIFE SCIENCES

60. *Body Types* A study on body types gave the following results: 45% were short; 25% were short and overweight; and 24% were tall and not overweight. Find the probabilities that a person is the following.

   a. Overweight

   b. Short, but not overweight

   c. Tall and overweight

*Problem 3 from the 2005 Sample Exam P of the Education and Examination Committee of the Society of Actuaries. Reprinted by permission of the Society of Actuaries.

61. *Color Blindness* Color blindness is an inherited characteristic that is more common in males than in females. If M represents male and C represents red-green color blindness, we use the relative frequencies of the incidences of males and red-green color blindness as probabilities to get

$$P(C) = 0.039, P(M \cap C) = 0.035, P(M \cup C) = 0.491.*$$

Find the following probabilities.

a. $P(C')$ **b.** $P(M)$ **c.** $P(M')$

d. $P(M' \cap C')$ **e.** $P(C \cap M')$ **f.** $P(C \cup M')$

62. *Genetics* Gregor Mendel, an Austrian monk, was the first to use probability in the study of genetics. In an effort to understand the mechanism of character transmittal from one generation to the next in plants, he counted the number of occurrences of various characteristics. Mendel found that the flower color in certain pea plants obeyed this scheme:

Pure red crossed with pure white produces red.

From its parents, the red offspring received genes for both red (R) and white (W), but in this case red is *dominant* and white *recessive*, so the offspring exhibits the color red. However, the offspring still carries both genes, and when two such offspring are crossed, several things can happen in the third generation. The table below, which is called a *Punnet square*, shows the equally likely outcomes.

		Second Parent	
		R	*W*
First Parent	*R*	RR	RW
	W	WR	WW

Use the fact that red is dominant over white to find the following. Assume that there are an equal number of red and white genes in the population.

a. P(a flower is red)   **b.** P(a flower is white)

63. *Genetics* Mendel found no dominance in snapdragons, with one red gene and one white gene producing pink-flowered offspring. These second-generation pinks, how-

ever, still carry one red and one white gene, and when they are crossed, the next generation still yields the Punnet square from Exercise 62. Find each probability.

a. P(red)   **b.** P(pink)   **c.** P(white)

(Mendel verified these probability ratios experimentally and did the same for many characteristics other than flower color. His work, published in 1866, was not recognized until 1890.)

64. *Genetics* In most animals and plants, it is very unusual for the number of main parts of the organism (such as arms, legs, toes, or flower petals) to vary from generation to generation. Some species, however, have *meristic variability,* in which the number of certain body parts varies from generation to generation. One researcher studied the front feet of certain guinea pigs and produced the following probabilities.[†]

$$P(\text{only four toes, all perfect}) = 0.77$$
$$P(\text{one imperfect toe and four good ones}) = 0.13$$
$$P(\text{exactly five good toes}) = 0.10$$

Find the probability of each event.

a. No more than four good toes

b. Five toes, whether perfect or not

65. *Doctor Visit* The probability that a visit to a primary care physician's (PCP) office results in neither lab work nor referral to a specialist is 35%. Of those coming to a PCP's office, 30% are referred to specialists and 40% require lab work. Determine the probability that a visit to a PCP's office results in both lab work and referral to a specialist.[‡] (Choose one of the following. *Hint:* Use the union rule for probability.)

a. 0.05   **b.** 0.12   **c.** 0.18

d. 0.25   **e.** 0.35

66. *Shoulder Injuries* Among a large group of patients recovering from shoulder injuries, it is found that 22% visit both a physical therapist and a chiropractor, whereas 12% visit neither of these. The probability that a patient visits a chiropractor exceeds by 0.14 the probability that a patient visits a physical therapist. Determine the probability that a randomly chosen member of this group visits a physical

*The probabilities of a person being male or female are from *The World Almanac and Book of Facts,* 1995. The probabilities of a male and female being color-blind are from *Parsons' Diseases of the Eye* (18th ed.) by Stephen J. H. Miller, Churchill Livingstone, 1990, p. 269. This reference gives a range of 3 to 4% for the probability of gross color blindness in men; we used the midpoint of this range.
†Wright, J. R., Data from "An Analysis of Variability in Guinea Pigs," *Genetics,* Vol. 19, pp. 506–536.
‡Problem 2 from the 2005 Sample Exam P of the *Education and Examination Committee of the Society of Actuaries.* Reprinted by permission of the Society of Actuaries.

therapist.* (Choose one of the following. *Hint:* Use the union rule for probability, and let $x = P$(patient visits a physical therapist).)

a. 0.26   **b.** 0.38   **c.** 0.40

d. 0.48   **e.** 0.62

67. *Health Plan* An insurer offers a health plan to the employees of a large company. As part of this plan, the individual employees may choose exactly two of the supplementary coverages A, B, and C, or they may choose no supplementary coverage. The proportions of the company's employees that choose coverages A, B, and C are 1/4, 1/3, and 5/12, respectively. Determine the probability that a randomly chosen employee will choose no supplementary coverage.[†] (Choose one of the following. *Hint:* Draw a Venn diagram with three sets, and let $x = P(A \cap B)$. Use the fact that 4 of the 8 regions in the Venn diagram have a probability of 0.)

a. 0   **b.** 47/144   **c.** 1/2

d. 97/144   **e.** 7/9

SOCIAL SCIENCES

---

68. *Presidential Candidates* In 2002, *The New York Times* columnist William Safire gave the following odds against various prominent Democrats receiving their party's presidential nomination in 2004.[‡]

> Al Gore: 2 to 1
> Tom Daschle: 4 to 1
> John Kerry: 4 to 1
> Chris Dodd: 4 to 1
> Joe Lieberman: 5 to 1
> Joe Biden: 5 to 1
> Pat Leahy: 6 to 1
> Russell Feingold: 8 to 1
> John Edwards: 9 to 1
> Dick Gephardt: 15 to 1

John Allen Paulos observed that there is something wrong with those odds.[§] Translate these odds into probabilities of winning the nomination, and then explain why these are not possible.

69. *Earnings* The following data were gathered for 130 adult U.S. workers: 55 were women; 3 women earned more than

$40,000; and 62 men earned $40,000 or less. Find the probability that an individual is

a. a woman earning $40,000 or less;

b. a man earning more than $40,000;

c. a man or is earning more than $40,000;

d. a woman or is earning $40,000 or less.

70. *Expenditures for Music* A survey of 100 people about their music expenditures gave the following information: 38 bought rock music; 20 were teenagers who bought rock music; and 26 were teenagers. Find the probabilities that a person is

a. a teenager who buys nonrock music;

b. someone who buys rock music or is a teenager;

c. not a teenager;

d. not a teenager, but a buyer of rock music.

71. *Refugees* In a refugee camp in southern Mexico, it was found that 90% of the refugees came to escape political oppression, 80% came to escape abject poverty, and 70% came to escape both. What is the probability that a refugee in the camp was not poor nor seeking political asylum?

72. *Community Activities* At the first meeting of a committee to plan a local Lunar New Year celebration, the persons attending are 3 Chinese men, 4 Chinese women, 3 Vietnamese women, 2 Vietnamese men, 4 Korean women, and 2 Korean men. A chairperson is selected at random. Find the probabilities that the chairperson is the following.

a. Chinese

b. Korean or a woman

c. A man or Vietnamese

d. Chinese or Vietnamese

e. Korean and a woman

73. *Elections* If the odds that a given candidate will win an election are 3 to 2, what is the probability that the candidate will lose?

74. *Military* There were 212,156 female military personnel in 2004 in various ranks and military branches, as listed in the table on the next page.[‖]

---

*Problem 8 from the 2005 Sample Exam P of the *Education and Examination Committee of the Society of Actuaries.* Reprinted by permission of the Society of Actuaries.

[†]Problem 15 from the 2005 Sample Exam P of the *Education and Examination Committee of the Society of Actuaries.* Reprinted by permission of the Society of Actuaries.

[‡]Safire, William, "The Henry Poll," *The New York Times*, June 25, 2001, p. A17.

[§]http://abcnews.go.com/sections/scitech/DailyNews/safire010628.html.

[‖]*Selected Manpower Statistics, Fiscal Year 2004*, U.S. Department of Defense, p. 31.

	Army (A)	Air Force (B)	Navy (C)	Marines (D)
Officers (O)	12,309	13,596	8111	1096
Enlisted (E)	60,395	59,436	45,415	9683
Cadets & Midshipmen (M)	639	754	722	0

a. Convert the numbers in the table to probabilities.

b. Find the probability that a randomly selected woman is in the Army.

c. Find the probability that a randomly selected woman is an officer in the Navy or Marine Corps.

d. $P(A \cup B)$

e. $P(E \cup (C \cup D))$

75. *Perceptions of Threat* Research has been carried out to measure the amount of intolerance that citizens of Russia have for left-wing Communists and right-wing Fascists, as indicated in the first table below. Note that the numbers are given as percents and each row sums to 100 (except for rounding).*

a. Find the probability that a randomly chosen citizen of Russia would be somewhat or extremely intolerant of right-wing Fascists.

b. Find the probability that a randomly chosen citizen of Russia would be completely tolerant of left-wing Communists.

c. Compare your answers to parts a and b and provide possible reasons for these numbers.

76. *Perceptions of Threat* Research has been carried out to measure the amount of intolerance that U.S. citizens have for left-wing Communists and right-wing Fascists, as indicated in the second table below. Note that the numbers are given as percents and each row sums to 100 (except for rounding).*

a. Find the probability that a randomly chosen U.S. citizen would have at least some intolerance of right-wing Fascists.

b. Find the probability that a randomly chosen U.S. citizen would have at least some intolerance of left-wing Communists.

c. Compare your answers to parts a and b and provide possible reasons for these numbers.

d. Compare these answers to the answers to Exercise 75.

Russia	None at All	Don't Know	Not Very Much	Somewhat	Extremely
Left-Wing Communists	47.8	6.7	31.0	10.5	4.1
Right-Wing Fascists	3.0	3.2	7.1	27.1	59.5

United States	None at All	Don't Know	Not Very Much	Somewhat	Extremely
Left-Wing Communists	13.0	2.7	33.0	34.2	17.1
Right-Wing Fascists	10.1	3.3	20.7	43.1	22.9

*Gibson, J. L., "Putting Up with Fellow Russians: An Analysis of Political Tolerance in the Fledgling Russian Democracy," *Political Research Quarterly*, Vol. 51, No. 1, Mar. 1998, pp. 37–68.

77. *Weather* If the odds that it will rain are 4 to 7, what is the probability of rain? Interpret your answer.

78. *Olympics* In recent winter Olympics, each part of the women's figure skating program has 12 judges, but the scores of only 9 of the judges are randomly selected for the final results.* As we will see in the next chapter, there are 220 possible ways for the 9 judges whose scores are counted to be selected. *The New York Times* examined those 220 possibilities for the short program in the 2006 Olympics, based on the published scores of the judges, and listed what the results would have been for each, as shown below.

a. The winner of the short program was Sasha Cohen. For a random combination of 9 judges, what is the probability of that outcome?

b. The second place finisher in the short program was Irina Slutskaya. For a random combination of 9 judges, what is the probability of that outcome?

c. The third place finisher in the short program was Shizuka Arakawa. For a random combination of 9 judges, what is the probability of that outcome? Do not include outcomes that include a tie.

Outcome	1. Slutskaya 2. Cohen 3. Arakawa	1. Slutskaya 2. Arakawa 3. Cohen	1. Slutskaya 2, 3. Arakawa and Cohen tied	1. Cohen 2. Slutskaya 3. Arakawa	1. Cohen 2. Arakawa 3. Slutskaya
Number of Possible Judging Combinations	92	33	3	67	25

7.5 Conditional Probability; Independent Events

? THINK ABOUT IT

What is the probability that a broker who uses research picks stocks that go up?

The training manager for a large brokerage firm has noticed that some of the firm's stockbrokers use the firm's research advice, while other brokers tend to follow their own feelings of which stocks will go up. To see whether the research department performs better than brokers' feelings, the manager surveyed 100 brokers, with results as shown in the following table.

	Picked Stocks That Went Up (A)	Didn't Pick Stocks That Went Up (A')	Totals
Used Research (B)	30	15	45
Didn't Use Research (B')	30	25	55
Totals	60	40	100

The New York Times, Feb. 23, 2006, p. D3.

Letting A represent the event "picked stocks that went up," and letting B represent the event "used research," we can find the following probabilities.

$$P(A) = \frac{60}{100} = 0.6 \qquad P(A') = \frac{40}{100} = 0.4$$

$$P(B) = \frac{45}{100} = 0.45 \qquad P(B') = \frac{55}{100} = 0.55$$

To answer the question asked at the beginning of this section, suppose we want to find the probability that a broker using research will pick stocks that go up. From the table, of the 45 brokers who use research, 30 picked stocks that went up, with

$$P(\text{broker who uses research picks stocks that go up}) = \frac{30}{45} \approx 0.6667.$$

This is a different number than the probability that a broker picks stocks that go up, 0.6, since we have additional information (the broker uses research) that has *reduced the sample space*. It other words, we found the probability that a broker picks stocks that go up, A, given the additional information that the broker uses research, B. This is called the *conditional probability* of event A, given that event B has occurred, written $P(A|B)$. ($P(A|B)$ may also be read as "the probability of A given B.")

In the example above,

$$P(A|B) = \frac{30}{45},$$

which can be written as

$$P(A|B) = \frac{30/100}{45/100} = \frac{P(A \cap B)}{P(B)},$$

where $P(A \cap B)$ represents, as usual, the probability that both A and B will occur.

To generalize this result, assume that E and F are two events for a particular experiment, and that all events in the sample space S are equally likely. Using the fundamental principle of probability,

$$P(F) = \frac{n(F)}{n(S)} \qquad \text{and} \qquad P(E \cap F) = \frac{n(E \cap F)}{n(S)}.$$

We now want $P(E|F)$, the probability that E occurs given that F has occurred. Since we assume F has occurred, reduce the sample space to F: look only at the elements inside F. See Figure 20. Of these $n(F)$ elements, there are $n(E \cap F)$ elements where E also occurs. This makes

$$P(E|F) = \frac{n(E \cap F)}{n(F)}.$$

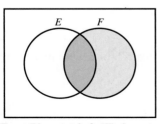

Event F has a total of $n(F)$ elements.

FIGURE 20

Divide numerator and denominator by $n(S)$ to get

$$P(E|F) = \frac{n(E \cap F)/n(S)}{n(F)/n(S)} = \frac{P(E \cap F)}{P(F)}.$$

This last result motivates the definition of conditional probability.

CONDITIONAL PROBABILITY

The **conditional probability** of event E given event F, written $P(E|F)$, is

$$P(E|F) = \frac{P(E \cap F)}{P(F)}, \quad \text{where } P(F) \neq 0.$$

This definition tells us that, for equally likely outcomes, conditional probability is found by *reducing the sample space to event F*, and then finding the number of outcomes in F that are also in event E. Thus,

$$P(E|F) = \frac{n(E \cap F)}{n(F)}.$$

Although the definition of conditional probability was motivated by an example with equally likely outcomes, it is valid in all cases. For an intuitive explanation, think of the formula as giving the probability that both E and F occur compared with the entire probability of F.

EXAMPLE 1   **Stocks**

Use the information given in the chart at the beginning of this section to find the following probabilities.

(a) $P(B|A)$

▶**Solution** This represents the probability that the broker used research, given that the broker picked stocks that went up. Reduce the sample space to A. Then find $n(A \cap B)$ and $n(A)$.

$$P(B|A) = \frac{P(B \cap A)}{P(A)} = \frac{n(A \cap B)}{n(A)} = \frac{30}{60} = \frac{1}{2}$$

If a broker picked stocks that went up, then the probability is $1/2$ that the broker used research.

(b) $P(A'|B)$

▶**Solution** In words, this is the probability that a broker picks stocks that do not go up, even though he used research.

$$P(A'|B) = \frac{n(A' \cap B)}{n(B)} = \frac{15}{45} = \frac{1}{3}$$

(c) $P(B'|A')$

▶**Solution** Here, we want the probability that a broker who picked stocks that did not go up did not use research.

$$P(B'|A') = \frac{n(B' \cap A')}{n(A')} = \frac{25}{40} = \frac{5}{8}$$

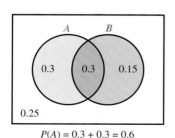

$P(A) = 0.3 + 0.3 = 0.6$

FIGURE 21

Venn diagrams are useful for illustrating problems in conditional probability. A Venn diagram for Example 1, in which the probabilities are used to indicate the number in the set defined by each region, is shown in Figure 21. In the diagram,

$P(B|A)$ is found by reducing the sample space to just set A. Then $P(B|A)$ is the ratio of the number in that part of set B that is also in A to the number in set A, or $0.3/0.6 = 0.5$.

EXAMPLE 2 **Conditional Probabilities**
Given $P(E) = 0.4$, $P(F) = 0.5$, and $P(E \cup F) = 0.7$, find $P(E|F)$.

▶**Solution** Find $P(E \cap F)$ first. By the union rule,

$$P(E \cup F) = P(E) + P(F) - P(E \cap F)$$
$$0.7 = 0.4 + 0.5 - P(E \cap F)$$
$$P(E \cap F) = 0.2.$$

$P(E|F)$ is the ratio of the probability of that part of E that is in F to the probability of F, or

$$P(E|F) = \frac{P(E \cap F)}{P(F)} = \frac{0.2}{0.5} = \frac{2}{5}.$$

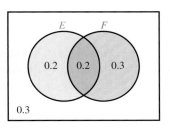

FIGURE 22

The Venn diagram in Figure 22 illustrates Example 2.

EXAMPLE 3 **Tossing Coins**
Two fair coins were tossed, and it is known that at least one was a head. Find the probability that both were heads.

▶**Solution** At first glance the answer to this question appears to be $1/2$. Using mathematics, however, we will see otherwise. The sample space has four equally likely outcomes, $S = \{hh, ht, th, tt\}$. Define two events:

$$E_1 = \text{at least 1 head} = \{hh, ht, th\},$$

and

$$E_2 = \text{2 heads} = \{hh\}.$$

Since there are four equally likely outcomes, $P(E_1) = 3/4$. Also, $P(E_1 \cap E_2) = 1/4$. We want the probability that both were heads, given that at least one was a head; that is, we want to find $P(E_2|E_1)$. Because of the condition that at least one coin was a head, the reduced sample space is

$$\{hh, ht, th\}.$$

Since only one outcome in this reduced sample space is 2 heads,

$$P(E_2|E_1) = \frac{1}{3}.$$

Alternatively, use the definition given above.

$$P(E_2|E_1) = \frac{P(E_2 \cap E_1)}{P(E_1)} = \frac{1/4}{3/4} = \frac{1}{3}$$

EXAMPLE 4 **Playing Cards**
Two cards are drawn from a standard deck, one after another without replacement. Find the probability that the second card is red, given that the first card is red.

▶**Solution** According to the conditional probability formula,

$$P(\text{second card is red} \mid \text{first card is red})$$
$$= \frac{P(\text{second card is red and the first card is red})}{P(\text{first card is red})}.$$

We will soon see how to compute probabilities such as the one in the numerator. But there is a much simpler way to calculate this conditional probability. We only need to observe that with one red card gone, there are 51 cards left, 25 of which are red, so

$$P(\text{second card is red} \mid \text{first card is red}) = \frac{25}{51}.$$

It is important not to confuse $P(A \mid B)$ with $P(B \mid A)$. For example, in a criminal trial, a prosecutor may point out to the jury that the probability of the defendant's DNA profile matching that of a sample taken at the scene of the crime, given that the defendant is innocent, $P(D \mid I)$, is very small. What the jury must decide, however, is the probability that the defendant is innocent, given that the defendant's DNA profile matches the sample, $P(I \mid D)$. Confusing the two is an error sometimes called "the prosecutor's fallacy," and the 1990 conviction of a rape suspect in England was overturned by a panel of judges, who ordered a retrial, because the fallacy made the original trial unfair.*

In the next section, we will see how to compute $P(A \mid B)$ when we know $P(B \mid A)$.

Product Rule   If $P(E) \neq 0$ and $P(F) \neq 0$, then the definition of conditional probability shows that

$$P(E \mid F) = \frac{P(E \cap F)}{P(F)} \qquad \text{and} \qquad P(F \mid E) = \frac{P(F \cap E)}{P(E)}.$$

Using the fact that $P(E \cap F) = P(F \cap E)$, and solving each of these equations for $P(E \cap F)$, we obtain the following rule.

PRODUCT RULE OF PROBABILITY

If E and F are events, then $P(E \cap F)$ may be found by either of these formulas.

$$P(E \cap F) = P(F) \cdot P(E \mid F) \qquad \text{or} \qquad P(E \cap F) = P(E) \cdot P(F \mid E)$$

The product rule gives a method for finding the probability that events E and F both occur, as illustrated by the next few examples.

EXAMPLE 5   **Business Majors**

In a class with 2/5 women and 3/5 men, 25% of the women are business majors. Find the probability that a student chosen from the class at random is a female business major.

*Pringle, David, "Who's the DNA Fingerprinting Pointing At?" *New Scientist*, Jan. 29, 1994, pp. 51–52.

▶**Solution** Let B and W represent the events "business major" and "woman," respectively. We want to find $P(B \cap W)$. By the product rule,

$$P(B \cap W) = P(W) \cdot P(B|W).$$

Using the given information, $P(W) = 2/5 = 0.4$ and $P(B|W) = 0.25$. Thus,

$$P(B \cap W) = 0.4(0.25) = 0.10.$$

The next examples show how a tree diagram is used with the product rule to find the probability of a sequence of events.

EXAMPLE 6 **Advertising**
A company needs to hire a new director of advertising. It has decided to try to hire either person A or B, who are assistant advertising directors for its major competitor. To decide between A and B, the company does research on the campaigns managed by either A or B (no campaign is managed by both), and finds that A is in charge of twice as many advertising campaigns as B. Also, A's campaigns have satisfactory results 3 out of 4 times, while B's campaigns have satisfactory results only 2 out of 5 times. Suppose one of the competitor's advertising campaigns (managed by A or B) is selected randomly.

We can represent this situation schematically as follows. Let A denote the event "person A does the job" and B the event "person B does the job." Notice that in this situation, A and B are complementary events, that is, $A = B'$, and $A \cup B$ is the sample space. Let S be the event "satisfactory results" and U the event "unsatisfactory results." Then the given information can be summarized in the tree diagram in Figure 23. Since A does twice as many jobs as B, we have $P(A) = 2/3$ and $P(B) = 1/3$, as noted on the first-stage branches of the tree. When A does a job, the probability of satisfactory results is 3/4, and of unsatisfactory results, 1/4, as noted on the second-stage branches. Similarly, the probabilities when B does the job are noted on the remaining second-stage branches. The composite branches labeled 1–4 represent the four mutually exclusive possibilities for the running and outcome of the selected campaign.

(a) Find the probability that A is in charge of the selected campaign and that it produces satisfactory results.

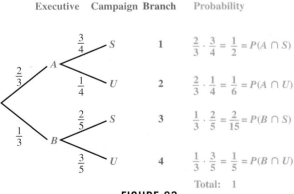

FIGURE 23

►**Solution** We are asked to find $P(A \cap S)$. We know that when A does the job, the probability of success is 3/4, that is, $P(S|A) = 3/4$. Hence, by the product rule,

$$P(A \cap S) = P(A) \cdot P(S|A) = \frac{2}{3} \cdot \frac{3}{4} = \frac{1}{2}.$$

The event $A \cap S$ is represented by branch 1 of the tree, and as we have just seen, its probability is the product of the probabilities of the pieces that make up that branch.

(b) Find the probability that B runs the campaign and that it produces satisfactory results.

►**Solution** We must find $P(B \cap S)$. The event is represented by branch 3 of the tree and, as before, its probability is the product of the probabilities of the pieces of that branch:

$$P(B \cap S) = P(B) \cdot P(S|B) = \frac{1}{3} \cdot \frac{2}{5} = \frac{2}{15}.$$

(c) What is the probability that the selected campaign is satisfactory?

►**Solution** The event S is the union of the mutually exclusive events $A \cap S$ and $B \cap S$, which are represented by branches 1 and 3 of the diagram. By the union rule,

$$P(S) = P(A \cap S) + P(B \cap S) = \frac{1}{2} + \frac{2}{15} = \frac{19}{30}.$$

Thus, the probability of an event that appears on several branches is the sum of the probabilities of each of these branches.

(d) What is the probability that the selected campaign is unsatisfactory?

►**Solution** $P(U)$ can be read from branches 2 and 4 of the tree.

$$(A \cap U) + (B \cap U)$$

$$P(U) = \frac{1}{6} + \frac{1}{5} = \frac{11}{30}$$

Alternatively, since U is the complement of S,

$$P(U) = 1 - P(S) = 1 - \frac{19}{30} = \frac{11}{30}.$$

EXAMPLE 7   **Environmental Inspections**
The Environmental Protection Agency is considering inspecting 6 plants for environmental compliance: 3 in Chicago, 2 in Los Angeles, and 1 in New York. Due to a lack of inspectors, they decide to inspect two plants selected at random, one this month and one next month, with each plant equally likely to be selected, but no plant selected twice. What is the probability that 1 Chicago plant and 1 Los Angeles plant are selected?

►**Solution** A tree diagram showing the various possible outcomes is given in Figure 24. In this diagram, the events of inspecting a plant in Chicago, Los Angeles, and New York are represented by C, LA, and NY, respectively. For the first inspection, $P(C \text{ first}) = 3/6 = 1/2$ because 3 of the 6 plants are in Chicago, and

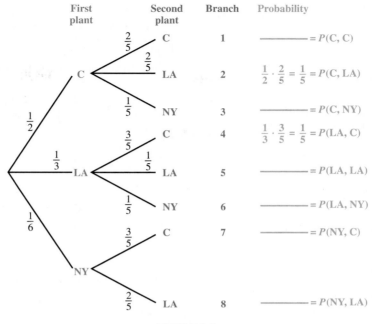

First plant | Second plant | Branch | Probability

$\frac{2}{5}$ C 1 ——— $= P(C, C)$

$\frac{2}{5}$ LA 2 $\frac{1}{2} \cdot \frac{2}{5} = \frac{1}{5} = P(C, LA)$

$\frac{1}{5}$ NY 3 ——— $= P(C, NY)$

$\frac{3}{5}$ C 4 $\frac{1}{3} \cdot \frac{3}{5} = \frac{1}{5} = P(LA, C)$

$\frac{1}{5}$ LA 5 ——— $= P(LA, LA)$

$\frac{1}{5}$ NY 6 ——— $= P(LA, NY)$

$\frac{3}{5}$ C 7 ——— $= P(NY, C)$

$\frac{2}{5}$ LA 8 ——— $= P(NY, LA)$

FIGURE 24

all plants are equally likely to be selected. For the second inspection, $P(\text{LA second} \mid \text{C first}) = 2/5$. One plant has been removed, leaving 5, of which 2 are in Los Angeles.

We want to find the probability of selecting exactly 1 Chicago plant and 1 Los Angeles plant. This event can occur in two ways: inspecting Chicago this month and Los Angeles next month (branch 2 of the tree diagram), or inspecting Los Angeles this month and Chicago next month (branch 4). For branch 2,

$$P(\text{C first}) \cdot P(\text{LA second} \mid \text{C first}) = \frac{1}{2} \cdot \frac{2}{5} = \frac{1}{5}.$$

For branch 4, where Los Angeles is inspected first,

$$P(\text{LA first}) \cdot P(\text{C second} \mid \text{LA first}) = \frac{1}{3} \cdot \frac{3}{5} = \frac{1}{5}.$$

Since the two events are mutually exclusive, the final probability is the sum of these two probabilities.

$$\begin{aligned} P(1\,\text{C}, 1\,\text{LA}) &= P(\text{C first}) \cdot P(\text{LA second} \mid \text{C first}) \\ &\quad + P(\text{LA first}) \cdot P(\text{C second} \mid \text{LA first}) \\ &= \frac{2}{5} \end{aligned}$$

The product rule is often used with *stochastic processes*, which are mathematical models that evolve over time in a probabilistic manner. For example, selecting factories at random for inspection is such a process, in which the probabilities change with each successive selection.

▶**FOR REVIEW**

You may wish to refer to the picture of a deck of cards shown in Figure 17 (Section 7.3) and the description accompanying it.

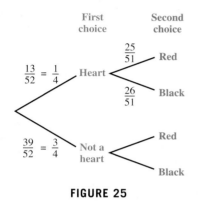

FIGURE 25

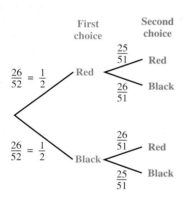

FIGURE 26

| EXAMPLE 8 | **Playing Cards** |

Two cards are drawn from a standard deck, one after another without replacement.

(a) Find the probability that the first card is a heart and the second card is red.

▶**Solution** Start with the tree diagram in Figure 25. On the first draw, since there are 13 hearts among the 52 cards, the probability of drawing a heart is $13/52 = 1/4$. On the second draw, since a (red) heart has been drawn already, there are 25 red cards in the remaining 51 cards. Thus, the probability of drawing a red card on the second draw, given that the first is a heart, is $25/51$. By the product rule of probability,

$$P(\text{heart first and red second})$$
$$= P(\text{heart first}) \cdot P(\text{red second}|\text{heart first})$$
$$= \frac{1}{4} \cdot \frac{25}{51} = \frac{25}{204} \approx 0.123.$$

(b) Find the probability that the second card is red.

▶**Solution** To solve this, we need to fill out the bottom branch of the tree diagram in Figure 25. Unfortunately, if the first card is not a heart, it is not clear how to find the probability that the second card is red, because it depends upon whether the first card is red or black. One way to solve this problem would be to divide the bottom branch into two separate branches: diamond and black card (club or spade). There is a simpler way, however, since we don't care whether or not the first card is a heart, as we did in part (a). Instead, we'll consider whether the first card is red or black, and then do the same for the second card. The result, with the corresponding probabilities, is in Figure 26. The probability that the second card is red is found by multiplying the probabilities along the two branches and adding.

$$P(\text{red second}) = \frac{1}{2} \cdot \frac{25}{51} + \frac{1}{2} \cdot \frac{26}{51}$$
$$= \frac{1}{2}$$

The probability is $1/2$, exactly the same as the probability that any card is red. If we know nothing about the first card, there is no reason for the probability of the second card to be anything other than $1/2$.

Independent Events   Suppose, in Example 8(a), that we draw the two cards *with* replacement rather than without replacement (that is, we put the first card back before drawing the second card). If the first card is a heart, then the probability of drawing a red card on the second draw is $26/52$, rather than $25/51$, because there are still 52 cards in the deck, 26 of them red. In this case, $P(\text{red second}|\text{heart first})$ is the same as $P(\text{red second})$. The value of the second card is not affected by the value of the first card. We say that the event that the second card is red is *independent* of the event that the first card is a heart since the knowledge of the first card does not influence what happens to the second card. On the other hand, when we draw without replacement, the events that the first card is a heart and that the second card is red are *dependent* events. The fact that the first card is a heart means there is one less red card in the deck, influencing the probability that the second card is red.

As another example, consider tossing a fair coin twice. If the first toss shows heads, the probability that the next toss is heads is still $1/2$. Coin tosses are independent events, since the outcome of one toss does not influence the outcome of the next toss. Similarly, rolls of a fair die are independent events. On the other hand, the events "the milk is old" and "the milk is sour" are dependent events; if the milk is old, there is an increased chance that it is sour. Also, in the example at the beginning of this section, the events A (broker picked stocks that went up) and B (broker used research) are dependent events, because information about the use of research affected the probability of picking stocks that go up. That is, $P(A|B)$ is different from $P(A)$.

If events E and F are independent, then the knowledge that E has occurred gives no (probability) information about the occurrence or nonoccurrence of event F. That is, $P(F)$ is exactly the same as $P(F|E)$, or

$$P(F|E) = P(F).$$

This, in fact, is the formal definition of independent events.

INDEPENDENT EVENTS

Events E and F are **independent events** if

$$P(F|E) = P(F) \qquad \text{or} \qquad P(E|F) = P(E).$$

If the events are not independent, they are **dependent events**.

When E and F are independent events, then $P(F|E) = P(F)$ and the product rule becomes

$$P(E \cap F) = P(E) \cdot P(F|E) = P(E) \cdot P(F).$$

Conversely, if this equation holds, then it follows that $P(F) = P(F|E)$. Consequently, we have this useful fact:

PRODUCT RULE FOR INDEPENDENT EVENTS

Events E and F are independent events if and only if

$$P(E \cap F) = P(E) \cdot P(F).$$

EXAMPLE 9 **Calculator**

A calculator requires a keystroke assembly and a logic circuit. Assume that 99% of the keystroke assemblies are satisfactory and 97% of the logic circuits are satisfactory. Find the probability that a finished calculator will be satisfactory.

▶**Solution** If the failure of a keystroke assembly and the failure of a logic circuit are independent events, then

$$P(\text{satisfactory calculator})$$
$$= P(\text{satisfactory keystroke assembly}) \cdot P(\text{satisfactory logic circuit})$$
$$= (0.99)(0.97) \approx 0.96.$$

(The probability of a defective calculator is $1 - 0.96 = 0.04$.)

CAUTION It is common for students to confuse the ideas of *mutually exclusive* events and *independent* events. Events E and F are mutually exclusive if $E \cap F = \emptyset$. For example, if a family has exactly one child, the only possible outcomes are $B = \{\text{boy}\}$ and $G = \{\text{girl}\}$. These two events are mutually exclusive. The events are *not* independent, however, since $P(G|B) = 0$ (if a family with only one child has a boy, the probability it has a girl is then 0). Since $P(G|B) \neq P(G)$, the events are not independent.

Of all the families with exactly two children, the events $G_1 = \{\text{first child is a girl}\}$ and $G_2 = \{\text{second child is a girl}\}$ are independent, since $P(G_2|G_1)$ equals $P(G_2)$. However, G_1 and G_2 are not mutually exclusive, since $G_1 \cap G_2 = \{\text{both children are girls}\} \neq \emptyset$. ∎

To show that two events E and F are independent, show that $P(F|E) = P(F)$ or that $P(E|F) = P(E)$ or that $P(E \cap F) = P(E) \cdot P(F)$. Another way is to observe that knowledge of one outcome does not influence the probability of the other outcome, as we did for coin tosses.

NOTE In some cases, it may not be apparent from the physical description of the problem whether two events are independent or not. For example, it is not obvious whether the event that a baseball player gets a hit tomorrow is independent of the event that he got a hit today. In such cases, it is necessary to calculate whether $P(F|E) = P(F)$, or, equivalently, whether $P(E \cap F) = P(E) \cdot P(F)$. ∎

EXAMPLE 10 **Snow in Manhattan**
On a typical January day in Manhattan the probability of snow is 0.10, the probability of a traffic jam is 0.80, and the probability of snow or a traffic jam (or both) is 0.82. Are the event "it snows" and the event "a traffic jam occurs" independent?

▶**Solution** Let S represent the event "it snows" and T represent the event "a traffic jam occurs." We must determine whether

$$P(T|S) = P(T) \qquad \text{or} \qquad P(S|T) = P(S).$$

We know $P(S) = 0.10$, $P(T) = 0.8$, and $P(S \cup T) = 0.82$. We can use the union rule (or a Venn diagram) to find $P(S \cap T) = 0.08$, $P(T|S) = 0.8$, and $P(S|T) = 0.1$. Since

$$P(T|S) = P(T) = 0.8 \qquad \text{and} \qquad P(S|T) = P(S) = 0.1,$$

the events "it snows" and "a traffic jam occurs" are independent.

Although we showed $P(T|S) = P(T)$ and $P(S|T) = P(S)$ in Example 10, only one of these results is needed to establish independence. It is also important to note that independence of events does not necessarily follow intuition; it is established from the mathematical definition of independence.

➤ 7.5 Exercises

If a single fair die is rolled, find the probabilities of the following results.

1. A 2, given that the number rolled was odd

2. A 4, given that the number rolled was even

3. An even number, given that the number rolled was 6

If two fair dice are rolled, find the probabilities of the following results.

4. A sum of 8, given that the sum is greater than 7

5. A sum of 6, given that the roll was a "double" (two identical numbers)

6. A double, given that the sum was 9

If two cards are drawn without replacement from an ordinary deck, find the probabilities of the following results.

7. The second is a heart, given that the first is a heart.

8. The second is black, given that the first is a spade.

9. The second is a face card, given that the first is a jack.

10. The second is an ace, given that the first is not an ace.

11. A jack and a 10 are drawn.

12. An ace and a 4 are drawn.

13. Two black cards are drawn.

14. Two hearts are drawn.

15. In your own words, explain how to find the conditional probability $P(E \mid F)$.

Decide whether each of the following pairs of events are dependent or independent.

16. A red and a green die are rolled. A is the event that the red die comes up even, and B is the event that the green die comes up even.

17. C is the event that it rains more than 10 days in Chicago next June, and D is the event that it rains more than 15 days.

18. E is the event that a resident of Texas lives in Dallas, and F is the event that a resident of Texas lives in either Dallas or Houston.

19. A coin is flipped. G is the event that today is Tuesday, and H is the event that the coin comes up heads.

In the previous section, we described an experiment in which the numbers 1, 2, 3, 4, and 5 are written on slips of paper, and 2 slips are drawn at random one at a time without replacement. Find each probability in Exercises 20 and 21.

20. The probability that the first number is 3, given the following.

   a. The sum is 7.

   b. The sum is 8.

21. The probability that the sum is 8, given the following.

   a. The first number is 5.

   b. The first number is 4.

22. Suppose two dice are rolled. Let A be the event that the sum of the two dice is 7. Find an event B related to numbers on the dice such that A and B are

   a. independent;

   b. dependent.

23. Your friend asks you to explain how the product rule for independent events differs from the product rule for dependent events. How would you respond?

24. Another friend asks you to explain how to tell whether two events are dependent or independent. How would you reply? (Use your own words.)

25. A student reasons that the probability in Example 3 of both coins being heads is just the probability that the other coin is a head, that is, 1/2. Explain why this reasoning is wrong.

26. The following problem, submitted by Daniel Hahn of Blairstown, Iowa, appeared in the "Ask Marilyn" column of *Parade* magazine.*

"You discover two booths at a carnival. Each is tended by an honest man with a pair of covered coin shakers. In each shaker is a single coin, and you are allowed to bet upon the chance that both coins in that booth's shakers are heads after the man in the booth shakes them, does an inspection, and can tell you that at least one of the shakers contains a head. The difference is that the man in the first booth always looks inside both of his shakers, whereas the man in the second booth looks inside only one of the shakers. Where will you stand the best chance?"

27. The following question was posed in *Chance News* by Craig Fox and Yoval Rotenstrich.[†] You are playing a game in which a fair coin is flipped and a fair die is rolled. You win a prize if both the coin comes up heads and a 6 is rolled on the die. Now suppose the coin is tossed and the die is rolled, but you are not allowed to see either result. You are told, however, that either the head or the 6 occurred. You are then offered the chance to cancel the game and play a new game in which a die is rolled (there is no coin), and you win a prize if a 6 is rolled.

a. Is it to your advantage to switch to the new game, or to stick with the original game? Answer this question by calculating your probability of winning in each case.

b. Many people erroneously think that it's better to stick with the original game. Discuss why this answer might seem intuitive, but why it is wrong.

28. Suppose a male defendant in a court trial has a mustache, beard, tattoo, and an earring. Suppose, also, that an eyewitness has identified the perpetrator as someone with these characteristics. If the respective probabilities for the male population in this region are 0.35, 0.30, 0.10, and 0.05, is it fair to multiply these probabilities together to conclude that the probability that a person having these characteristics is 0.000525, or 21 in 40,000, and thus decide that the defendant must be guilty?

29. In a two-child family, if we assume that the probabilities of a male child and a female child are each 0.5, are the events *both children are the same sex* and *at most one male* independent? Are they independent for a three-child family?

30. Let A and B be independent events with $P(A) = \dfrac{1}{4}$ and $P(B) = \dfrac{1}{5}$. Find $P(A \cap B)$ and $P(A \cup B)$.

31. If A and B are events such that $P(A) = 0.5$ and $P(A \cup B) = 0.7$, find $P(B)$ when

a. A and B are mutually exclusive;

b. A and B are independent.

32. Laura Johnson, a game show contestant, could win one of two prizes: a shiny new Porsche or a shiny new penny. Laura is given two boxes of marbles. The first box has 50 pink marbles in it and the second box has 50 blue marbles in it. The game show host will pick someone from the audience to be blindfolded and then draw a marble from one of the two boxes. If a pink marble is drawn, she wins the Porsche. Otherwise, Laura wins the penny.[‡] Can Laura increase her chances of winning by redistributing some of the marbles from one box to the other? Explain.

---

*Source: *Parade* magazine, June 12, 1994, p. 18. © 1994 Marilyn vos Savant. Initially published in *Parade* magazine. All rights reserved.

[†]*Chance News* 10.01, Jan 16, 2001.

[‡]This problem is based on the "Puzzler of the Week: Prison Marbles" from the week of Sept. 7, 1996, on National Public Radio's *Car Talk*.

Applications

Banking *The Midtown Bank has found that most customers at the tellers' windows either cash a check or make a deposit. The following table indicates the transactions for one teller for one day.*

	Cash Check	No Check	Totals
Make Deposit	60	20	80
No Deposit	30	10	40
Totals	90	30	120

Letting C represent "cashing a check" and D represent "making a deposit," express each probability in words and find its value.

33. $P(C|D)$ **34.** $P(D'|C)$ **35.** $P(C'|D')$

36. $P(C'|D)$ **37.** $P[(C \cap D)']$

38. *Airline Delays* In February 2006, the major U.S. airline with the fewest delays was US Airways, for which 79.2% of their flights arrived on time.* Assume that the event that a given flight arrives on time is independent of the event that another flight arrives on time.

    a. Chrissy Jenkins plans to take four separate flights for her publisher next month on US Airways. Assuming that the airline has the same on-time performance as in February 2006, what is the probability that all four flights arrive on time?

    b. Discuss how realistic it is to assume that the on-time arrivals of the different flights are independent.

39. *Backup Computers* Corporations where a computer is essential to day-to-day operations, such as banks, often have a second backup computer in case the main computer fails. Suppose there is a 0.003 chance that the main computer will fail in a given time period, and a 0.005 chance that the backup computer will fail while the main computer is being repaired. Assume these failures represent independent events, and find the fraction of the time that the corporation can assume it will have computer service. How realistic is our assumption of independence?

40. *ATM Transactions* Among users of automated teller machines (ATMs), 92% use ATMs to withdraw cash, and 32% use them to check their account balance.[†] Suppose that 96% use ATMs to either withdraw cash or check their account balance (or both). Given a woman who uses an ATM to check her account balance, what is the probability that she also uses an ATM to get cash?

Quality Control *A bicycle factory runs two assembly lines, A and B. If 95% of line A's products pass inspection, while only 85% of line B's products pass inspection, and 60% of the factory's bikes come off assembly line A (the rest off B), find the probabilities that one of the factory's bikes did not pass inspection and came off the following.*

41. Assembly line A   **42.** Assembly line B

43. Find the probability that one of the factory's bikes did not pass inspection.

44. *Genetics* Both of a certain pea plant's parents had a gene for red and a gene for white flowers. (See Exercise 62 in Section 7.4.) If the offspring has red flowers, find the probability that it combined a gene for red and a gene for white (rather than 2 for red).

Genetics *Assuming that boy and girl babies are equally likely, fill in the remaining probabilities on the tree diagram on the next page and use the following information to find the probability that a family with three children has all girls, given the following.*

45. The first is a girl.

46. The third is a girl.

47. The second is a girl.

48. At least 2 are girls.

49. At least 1 is a girl.

Air Travel Consumer Report, U.S. Department of Transportation, April 2006, http://airconsumer.ost.dot.gov/reports/atcr06.htm.
[†]*Chicago Tribune*, Dec. 18, 1995, Sec. 4, p. 1.

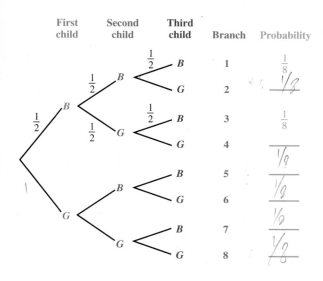

First child	Second child	Third child	Branch	Probability

(Tree diagram showing probabilities for three children, each branch $\frac{1}{2}$)

Branch 1: B, probability $\frac{1}{8}$
Branch 2: G
Branch 3: B, probability $\frac{1}{8}$
Branch 4: G
Branch 5: B
Branch 6: G
Branch 7: B
Branch 8: G

Color Blindness The following table shows frequencies for red-green color blindness, where M represents "person is male" and C represents "person is color-blind." Use this table to find the following probabilities. (See Exercise 61, Section 7.4.)

	M	**M'**	**Totals**
C	0.035	0.004	0.039
C'	0.452	0.509	0.961
Totals	0.487	0.513	1.000

52. $P(M)$ **53.** $P(C)$

54. $P(M \cap C)$ **55.** $P(M \cup C)$

56. $P(M|C)$ **57.** $P(C|M)$

58. $P(M'|C)$

59. Are the events C and M, described above, dependent? What does this mean?

60. *Color Blindness* A scientist wishes to determine whether there is a relationship between color blindness (C) and deafness (D).

a. Suppose the scientist found the probabilities listed in the table. What should the findings be? (See Exercises 52–59.)

b. Explain what your answer tells us about color blindness and deafness.

	D	**D'**	**Totals**
C	0.0008	0.0392	0.0400
C'	0.0192	0.9408	0.9600
Totals	0.0200	0.9800	1.0000

50. *AIDS* The following table gives the estimated numbers of cases of HIV/AIDS diagnosed in 2004 for areas of the United States with confidential name-based HIV infection reporting for adults, based on gender and method of transmission.*

Method of Transmission	Male	Female	Totals
Homosexual contact	18,203	0	18,203
Heterosexual contact	4581	8102	12,683
Injection drug use	3826	2134	5960
Other	1533	174	1707
Totals	28,143	10,410	38,553

a. Find the probability that a male in this group contracted AIDS via homosexual contact.

b. Find the probability that a female in this group contracted AIDS via injection drug use.

51. *Medical Experiment* A medical experiment showed that the probability that a new medicine is effective is 0.75, the probability that a patient will have a certain side effect is 0.4, and the probability that both events occur is 0.3. Decide whether these events are dependent or independent.

61. *Obesity* In 2002, 66.9% of men and 50.0% of women in the United States were overweight.† Given that 48.3% of adult Americans are men and 51.7% are women,‡ find the probability that a randomly selected adult fits the following description.

a. An overweight man **b.** Overweight

c. Are the events that an adult American is a man and that an adult American is overweight independent? Explain.

*Centers for Disease Control and Prevention, HIV/AIDS Surveillance Report, http://www.cdc.gov/hiv/topics/surveillance/resources/reports/2004report/table1.htm.
†*Time Almanac 2006*, p. 553.
‡Ibid, p. 121.

62. *Hospital Insurance* An insurance company pays hospital claims. The number of claims that include emergency room or operating room charges is 85% of the total number of claims. The number of claims that do not include emergency room charges is 25% of the total number of claims. The occurrence of emergency room charges is independent of the occurrence of operating room charges on hospital claims. Calculate the probability that a claim submitted to the insurance company includes operating room charges.* (Choose one of the following.)

   a. 0.10   **b.** 0.20   **c.** 0.25   **d.** 0.40   **e.** 0.80

63. *Blood Pressure* A doctor is studying the relationship between blood pressure and heartbeat abnormalities in her patients. She tests a random sample of her patients and notes their blood pressures (high, low, or normal) and their heartbeats (regular or irregular). She finds that:

   (i) 14% have high blood pressure.

   (ii) 22% have low blood pressure.

   (iii) 15% have an irregular heartbeat.

   (iv) Of those with an irregular heartbeat, one-third have high blood pressure.

   (v) Of those with normal blood pressure, one-eighth have an irregular heartbeat.

   What portion of the patients selected have a regular heartbeat and low blood pressure?[†] (Choose one of the following. *Hint:* Make a table similar to the one for Exercises 52–59.)

   a. 2%   **b.** 5%   **c.** 8%   **d.** 9%   **e.** 20%

64. *Breast Cancer* To explain why the chance of a woman getting breast cancer in the next year goes up each year, while the chance of a woman getting breast cancer in her lifetime goes down, Ruma Falk made the following analogy.[‡] Suppose you are looking for a letter that you may have lost. You have 8 drawers in your desk. There is a probability of 0.1 that the letter is in any one of the 8 drawers, and a probability of 0.2 that the letter is not in any of the drawers.

   a. What is the probability that the letter is in drawer 1?

   b. Given that the letter is not in drawer 1, what is the probability that the letter is in drawer 2?

   c. Given that the letter is not in drawer 1 or 2, what is the probability that the letter is in drawer 3?

   d. Given that the letter is not in drawers 1–7, what is the probability that the letter is in drawer 8?

   e. Based on your answers to parts a–d, what is happening to the probability that the letter is in the next drawer?

   f. What is the probability that the letter is in some drawer?

   g. Given that the letter is not in drawer 1, what is the probability that the letter is in some drawer?

   h. Given that the letter is not in drawer 1 or 2, what is the probability that the letter is in some drawer?

   i. Given that the letter is not in drawers 1–7, what is the probability that the letter is in some drawer?

   j. Based on your answers to parts f–i, what is happening to the probability that the letter is in some drawer?

65. *Drug Screening* In searching for a new drug with commercial possibilities, drug company researchers use the ratio

$$N_S : N_A : N_P : 1.$$

That is, if the company gives preliminary screening to N_S substances, it may find that N_A of them are worthy of further study, with N_P of these surviving into full-scale development. Finally, 1 of the substances will result in a marketable drug. Typical numbers used by Smith, Kline, and French Laboratories in planning research budgets might be $2000 : 30 : 8 : 1$.[§] Use this ratio for parts a–f.

   a. Suppose a compound has been chosen for preliminary screening. Find the probability that the compound will survive and become a marketable drug.

   b. Find the probability that the compound will not lead to a marketable drug.

   c. Suppose the number of such compounds receiving preliminary screening is a. Set up the probability that none of them produces a marketable drug. (Assume independence throughout these exercises.)

   d. Use your results from part c to find the probability that at least one of the drugs will prove marketable.

   e. Suppose now that N scientists are employed in the preliminary screening, and that each scientist can screen c compounds per year. Find the probability that no marketable drugs will be discovered in a year.

   f. Find the probability that at least one marketable drug will be discovered.

---

*Problem 37 from May 2003 Course 1 Examination of the *Education and Examination Committee of the Society of Actuaries*. Reprinted by permission of the Society of Actuaries.

[†]Problem 12 from the 2005 Sample Exam P of the *Education and Examination Committee of the Society of Actuaries*. Reprinted by permission of the Society of Actuaries.

[‡]Falk, Ruma, *Chance News*, July 23, 1995.

[§]Pyle, E. B., III, B. Douglas, G. W. Ebright, W. J. Westlake, and A. B. Bender, "Scientific Manpower Allocation to New Drug Screening Programs," *Management Science*, Vol. 19, No. 12, August 1973. Copyright © 1973 by The Institute of Management Sciences. Reprinted by permission.

Hockey The table below lists the number of head and neck injuries for 319 ice hockey players' exposures wearing either a full shield or half shield in the Canadian Inter-University Athletics Union during the 1997–1998 season.*

For a randomly selected injury, find each probability.

66. $P(A)$ **67.** $P(C|F)$

68. $P(A|H)$ **69.** $P(B'|H')$

70. Are the events A and H independent events?[†]

	Half Shield (*H*)	Full Shield (*F*)	Totals
Head and Face Injuries (*A*)	95	34	129
Concussions (*B*)	41	38	79
Neck Injuries (*C*)	9	7	16
Other Injuries (*D*)	202	150	352
Totals	347	229	576

SOCIAL SCIENCES

71. *Working Women* A survey has shown that 52% of the women in a certain community work outside the home. Of these women, 64% are married, while 86% of the women who do not work outside the home are married. Find the probabilities that a woman in that community can be categorized as follows.

a. Married

b. A single woman working outside the home

PHYSICAL SCIENCES

72. *Rain Forecasts* In a letter to the journal *Nature*, Robert A. J. Matthews gives the following table of outcomes of forecast and weather over 1000 1-hour walks, based on the United Kingdom's Meteorological office's 83% accuracy in 24-hour forecasts.[‡]

	Rain	No Rain	Totals
Forecast of Rain	66	156	222
Forecast of No Rain	14	764	778
Totals	80	920	1000

a. Verify that the probability that the forecast called for rain, given that there was rain, is indeed 83%. Also verify that the probability that the forecast called for no rain, given that there was no rain, is also 83%.

b. Calculate the probability that there was rain, given that the forecast called for rain.

c. Calculate the probability that there was no rain, given that the forecast called for no rain.

d. Observe that your answer to part c is higher than 83%, and that your answer to part b is much lower. Discuss which figure best describes the accuracy of the weather forecast in recommending whether or not you should carry an umbrella.

73. *Earthquakes* There are seven geologic faults (and possibly more) capable of generating a magnitude 6.7 earthquake in the region around San Francisco.[§] Their probabilities of rupturing by the year 2032 are 27%, 21%, 11%, 10%, 4%, 3%, and 3%.

a. Calculate the probability that at least one of these faults erupts by the year 2032, assuming that these are independent events.

b. Scientists forecast a 62% chance of an earthquake with magnitude at least 6.7 in the region around San Francisco by the year 2032. Compare this with your answer from part a. Consider the realism of the assumption of independence. Also consider the role of roundoff. For example, the probability of 10% for one of the faults is presumably rounded to the nearest percent, with the actual probability between 9.5% and 10.5%.

---

*Benson, Brian, Nicholas Nohtaki, M. Sarah Rose, and Willem Meeuwisse, "Head and Neck Injuries Among Ice Hockey Players Wearing Full Face Shields vs. Half Face Shields," *JAMA*, Vol. 282, No. 24, Dec. 22/29, 1999, pp. 2328–2332.

[†]We are assuming here and in other exercises that the events consist entirely of the numbers given in the table. If the numbers are interpreted as a sample of all people fitting the description of the events, then testing for independence is more complicated, requiring a technique from statistics known as a *contingency table*.

[‡]Matthews, Robert A. J., *Nature*, Vol. 382, Aug. 29, 1996, p. 3.

[§]*Science News*, Vol. 169, April 15, 2006, pp. 234–236.

74. *Reliability* The probability that a key component of a space rocket will fail is 0.03.

    a. How many such components must be used as backups to ensure that the probability of at least one of the components working is 0.999999 or more?

    b. Is it reasonable to assume independence here?

GENERAL INTEREST

75. *Titanic* The following table lists the number of passengers who were on the Titanic and the number of passengers who survived, according to class of ticket.*

	Children		Women		Men		Totals	
	On	Survived	On	Survived	On	Survived	On	Survived
First Class	6	6	144	140	175	57	325	203
Second Class	24	24	165	76	168	14	357	114
Third Class	79	27	93	80	462	75	634	182
Totals	109	57	402	296	805	146	1316	499

Use this information to determine the following (round answers to four decimal places).

    a. What is the probability that a randomly selected passenger was second class?

    b. What is the overall probability of surviving?

    c. What is the probability of a first-class passenger surviving?

    d. What is the probability of a child who was also in the third class surviving?

    e. Given that the survivor is from first class, what is the probability that she was a woman?

    f. Given that a male has survived, what is the probability that he was in third class?

    g. Are the events third-class survival and male survival independent events? What does this imply?

76. *Real Estate* A real estate agent trying to sell you an attractive beachfront house claims that it will not collapse unless it is subjected simultaneously to extremely high winds and extremely high waves. According to weather service records, there is a 0.001 probability of extremely high winds, and the same for extremely high waves. The real estate agent claims, therefore, that the probability of both occurring is $(0.001)(0.001) = 0.000001$. What is wrong with the agent's reasoning?

77. *Age and Loans* Suppose 20% of the population are 65 or over, 26% of those 65 or over have loans, and 53% of those under 65 have loans. Find the probabilities that a person fits into the following categories.

    a. 65 or over and has a loan

    b. Has a loan

78. *Women Joggers* In a certain area, 15% of the population are joggers and 40% of the joggers are women. If 55% of those who do not jog are women, find the probabilities that an individual from that community fits the following descriptions.

    a. A woman jogger   **b.** Not a jogger   **c.** A woman

    d. Are the events that a person is a woman and a person is a jogger independent? Explain.

79. *Diet Soft Drinks* Two-thirds of the population are on a diet at least occasionally. Of this group, 4/5 drink diet soft drinks, while 1/2 of the rest of the (nondieting) population drink diet soft drinks. Find the probabilities that a person fits into the following categories.

    a. Drinks diet soft drinks

    b. Diets, but does not drink diet soft drinks

80. *Driver's License Test* The Motor Vehicle Department has found that the probability of a person passing the test for a driver's license on the first try is 0.75. The probability that an individual who fails on the first test will pass on the second try is 0.80, and the probability that an individual who fails the first and second tests will pass the third time is 0.70. Find the probabilities that an individual will do the following.

    a. Fail both the first and second tests

    b. Fail three times in a row

    c. Require at least two tries

---

*Takis, Sandra L., "Titanic: A Statistical Exploration," *Mathematics Teacher*, Vol. 92, No. 8, Nov. 1999, pp. 660–664.

81. *Ballooning* A pair of mathematicians in a hot air balloon were told that there are four independent burners, any one of which is sufficient to keep the balloon aloft. If the probability of any one burner failing during a flight is 0.001, what is the probability that the balloon will crash due to all four burners failing?

82. *Speeding Tickets* A smooth-talking young man has a 1/3 probability of talking a policeman out of giving him a speeding ticket. The probability that he is stopped for speeding during a given weekend is 1/2. Find the probabilities of the events in parts a and b.

a. He will receive no speeding tickets on a given weekend.

b. He will receive no speeding tickets on 3 consecutive weekends.

c. We have assumed that what happens on the second or third weekend is the same as what happened on the first weekend. Is this realistic? Will driving habits remain the same after getting a ticket?

83. *Luxury Cars* In one area, 4% of the population drive luxury cars. However, 17% of the CPAs drive luxury cars. Are the events "person drives a luxury car" and "person is a CPA" independent?

84. *Studying* A teacher has found that the probability that a student studies for a test is 0.60, the probability that a student gets a good grade on a test is 0.70, and the probability that both occur is 0.52.

a. Are these events independent?

b. Given that a student studies, find the probability that the student gets a good grade.

c. Given that a student gets a good grade, find the probability that the student studied.

85. *Football* A football coach whose team is 14 points behind needs two touchdowns to win. Each touchdown is worth 6 points. After a touchdown, the coach can choose either a 1-point kick, which is almost certain to succeed, or a 2-point conversion, which is roughly half as likely to succeed. After the first touchdown, the coach must decide whether to go for 1 or 2 points. If the 2-point conversion is successful, the almost certain 1-point kick after the second touchdown will win the game. If the 2-point conversion fails, the team can try another 2-point conversion after the second touchdown to tie. Some coaches, however, prefer to go for the almost certain 1-point kick after the first touchdown, hoping that the momentum will help them get a 2-point conversion after the second touchdown and win the game. They fear that an unsuccessful 2-point conversion after the first touchdown will discourage the team, which can then at best tie.*

a. Draw a tree diagram for the 1-point kick after the first touchdown and the 2-point conversion after the second touchdown. Letting the probability of success for the 1-point kick and the 2-point conversion be k and r, respectively, show that

$$P(\text{win}) = kr,$$
$$P(\text{tie}) = r(1 - k), \quad \text{and}$$
$$P(\text{lose}) = 1 - r.$$

b. Consider the case of trying for a 2-point conversion after the first touchdown. If it succeeds, try a 1-point kick after the second touchdown. If the 2-point conversion fails, try another one after the second touchdown. Draw a tree diagram and use it to show that

$$P(\text{win}) = kr,$$
$$P(\text{tie}) = r(2 - k - r), \quad \text{and}$$
$$P(\text{lose}) = (1 - r)^2.$$

c. What can you say about the probability of winning under each strategy?

d. Given that $r < 1$, which strategy has a smaller probability of losing? What does this tell you about the value of the two strategies?

*Schielack, Vincent P., Jr., "The Football Coach's Dilemma: Should We Go for 1 or 2 Points First?" *The Mathematics Teacher*, Vol. 88, No. 9, Dec. 1995, pp. 731–733.

7.6 Bayes' Theorem

? *THINK ABOUT IT*

What is the probability that a particular defective item was produced by a new machine operator?

This question and others like it are answered using Bayes' theorem, discussed in this section.

Suppose the probability that a person gets lung cancer, given that the person smokes a pack or more of cigarettes daily, is known. For a research project, it might be necessary to know the probability that a person smokes a pack or more of cigarettes daily, given that the person has lung cancer. More generally, if $P(E|F)$ is known for two events E and F, can $P(F|E)$ be found? The answer is yes, we can find $P(F|E)$ using the formula to be developed in this section. To develop this formula, we can use a tree diagram to find $P(F|E)$. Since $P(E|F)$ is known, the first outcome is either F or F'. Then for each of these outcomes, either E or E' occurs, as shown in Figure 27.

The four cases have the probabilities shown on the right. By the definition of conditional probability and the product rule,

$$P(F|E) = \frac{P(F \cap E)}{P(E)} = \frac{P(F) \cdot P(E|F)}{P(F) \cdot P(E|F) + P(F') \cdot P(E|F')}.$$

Notice that $P(E)$ is the sum of the first and third cases in the tree diagram. This result is a special case of Bayes' theorem, which is generalized later in this section.

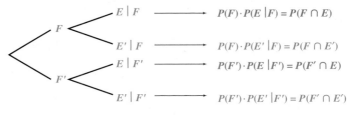

FIGURE 27

BAYES' THEOREM (SPECIAL CASE)

$$P(F|E) = \frac{P(F) \cdot P(E|F)}{P(F) \cdot P(E|F) + P(F') \cdot P(E|F')}$$

EXAMPLE 1   **Worker Errors**

For a fixed length of time, the probability of a worker error on a certain production line is 0.1, the probability that an accident will occur when there is a worker error is 0.3, and the probability that an accident will occur when there is no worker error is 0.2. Find the probability of a worker error if there is an accident.

▶**Solution** Let E represent the event of an accident, and let F represent the event of worker error. From the information given,

$$P(F) = 0.1, \qquad P(E|F) = 0.3, \qquad \text{and} \qquad P(E|F') = 0.2.$$

These probabilities are shown on the tree diagram in Figure 28.

Find $P(F|E)$ by dividing the probability that both E and F occur, given by branch 1, by the probability that E occurs, given by the sum of branches 1 and 3.

$$P(F|E) = \frac{P(F) \cdot P(E|F)}{P(F) \cdot P(E|F) + P(F') \cdot P(E|F')}$$

$$= \frac{(0.1)(0.3)}{(0.1)(0.3) + (0.9)(0.2)} = \frac{0.03}{0.21} = \frac{1}{7} \approx 0.1429$$

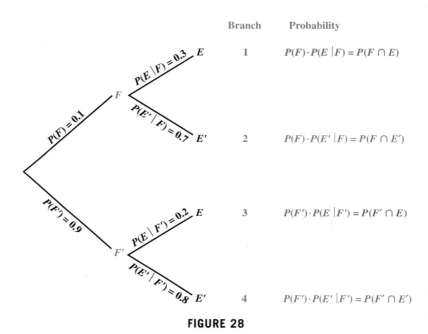

FIGURE 28

The special case of Bayes' theorem can be generalized to more than two events with the tree diagram in Figure 29. This diagram shows the paths that can produce an event E. We assume that the events $F_1, F_2, \ldots, F_n$ are mutually exclusive events (that is, disjoint events) whose union is the sample space, and that E is an event that has occurred. See Figure 30.

The probability $P(F_i|E)$, where $1 \le i \le n$, can be found by dividing the probability for the branch containing $P(E|F_i)$ by the sum of the probabilities of all the branches producing event E.

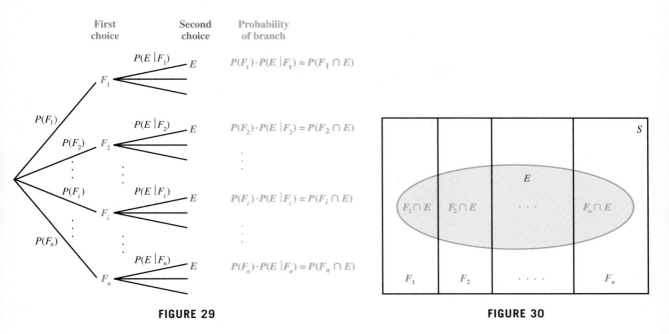

FIGURE 29   FIGURE 30

BAYES' THEOREM

$$P(F_i|E) = \frac{P(F_i) \cdot P(E|F_i)}{P(F_1) \cdot P(E|F_1) + P(F_2) \cdot P(E|F_2) + \cdots + P(F_n) \cdot P(E|F_n)}$$

This result is known as **Bayes' theorem**, after the Reverend Thomas Bayes (1702–1761), whose paper on probability was published about three years after his death.

The statement of Bayes' theorem can be daunting. Actually, it is easier to remember the formula by thinking of the tree diagram that produced it. Go through the following steps.

USING BAYES' THEOREM

1. Start a tree diagram with branches representing $F_1, F_2, \ldots, F_n$. Label each branch with its corresponding probability.

2. From the end of each of these branches, draw a branch for event E. Label this branch with the probability of getting to it, $P(E|F_i)$.

3. You now have n different paths that result in event E. Next to each path, put its probability—the product of the probabilities that the first branch occurs, $P(F_i)$, and that the second branch occurs, $P(E|F_i)$; that is, the product $P(F_i) \cdot P(E|F_i)$, which equals $P(F_i \cap E)$.

4. $P(F_i|E)$ is found by dividing the probability of the branch for F_i by the sum of the probabilities of all the branches producing event E.

EXAMPLE 2 **Machine Operators**

Based on past experience, a company knows that an experienced machine operator (one or more years of experience) will produce a defective item 1% of the time. Operators with some experience (up to one year) have a 2.5% defect rate, and new operators have a 6% defect rate. At any one time, the company has 60% experienced operators, 30% with some experience, and 10% new operators. Find the probability that a particular defective item was produced by a new operator.

▶**Solution** Let E represent the event "item is defective," F_1 represent "item was made by an experienced operator," F_2 represent "item was made by an operator with some experience," and F_3 represent "item was made by a new operator." Then

$$P(F_1) = 0.60 \qquad P(E|F_1) = 0.01$$
$$P(F_2) = 0.30 \qquad P(E|F_2) = 0.025$$
$$P(F_3) = 0.10 \qquad P(E|F_3) = 0.06.$$

We need to find $P(F_3|E)$, the probability that an item was produced by a new operator, given that it is defective. First, draw a tree diagram using the given information, as in Figure 31. The steps leading to event E are shown in red.

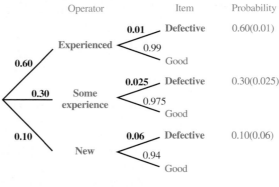

FIGURE 31

Find $P(F_3|E)$ with the bottom branch of the tree in Figure 31: Divide the probability for this branch by the sum of the probabilities of all the branches leading to E, or

$$P(F_3|E) = \frac{0.10(0.06)}{0.60(0.01) + 0.30(0.025) + 0.10(0.06)} = \frac{0.006}{0.0195} = \frac{4}{13} \approx 0.3077.$$

In a similar way, the probability that the defective item was produced by an operator with some experience is

$$P(F_2|E) = \frac{0.30(0.025)}{0.60(0.01) + 0.30(0.025) + 0.10(0.06)} = \frac{0.0075}{0.0195} = \frac{5}{13} \approx 0.3846.$$

Finally, the probability that the defective item was produced by an experienced operator is $P(F_1|E) = 4/13 \approx 0.3077$. Check that $P(F_1|E) + P(F_2|E) + P(F_3|E) = 1$ (that is, the defective item was made by *someone*).

EXAMPLE 3

Manufacturing

A manufacturer buys items from six different suppliers. The fraction of the total number of items obtained from each supplier, along with the probability that an item purchased from that supplier is defective, are shown in the following table.

Supplier	Fraction of Total Supplied	Probability of Defect
1	0.05	0.04
2	0.12	0.02
3	0.16	0.07
4	0.23	0.01
5	0.35	0.03
6	0.09	0.05

Find the probability that a defective item came from supplier 5.

▶**Solution** Let F_1 be the event that an item came from supplier 1, with F_2, F_3, F_4, F_5, and F_6 defined in a similar manner. Let E be the event that an item is defective. We want to find $P(F_5|E)$. Use the probabilities in the table above to prepare a tree diagram, or work with the rows of the table to get

$$P(F_5|E) = \frac{(0.35)(0.03)}{(0.05)(0.04) + (0.12)(0.02) + (0.16)(0.07) + (0.23)(0.01) + (0.35)(0.03) + (0.09)(0.05)}$$

$$= \frac{0.0105}{0.0329} \approx 0.319.$$

There is about a 32% chance that a defective item came from supplier 5. Even though supplier 5 has only 3% defectives, his probability of being "guilty" is relatively high, about 32%, because of the large fraction supplied by 5.

CAUTION Notice that the 0.04 in the upper right of the previous table represents the probability of a defective item *given* that the item came from supplier 1. In contrast, the probability of 0.035 in the table for Exercises 52–59 of the previous section represents the probability that a person is color-blind *and* male. The tables in this section represent probability in a different way than those of the previous section. Tables that you encounter outside of this course might represent probability in either way. You can usually tell what is intended by the context, but be careful! ■

➔ 7.6 Exercises

For two events M and N, $P(M) = 0.4$, $P(N|M) = 0.3$, and $P(N|M') = 0.4$. Find the following.

1. $P(M|N)$

2. $P(M'|N)$

For mutually exclusive events R_1, R_2, and R_3, we have $P(R_1) = 0.15$, $P(R_2) = 0.55$, and $P(R_3) = 0.30$. Also, $P(Q|R_1) = 0.40$, $P(Q|R_2) = 0.20$, and $P(Q|R_3) = 0.70$. Find the following.

3. $P(R_1|Q)$ **4.** $P(R_2|Q)$ **5.** $P(R_3|Q)$ **6.** $P(R_1'|Q)$

Suppose you have three jars with the following contents: 2 black balls and 1 white ball in the first, 1 black ball and 2 white balls in the second, and 1 black ball and 1 white ball in the third. One jar is to be selected, and then 1 ball is to be drawn from the selected jar. If the probabilities of selecting the first, second, or third jar are 1/2, 1/3, and 1/6, respectively, find the probabilities that if a white ball is drawn, it came from the following jars.

7. The second jar   **8.** The third jar

➤ Applications

BUSINESS AND ECONOMICS

9. *Employment Test* A manufacturing firm finds that 70% of its new hires turn out to be good workers and 30% become poor workers. All current workers are given a reasoning test. Of the good workers, 85% pass it; 35% of the poor workers pass it. Assume that these figures will hold true in the future. If the company makes the test part of its hiring procedure and only hires people who meet the previous requirements and also pass the test, what percent of the new hires will turn out to be good workers?

Job Qualifications Of all the people applying for a certain job, 75% are qualified and 25% are not. The personnel manager claims that she approves qualified people 85% of the time; she approves an unqualified person 20% of the time. Find each probability.

10. A person is qualified if he or she was approved by the manager.

11. A person is unqualified if he or she was approved by the manager.

Quality Control A building contractor buys 70% of his cement from supplier A, and 30% from supplier B. A total of 90% of the bags from A arrive undamaged, while 95% of the bags from B arrive undamaged. Give the probabilities that a damaged bag is from the following sources.

12. Supplier A   **13.** Supplier B

Appliance Reliability Companies A, B, and C produce 15%, 40%, and 45%, respectively, of the major appliances sold in a certain area. In that area, 1% of the company A appliances, $1\frac{1}{2}$% of the company B appliances, and 2% of the company C appliances need service within the first year. Suppose a defective appliance is chosen at random; find the probabilities that it was manufactured by the following companies.

14. Company A   **15.** Company B

Television Advertising On a given weekend in the fall, a tire company can buy television advertising time for a college football game, a baseball game, or a professional football game. If the company sponsors the college football game, there is a 70% chance of a high rating, a 50% chance if they sponsor a baseball game, and a 60% chance if they sponsor a professional football game. The probabilities of the company sponsoring these various games are 0.5, 0.2, and 0.3, respectively. Suppose the company does get a high rating; find the probabilities that it sponsored the following.

16. A college football game

17. A professional football game

18. *Auto Insurance* An auto insurance company insures drivers of all ages. An actuary compiled the following statistics on the company's insured drivers:

Age of Driver	Probability of Accident	Portion of Company's Insured Drivers
16–20	0.06	0.08
21–30	0.03	0.15
31–65	0.02	0.49
66–99	0.04	0.28

A randomly selected driver that the company insures has an accident. Calculate the probability that the driver was age 16–20.* (Choose one of the following.)

     a. 0.13   **b.** 0.16   **c.** 0.19   **d.** 0.23   **e.** 0.40

---

*Problem 8 from May 2003 Course 1 Examination of the *Education and Examination Committee of the Society of Actuaries*. Reprinted by permission of the Society of Actuaries.*

19. *Life Insurance* An insurance company issues life insurance policies in three separate categories: standard, preferred, and ultra-preferred. Of the company's policyholders, 50% are standard, 40% are preferred, and 10% are ultra-preferred. Each standard policyholder has probability 0.010 of dying in the next year, each preferred policyholder has probability 0.005 of dying in the next year, and each ultra-preferred policyholder has probability 0.001 of dying in the next year. A policyholder dies in the next year. What is the probability that the deceased policyholder was ultra-preferred? * (Choose one of the following.)

  a. 0.0001 **b.** 0.0010 **c.** 0.0071 **d.** 0.0141 **e.** 0.2817

20. *Automobile Collisions* An actuary studied the likelihood that different types of drivers would be involved in at least one collision during any one-year period. The results of the study are presented below.

Type of Driver	Percentage of All Drivers	Probability of at Least One Collision
Teen	8%	0.15
Young Adult	16%	0.08
Midlife	45%	0.04
Senior	31%	0.05
Total	100%	

Given that a driver has been involved in at least one collision in the past year, what is the probability that the driver is a young adult driver?[†] (Choose one of the following.)

  a. 0.06 **b.** 0.16 **c.** 0.19 **d.** 0.22 **e.** 0.25

21. *Shipping Errors* The following information pertains to three shipping terminals operated by Krag Corp.[‡]

Terminal	Percentage of Cargo Handled	Percentage of Error
Land	50	2
Air	40	4
Sea	10	14

Krag's internal auditor randomly selects one set of shipping documents, ascertaining that the set selected contains an error. Which of the following gives the probability that the error occurred in the Land Terminal?

  a. 0.02   **b.** 0.10

  c. 0.25   **d.** 0.50

22. *Mortgage Defaults* A bank finds that the relationship between mortgage defaults and the size of the down payment is given by the following table.

Down Payment	Number of Mortgages with This Down Payment	Probability of Default
5%	1260	0.06
10%	700	0.04
20%	560	0.02
25%	280	0.01

  a. If a default occurs, what is the probability that it is on a mortgage with a 5% down payment?

  b. What is the probability that a mortgage that is paid to maturity has a 10% down payment?

LIFE SCIENCES

23. *Colorectal Cancer* Researchers found that only one out of 24 physicians could give the correct answer to the following problem: "The probability of colorectal cancer can be given as 0.3%. If a person has colorectal cancer, the probability that the hemoccult test is positive is 50%. If a person does not have colorectal cancer, the probability that he still tests positive is 3%. What is the probability that a person who tests positive actually has colorectal cancer?"[§] What is the correct answer?

24. *Hepatitis Blood Test* The probability that a person with certain symptoms has hepatitis is 0.8. The blood test used to confirm this diagnosis gives positive results for 90% of people with the disease and 5% of those without the disease. What is the probability that an individual who has the symptoms and who reacts positively to the test actually has hepatitis?

---

*Problem 20 from the 2005 Sample Exam P of the *Education and Examination Committee of the Society of Actuaries*. Reprinted by permission of the Society of Actuaries.
[†]Problem 23 from the 2005 Sample Exam P of the *Education and Examination Committee of the Society of Actuaries*. Reprinted by permission of the Society of Actuaries.
[‡]Uniform CPA Examination, Nov. 1989.
[§]Hoffrage, Ulrich, Samuel Lindsey, Ralph Hertwig, and Gerd Gigerenzer, *Science*, Vol. 290, Dec. 22, 2000, pp. 2261–2262.

25. *Sensitivity and Specificity* The sensitivity of a medical test is defined as the probability that a test will be positive given that a person has a disease, written $P(T^+|D^+)$. The specificity of a test is defined as the probability that a test will be negative given that the person does not have the disease, written $P(T^-|D^-)$. For example, the sensitivity and specificity for breast cancer during a clinical breast examination by a trained expert is approximately 0.54 and 0.94, respectively.*

a. If 2% of U.S. women have breast cancer,[†] find the probability that a woman who tests positive during a clinical breast examination actually has breast cancer.

b. Given that a woman tests negative during a clinical breast examination, find the probability that she does not have breast cancer.

c. Using the information above, how many false positives would you expect for every 1000 clinical breast examinations?

26. *Test for HIV* A test for the virus that causes AIDS, developed by Octopus Diagnostics Research of Hantsport, Nova Scotia, shows the presence or absence of HIV in a drop of blood in two minutes, compared with five days for other tests.[‡] Preliminary results indicate a false positive rate (an indication that the HIV virus is present when it is not) of less than 2%, and a false negative rate (a failure to detect the presence of the HIV virus) of up to 5%. Assume for this exercise that these rates are exactly 2% and 5%. In 2001, there were 950,000 people in North America with the HIV virus, out of a population of 491 million.[§] Suppose a resident of North America is chosen at random and given this test. If the result is positive, what is the probability that the person actually has the HIV virus?

27. *Smokers* A health study tracked a group of persons for five years. At the beginning of the study, 20% were classified as heavy smokers, 30% as light smokers, and 50% as nonsmokers. Results of the study showed that light smokers were twice as likely as nonsmokers to die during the five-year study, but only half as likely as heavy smokers. A

randomly selected participant from the study died over the five-year period. Calculate the probability that the participant was a heavy smoker.[‖] (Choose one of the following. *Hint:* Let $x = P$(a nonsmoker dies).)

a. 0.20   **b.** 0.25   **c.** 0.35   **d.** 0.42   **e.** 0.57

28. *Emergency Room* Upon arrival at a hospital's emergency room, patients are categorized according to their condition as critical, serious, or stable. In the past year:

   (i) 10% of the emergency room patients were critical;

   (ii) 30% of the emergency room patients were serious;

   (iii) the rest of the emergency room patients were stable;

   (iv) 40% of the critical patients died;

   (v) 10% of the serious patients died; and

   (vi) 1% of the stable patients died.

Given that a patient survived, what is the probability that the patient was categorized as serious upon arrival?[#] (Choose one of the following.)

a. 0.06   **b.** 0.29   **c.** 0.30   **d.** 0.39   **e.** 0.64

29. *Blood Test* A blood test indicates the presence of a particular disease 95% of the time when the disease is actually present. The same test indicates the presence of the disease 0.5% of the time when the disease is not present. One percent of the population actually has the disease. Calculate the probability that a person has the disease, given that the test indicates the presence of the disease.** (Choose one of the following.)

a. 0.324   **b.** 0.657   **c.** 0.945   **d.** 0.950   **e.** 0.995

30. *Circulation* The probability that a randomly chosen male has a circulation problem is 0.25. Males who have a circulation problem are twice as likely to be smokers as those who do not have a circulation problem. What is the conditional probability that a male has a circulation problem, given that he is a smoker? [††] (Choose one of the following.)

a. 1/4   **b.** 1/3   **c.** 2/5   **d.** 1/2   **e.** 2/3

---

*Barton, Mary B., Russell Harris, and Suzanne Fletcher, "Does This Patient Have Breast Cancer, The Screening Clinical Breast Examinations: Should It Be Done? How?" *JAMA*, Vol. 282, No. 13, Oct. 6, 1999, pp. 1270–1280.

[†]*The World Almanac and Book of Facts 2000*, p. 902.

[‡]*Maclean's*, Feb. 17, 1997, p. 70.

[§]*The World Almanac and Book of Facts 2003*, pp. 857, 859.

[‖]Problem 31 from May 2003 Course 1 Examination of the *Education and Examination Committee of the Society of Actuaries*. Reprinted by permission of the Society of Actuaries.

[#]Problem 21 from the 2005 Sample Exam P of the *Education and Examination Committee of the Society of Actuaries*. Reprinted by permission of the Society of Actuaries.

**Problem 25 from the 2005 Sample Exam P of the *Education and Examination Committee of the Society of Actuaries*. Reprinted by permission of the Society of Actuaries.

[††]Problem 26 from the 2005 Sample Exam P of the *Education and Examination Committee of the Society of Actuaries*. Reprinted by permission of the Society of Actuaries.

SOCIAL SCIENCES

31. *Binge Drinking* A 1995 study by the Harvard School of Public Health reported that 86% of male students who live in a fraternity house are binge drinkers. The figure for fraternity members who are not residents of a fraternity house is 71%, while the figure for men who do not belong to a fraternity is 45%.* Suppose that 10% of U.S. male students live in a fraternity house, 15% belong to a fraternity but do not live in a fraternity house, and 75% do not belong to a fraternity.

  a. What is the probability that a randomly selected male student is a binge drinker?

  b. If a randomly selected male student is a binge drinker, what is the probability that he lives in a fraternity house?

32. *Murder* During the murder trial of O. J. Simpson, Alan Dershowitz, an advisor to the defense team, stated on television that only about 0.1% of men who batter their wives actually murder them. Statistician I. J. Good observed that even if, given that a husband is a batterer, the probability he is guilty of murdering his wife is 0.001, what we really want to know is the probability that the husband is guilty, given that the wife was murdered.[†] Good estimates the probability of a battered wife being murdered, given that her husband is not guilty, as 0.001. The probability that she is murdered if her husband is guilty is 1, of course. Using these numbers and Dershowitz's 0.001 probability of the husband being guilty, find the probability that the husband is guilty, given that the wife was murdered.

Never-Married Adults by Age Group The following tables give the proportion of men and of women 18 and older in each age group in 2003, as well as the proportion in each group who have never been married.[‡]

	Men	
Age	Proportion of Population	Proportion Never Married
18–24	0.135	0.895
25–34	0.191	0.434
35–44	0.212	0.195
45–64	0.320	0.088
65 or over	0.142	0.074

	Women	
Age	Proportion of Population	Proportion Never Married
18–24	0.123	0.806
25–34	0.179	0.311
35–44	0.203	0.132
45–64	0.316	0.075
65 or over	0.179	0.037

33. Find the probability that a randomly selected man who has never married is between 35 and 44 years old (inclusive).

34. Find the probability that a randomly selected woman who has been married is between 18 and 24 (inclusive).

35. Find the probability that a randomly selected woman who has never been married is between 45 and 64 (inclusive).

Seat Belt Effectiveness *A federal study showed that in 1990, 49% of all those involved in a fatal car crash wore seat belts. Of those in a fatal crash who wore seat belts, 44% were injured and 27% were killed. For those not wearing seat belts, the comparable figures were 41% and 50%, respectively.*[§]

36. Find the probability that a randomly selected person who was killed in a car crash was wearing a seat belt.

37. Find the probability that a randomly selected person who was unharmed in a fatal crash was not wearing a seat belt.

GENERAL INTEREST

38. *Automobile Accidents* A study of automobile accidents produced the following data:

Model Year	Proportion of All Vehicles	Probability of Involvement in an Accident
1997	0.16	0.05
1998	0.18	0.02
1999	0.20	0.03
Other	0.46	0.04

---

*The New York Times, Dec. 6, 1995, p. B16.
[†]Good, I. J., "When Batterer Turns Murderer," *Nature*, Vol. 375, No. 15, June 15, 1995, p. 541.
[‡]From data in *The New York Times 2006 Almanac*, p. 289.
[§]National Highway Traffic Safety Administration, Office of Driver and Pedestrian Research: "Occupant Protection Trends in 19 Cities," Nov. 1989, and "Use of Automatic Safety Belt Systems in 19 Cities, Feb. 1991.

An automobile from one of the model years 1997, 1998, and 1999 was involved in an accident. Determine the probability that the model year of this automobile is 1997.* (Choose one of the following. *Hint:* Be sure to ignore the "Other" branch of the tree.)

a. 0.22   **b.** 0.30   **c.** 0.33   **d.** 0.45   **e.** 0.50

39. *Terrorists* John Allen Paulos has pointed out a problem with massive, untargeted wiretaps.[†] To illustrate the problem, he supposes that one out of every million Americans has terrorist ties. Furthermore, he supposes that the terrorist profile is 99% accurate, so that if a person has terrorist ties, the profile will pick them up 99% of the time, and if the person does not have terrorist ties, the profile will accidentally pick them up only 1% of the time. Given that the profile has picked up a person, what is the probability that the person actually has terrorist ties? Discuss how your answer affects your opinion on domestic wiretapping.

40. *Three Prisoners* The famous "problem of three prisoners" is as follows.[‡]

Three men, A, B, and C, were in jail. A knew that one of them was to be set free and the other two were to be executed. But he didn't know who was the one to be spared. To the jailer who did know, A said, "Since two out of the three will be executed, it is certain that either B or C will be, at least. You will give me no information about my own chances if you give me the name of one man, B or C, who is going to be executed." Accepting this argument after some thinking, the jailer said "B will be executed." Thereupon A felt happier because now either he or C would go free, so his chance had increased from 1/3 to 1/2.

a. Assume that initially each of the prisoners is equally likely to be set free. Assume also that if both B and C are to be executed, the jailer is equally likely to name either B or C. Show that A is wrong, and that his probability of being freed, given that the jailer says B will be executed, is still 1/3.

b. Now assume that initially the probabilities of A, B, and C being freed are 1/4, 1/4, and 1/2, respectively. As in part a, assume also that if both B and C are to be executed, the jailer is equally likely to name either B or C. Now show that A's probability of being freed, given that the jailer says B will be executed, actually drops to 1/5. Discuss the reasonableness of this answer, and why this result might violate someone's intuition.

Chapter 7 Review

▶ Chapter Summary

We began this chapter by introducing sets, which are collections of objects. We introduced the following set operations:

- complement (A' is the set of elements not in A),
- intersection ($A \cap B$ is the set of elements belonging to both set A and set B), and
- union ($A \cup B$ is the set of elements belonging to either set A or set B).

We used tree diagrams and Venn diagrams to define and study concepts in set operations as well as in probability. We introduced the following terms:

- experiment (an activity or occurrence with an observable result),
- trial (a repetition of an experiment),
- outcome (a result of a trial),

*Problem 27 from the 2005 Sample Exam P of the *Education and Examination Committee of the Society of Actuaries.* Reprinted by permission of the Society of Actuaries.
[†]http://abcnews.go.com/Technology/WhosCounting/story?id=1560771.
[‡]Shimojo, Shinsuke, and Shin'ichi Ichikawa, "Intuitive Reasoning About Probability: Theoretical and Experimental Analyses of the 'Problem of Three Prisoners,'" *Cognition,* Vol. 32, 1989, pp. 1–24.

- sample space (the set of all possible outcomes for an experiment), and
- event (a subset of a sample space).

We investigated how to compute various probabilities and we explored some of the properties of probability. In particular, we studied the following concepts:

- empirical probability (based on how frequently an event actually occurred),
- conditional probability (in which some other event is assumed to have occurred),
- odds (an alternative way of expressing probability),
- independent events (in which the occurrence of one event does not affect the probability of another), and
- Bayes' theorem (used to calculate certain types of conditional probability).

Throughout the chapter, many applications of probability were introduced and analyzed. In the next two chapters, we will employ these techniques to further our study into the fields of probability and statistics.

SETS SUMMARY

Number of Subsets   A set of k distinct elements has 2^k subsets.

Disjoint Sets   If sets A and B are disjoint, then

$$A \cap B = \emptyset \quad \text{and} \quad n(A \cap B) = 0.$$

Union Rule for Sets   For any sets A and B,

$$n(A \cup B) = n(A) + n(B) - n(A \cap B).$$

PROBABILITY SUMMARY

Basic Probability Principle   Let S be a sample space of equally likely outcomes, and let event E be a subset of S. Then the probability that event E occurs is

$$P(E) = \frac{n(E)}{n(S)}.$$

Mutually Exclusive Events   If E and F are mutually exclusive events,

$$E \cap F = \emptyset \quad \text{and} \quad P(E \cap F) = 0.$$

Union Rule   For any events E and F from a sample space S,

$$P(E \cup F) = P(E) + P(F) - P(E \cap F).$$

Complement Rule $P(E) = 1 - P(E') \quad \text{and} \quad P(E') = 1 - P(E)$

Odds   The odds in favor of event E are $\dfrac{P(E)}{P(E')}$, $P(E') \neq 0$.

If the odds favoring event E are m to n, then

$$P(E) = \frac{m}{m + n} \quad \text{and} \quad P(E') = \frac{n}{m + n}.$$

Properties of Probability   **1.** For any event E in sample space S, $0 \leq P(E) \leq 1$.

2. The sum of the probabilities of all possible distinct outcomes is 1.

Conditional Probability   The conditional probability of event E, given that event F has occurred, is

$$P(E|F) = \frac{P(E \cap F)}{P(F)}, \quad \text{where } P(F) \neq 0.$$

For equally likely outcomes, conditional probability is found by reducing the sample space to event F; then

$$P(E|F) = \frac{n(E \cap F)}{n(F)}.$$

Product Rule of Probability If E and F are events, then $P(E \cap F)$ may be found by either of these formulas.

$$P(E \cap F) = P(F) \cdot P(E|F) \quad \text{or} \quad P(E \cap F) = P(E) \cdot P(F|E)$$

Independent Events If E and F are independent events,

$$P(E|F) = P(E), \quad P(F|E) = P(F), \quad \text{and} \quad P(E \cap F) = P(E) \cdot P(F).$$

Bayes' Theorem $P(F_i|E) = \dfrac{P(F_i) \cdot P(E|F_i)}{P(F_1) \cdot P(E|F_1) + P(F_2) \cdot P(E|F_2) + \cdots + P(F_n) \cdot P(E|F_n)}$

 **Key Terms**

7.1 set	**intersection**	**simple event**	**empirical probability**
element (member)	**disjoint sets**	**certain event**	**probability distribution**
empty set	**union**	**impossible event**	**7.5 conditional probability**
set-builder notation	**7.2 union rule for sets**	**mutually exclusive**	**product rule**
universal set	**7.3 experiment**	**events**	**independent events**
subset	**trial**	**probability**	**dependent events**
tree diagram	**outcome**	**7.4 union rule for**	**7.6 Bayes' theorem**
Venn diagram	**sample space**	**probability**	
complement	**event**	**odds**	

Concept Check

Determine whether each of the following statements is true or false, and explain why.

1. A set is a subset of itself.

2. A set has more subsets than it has elements.

3. The union of two sets always has more elements than either set.

4. The intersection of two sets always has fewer elements than either set.

5. The number of elements in the union of two sets can be found by adding the number of elements in each set.

6. The probability of an event is always at least 0 and no larger than 1.

7. The probability of the union of two events can be found by adding the probability of each event.

8. The probability of drawing the Queen of Hearts from a deck of cards is an example of empirical probability.

9. If two events are mutually exclusive, then they are independent.

10. The probability of two independent events can be found by multiplying the probabilities of each event.

11. The probability of an event E given an event F is the same as the probability of F given E.

12. Bayes' theorem can be useful for calculating conditional probability.

→ Chapter 7 Review Exercises

Write true or false for each statement.

1. $9 \in \{8, 4, -3, -9, 6\}$

2. $4 \notin \{3, 9, 7\}$

3. $2 \notin \{0, 1, 2, 3, 4\}$

4. $0 \in \{0, 1, 2, 3, 4\}$

5. $\{3, 4, 5\} \subseteq \{2, 3, 4, 5, 6\}$

6. $\{1, 2, 5, 8\} \subseteq \{1, 2, 5, 10, 11\}$

7. $\{3, 6, 9, 10\} \subseteq \{3, 9, 11, 13\}$

8. $\emptyset \subseteq \{1\}$

9. $\{2, 8\} \nsubseteq \{2, 4, 6, 8\}$

10. $0 \subseteq \emptyset$

In Exercises 11–20, let $U = \{a, b, c, d, e, f, g, h\}$, $K = \{c, d, e, f, h\}$, and $R = \{a, c, d, g\}$. Find the following.

11. The number of subsets of K

12. The number of subsets of R

13. K'

14. R'

15. $K \cap R$

16. $K \cup R$

17. $(K \cap R)'$

18. $(K \cup R)'$

19. $\emptyset'$

20. U'

In Exercises 21–26, let $U = \{$all employees of the K. O. Brown Company$\}$;
$A = \{$employees in the accounting department$\}$;
$B = \{$employees in the sales department$\}$;
$C = \{$female employees$\}$;
$D = \{$employees with an MBA degree$\}$.

Describe each set in words.

21. $A \cap C$

22. $B \cap D$

23. $A \cup D$

24. $A' \cap D$

25. $B' \cap C'$

26. $(B \cup C)'$

Draw a Venn diagram and shade each set.

27. $A \cup B'$

28. $A' \cap B$

29. $(A \cap B) \cup C$

30. $(A \cup B)' \cap C$

Write the sample space for each experiment.

31. Rolling a die

32. Drawing a card from a deck containing only the 13 spades

33. Measuring the weight of a person to the nearest half pound (the scale will not measure more than 300 lb)

34. Tossing a coin 4 times

A jar contains 5 balls labeled 3, 5, 7, 9, and 11, respectively, while a second jar contains 4 red and 2 green balls. An experiment consists of pulling 1 ball from each jar, in turn. In Exercises 35–37, write each set using set notation.

35. The sample space

36. Event E: the number on the first ball is greater than 5

37. Event F: the second ball is green

38. Are the outcomes in the sample space in Exercise 35 equally likely?

In Exercises 39–45, find the probability of each event when a single card is drawn from an ordinary deck.

39. A heart

40. A red queen

41. A face card

42. Black or a face card

43. Red, given that it is a queen

44. A jack, given that it is a face card

45. A face card, given that it is a king

46. Describe what is meant by disjoint sets.

47. Describe what is meant by mutually exclusive events.

48. How are disjoint sets and mutually exclusive events related?

49. Define independent events.

50. Are independent events always mutually exclusive? Are they ever mutually exclusive?

51. An uproar has raged since September 1990 over the answer to a puzzle* published in *Parade* magazine, a supplement of the Sunday newspaper. In the "Ask Marilyn" column, Marilyn vos Savant answered the following question: "Suppose you're on a game show, and you're given the choice of three doors. Behind one door is a car; behind the others, goats. You pick a door, say number 1, and the host, who knows what's behind the other doors, opens another door, say number 3, which has a goat. He then says to you, 'Do you want to pick door number 2?' Is it to your advantage to take the switch?"

Ms. vos Savant estimates that she has since received some 10,000 letters; most of them, including many from mathematicians and statisticians, disagreed with her answer. Her answer has been debated by both professionals and amateurs, and tested in classes at all levels, from grade school to graduate school. But by performing the experiment repeatedly, it can be shown that vos Savant's answer was correct. Find the probabilities of getting the car if you switch or do not switch, and then answer the question yourself. (*Hint:* Consider the sample space.)

Find the odds in favor of a card drawn from an ordinary deck being the following.

52. A club

53. A black jack

54. A red face card or a queen

Find the probabilities of getting the following sums when two fair dice are rolled.

55. 8

56. 0

57. At least 10

58. No more than 5

59. An odd number greater than 8

60. 12, given that the sum is greater than 10

61. 7, given that at least one die shows a 4

62. At least 9, given that at least one die shows a 5

63. Suppose $P(E) = 0.51$, $P(F) = 0.37$, and $P(E \cap F) = 0.22$. Find the following.

   a. $P(E \cup F)$ **b.** $P(E \cap F')$ **c.** $P(E' \cup F)$ **d.** $P(E' \cap F')$

64. Box A contains 5 red balls and 1 black ball; box B contains 2 red balls and 3 black balls. A box is chosen, and a ball is selected from it. The probability of choosing box A is 3/8. If the selected ball is black, what is the probability that it came from box A?

65. Find the probability that the ball in Exercise 64 came from box B, given that it is red.

66. An urn contains 10 balls: 4 red and 6 blue. A second urn contains 16 red balls and an unknown number of blue balls. A single ball is drawn from each urn. The probability that both balls are the same color is 0.44. Calculate the number of blue balls in the second urn.[†] (Choose one of the following.)

   a. 4   **b.** 20   **c.** 24   **d.** 44   **e.** 64

Source: Parade magazine, Sept. 9, 1990, p. 13. © 1990 Marilyn vos Savant. Initially published in *Parade* magazine. All rights reserved.

[†]Problem 4 from the 2005 Sample Exam P of the *Education and Examination Committee of the Society of Actuaries*. Reprinted by permission of the Society of Actuaries.

Applications

Appliance Repairs Of the appliance repair shops listed in the phone book, 80% are competent and 20% are not. A competent shop can repair an appliance correctly 95% of the time; an incompetent shop can repair an appliance correctly 55% of the time. Suppose an appliance was repaired correctly. Find the probabilities that it was repaired by the following.

67. A competent shop

68. An incompetent shop

Suppose an appliance was repaired incorrectly. Find the probabilities that it was repaired by the following.

69. A competent shop

70. An incompetent shop

71. Find the probability that an appliance brought to a shop chosen at random is repaired correctly.

72. Are the events that a repair shop is competent and that the repair is done correctly independent? Explain.

73. *Sales* A company sells printers and copiers. Let *E* be the event "a customer buys a printer," and let *F* be the event "a customer buys a copier." Write the following using ∩, ∪, or ′ as necessary.

a. A customer buys neither machine.

b. A customer buys at least one of the machines.

74. *Defective Items* A sample shipment of five hair dryers is chosen at random. The probability of exactly 0, 1, 2, 3, 4, or 5 hair dryers being defective is given in the following table.

Number Defective	0	1	2	3	4	5
Probability	0.34	0.26	0.18	0.12	0.07	0.03

Find the probabilities that the following numbers of hair dryers are defective.

a. No more than 3

b. At least 3

75. *Defective Items* A manufacturer buys items from four different suppliers. The fraction of the total number of items that is obtained from each supplier, along with the probability that an item purchased from that supplier is defective, is shown in the table below.

Supplier	Fraction of Total Supplied	Probability of Defective
1	0.17	0.01
2	0.39	0.02
3	0.35	0.05
4	0.09	0.03

a. Find the probability that a randomly selected item is defective.

b. Find the probability that a defective item came from supplier 4.

c. Find the probability that a defective item came from supplier 2.

d. Are the events that an item came from supplier 4 and that the item is defective independent? Explain.

76. *Car Buyers* The table shows the results of a survey of buyers of a certain model of car.

Car Type	Satisfied	Not Satisfied	Totals
New	300	100	
Used	450		600
Totals		250	

a. Complete the table.

b. How many buyers were surveyed?

c. How many bought a new car and were satisfied?

d. How many were not satisfied?

e. How many bought used cars?

f. How many of those who were not satisfied had purchased a used car?

g. Rewrite the event stated in part f using the expression "given that."

h. Find the probability of the outcome in parts f and g.

i. Find the probability that a used-car buyer is not satisfied.

j. You should have different answers in parts h and i. Explain why.

k. Are the events that a car is new and that the customer is satisfied independent? Explain.

77. *Auto Insurance* An insurance company examines its pool of auto insurance customers and gathers the following information:

  (i) All customers insure at least one car.

  (ii) 70% of the customers insure more than one car.

  (iii) 20% of the customers insure a sports car.

  (iv) Of those customers who insure more than one car, 15% insure a sports car.

Calculate the probability that a randomly selected customer insures exactly one car and that car is not a sports car.* (Choose one of the following. *Hint:* Draw a tree diagram, and let x be the probability that a customer who insures exactly one car insures a sports car.)

a. 0.13   **b.** 0.21   **c.** 0.24   **d.** 0.25   **e.** 0.30

78. *Auto Insurance* An auto insurance company has 10,000 policyholders. Each policyholder is classified as:

 (i) young or old;

 (ii) male or female; and

 (iii) married or single.

Of these policyholders, 3000 are young, 4600 are male, and 7000 are married. The policyholders can also be classified as 1320 young males, 3010 married males, and 1400 young married persons. Finally, 600 of the policyholders are young married males. How many of the company's policyholders are young, female, and single?[†] (Choose one of the following.)

a. 280   **b.** 423   **c.** 486   **d.** 880   **e.** 896

79. *Auto Insurance* An actuary studying the insurance preferences of automobile owners makes the following conclusions:

 (i) An automobile owner is twice as likely to purchase collision coverage as disability coverage.

 (ii) The event that an automobile owner purchases collision coverage is independent of the event that he or she purchases disability coverage.

 (iii) The probability that an automobile owner purchases both collision and disability coverages is 0.15.

What is the probability that an automobile owner purchases neither collision nor disability coverage?[‡] (Choose one of the following.)

a. 0.18   **b.** 0.33   **c.** 0.48   **d.** 0.67   **e.** 0.82

80. *Insurance* An insurance company estimates that 40% of policyholders who have only an auto policy will renew next year and 60% of policyholders who have only a homeowners policy will renew next year. The company esti-

mates that 80% of policyholders who have both an auto and a homeowners policy will renew at least one of these policies next year. Company records show that 65% of policyholders have an auto policy, 50% of policyholders have a homeowners policy, and 15% of policyholders have both an auto and a homeowners policy. Using the company's estimates, calculate the percentage of policyholders that will renew at least one policy next year.[§] (Choose one of the following.)

a. 20   **b.** 29   **c.** 41   **d.** 53   **e.** 70

LIFE SCIENCES

81. *Sickle Cell Anemia* The square below shows the four possible (equally likely) combinations when both parents are carriers of the sickle cell anemia trait. Each carrier parent has normal cells (N) and trait cells (T).

a. Complete the table.

b. If the disease occurs only when two trait cells combine, find the probability that a child born to these parents will have sickle cell anemia.

c. The child will carry the trait but not have the disease if a normal cell combines with a trait cell. Find this probability.

d. Find the probability that the child is neither a carrier nor has the disease.

		Second Parent	
		N_2	T_2
First Parent	N_1		N_1T_2
	T_1		

82. *Blood Antigens* In Exercise 44 of Section 7.2, we described the eight types of human blood. The percentage of the population having each type is as follows:[‖]

O^+: 38%; O^-: 8%; A^+: 32%; A^-: 7%;
B^+: 9%; B^-: 2%; AB^+: 3%; AB^-: 1%.

---

*Problem 5 from May 2003 Course 1 Examination of the *Education and Examination Committee of the Society of Actuaries.* Reprinted by permission of the Society of Actuaries.
[†]Problem 5 from the 2005 Sample Exam P of the *Education and Examination Committee of the Society of Actuaries.* Reprinted by permission of the Society of Actuaries.
[‡]Problem 11 from the 2005 Sample Exam P of the *Education and Examination Committee of the Society of Actuaries.* Reprinted by permission of the Society of Actuaries.
[§]Problem 18 from May 2003 Course 1 Examination of the *Education and Examination Committee of the Society of Actuaries.* Reprinted by permission of the Society of Actuaries.
[‖]Young, Victoria, "A Matter of Survival," *The Mathematics Teacher,* Vol. 95, No. 2, Feb. 2002, pp. 100–112.

When a person receives a blood transfusion, it is important that the blood be compatible, which means that it introduces no new antigens into the recipient's blood. The following diagram helps illustrate what blood types are compatible.

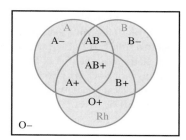

The universal blood type is O⁻, since it has none of the additional antigens. The circles labeled A, B, and Rh contain blood types with the A antigen, B antigen, and Rh antigen, respectively. A person with O⁻ blood can only be transfused with O⁻ blood, because any other type would introduce a new antigen. Thus the probability that blood from a random donor is compatible is just 8%. A person with AB⁺ blood already has all antigens, so the probability that blood from a random donor is compatible is 100%. Find the probability that blood from a random donor is compatible with a person with each blood type.

a. O⁺ **b.** A⁺ **c.** B⁺

d. A⁻ **e.** B⁻ **f.** AB⁻

83. *Heart Disease* A public health researcher examines the medical records of a group of 937 men who died in 1999 and discovers that 210 of the men died from causes related to heart disease. Moreover, 312 of the 937 men had at least one parent who suffered from heart disease, and, of these 312 men, 102 died from causes related to heart disease. Determine the probability that a man randomly selected from this group died of causes related to heart disease, given that neither of his parents suffered from heart disease.* (Choose one of the following.)

a. 0.115 **b.** 0.173 **c.** 0.224 **d.** 0.327 **e.** 0.514

84. *Risk Factors* An actuary is studying the prevalence of three health risk factors, denoted by A, B, and C, within a population of women. For each of the three factors, the probability is 0.1 that a woman in the population has only this risk factor (and no others). For any two of the three factors, the probability is 0.12 that she has exactly these two risk factors (but not the other). The probability that a woman has all three risk factors, given that she has A and B, is 1/3. What is the probability that a woman has none of the three risk factors, given that she does not have risk factor A?[†] (Choose one of the following.)

a. 0.280 **b.** 0.311 **c.** 0.467 **d.** 0.484 **e.** 0.700

SOCIAL SCIENCES

85. *Elections* In the 2004 presidential elections, George W. Bush won 50.72% of the popular vote, as opposed to 48.27% for John Kerry and 1.01% for other candidates.[‡] According to an election day poll, 50% of those who voted for Bush were male, while 42% of those who voted for Kerry were male.[§] For this exercise, assume that 50% of the other voters were male.

a. Find the percentage of the voters who were male. Compare this with the figure of 46% reported in the survey.

b. Find the probability that a randomly selected male voter voted for Bush.

c. Find the probability that a randomly selected female voter voted for Bush.

86. *Television Viewing Habits* A telephone survey of television viewers revealed the following information:

    20 watch situation comedies;
    19 watch game shows;
    27 watch movies;
    19 watch movies but not game shows;
    15 watch situation comedies but not game shows;
    10 watch both situation comedies and movies;
     3 watch all three;
     7 watch none of these.

a. How many viewers were interviewed?

b. How many viewers watch comedies and movies but not game shows?

c. How many viewers watch only movies?

d. How many viewers do not watch movies?

---

*Problem 6 from the 2005 Sample Exam P of the *Education and Examination Committee of the Society of Actuaries*. Reprinted by permission of the Society of Actuaries.
[†]Problem 13 from the 2005 Sample Exam P of the *Education and Examination Committee of the Society of Actuaries*. Reprinted by permission of the Society of Actuaries.
[‡]*Time Almanac 2006*, p. 45.
[§]*The New York Times*, Nov. 3, 2004, p. P4.

87. *Randomized Response Method for Getting Honest Answers to Sensitive Questions** Basically, this is a method to guarantee that an individual who answers sensitive question will remain anonymous, thus encouraging a truthful response. This method is, in effect, an application of the formula for finding the probability of an intersection, and operates as follows. Questions *A* and *B* are posed, one of which is sensitive and the other not. The probability of receiving a "yes" to the nonsensitive question must be known. For example, one could ask

> *A*: Does your Social Security number end in an odd digit? (Nonsensitive)
>
> *B*: Have you ever intentionally cheated on your income tax? (Sensitive)

We know that $P(\text{answer yes}|\text{answer } A) = 1/2$. We wish to approximate $P(\text{answer yes}|\text{answer } B)$. The subject is asked to flip a coin and answer *A* if the coin comes up heads and otherwise to answer *B*. In this way, the interviewer does not know which question the subject is answering. Thus, a "yes" answer is not incriminating. There is no way for the interviewer to know whether the subject is saying "Yes, my Social Security number ends in an odd digit" or "Yes, I have intentionally cheated on my income taxes." The percentage of subjects in the group answering "yes" is used to approximate $P(\text{answer yes})$.

a. Use the fact that the event "answer yes" is the union of the event "answer yes and answer *A*" with the event "answer yes and answer *B*" to prove that

$$P(\text{answer yes}|\text{answer } B)$$
$$= \frac{P(\text{answer yes}) - P(\text{answer yes}|\text{answer } A) \cdot P(\text{answer } A)}{P(\text{answer } B)}.$$

b. If this technique is tried on 100 subjects and 60 answered "yes," what is the approximate probability that a person randomly selected from the group has intentionally cheated on income taxes?

88. *Police Lineup* To illustrate the difficulties with eyewitness identifications from police lineups, John Allen Paulos considers a "lineup" of three pennies, in which we know that two are fair (innocent) and the third (the culprit) has a 75%

probability of landing heads.[†] The probability of picking the culprit by chance is, of course, 1/3. Suppose we observe three heads in a row on one of the pennies. If we then guess that this penny is the culprit, what is the probability that we're right?

89. *SIDS* On July 15, 2005, a panel in England ruled that Roy Meadow, a renowned expert on child abuse and co-founder of London's Royal College of Paediatrics and Child Health, should be erased from the register of physicians in Britain for his faulty statistics at the trial of Sally Clark, who was convicted of murdering her first two babies.[‡] Meadow testified at the trial that the probability of a baby dying of sudden death syndrome (SIDS) is $1/8543$. He then calculated that the probability of two babies in a family dying of SIDS is $(1/8543)^2 \approx 1/73,000,000$. With such a small probability of both babies dying of SIDS, he concluded that the babies were instead murdered. What assumption did Meadow make in doing this calculation? Discuss reasons why this assumption may be invalid. (*Note:* Clark spent three years in prison before her conviction was reversed.)

PHYSICAL SCIENCES

90. *Earthquake* It has been reported that government scientists have predicted that the odds for a major earthquake occurring in the San Francisco Bay area during the next 30 years are 9 to 1.[§] What is the probability that a major earthquake will occur during the next 30 years in San Francisco?

GENERAL INTEREST

91. *Making a First Down* A first down is desirable in football—it guarantees four more plays by the team making it, assuming no score or turnover occurs in the plays. After getting a first down, a team can get another by advancing the ball at least 10 yards. During the four plays given by a first down, a team's position will be indicated by a phrase such as "third and 4," which means that the team has already had two of its four plays, and that 4 more yards are needed to get 10 yards necessary for another first down. An article in a management journal[‖] offers the following

*Milton, J. S. and J. J. Corbet, *Applied Statistics with Probability.* Copyright © 1979 by Litton Educational Publishing, Inc. Reprinted by permission of Brooks/Cole Publishing Company, Monterey, California.

†John Allen Paulos, "Coins and Confused Eyewitnesses: Calculating the Probability of Picking the Wrong Guy," *Who's Counting*, Feb. 1, 2001. http://more.abcnews.go.com/sections/science/ whoscounting _index/whoscounting_index.html.

‡*Science*, Vol. 309, July 22, 2005, p. 543.

§*The San Francisco Chronicle*, June 8, 1994, p. A1.

‖Carter, Virgil and Robert Machols, "Optimal Strategies on Fourth Down," *Management Science*, Vol. 24, No. 16, Dec. 1978. Copyright © 1978 by The Institute of Management Sciences.

results for 189 games for a particular National Football League season. "Trials" represents the number of times a team tried to make a first down, given that it was currently playing either a third or a fourth down. Here, n represents the number of yards still needed for a first down.

n	Trials	Successes	Probability of Making First Down with n Yards to Go
1	543	388	
2	327	186	
3	356	146	
4	302	97	
5	336	91	

a. Complete the table.

b. Why is the sum of the answers in the table not equal to 1?

92. *States* Of the 50 United States, the following is true:

22 are west of the Mississippi River (western states);*

22 had populations less than 3 million in the 2000 census (small states);

26 begin with the letters A through M (early states);

9 are large late (beginning with the letters N through Z) eastern states;

13 are small western states;

10 are small early states;

5 are small early western states.

a. How many western states had populations more than 3 million in the 2000 census and begin with the letters N through Z?

b. How many states east of the Mississippi had populations more than 3 million in the 2000 census?

93. *Music* Country-western songs often emphasize three basic themes: love, prison, and trucks. A survey of the local country-western radio station produced the following data:

12 songs were about a truckdriver who was in love while in prison;

13 were about a prisoner in love;

28 were about a person in love;

18 were about a truckdriver in love;

33 were about people not in prison;

18 were about prisoners;

15 were about truckdrivers who were in prison;

16 were about truckdrivers who were not in prison.

a. How many songs were surveyed?

Find the number of songs about

b. truckdrivers;

c. prisoners;

d. truckdrivers in prison;

e. people not in prison;

f. people not in love.

94 *Gambling* The following puzzle was featured on the Puzzler part of the radio program *Car Talk* on February 23, 2002.[†] A con man puts three cards in a bag; one card is green on both sides, one is red on both sides, and the third is green on one side and red on the other. He lets you pick one card out of the bag and put it on a table, so you can see that a red side is face up, but neither of you can see the other side. He offers to bet you even money that the other side is also red. In other words, if you bet $1, you lose if the other side is red but get back $2 if the other side is green. Is this a good bet? What is the probability that the other side is red?

95. *Missiles* In his novel *Debt of Honor*, Tom Clancy writes the following:[‡]

"There were ten target points—missile silos, the intelligence data said, and it pleased the Colonel [Zacharias] to be eliminating the hateful things, even though the price of that was the lives of other men. There were only three of them [bombers], and his bomber, like the others, carried only eight weapons [smart bombs]. The total number of weapons carried for the mission was only twenty-four, with two designated for each silo, and Zacharias's last four for the last target. Two bombs each. Every bomb had a 95% probability of hitting within four meters of the aim point, pretty good numbers really, except that this sort of mission had precisely no margin for error. Even the paper probability was less than half a percent chance of a double miss, but that number times ten targets meant a 5% chance that [at least] one missile would survive, and that could not be tolerated."

Determine whether the calculations in this quote are correct by the following steps.

a. Given that each bomb had a 95% probability of hitting the missile silo on which it was dropped, and that two bombs were dropped on each silo, what is the probability of a double miss?

---

*We count here states such as Minnesota, which has more than half of its area to the west of the Mississippi.

[†]http://www.cartalk.com/content/puzzler/2002.html.

[‡]Clancy, Tom, *Debt of Honor*, New York: G. P. Putnam's Sons, 1994, pp. 686–687.

b. What is the probability that a specific silo was destroyed (that is, that at least one bomb of the two bombs struck the silo)?

c. What is the probability that all ten silos were destroyed?

d. What is the probability that at least one silo survived? Does this agree with the quote?

e. What assumptions need to be made for the calculations in parts a through d to be valid? Discuss whether these assumptions seem reasonable.

96 *Viewing Habits* A survey of a group's viewing habits over the last year revealed the following information:

(i) 28% watched gymnastics;

(ii) 29% watched baseball;

(iii) 19% watched soccer;

(iv) 14% watched gymnastics and baseball;

(v) 12% watched baseball and soccer;

(vi) 10% watched gymnastics and soccer;

(vii) 8% watched all three sports.

Calculate the percentage of the group that watched none of the three sports during the last year.* (Choose one of the following.)

a. 24   **b.** 36   **c.** 41   **d.** 52   **e.** 60

---

*Problem 1 from May 2003 Course 1 Examination of the *Education and Examination Committee of the Society of Actuaries*. Reprinted by permission of the Society of Actuaries.

Medical Diagnosis

When a patient is examined, information (typically incomplete) is obtained about his or her state of health. Probability theory provides a mathematical model appropriate for this situation, as well as a procedure for quantitatively interpreting such partial information to arrive at a reasonable diagnosis.*

To develop a model, we list the states of health that can be distinguished in such a way that the patient can be in one and only one state at the time of the examination. For each state of health H, we associate a number, $P(H)$, between 0 and 1 such that the sum of all these numbers is 1. This number $P(H)$ represents the probability, before examination, that a patient is in the state of health H, and $P(H)$ may be chosen subjectively from medical experience, using any information available prior to the examination. The probability may be most conveniently established from clinical records; that is, a mean probability is established for patients in general, although the number would vary from patient to patient. Of course, the more information that is brought to bear in establishing $P(H)$, the better the diagnosis.

For example, limiting the discussion to the condition of a patient's heart, suppose there are exactly three states of health, with probabilities as follows.

	State of Health, H	$P(H)$
H_1	Patient has a normal heart	0.8
H_2	Patient has minor heart irregularities	0.15
H_3	Patient has a severe heart condition	0.05

Having selected $P(H)$, the information from the examination is processed. First, the results of the examination must be classified. The examination itself consists of observing the state of a number of characteristics of the patient. Let us assume that the examination for a heart condition consists of a stethoscope examination and a cardiogram. The outcome of such an examination, C, might be one of the following:

C_1 = stethoscope shows normal heart
   and cardiogram shows normal heart;

C_2 = stethoscope shows normal heart
   and cardiogram shows minor irregularities;

and so on.

It remains to assess for each state of health H the conditional probability $P(C|H)$ of each examination outcome C using only the knowledge that a patient is in a given state of health. (This may be based on the medical knowledge and clinical experience of the doctor.) The conditional probabilities $P(C|H)$ will not vary from patient to patient (although they should be reviewed periodically), so that they may be built into a diagnostic system.

Suppose the result of the examination is C_1. Let us assume the following probabilities:

$$P(C_1|H_1) = 0.9,$$
$$P(C_1|H_2) = 0.4,$$
$$P(C_1|H_3) = 0.1.$$

Now, for a given patient, the appropriate probability associated with each state of health H, after examination, is $P(H|C)$, where C is the outcome of the examination. This can be calculated by using Bayes' theorem. For example, to find $P(H_1|C_1)$—that is, the probability that the patient has a normal heart given that the examination showed a normal stethoscope examination and a normal cardiogram—we use Bayes' theorem as follows:

$$P(H_1|C_1)$$
$$= \frac{P(C_1|H_1)P(H_1)}{P(C_1|H_1)P(H_1) + P(C_1|H_2)P(H_2) + P(C_1|H_3)P(H_3)}$$
$$= \frac{(0.9)(0.8)}{(0.9)(0.8) + (0.4)(0.15) + (0.1)(0.05)} \approx 0.92.$$

Hence, the probability is about 0.92 that the patient has a normal heart on the basis of the examination results. This means that in 8 out of 100 patients, some abnormality will be present and not be detected by the stethoscope or the cardiogram.

*Wright. Roger, "Probabilistic Medical Diagnosis," *Some Mathematical Models in Biology*, rev. ed., Robert M. Thrall, ed., University of Michigan, 1967. Used by permission of Robert M. Thrall.

EXERCISES

1. Find $P(H_2|C_1)$.

2. Assuming the following probabilities, find $P(H_1|C_2)$.

$$P(C_2|H_1) = 0.2 \qquad P(C_2|H_2) = 0.8 \qquad P(C_2|H_3) = 0.3$$

3. Assuming the probabilities of Exercise 2, find $P(H_3|C_2)$.

DIRECTIONS FOR GROUP PROJECT

Find an article on medical decision making from a medical journal and develop a doctor–patient scenario for that particular decision. Then create a role-playing activity where the doctor and nurse present the various options and the mathematics associated with making such a decision to a patient. Make sure to present the mathematics in a manner that the average patient might understand. (Hint: Many leading medical journals include articles on medical decision making. One particular journal that certainly includes such research is Medical Decision Making.*)*

8

Counting Principles; Further Probability Topics

If you have 31 ice cream flavors available, how many different three-scoop cones can you make? The answer, which is surprisingly large, involves counting permutations or combinations, the subject of the first two sections in this chapter. The counting formulas we will develop have important applications in probability theory.

In this chapter, we continue our discussion of probability theory. To use the basic definition of probability, $P(E) = n(E)/n(S)$ (where S is the sample space with equally likely outcomes), up to now we have simply listed the outcomes in S and in E. However, when S has many outcomes, listing them all becomes very tedious. In the first two sections of this chapter, we introduce methods for counting the number of outcomes in a set without actually listing them, and then we use this approach in the third section to find probabilities. In the section on binomial probability (repeated independent trials of an experiment with only two possible outcomes), we introduce a formula for finding the probability of a certain number of successes in a number of trials. The final section continues the discussion of probability distributions that we began in Chapter 7.

8.1 The Multiplication Principle; Permutations

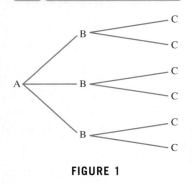

FIGURE 1

? THINK ABOUT IT

In how many ways can seven panelists be seated in a row of seven chairs?

Before answering this question, let's begin with a simpler example. If there are 3 roads from town A to town B and 2 roads from town B to town C, in how many ways can a person travel from A to C by way of B? For each of the 3 roads from A there are 2 different routes leading from B to C, or a total of $3 \cdot 2 = 6$ different ways for the trip, as shown in Figure 1. This example illustrates a general principle of counting, called the **multiplication principle**.

MULTIPLICATION PRINCIPLE

Suppose n choices must be made, with

$$m_1 \text{ ways to make choice 1,}$$

and for each of these ways,

$$m_2 \text{ ways to make choice 2,}$$

and so on, with

$$m_n \text{ ways to make choice } n.$$

Then there are

$$m_1 \cdot m_2 \cdot \cdots \cdot m_n$$

different ways to make the entire sequence of choices.

EXAMPLE 1 **Combination Lock**

A certain combination lock can be set to open to any 3-letter sequence.

(a) How many sequences are possible?

▶**Solution** Since there are 26 letters in the alphabet, there are 26 choices for each of the 3 letters. By the multiplication principle, there are $26 \cdot 26 \cdot 26 = 17{,}576$ different sequences.

(b) How many sequences are possible if no letter is repeated?

▶**Solution** There are 26 choices for the first letter. It cannot be used again, so there are 25 choices for the second letter and then 24 choices for the third letter. Consequently, the number of such sequences is $26 \cdot 25 \cdot 24 = 15{,}600$.

EXAMPLE 2 Morse Code

Morse code uses a sequence of dots and dashes to represent letters and words. How many sequences are possible with at most 3 symbols?

▶**Solution** "At most 3" means "1 or 2 or 3" here. Each symbol may be either a dot or a dash. Thus the following number of sequences are possible in each case.

Number of Symbols	Number of Sequences
1	**2**
2	$\mathbf{2 \cdot 2 = 4}$
3	$\mathbf{2 \cdot 2 \cdot 2 = 8}$

Altogether, $2 + 4 + 8 = 14$ different sequences are possible.

EXAMPLE 3 I Ching

yin   yang

FIGURE 2

An ancient Chinese philosophical work known as the *I Ching (Book of Changes)* is often used as an oracle from which people can seek and obtain advice. The philosophy describes the duality of the universe in terms of two primary forces: *yin* (passive, dark, receptive) and *yang* (active, light, creative). Figure 2 shows the traditional symbol for yin and yang. The yin energy can also be represented by a broken line (– –) and the yang by a solid line (—). These lines are written on top of one another in groups of three, known as *trigrams*. For example, the trigram ☱ is called *Tui*, the Joyous, and has the image of a lake.

(a) How many trigrams are there altogether?

▶**Solution** Think of choosing between the 2 types of lines for each of the 3 positions in the trigram. There will be 2 choices for each position, so there are $2 \cdot 2 \cdot 2 = 8$ different trigrams.

(b) The trigrams are grouped together, one on top of the other, in pairs known as *hexagrams*. Each hexagram represents one aspect of the *I Ching* philosophy. How many hexagrams are there?

▶**Solution** For each position in the hexagram there are 8 possible trigrams, giving $8 \cdot 8 = 64$ hexagrams.

EXAMPLE 4 Books

A teacher has 5 different books that he wishes to arrange side by side. How many different arrangements are possible?

▶**Solution** Five choices will be made, one for each space that will hold a book. Any of the 5 books could be chosen for the first space. There are 4 choices for the second space, since 1 book has already been placed in the first space; there are 3 choices for the third space, and so on. By the multiplication principle, the number of different possible arrangements is $5 \cdot 4 \cdot 3 \cdot 2 \cdot 1 = 120$.

FOR REVIEW

The natural numbers, also referred to as the positive integers, are the numbers 1, 2, 3, 4, etc.

The use of the multiplication principle often leads to products such as $5 \cdot 4 \cdot 3 \cdot 2 \cdot 1$, the product of all the natural numbers from 5 down to 1. If n is a natural number, the symbol $n!$ (read "*n factorial*") denotes the product of all the natural numbers from n down to 1. If $n = 1$, this formula is understood to give $1! = 1$.

FACTORIAL NOTATION

For any natural number n,

$$n! = n(n - 1)(n - 2) \cdots (3)(2)(1).$$

Also, by definition,

$$0! = 1.$$

With this symbol, the product $5 \cdot 4 \cdot 3 \cdot 2 \cdot 1$ can be written as $5!$. Also, $3! = 3 \cdot 2 \cdot 1 = 6$. The definition of $n!$ could be used to show that $n[(n - 1)]! = n!$ for all natural numbers $n \geq 2$. It is helpful if this result also holds for $n = 1$. This can happen only if $0!$ equals 1, as defined above.

Most calculators have an $n!$ key. A calculator with a 10-digit display and scientific notation capability will usually give the exact value of $n!$ for $n \leq 13$, and approximate values of $n!$ for $14 \leq n \leq 69$. The value of $70!$ is approximately 1.198×10^{100}, which is too large for most calculators. To see how large $70!$ is, suppose a computer counted the numbers from 1 to $70!$ at a rate of 1 billion numbers per second. If the computer started when the universe began, by now it would only be done with a tiny fraction of the total.

On many graphing calculators, the factorial of a number is accessible through a menu. On the TI-83/84 Plus, for example, this menu is found by pressing the MATH key, and then selecting PRB (for probability).

EXAMPLE 5 **Books**

Suppose the teacher in Example 4 wishes to place only 3 of the 5 books on his desk. How many arrangements of 3 books are possible?

▶**Solution** The teacher again has 5 ways to fill the first space, 4 ways to fill the second space, and 3 ways to fill the third. Since he wants to use only 3 books, only 3 spaces can be filled (3 events) instead of 5, for $5 \cdot 4 \cdot 3 = 60$ arrangements.

Permutations   The answer 60 in Example 5 is called the number of *permutations* of 5 things taken 3 at a time. A **permutation** of r (where $r \geq 1$) elements from a set of n elements is any specific ordering or arrangement, *without repetition*, of the r elements. Each rearrangement of the r elements is a different permutation. The number of permutations of n things taken r at a time (with $r \leq n$) is written $P(n, r)$. Based on the work in Example 5,

$$P(5, 3) = 5 \cdot 4 \cdot 3 = 60.$$

Factorial notation can be used to express this product as follows.

$$5 \cdot 4 \cdot 3 = 5 \cdot 4 \cdot 3 \cdot \frac{2 \cdot 1}{2 \cdot 1} = \frac{5 \cdot 4 \cdot 3 \cdot 2 \cdot 1}{2 \cdot 1} = \frac{5!}{2!} = \frac{5!}{(5 - 3)!}$$

This example illustrates the general rule of permutations, which can be stated as follows.

PERMUTATIONS

If $P(n, r)$ (where $r \leq n$) is the number of permutations of n elements taken r at a time, then

$$P(n, r) = \frac{n!}{(n - r)!}.$$

CAUTION The letter P here represents *permutations*, not *probability*. In probability notation, the quantity in parentheses describes an *event*. In permutations notation, the quantity in parentheses always comprises *two numbers*. ■

The proof of the permutations rule follows the discussion in Example 5. There are n ways to choose the first of the r elements, $n - 1$ ways to choose the second, and $n - r + 1$ ways to choose the rth element, so that

$$P(n, r) = n(n - 1)(n - 2) \cdots (n - r + 1).$$

Now multiply on the right by $(n - r)!/(n - r)!$.

$$P(n, r) = n(n - 1)(n - 2) \cdots (n - r + 1) \cdot \frac{(n - r)!}{(n - r)!}$$

$$= \frac{n(n - 1)(n - 2) \cdots (n - r + 1)(n - r)!}{(n - r)!}$$

$$= \frac{n!}{(n - r)!}$$

NOTE Because we defined 0! equal to 1, the formula for permutations gives the special case

$$P(n, n) = \frac{n!}{(n - n)!} = \frac{n!}{0!} = \frac{n!}{1} = n!.$$

This result also follows from the multiplication principle, because $P(n, n)$ gives the number of permutations of n objects, and there are n choices for the first object, $n - 1$ for the second, and so on, down to just 1 choice for the last object. Example 4 illustrated this idea. ■

The number of permutations of a set with n elements is $n!$.

To find $P(n, r)$, we can use either the permutations formula or direct application of the multiplication principle, as the following example shows.

EXAMPLE 6   Politics

In mid 2007, eight candidates sought the Democratic nomination for president. In how many ways could voters rank their first, second, and third choices?

▶ Solution

METHOD 1
Calculating by Hand

This is the same as finding the number of permutations of 8 elements taken 3 at a time. Since there are 3 choices to be made, the multiplication principle gives $P(8, 3) = 8 \cdot 7 \cdot 6 = 336$. Alternatively, use the permutations formula to get

$$P(8, 3) = \frac{8!}{(8 - 3)!} = \frac{8!}{5!} = \frac{8 \cdot 7 \cdot 6 \cdot 5 \cdot 4 \cdot 3 \cdot 2 \cdot 1}{5 \cdot 4 \cdot 3 \cdot 2 \cdot 1} = 8 \cdot 7 \cdot 6 = 336.$$

METHOD 2
Graphing Calculator

Graphing calculators have the capacity to compute permutations. For example, on a TI-83/84 Plus, $P(8, 3)$ can be calculated by inputting 8 followed by nPr (found in the MATH-PRB menu), and a 3 yielding 336, as shown in Figure 3.

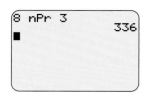

FIGURE 3

METHOD 3
Spreadsheet

Spreadsheets can also compute permutations. For example, in Microsoft Excel, $P(8, 3)$ can be calculated by inputting 8 and 3 in cells, say, A1 and B1, and then typing "=FACT(A1)/FACT(A1-B1)" in cell C1 or, for that matter, any other cell.

CAUTION   When calculating the number of permutations with the formula, do not try to cancel unlike factorials. For example,

$$\frac{8!}{4!} \neq 2! = 2 \cdot 1 = 2.$$

$$\frac{8!}{4!} = \frac{8 \cdot 7 \cdot 6 \cdot 5 \cdot 4 \cdot 3 \cdot 2 \cdot 1}{4 \cdot 3 \cdot 2 \cdot 1} = 8 \cdot 7 \cdot 6 \cdot 5 = 1680.$$

Always write out the factors first, then cancel where appropriate. ■

EXAMPLE 7   Permutations

Find the following.

(a) The number of permutations of the letters A, B, and C

▶ Solution By the formula for $P(n, r)$ with both n and r equal to 3,

$$P(3, 3) = \frac{3!}{(3 - 3)!} = \frac{3!}{0!} = \frac{3!}{1} = 3 \cdot 2 \cdot 1 = 6.$$

The 6 permutations (or arrangements) are

$$ABC, \quad ACB, \quad BAC, \quad BCA, \quad CAB, \quad CBA.$$

(b) The number of permutations if just 2 of the letters A, B, and C are to be used

▶**Solution** Find $P(3, 2)$.

$$P(3, 2) = \frac{3!}{(3 - 2)!} = \frac{3!}{1!} = 3! = 6$$

This result is exactly the same answer as in part (a). This is because, in the case of $P(3, 3)$, after the first 2 choices are made, the third is already determined, as shown in the table below.

First Two Letters	AB	AC	BA	BC	CA	CB
Third Letter	C	B	C	A	B	A

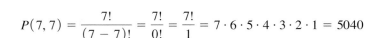

EXAMPLE 8 **Television**

A televised talk show will include 4 women and 3 men as panelists.

(a) In how many ways can the panelists be seated in a row of 7 chairs?

▶**Solution** Find $P(7, 7)$, the total number of ways to seat 7 panelists in 7 chairs.

$$P(7, 7) = \frac{7!}{(7 - 7)!} = \frac{7!}{0!} = \frac{7!}{1} = 7 \cdot 6 \cdot 5 \cdot 4 \cdot 3 \cdot 2 \cdot 1 = 5040$$

There are 5040 ways to seat the 7 panelists.

(b) In how many ways can the panelists be seated if the men and women are to be alternated?

▶**Solution** Use the multiplication principle. In order to alternate men and women, a woman must be seated in the first chair (since there are 4 women and only 3 men), any of the men next, and so on. Thus there are 4 ways to fill the first seat, 3 ways to fill the second seat, 3 ways to fill the third seat (with any of the 3 remaining women), and so on. This gives

$$4 \cdot 3 \cdot 3 \cdot 2 \cdot 2 \cdot 1 \cdot 1 = 144$$

ways to seat the panelists.

(c) In how many ways can the panelists be seated if the men must sit together, and the women must also sit together?

▶**Solution** Use the multiplication principle. We first must decide how to arrange the two groups (men and women). There are 2! ways of doing this. Next, there are 4! ways of arranging the women and 3! ways of arranging the men, for a total of

$$2! \, 4! \, 3! = 2 \cdot 24 \cdot 6 = 288$$

ways.

(d) In how many ways can one woman and one man from the panel be selected?

▶**Solution** There are 4 ways to pick the woman and 3 ways to pick the man, for a total of

$$4 \cdot 3 = 12$$

ways.

NOTE It might help you to add spaces into which you can put the numbers, and below each space denote briefly which choice you're making in each space, such as W_1 for the first woman and M_1 for the first man. For instance, in Example 8(b), we could write the solution in the following manner.

$$\underline{4} \cdot \underline{3} \cdot \underline{3} \cdot \underline{2} \cdot \underline{2} \cdot \underline{1} \cdot \underline{1} = 144$$
$$W_1 \quad M_1 \quad W_2 \quad M_2 \quad W_3 \quad M_3 \quad W_4$$

If the n objects in a permutation are not all distinguishable—that is, if there are n_1 of type 1, n_2 of type 2, and so on for r different types, then the number of **distinguishable permutations** is

$$\frac{n!}{n_1! \, n_2! \cdots n_r!}.$$

For example, suppose we want to find the number of permutations of the numbers 1, 1, 4, 4, 4. We cannot distinguish between the two 1's or among the three 4's, so using 5! would give too many distinguishable arrangements. Since the two 1's are indistinguishable and account for 2! of the permutations, we divide 5! by 2!. Similarly, we also divide by 3! to account for the three indistinguishable 4's. This gives

$$\frac{5!}{2! \, 3!} = 10$$

permutations.

EXAMPLE 9 Mississippi

In how many ways can the letters in the word *Mississippi* be arranged?

▶**Solution** This word contains 1 m, 4 i's, 4 s's, and 2 p's. To use the formula, let $n = 11, n_1 = 1, n_2 = 4, n_3 = 4$, and $n_4 = 2$ to get

$$\frac{11!}{1! \, 4! \, 4! \, 2!} = 34{,}650$$

arrangements.

NOTE If Example 9 had asked for the number of ways that the letters in a word with 11 *different* letters could be arranged, the answer would be $11! = 39{,}916{,}800$. ■

EXAMPLE 10 Yogurt

A student buys 3 cherry yogurts, 2 raspberry yogurts, and 2 blueberry yogurts. She puts them in her dormitory refrigerator to eat one a day for the next week. Assuming yogurts of the same flavor are indistinguishable, in how many ways can she select yogurts to eat for the next week?

►**Solution** This problem is again one of distinguishable permutations. The 7 yogurts can be selected in 7! ways, but since the 3 cherry, 2 raspberry, and 2 blueberry yogurts are indistinguishable, the total number of distinguishable orders in which the yogurts can be selected is

$$\frac{7!}{3!\,2!\,2!} = 210.$$

➡ **8.1 Exercises**

In Exercises 1–12, evaluate the factorial or permutation.

1. 6!
2. 7!
3. 15!
4. 16!

5. $P(13, 2)$
6. $P(12, 3)$
7. $P(38, 17)$
8. $P(33, 19)$

9. $P(n, 0)$
10. $P(n, n)$
11. $P(n, 1)$
12. $P(n, n - 1)$

13. How many different types of homes are available if a builder offers a choice of 6 basic plans, 3 roof styles, and 2 exterior finishes?

14. A menu offers a choice of 3 salads, 8 main dishes, and 7 desserts. How many different meals consisting of one salad, one main dish, and one dessert are possible?

15. A couple has narrowed down the choice of a name for their new baby to 4 first names and 5 middle names. How many different first- and middle-name arrangements are possible?

16. In a club with 16 members, how many ways can a slate of 3 officers consisting of president, vice-president, and secretary/treasurer be chosen?

17. Define *permutation* in your own words.

18. In Example 7, there are six 3-letter permutations of the letters A, B, and C. How many 3-letter subsets (unordered groups of letters) are there?

19. In Example 7, how many unordered 2-letter subsets of the letters A, B, and C are there?

20. Find the number of distinguishable permutations of the letters in each word.

  a. initial
  b. little
  c. decreed

21. A printer has 5 A's, 4 B's, 2 C's, and 2 D's. How many different "words" are possible that use all these letters? (A "word" does not have to have any meaning here.)

22. Wing has different books to arrange on a shelf: 4 blue, 3 green, and 2 red.

  a. In how many ways can the books be arranged on a shelf?

  b. If books of the same color are to be grouped together, how many arrangements are possible?

  c. In how many distinguishable ways can the books be arranged if books of the same color are identical but need not be grouped together?

  d. In how many ways can you select 3 books, one of each color, if the order in which the books are selected does not matter?

  e. In how many ways can you select 3 books, one of each color, if the order in which the books are selected matters?

23. A child has a set of differently shaped plastic objects. There are 3 pyramids, 4 cubes, and 7 spheres.

  a. In how many ways can she arrange the objects in a row if each is a different color?

b. How many arrangements are possible if objects of the same shape must be grouped together and each object is a different color?

c. In how many distinguishable ways can the objects be arranged in a row if objects of the same shape are also the same color, but need not be grouped together?

d. In how many ways can you select 3 objects, one of each shape, if the order in which the objects are selected does not matter and each object is a different color?

e. In how many ways can you select 3 objects, one of each shape, if the order in which the objects are selected matters and each object is a different color?

24. Some students find it puzzling that $0! = 1$, and think that $0!$ should equal 0. If this were true, what would be the value of $P(4, 4)$ using the permutations formula?

25. If you already knew the value of 9!, how could you find the value of 10! quickly?

26. Given that 450! is approximately equal to $1.7333687 \times 10^{1000}$ (to 8 digits of accuracy), find 451! to 7 digits of accuracy.

27. When calculating $n!$, the number of ending zeros in the answer can be determined prior to calculating the actual number by finding the number of times 5 can be factored from $n!$. For example, 7! only has one 5 occurring in its calculation, and so there is only one ending zero in 5040. The number 10! has two 5's (one from the 5 and one from the 10) and so there must be two ending zeros in the answer 3,628,800. Use this idea to determine the number of zeros that occur in the following factorials, and then explain why this works.

    a. 13!   **b.** 27!   **c.** 75!

28. Because of the view screen, calculators only show a fixed number of digits, often 10 digits. Thus, an approximation of a number will be shown by only including the 10 largest place values of the number. Using the ideas from the previous exercise, determine if the following numbers are correct or if they are incorrect by checking if they have the correct number of ending zeros. (*Note:* Just because a number has the correct number of zeros does not imply that it is correct.)

    a. $12! = 479,001,610$ **b.** $23! = 25,852,016,740,000,000,000,000$

    c. $15! = 1,307,643,680,000$ **d.** $14! = 87,178,291,200$

▶ Applications

BUSINESS AND ECONOMICS

29. *Automobile Manufacturing* An automobile manufacturer produces 8 models, each available in 7 different exterior colors, with 4 different upholstery fabrics and 5 interior colors. How many varieties of automobile are available?

LIFE SCIENCES

30. *Drug Sequencing* Twelve drugs have been found to be effective in the treatment of a disease. It is believed that the sequence in which the drugs are administered is important in the effectiveness of the treatment. In how many different sequences can 5 of the 12 drugs be administered?

31. *Insect Classification* A biologist is attempting to classify 52,000 species of insects by assigning 3 initials to each species. Is it possible to classify all the species in this way? If not, how many initials should be used?

32. *Genetics Experiment* In how many ways can 7 of 11 monkeys be arranged in a row for a genetics experiment?

SOCIAL SCIENCES

33. *Social Science Experiment* In an experiment on social interaction, 6 people will sit in 6 seats in a row. In how many ways can this be done?

34. *Election Ballots* In an election with 3 candidates for one office and 6 candidates for another office, how many different ballots may be printed?

GENERAL INTEREST

35. *Course Scheduling* A business school gives courses in typing, shorthand, transcription, business English, technical writing, and accounting. In how many ways can a student arrange a schedule if 3 courses are taken? Assume that the order in which courses are scheduled matters.

36. *Course Scheduling* If your college offers 400 courses, 25 of which are in mathematics, and your counselor arranges your schedule of 4 courses by random selection, how many schedules are possible that do not include a math course? Assume that the order in which courses are scheduled matters.

37. *Baseball Teams* A baseball team has 19 players. How many 9-player batting orders are possible?

38. *Union Elections* A chapter of union Local 715 has 35 members. In how many different ways can the chapter select a president, a vice-president, a treasurer, and a secretary?

39. *Programming Music* A concert to raise money for an economics prize is to consist of 5 works: 2 overtures, 2 sonatas, and a piano concerto.

  a. In how many ways can the program be arranged?

  b. In how many ways can the program be arranged if an overture must come first?

40. *Programming Music* A zydeco band from Louisiana will play 5 traditional and 3 original Cajun compositions at a concert. In how many ways can they arrange the program if

  a. they begin with a traditional piece?

  b. an original piece will be played last?

41. *Television Scheduling* The television schedule for a certain evening shows 8 choices from 8 to 9 P.M., 5 choices from 9 to 10 P.M., and 7 choices from 10 to 11 P.M. In how many different ways could a person schedule that evening of television viewing from 8 to 11 P.M.? (Assume each program that is selected is watched for an entire hour.)

42. *Radio Station Call Letters* How many different 4-letter radio station call letters can be made if

  a. the first letter must be K or W and no letter may be repeated?

  b. repeats are allowed, but the first letter is K or W?

  c. the first letter is K or W, there are no repeats, and the last letter is R?

43. *Telephone Numbers* How many 7-digit telephone numbers are possible if the first digit cannot be zero and

  a. only odd digits may be used?

  b. the telephone number must be a multiple of 10 (that is, it must end in zero)?

  c. the telephone number must be a multiple of 100?

  d. the first 3 digits are 481?

  e. no repetitions are allowed?

Telephone Area Codes Several years ago, the United States began running out of telephone numbers. Telephone companies introduced new area codes as numbers were used up, and eventually almost all area codes were used up.

44. a. Until recently, all area codes had a 0 or 1 as the middle digit, and the first digit could not be 0 or 1. How many area codes are there with this arrangement? How many telephone numbers does the current 7-digit sequence permit per area code? (The 3-digit sequence that follows the area code cannot start with 0 or 1. Assume there are no other restrictions.)

  b. The actual number of area codes under the previous system was 152. Explain the discrepancy between this number and your answer to part a.

45. The shortage of area codes was avoided by removing the restriction on the second digit. (This resulted in problems for some older equipment, which used the second digit to determine that a long-distance call was being made.) How many area codes are available under the new system?

46. *License Plates* For many years, the state of California used 3 letters followed by 3 digits on its automobile license plates.

  a. How many different license plates are possible with this arrangement?

  b. When the state ran out of new numbers, the order was reversed to 3 digits followed by 3 letters. How many new license plate numbers were then possible?

  c. Several years ago, the numbers described in b were also used up. The state then issued plates with 1 letter followed by 3 digits and then 3 letters. How many new license plate numbers will this provide?

47. *Social Security Numbers* A social security number has 9 digits. How many social security numbers are there? The U.S. population in 2005 was about 296 million. Is it possible for every U.S. resident to have a unique social security number? (Assume no restrictions.)

48. *Postal Zip Codes* The U.S. Postal Service currently uses 5-digit zip codes in most areas. How many zip codes are possible if there are no restrictions on the digits used? How many would be possible if the first number could not be 0?

49. *Postal Zip Codes* The U.S. Postal Service is encouraging the use of 9-digit zip codes in some areas, adding 4 digits after the usual 5-digit code. How many such zip codes are possible with no restrictions?

50. *Games* The game of Sets* uses a special deck of cards. Each card has either one, two, or three identical shapes, all of the same color and style. There are three possible shapes: squiggle, diamond, and oval. There are three possible colors: green, purple, and red. There are three possible styles: solid, shaded, or outline. The deck consists of all possible combinations of shape, color, style, and number of shapes. How many cards are in the deck?

51. *Games* In the game of Scattergories,† the players take 12 turns. In each turn, a 20-sided die is rolled; each side has a letter. The players must then fill in 12 categories (e.g., vegetable, city, etc.) with a word beginning with the letter rolled. Considering that a game consists of 12 rolls of the 20-sided die, and that rolling the same side more than once is allowed, how many possible games are there?

52. *Games* The game of Twenty Questions consists of asking 20 questions to determine a person, place, or thing that the other person is thinking of. The first question, which is always "Is it an animal, vegetable, or mineral?" has three possible answers. All the other questions must be answered "Yes" or "No." How many possible objects can be distinguished in this game, assuming that all 20 questions are asked? Are 20 questions enough?

53. *Traveling Salesman* In the famous Traveling Salesman Problem, a salesman starts in any one of a set of cities, visits every city in the set once, and returns to the starting city. He would like to complete this circuit with the shortest possible distance.

a. Suppose the salesman has 10 cities to visit. Given that it does not matter what city he starts in, how many different circuits can he take?

b. The salesman decides to check all the different paths in part a to see which is shortest, but realizes that a circuit has the same distance whichever direction it is traveled. How many different circuits must he check?

c. Suppose the salesman has 70 cities to visit. Would it be feasible to have a computer check all the different circuits? Explain your reasoning.

54. *Circular Permutations* Circular permutations arise in applications involving arrangements around a closed loop, as in the previous exercise. Here are two examples.

a. A ferris wheel has 20 seats. How many ways can 20 students arrange themselves on the ferris wheel if each student takes a different seat? We consider two arrangements to be identical if they differ only by rotations of the wheel.

b. A necklace is to be strung with 15 beads, each of a different color. In how many ways can the beads be arranged? We consider two arrangements to be identical if they differ only by rotations of the necklace or by flipping the necklace over. (*Hint:* If every arrangement is counted twice, the correct number of arrangements can be found by dividing by 2.)

8.2 Combinations

? **THINK ABOUT IT** In how many ways can a manager select 4 employees for promotion from 12 eligible employees?

As we shall see, permutations alone cannot be used to answer this question, but combinations will provide the answer.

In the previous section, we saw that there are 60 ways that a teacher can arrange 3 of 5 different books on his desk. That is, there are 60 permutations of 5 books taken 3 at a time. Suppose now that the teacher does not wish to arrange the books on his desk, but rather wishes to choose, without regard to order, any 3 of the 5 books for a book sale to raise money for his school. In how many ways can this be done?

At first glance, we might say 60 again, but this is incorrect. The number 60 counts all possible *arrangements* of 3 books chosen from 5. The following

6 arrangements, however, would all lead to the same set of 3 books being given to the book sale.

mystery-biography-textbook	biography-textbook-mystery
mystery-textbook-biography	textbook-biography-mystery
biography-mystery-textbook	textbook-mystery-biography

The list shows 6 different *arrangements* of 3 books, but only one *subset* of 3 books. A subset of items listed *without regard to order* is called a **combination**. The number of combinations of 5 things taken 3 at a time is written $\binom{5}{3}$, and read "5 over 3" or "5 choose 3."* Since they are subsets, combinations are *not ordered*.

To evaluate $\binom{5}{3}$, start with the $5 \cdot 4 \cdot 3$ *permutations* of 5 things taken 3 at a time. Since combinations are not ordered, find the number of combinations by dividing the number of permutations by the number of ways each group of 3 can be ordered; that is, divide by 3!.

$$\binom{5}{3} = \frac{5 \cdot 4 \cdot 3}{3!} = \frac{5 \cdot 4 \cdot 3}{3 \cdot 2 \cdot 1} = 10$$

There are 10 ways that the teacher can choose 3 books for the book sale.

Generalizing this discussion gives the following formula for the number of combinations of n elements taken r at a time:

$$\binom{n}{r} = \frac{P(n, r)}{r!}.$$

Another version of this formula is found as follows.

$$\binom{n}{r} = \frac{P(n, r)}{r!}$$

$$= \frac{n!}{(n - r)!} \cdot \frac{1}{r!}$$

$$= \frac{n!}{(n - r)! \, r!}$$

The steps above lead to the following result.

COMBINATIONS

If $\binom{n}{r}$ denotes the number of combinations of n elements taken r at a time, where $r \leq n$, then

$$\binom{n}{r} = \frac{n!}{(n - r)! \, r!}.$$

---

*Other common notations for $\binom{n}{r}$ are $_nC_r$, C_r^n, and $C(n, r)$.

EXAMPLE 1 **Committees**

How many committees of 3 people can be formed from a group of 8 people?

►**Solution**

METHOD 1
Calculating by Hand

A committee is an unordered group, so use the combinations formula for $\binom{8}{3}$.

$$\binom{8}{3} = \frac{8!}{5!3!} = \frac{8 \cdot 7 \cdot 6 \cdot 5 \cdot 4 \cdot 3 \cdot 2 \cdot 1}{5 \cdot 4 \cdot 3 \cdot 2 \cdot 1 \cdot 3 \cdot 2 \cdot 1} = \frac{8 \cdot 7 \cdot 6}{3 \cdot 2 \cdot 1} = 56$$

METHOD 2
Graphing Calculator

Graphing calculators have the capacity to compute combinations. For example, on a TI-83/84 Plus, $\binom{8}{3}$ can be calculated by inputting 8 followed by `nCr` (found in the `MATH-PRB` menu) and a 3 yielding 56, as shown in Figure 4.

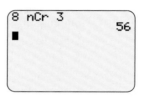

FIGURE 4

METHOD 3
Spreadsheet

Spreadsheets can also compute combinations. For example, in Microsoft Excel, $\binom{8}{3}$ can be calculated by inputting 8 and 3 in cells, say, A1 and B1, and then typing "`=FACT(A1)/(FACT(A1-B1)*FACT(B1))`" in cell C1 or, for that matter, any other cell.

Example 1 shows an alternative way to compute $\binom{n}{r}$. Take r or $n - r$, whichever is smaller. Write the factorial of this number in the denominator. In the numerator, write out a sufficient number of factors of $n!$ so there is one factor in the numerator for each factor in the denominator. For example, to calculate $\binom{8}{3}$ or $\binom{8}{5}$, write

$$\frac{8 \cdot 7 \cdot 6}{3 \cdot 2 \cdot 1} = 56.$$

The factors that are omitted (written in color in Example 1) cancel out of the numerator and denominator, so need not be included.

Notice from the previous discussion that $\binom{8}{3} = \binom{8}{5}$. (See Exercise 25 for a generalization of this idea.) One interpretation of this fact is that the number of ways to form a committee of 3 people chosen from a group of 8 is the same as the number of ways to choose the 5 people who are not on the committee.

Notice that this is *not* true with permutations: $P(8, 3) \neq P(8, 5)$.

EXAMPLE 2 Lawyers

Three lawyers are to be selected from a group of 30 to work on a special project.

(a) In how many different ways can the lawyers be selected?

▶**Solution** Here we wish to know the number of 3-element combinations that can be formed from a set of 30 elements. (We want combinations, not permutations, since order within the group of 3 doesn't matter.)

$$\binom{30}{3} = \frac{30!}{27!\,3!} = \frac{30 \cdot 29 \cdot 28 \cdot 27!}{27! \cdot 3 \cdot 2 \cdot 1}$$
$$= \frac{30 \cdot 29 \cdot 28}{3 \cdot 2 \cdot 1}$$
$$= 4060$$

There are 4060 ways to select the project group.

(b) In how many ways can the group of 3 be selected if a certain lawyer must work on the project?

▶**Solution** Since 1 lawyer already has been selected for the project, the problem is reduced to selecting 2 more from the remaining 29 lawyers.

$$\binom{29}{2} = \frac{29!}{27!\,2!} = \frac{29 \cdot 28 \cdot 27!}{27! \cdot 2 \cdot 1} = \frac{29 \cdot 28}{2 \cdot 1} = 29 \cdot 14 = 406$$

In this case, the project group can be selected in 406 ways.

(c) In how many ways can a nonempty group of at most 3 lawyers be selected from these 30 lawyers?

▶**Solution** Here, by "at most 3" we mean "1 or 2 or 3." (The number 0 is excluded because the group is nonempty.) Find the number of ways for each case.

Case	Number of Ways
1	$\binom{30}{1} = \dfrac{30!}{29!\,1!} = \dfrac{30 \cdot 29!}{29!\,(1)} = 30$
2	$\binom{30}{2} = \dfrac{30!}{28!\,2!} = \dfrac{30 \cdot 29 \cdot 28!}{28! \cdot 2 \cdot 1} = 435$
3	$\binom{30}{3} = \dfrac{30!}{27!\,3!} = \dfrac{30 \cdot 29 \cdot 28 \cdot 27!}{27! \cdot 3 \cdot 2 \cdot 1} = 4060$

The total number of ways to select at most 3 lawyers will be the sum

$$30 + 435 + 4060 = 4525.$$

EXAMPLE 3 Sales

A salesman has 10 accounts in a certain city.

(a) In how many ways can he select 3 accounts to call on?

▶**Solution** Within a selection of 3 accounts, the arrangement of the calls is not important, so there are

$$\binom{10}{3} = \frac{10!}{7!\,3!} = \frac{10 \cdot 9 \cdot 8}{3 \cdot 2 \cdot 1} = 120$$

ways he can make a selection of 3 accounts.

(b) In how many ways can he select at least 8 of the 10 accounts to use in preparing a report?

▶**Solution** "At least 8" means "8 or more," which is "8 or 9 or 10." First find the number of ways to choose in each case.

Case	Number of Ways
8	$\binom{10}{8} = \dfrac{10!}{2!\,8!} = \dfrac{10 \cdot 9}{2 \cdot 1} = 45$
9	$\binom{10}{9} = \dfrac{10!}{1!\,9!} = \dfrac{10}{1} = 10$
10	$\binom{10}{10} = \dfrac{10!}{0!\,10!} = 1$

He can select at least 8 of the 10 accounts in $45 + 10 + 1 = 56$ ways.

FOR REVIEW

Notice in Example 3 that to calculate the number of ways to select 8 or 9 or 10 accounts, we added the three numbers found. The union rule for sets from Chapter 7 says that when A and B are disjoint sets, the number of elements in A or B is the number of elements in A plus the number in B.

CAUTION When we are making a first decision *and* a second decision, we *multiply* to find the total number of ways. When we are making a decision in which the first choice *or* the second choice are valid choices, we *add* to find the total number of ways. ■

The formulas for permutations and combinations given in this section and in the previous section will be very useful in solving probability problems in the next section. Any difficulty in using these formulas usually comes from being unable to differentiate between them. Both permutations and combinations give the number of ways to choose r objects from a set of n objects. The differences between permutations and combinations are outlined in the following table.

Permutations	Combinations
Different orderings or arrangements of the r objects are different permutations.	Each choice or subset of r objects gives one combination. Order within the group of r objects does not matter.
$P(n, r) = \dfrac{n!}{(n - r)!}$	$\binom{n}{r} = \dfrac{n!}{(n - r)!\,r!}$
Clue words: arrangement, schedule, order	Clue words: group, committee, set, sample
Order matters!	**Order does not matter!**

In the next examples, concentrate on recognizing which formula should be applied.

EXAMPLE 4 **Permutations and Combinations**

For each problem, tell whether permutations or combinations should be used to solve the problem.

(a) How many 4-digit code numbers are possible if no digits are repeated?

▶**Solution** Since changing the order of the 4 digits results in a different code, use permutations.

(b) A sample of 3 light bulbs is randomly selected from a batch of 15. How many different samples are possible?

▶**Solution** The order in which the 3 light bulbs are selected is not important. The sample is unchanged if the items are rearranged, so combinations should be used.

(c) In a baseball conference with 8 teams, how many games must be played so that each team plays every other team exactly once?

▶**Solution** Selection of 2 teams for a game is an *unordered* subset of 2 from the set of 8 teams. Use combinations again.

(d) In how many ways can 4 patients be assigned to 6 different hospital rooms so that each patient has a private room?

▶**Solution** The room assignments are an *ordered* selection of 4 rooms from the 6 rooms. Exchanging the rooms of any 2 patients within a selection of 4 rooms gives a different assignment, so permutations should be used.

(e) Solve the problems in parts (a)–(d) above. The answers are given in the footnote.*

EXAMPLE 5 **Promotions**

A manager must select 4 employees for promotion; 12 employees are eligible.

(a) In how many ways can the 4 be chosen?

▶**Solution** Since there is no reason to differentiate among the 4 who are selected, use combinations.

$$\binom{12}{4} = \frac{12!}{8! \, 4!} = 495$$

(b) In how many ways can 4 employees be chosen (from 12) to be placed in 4 different jobs?

▶**Solution** In this case, once a group of 4 is selected, they can be assigned in many different ways (or arrangements) to the 4 jobs. Therefore, this problem requires permutations.

$$P(12, 4) = \frac{12!}{8!} = 11{,}880$$

EXAMPLE 6 **Playing Cards**

In how many ways can a full house of aces and eights (3 aces and 2 eights) occur in 5-card poker?

*(a) 5040   (b) 455   (c) 28   (d) 360

━▶**FOR REVIEW**

Examples 6 and 7 involve a
standard deck of 52 playing
cards, as shown in Figure 17 in
Chapter 7. Recall the discussion
that accompanies the
photograph.

▶**Solution** The arrangement of the 3 aces or the 2 eights does not matter, so we use combinations and the multiplication principle. There are $\binom{4}{3}$ ways to get 3 aces from the 4 aces in the deck, and $\binom{4}{2}$ ways to get 2 eights. By the multiplication principle, the number of ways to get 3 aces and 2 eights is

$$\binom{4}{3} \cdot \binom{4}{2} = 4 \cdot 6 = 24.$$

EXAMPLE 7   **Playing Cards**
Five cards are dealt from a standard 52-card deck.

(a) How many such hands have only face cards?

▶**Solution** The face cards are the king, queen, and jack of each suit. Since there are 4 suits, there are 12 face cards. The arrangement of the 5 cards is not important, so use combinations to get

$$\binom{12}{5} = \frac{12!}{7! \, 5!} = 792.$$

(b) How many such hands have exactly 2 hearts?

▶**Solution** There are 13 hearts in the deck, so the 2 hearts will be selected from those 13 cards. The other 3 cards must come from the remaining 39 cards that are not hearts. Use combinations and the multiplication principle to get

$$\binom{13}{2}\binom{39}{3} = 78 \cdot 9139 = 712{,}842.$$

Notice that the two top numbers in the combinations add up to 52, the total number of cards, and the two bottom numbers add up to 5, the number of cards in a hand.

(c) How many such hands have cards of a single suit?

▶**Solution** The total number of ways that 5 cards of a particular suit of 13 cards can occur is $\binom{13}{5}$. Since the arrangement of the 5 cards is not important, use combinations. There are four different suits, so the multiplication principle gives

$$4 \cdot \binom{13}{5} = 4 \cdot 1287 = 5148$$

ways to deal 5 cards of the same suit.

As Example 7 shows, often both combinations and the multiplication principle must be used in the same problem.

EXAMPLE 8   **Soup**
To illustrate the differences between permutations and combinations in another way, suppose 2 cans of soup are to be selected from 4 cans on a shelf: noodle (N), bean (B), mushroom (M), and tomato (T). As shown in Figure 5(a) on the next page, there are 12 ways to select 2 cans from the 4 cans if the order matters (if

noodle first and bean second is considered different from bean, then noodle, for example). On the other hand, if order is unimportant, then there are 6 ways to choose 2 cans of soup from the 4, as illustrated in Figure 5(b).

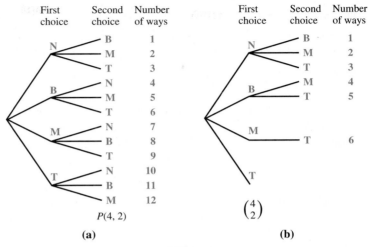

FIGURE 5

CAUTION It should be stressed that not all counting problems lend themselves to either permutations or combinations. Whenever a tree diagram or the multiplication principle can be used directly, it's often best to use it. ■

→ 8.2 Exercises

1. Define combinations in your own words.

Evaluate each combination.

2. $\binom{8}{3}$

3. $\binom{12}{5}$

4. $\binom{44}{20}$

5. $\binom{40}{18}$

6. $\binom{n}{0}$

7. $\binom{n}{n}$

8. $\binom{n}{1}$

9. $\binom{n}{n-1}$

10. In how many ways can a hand of 6 clubs be chosen from an ordinary deck?

11. Five cards are marked with the numbers 1, 2, 3, 4, and 5, then shuffled, and 2 cards are drawn.

a. How many different 2-card combinations are possible?

b. How many 2-card hands contain a number less than 3?

12. An economics club has 31 members.

a. If a committee of 4 is to be selected, in how many ways can the selection be made?

b. In how many ways can a committee of at least 1 and at most 3 be selected?

13. Use a tree diagram for the following.

a. Find the number of ways 2 letters can be chosen from the set {L, M, N} if order is important and repetition is allowed.

b. Reconsider part a if no repeats are allowed.

c. Find the number of combinations of 3 elements taken 2 at a time. Does this answer differ from part a or b?

14. Repeat Exercise 13 using the set {L, M, N, P}.

15. Explain the difference between a permutation and a combination.

16. Padlocks with digit dials are often referred to as "combination locks." According to the mathematical definition of combination, is this an accurate description? Explain.

In Exercises 17–24, decide whether each exercise involves permutations or combinations, and then solve the problem.

17. In a club with 9 male and 11 female members, how many 5-member committees can be chosen that have

    a. all men?   **b.** all women?   **c.** 3 men and 2 women?

18. In Exercise 17, how many committees can be selected that have

    a. at least 4 women?   **b.** no more than 2 men?

19. In a game of musical chairs, 12 children will sit in 11 chairs arranged in a row (one will be left out). In how many ways can this happen, if we count rearrangements of the children in the chairs as different outcomes?

20. A group of 3 students is to be selected from a group of 14 students to take part in a class in cell biology.

    a. In how many ways can this be done?

    b. In how many ways can the group who will not take part be chosen?

21. Marbles are being drawn without replacement from a bag containing 16 marbles.

    a. How many samples of 2 marbles can be drawn?

    b. How many samples of 4 marbles can be drawn?

    c. If the bag contains 3 yellow, 4 white, and 9 blue marbles, how many samples of 2 marbles can be drawn in which both marbles are blue?

22. There are 7 rotten apples in a crate of 26 apples.

    a. How many samples of 3 apples can be drawn from the crate?

    b. How many samples of 3 could be drawn in which all 3 are rotten?

    c. How many samples of 3 could be drawn in which there are two good apples and one rotten one?

23. A bag contains 5 black, 1 red, and 3 yellow jelly beans; you take 3 at random. How many samples are possible in which the jelly beans are

    a. all black?   **b.** all red?   **c.** all yellow?

    d. 2 black and 1 red?   **e.** 2 black and 1 yellow?

    f. 2 yellow and 1 black?   **g.** 2 red and 1 yellow?

24. In how many ways can 5 out of 9 plants be arranged in a row on a windowsill?

25. Show that $\binom{n}{r} = \binom{n}{n-r}$.

26. The following problem was posed on National Public Radio's *Weekend Edition*: In how many points can 6 circles intersect?*

    a. Find the answer for 6 circles.

    b. Find the general answer for *n* circles.

**Weekend Edition, National Public Radio, Oct. 23, 1994.

27. How many different dominoes can be formed from the numbers 0…6? (*Hint:* A domino may have the same number of dots on both halves of it or it may have a different number of dots on each half.)

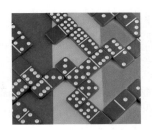

➤ Applications

28. *Secretarial Assignments* From a pool of 8 secretaries, 3 are selected to be assigned to 3 managers, one per manager. In how many ways can they be selected and assigned?

29. *Sales Schedules* A salesperson has the names of 6 prospects.

   a. In how many ways can she arrange her schedule if she calls on all 6?

   b. In how many ways can she arrange her schedule if she can call on only 4 of the 6?

30. *Worker Grievances* A group of 9 workers decides to send a delegation of 3 to their supervisor to discuss their grievances.

   a. How many delegations are possible?

   b. If it is decided that a particular worker must be in the delegation, how many different delegations are possible?

   c. If there are 4 women and 5 men in the group, how many delegations would include at least 1 woman?

31. *Hamburger Variety* Hamburger Hut sells regular hamburgers as well as a larger burger. Either type can include cheese, relish, lettuce, tomato, mustard, or catsup.

   a. How many different hamburgers can be ordered with exactly three extras?

   b. How many different regular hamburgers can be ordered with exactly three extras?

   c. How many different regular hamburgers can be ordered with at least five extras?

32. *Assembly Line Sampling* Five items are to be randomly selected from the first 50 items on an assembly line to determine the defect rate. How many different samples of 5 items can be chosen?

LIFE SCIENCES

33. *Research Participants* From a group of 16 smokers and 22 nonsmokers, a researcher wants to randomly select 8 smokers and 8 nonsmokers for a study. In how many ways can the study group be selected?

34. *Plant Hardiness* In an experiment on plant hardiness, a researcher gathers 6 wheat plants, 3 barley plants, and 2 rye plants. She wishes to select 4 plants at random.

   a. In how many ways can this be done?

   b. In how many ways can this be done if exactly 2 wheat plants must be included?

SOCIAL SCIENCES

35. *Legislative Committee* A legislative committee consists of 5 Democrats and 4 Republicans. A delegation of 3 is to be selected to visit a small Pacific island republic.

   a. How many different delegations are possible?

   b. How many delegations would have all Democrats?

   c. How many delegations would have 2 Democrats and 1 Republican?

   d. How many delegations would include at least 1 Republican?

36. *Political Committee* From 10 names on a ballot, 4 will be elected to a political party committee. In how many ways can the committee of 4 be formed if each person will have a different responsibility, and different assignments of responsibility are considered different committees?

37. *Judges* When Paul Martinek, publisher of *Lawyers Weekly USA*, was a guest on the television news program *The O'Reilly Factor*, he discussed a decision by a three-judge panel, chosen at random from judges in the Ninth Circuit in California.* The judges had ruled that the mandatory recitation of the Pledge of Allegience is unconstitutional because of the phrase "under God." According to Martinek, "Because there are 45 judges in the Ninth Circuit, there are 3000 different combinations of three-judge panels." Is this true? If not, what is the correct number?

38. *Bridge* How many different 13-card bridge hands can be selected from an ordinary deck?

39. *Poker* Five cards are chosen from an ordinary deck to form a hand in poker. In how many ways is it possible to get the following results?

a. 4 queens   **b.** No face card

c. Exactly 2 face cards   **d.** At least 2 face cards

e. 1 heart, 2 diamonds, and 2 clubs

40. *Poker* In poker, a flush consists of 5 cards with the same suit, such as 5 diamonds.

a. Find the number of ways of getting a flush consisting of cards with values from 5 to 10 by listing all the possibilities.

b. Find the number of ways of getting a flush consisting of cards with values from 5 to 10 by using combinations.

41. *Baseball* If a baseball coach has 5 good hitters and 4 poor hitters on the bench and chooses 3 players at random, in how many ways can he choose at least 2 good hitters?

42. *Softball* The coach of the Morton Valley Softball Team has 6 good hitters and 8 poor hitters. He chooses 3 hitters at random.

a. In how many ways can he choose 2 good hitters and 1 poor hitter?

b. In how many ways can he choose 3 good hitters?

c. In how many ways can he choose at least 2 good hitters?

43. *Flower Selection* Five orchids from a collection of 20 are to be selected for a flower show.

a. In how many ways can this be done?

b. In how many ways can the 5 be selected if 2 special plants must be included?

44. *Ice Cream Flavors* Baskin-Robbins advertises that it has 31 flavors of ice cream.

a. How many different double-scoop cones can be made? Assume that the order of the scoops matters.

b. How many different triple-scoop cones can be made?

c. How many different double-scoop cones can be made if order doesn't matter?

45. *Lottery* A state lottery game requires that you pick 6 different numbers from 1 to 99. If you pick all 6 winning numbers, you win the jackpot.

a. How many ways are there to choose 6 numbers if order is not important?

b. How many ways are there to choose 6 numbers if order matters?

46. *Lottery* In Exercise 45, if you pick 5 of the 6 numbers correctly, you win $250,000. In how many ways can you pick exactly 5 of the 6 winning numbers without regard to order?

47. *Pizza Varieties* A television commercial for Little Caesars pizza announced that with the purchase of two pizzas, one could receive free any combination of up to five toppings on each pizza. The commercial shows a young child waiting in line at Little Caesars who calculates that there are 1,048,576 possibilities for the toppings on the two pizzas.*

a. Verify the child's calculation. Use the fact that Little Caesars has 11 toppings to choose from. Assume that the order of the two pizzas matters; that is, if the first pizza has combination 1 and the second pizza has combination 2, that is different from combination 2 on the first pizza and combination 1 on the second.

b. In a letter to *The Mathematics Teacher*, Joseph F. Heiser argued that the two combinations described in part a should be counted as the same, so the child has actually overcounted. Give the number of possibilities if the order of the two pizzas doesn't matter.

48. *Pizza* In an ad for Pizza Hut, Jessica Simpson explains to the Muppets that there are more than 6 million possibilities for their 4forAll Pizza. Griffin Weber and Glenn Weber wrote an article explaining that the number of possibilities is far more than 6 million, as described below.†

a. Each pizza can have up to 3 toppings, out of 17 possible choices, or can be one of four specialty pizzas. Calculate the number of different pizzas possible.

b. Out of the total possible pizzas calculated in the first part of this exercise, a 4forAll Pizza consists of four pizzas in a box. Keeping in mind that the four pizzas could all be different, or there could be two or three different pizzas in the box, or all four pizzas could be the same, calculate the total number of 4forAll Pizzas possible.

c. The article considers another way of counting the number in part b. Suppose that only 8 pizzas were available, and they were listed in a row with lines separating each type, as in the following diagram:

$$A|B|C|D|E|F|G|H.$$

A person orders 4 pizzas by placing 4 X's in the desired places on the diagram, after which the letters can be

*Heiser, Joseph F., "Pascal and Gauss Meet Little Caesars," *Mathematics Teacher*, Vol. 87, Sept. 1994, p. 389.
†Weber, Griffin and Glenn Weber, "Pizza Combinatorics Revisited," *The College Mathematics Journal*, Vol. 37, No. 1, Jan. 2006, pp. 43–44.

ignored. For example, an order for 2 of A, 1 of C, and 1 of G would look like the following diagram.

$$XX||X|||X|$$

The number of ways this can be done is then the number of ways of arranging 11 objects, 4 of which are X and the other 7 of which are vertical lines, or

$$\binom{11}{4} = 330.$$

Use similar reasoning to verify the answer to part b.

49. *Cereal* The Post Corporation has introduced the cereal, *Create a Crunch*™, in which the consumers can combine ingredients to create their own unique cereal. Each box contains 8 packets of food goods. There are four types of cereal: Frosted Alpha Bits®, Cocoa Pebbles®, Fruity Pebbles®, and Honey Comb®. Also included in the box are four "Add-Ins": granola, blue rice cereal, marshmallows, and sprinkles.

a. What is the total number of breakfasts that can be made if a breakfast is defined as any one or more cereals or add-ins?

b. If Melissa Fischer chooses to mix one type of cereal with one add-in, how many different breakfasts can she make?

c. If Jane Fleming chooses to mix two types of cereal with three add-ins, how many different breakfasts can she make?

d. If Kevin Flores chooses to mix at least one type of cereal with at least one type of add-in, how many breakfasts can he make?

e. If Nicole Girrbach's favorite cereal is Fruity Pebbles®, how many different cereals can she make if each of her mixtures must include this cereal?

50. *Football* Writer Gregg Easterbrook, discussing ESPN's unsuccessful attempt to predict the winners for the six National Football League (NFL) divisions and the six wild-card slots, claimed that there were 180 different ways to make this forecast.* Reader Milton Eisner wrote in to tell him that the actual number is much larger.† To make the calculation, note that the NFL consists of two conferences, each of which consists of three divisions. Five of the divisions have five teams, while the other has six. There is one winner from each of the six divisions, plus three wild-card slots from each of the two conferences. How many ways can the six division winners and six wild-card slots be chosen?

51. *Music* In the opera *Amahl and the Night Visitors*, the shepherds sing a chorus involving 18 different names, a challenge for singers trying to remember the names in the correct order. (Two of the three authors of this textbook have sung this chorus in public.)

a. In how many ways can the names be arranged?

b. Not all the arrangements of names in part a could be sung, because 10 of the names have 3 syllables, 4 have 2 syllables, and 4 have 4 syllables. Of the 6 lines in the chorus, 4 lines consist of a 3-syllable name repeated, followed by a 2-syllable and then a 4-syllable name (e.g., Emily, Emily, Michael, Bartholomew), and 2 lines consist of a 3-syllable name repeated, followed by two more 3-syllable names (e.g., Josephine, Josephine, Angela, Jeremy). No names are repeated except where we've indicated. (If you think this is confusing, you should try memorizing the chorus.) How many arrangements of the names could fit this pattern?

52. *Committees* Suppose that out of 19 members of a club, two committees are to be formed. A nominating committee is to consist of 7 members, and a public relations committee is to consist of 5 members. No one can be on both committees.

a. Calculate the number of ways that the two committees can be formed, assuming that the nominating committee is formed first.

b. Calculate the number of ways that the two committees can be formed, assuming that the public relations committee is formed first. Verify that this answer is the same as that of part a.

c. Suppose the 7 members of the nominating committee wear red T-shirts, the 5 members of the public relations committee wear yellow T-shirts, and the remaining members of the club wear white T-shirts. A photographer lines up the members of the club to take a picture, but the picture is so blurry that people wearing the same color T-shirt are indistinguishable. In how many distinguishable ways can the club members line up? Explain why this answer is the same as the answers to parts a and b.

53. *Committee* A small department of 5 people decides to form a hiring committee. The only restriction on the size of the committee is that it must have at least 2 members.

a. Calculate the number of different committees possible by adding up the number of committees of different sizes.

b. Calculate the number of different committees possible by taking the total number of subsets of the 5 members and subtracting the number of committees that are invalid because they have too few members.

---

*http://slate.msn.com/id/95622/.
†http://slate.msn.com/id/96439/.

54. *Olympics* In recent Winter Olympics, there were 12 judges for each part of the women's figure skating program, but the scores of only 9 of the judges were randomly selected for the final results.*

a. In how many ways can the 9 judges whose scores are counted be selected?

b. Women's figure skating consists of a short program and a long program, with different judges for each part. How many different sets of judges' scores are possible for the entire event?

8.3 Probability Applications of Counting Principles

? THINK ABOUT IT If 3 engines are tested from a shipping container packed with 12 diesel engines, 2 of which are defective, what is the probability that at least 1 of the defective engines will be found (in which case the container will not be shipped)?

This problem theoretically could be solved with a tree diagram, but it would require a tree with a large number of branches. Many of the probability problems involving *dependent* events that were solved earlier by using tree diagrams can also be solved by using permutations or combinations. Permutations and combinations are especially helpful when the numbers involved are large.

To compare the method of using permutations or combinations with the method of tree diagrams used in Section 7.5, the first example repeats Example 7 from that section.

EXAMPLE 1 **Environmental Inspections**
The Environmental Protection Agency is considering inspecting 6 plants for environmental compliance: 3 in Chicago, 2 in Los Angeles, and 1 in New York. Due to a lack of inspectors, they decide to inspect 2 plants selected at random, 1 this month and 1 next month, with each plant equally likely to be selected, but no plant is selected twice. What is the probability that 1 Chicago plant and 1 Los Angeles plant are selected?

▶**Solution** Because the plants are selected one at a time, with one labeled as the first plant and the other as the second, we use permutations. There are two ways to select a Chicago plant and a Los Angeles plant. The first way is to select the Chicago plant followed by the Los Angeles plant, and the second is to select the Los Angeles plant followed by the Chicago plant. The Chicago plant can be selected from the 3 Chicago plants in $\binom{3}{1}$ ways, and the Los Angeles plant can be selected from the 2 Los Angeles plants in $\binom{2}{1}$ ways. By the multiplication principle and the union rule for sets, both results can occur in

$$\binom{3}{1}\binom{2}{1} + \binom{2}{1}\binom{3}{1} \text{ ways,}$$

*The New York Times, Feb. 23, 2006, p. D3.

giving the numerator of the probability fraction, $P(E) = n(E)/n(S)$. For the denominator, there are 6 ways to select the first plant and 5 ways to select the second, for a total of $6 \cdot 5$ ways. The required probability is

$$P(1 \text{ C and } 1 \text{ LA}) = \frac{\binom{3}{1}\binom{2}{1} + \binom{2}{1}\binom{3}{1}}{6 \cdot 5}$$

$$= \frac{3 \cdot 2 + 2 \cdot 3}{30} = \frac{12}{30} = \frac{2}{5}.$$

This agrees with the answer found earlier.

This example can be solved more simply by observing that the probability that 1 Chicago plant and 1 Los Angeles plant are selected should not depend upon the order in which the plants are selected, so we may use combinations. The numerator is simply the number of ways of selecting 1 Chicago plant out of 3 Chicago plants and 1 Los Angeles plant out of 2 Los Angeles plants. The denominator is just the number of ways of selecting 2 plants out of 6. Then

$$P(1 \text{ C and } 1 \text{ LA}) = \frac{\binom{3}{1}\binom{2}{1}}{\binom{6}{2}} = \frac{6}{15} = \frac{2}{5}.$$

This helps explain why combinations tend to be used more often than permutations in probability. Even if order matters in the original problem, it is sometimes possible to ignore order and use combinations. Be careful to do this only when the final result does not depend on the order of events. Order often does matter. (If you don't believe this, try getting dressed tomorrow morning and then taking your shower.)

Example 1 could also be solved using the tree diagram shown in Figure 6. Two of the branches correspond to drawing 1 Chicago plant and 1 Los Angeles

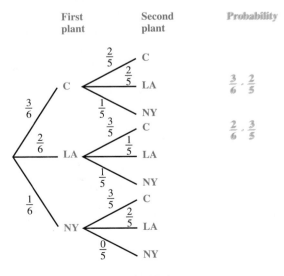

FIGURE 6

plant. The probability for each branch is calculated by multiplying the probabilities along the branch, as we did in the previous chapter. The resulting probabilities for the two branches are then added, giving the result

$$P(1 \text{ C and } 1 \text{ LA}) = \frac{3}{6} \cdot \frac{2}{5} + \frac{2}{6} \cdot \frac{3}{5} = \frac{2}{5}.$$

CAUTION The problems in the first two sections of this chapter asked how many ways a certain operation can be done. The problems in this section ask what is the probability that a certain event occurs; the solution involves answering questions about how many ways the event and the operation can be done.

- If a problem asks how many ways something can be done, the answer must be a nonnegative integer.

- If a problem asks for a probability, the answer must be a number between 0 and 1. ∎

EXAMPLE 2   **Nursing**

From a group of 22 nurses, 4 are to be selected to present a list of grievances to management.

(a) In how many ways can this be done?

▶**Solution** Four nurses from a group of 22 can be selected in $\binom{22}{4}$ ways. (Use combinations, since the group of 4 is an unordered set.)

$$\binom{22}{4} = \frac{22!}{18! \, 4!} = \frac{(22)(21)(20)(19)}{(4)(3)(2)(1)} = 7315$$

There are 7315 ways to choose 4 people from 22.

(b) One of the nurses is Julie Davis. Find the probability that Davis will be among the 4 selected.

▶**Solution**   The probability that Davis will be selected is given by $n(E)/n(S)$, where E is the event that the chosen group includes Davis, and S is the sample space for the experiment of choosing a group of 4. There is only $\binom{1}{1} = 1$ way to choose Davis. The number of ways that the other 3 nurses can be chosen from the remaining 21 nurses is

$$\binom{21}{3} = \frac{21!}{18! \, 3!} = 1330.$$

The probability that Davis will be one of the 4 chosen is

$$P(\text{Davis is chosen}) = \frac{n(E)}{n(S)} = \frac{\binom{1}{1}\binom{21}{3}}{\binom{22}{4}} = \frac{1330}{7315} \approx 0.1818.$$

Notice that the two numbers in red in the numerator, 1 and 21, add up to the number in red in the denominator, 22. This indicates that the 22 nurses have been split into two groups, one of size 1 (Davis) and the other of size 21 (the other nurses). Similarly, the green numbers indicate that the 4 nurses chosen consist of two groups of size 1 (Davis) and size 3 (the other nurses chosen).

(c) Find the probability that Davis will not be selected.

▶**Solution** The probability that Davis will not be chosen is $1 - 0.1818 = 0.8182$.

EXAMPLE 3 **Diesel Engines**

When shipping diesel engines abroad, it is common to pack 12 engines in one container that is then loaded on a rail car and sent to a port. Suppose that a company has received complaints from its customers that many of the engines arrive in nonworking condition. To help solve this problem, the company decides to make a spot check of containers after loading. The company will test 3 engines from a container at random; if any of the 3 are nonworking, the container will not be shipped until each engine in it is checked. Suppose a given container has 2 nonworking engines. Find the probability that the container will not be shipped.

▶**Solution** The container will not be shipped if the sample of 3 engines contains 1 or 2 defective engines. If $P(1 \text{ defective})$ represents the probability of exactly 1 defective engine in the sample, then

$$P(\text{not shipping}) = P(1 \text{ defective}) + P(2 \text{ defective}).$$

There are $\binom{12}{3}$ ways to choose the 3 engines for testing:

$$\binom{12}{3} = \frac{12!}{9! \, 3!} = 220.$$

There are $\binom{2}{1}$ ways of choosing 1 defective engine from the 2 in the container, and for each of these ways, there are $\binom{10}{2}$ ways of choosing 2 good engines from among the 10 in the container. By the multiplication principle, there are

$$\binom{2}{1}\binom{10}{2} = \frac{2!}{1! \, 1!} \cdot \frac{10!}{8! \, 2!} = 2 \cdot 45 = 90$$

ways of choosing a sample of 3 engines containing 1 defective engine with

$$P(1 \text{ defective}) = \frac{90}{220} = \frac{9}{22}.$$

There are $\binom{2}{2}$ ways of choosing 2 defective engines from the 2 defective engines in the container, and $\binom{10}{1}$ ways of choosing 1 good engine from among the 10 good engines, for

$$\binom{2}{2}\binom{10}{1} = 1 \cdot 10 = 10$$

ways of choosing a sample of 3 engines containing 2 defective engines. Finally,

$$P(2 \text{ defective}) = \frac{10}{220} = \frac{1}{22}$$

and

$$P(\text{not shipping}) = P(1 \text{ defective}) + P(2 \text{ defective})$$

$$= \frac{\binom{2}{1}\binom{10}{2}}{\binom{12}{3}} + \frac{\binom{2}{2}\binom{10}{1}}{\binom{12}{3}}$$

$$= \frac{9}{22} + \frac{1}{22} = \frac{10}{22} \approx 0.4545.$$

Notice that the probability is $1 - 0.4545 = 0.5455$ that the container will be shipped, even though it has 2 defective engines. The management must decide whether this probability is acceptable; if not, it may be necessary to test more than 3 engines from a container.

Observe that in Example 3, the complement of finding 1 or 2 defective engines is finding 0 defective engines. Then instead of finding the sum $P(1 \text{ defective}) + P(2 \text{ defective})$, the result in Example 3 could be found as $1 - P(0 \text{ defective})$.

$$P(\text{not shipping}) = 1 - P(0 \text{ defective in sample})$$

$$= 1 - \frac{\binom{2}{0}\binom{10}{3}}{\binom{12}{3}}$$

$$= 1 - \frac{1(120)}{220}$$

$$= 1 - \frac{120}{220} = \frac{100}{220} \approx 0.4545$$

➤**FOR REVIEW**
Recall that if E and E' are complements, then $P(E') = 1 - P(E)$. In Example 3, the event "0 defective in the sample" is the complement of the event "1 or 2 defective in the sample," since there are only 0 or 1 or 2 defective engines possible in the sample of 3 engines.

EXAMPLE 4 **Poker**

In a common form of the card game *poker*, a hand of 5 cards is dealt to each player from a deck of 52 cards. There are a total of

$$\binom{52}{5} = \frac{52!}{47! \, 5!} = 2,598,960$$

such hands possible. Find the probability of getting each of the following hands.

(a) A hand containing only hearts, called a *heart flush*

➤**Solution** There are 13 hearts in a deck, with

$$\binom{13}{5} = \frac{13!}{8! \, 5!} = \frac{(13)(12)(11)(10)(9)}{(5)(4)(3)(2)(1)} = 1287$$

different hands containing only hearts. The probability of a heart flush is

$$P(\text{heart flush}) = \frac{\binom{13}{5}\binom{39}{0}}{\binom{52}{5}} = \frac{1287}{2,598,960} \approx 0.0004952.$$

You don't really need the $\binom{39}{0}$, since this just equals 1, but it might help to remind you that you are choosing none of the 39 cards that remain after the hearts are removed.

(b) A flush of any suit (5 cards of the same suit)

▶**Solution** There are 4 suits in a deck, so

$$P(\text{flush}) = 4 \cdot P(\text{heart flush}) = 4 \cdot 0.0004952 \approx 0.001981.$$

(c) A full house of aces and eights (3 aces and 2 eights)

▶**Solution** There are $\binom{4}{3}$ ways to choose 3 aces from among the 4 in the deck, and $\binom{4}{2}$ ways to choose 2 eights.

$$P(3 \text{ aces, } 2 \text{ eights}) = \frac{\binom{4}{3} \cdot \binom{4}{2} \cdot \binom{44}{0}}{\binom{52}{5}} = \frac{4 \cdot 6 \cdot 1}{2,598,960} \approx 0.000009234$$

(d) Any full house (3 cards of one value, 2 of another)

▶**Solution**

METHOD 1
Standard Procedure

The 13 values in a deck give 13 choices for the first value. As in part (c), there are $\binom{4}{3}$ ways to choose the 3 cards from among the 4 cards that have that value. This leaves 12 choices for the second value (order *is* important here, since a full house of 3 aces and 2 eights is not the same as a full house of 3 eights and 2 aces). From the 4 cards that have the second value, there are $\binom{4}{2}$ ways to choose 2. The probability of any full house is then

$$P(\text{full house}) = \frac{13 \cdot \binom{4}{3} \cdot 12 \cdot \binom{4}{2}}{2,598,960} \approx 0.001441.$$

METHOD 2
Alternative Procedure

As an alternative way of counting the numerator, first count the number of different values in the hand.* Since there are 13 values from which to choose, and we need 2 different values (one for the set of 3 cards and one for the set of 2), there are $\binom{13}{2}$ ways to choose the values. Next, of the two values chosen, select the value for which there are 3 cards, which can be done $\binom{2}{1}$ ways. This automatically determines that the other value is the one for which there are 2 cards. Next, choose the suits for each value. For the value with 3 cards, there are $\binom{4}{3}$ values of the suits, and for the value with 2 cards, there are $\binom{4}{2}$ values. Putting this all together,

*We learned this approach from Professor Peter Grassi of Hofstra University.

$$P(\text{full house}) = \frac{\binom{13}{2} \cdot \binom{2}{1} \cdot \binom{4}{3} \cdot \binom{4}{2}}{2{,}598{,}960} \approx 0.001441.$$

EXAMPLE 5 **Music**

A music teacher has 3 violin pupils, Fred, Carl, and Helen. For a recital, the teacher selects a first violinist and a second violinist. The third pupil will play with the others, but not solo. If the teacher selects randomly, what is the probability that Helen is first violinist, Carl is second violinist, and Fred does not solo?

▶**Solution** Use *permutations* to find the number of arrangements in the sample space.

$$P(3, 3) = 3! = 6$$

(Think of this as filling the positions of first violin, second violin, and no solo.) The 6 arrangements are equally likely, since the teacher will select randomly. Thus, the required probability is $1/6$.

EXAMPLE 6 **Birthdays**

Suppose a group of n people is in a room. Find the probability that at least 2 of the people have the same birthday.

▶**Solution** "Same birthday" refers to the month and the day, not necessarily the same year. Also, ignore leap years, and assume that each day in the year is equally likely as a birthday. To see how to proceed, we first look at the case in which $n = 5$ and find the probability that *no 2 people* from among 5 people have the same birthday. There are 365 different birthdays possible for the first of the 5 people, 364 for the second (so that the people have different birthdays), 363 for the third, and so on. The number of ways the 5 people can have different birthdays is thus the number of permutations of 365 days taken 5 at a time or

$$P(365, 5) = 365 \cdot 364 \cdot 363 \cdot 362 \cdot 361.$$

The number of ways that 5 people can have the same birthday or different birthdays is

$$365 \cdot 365 \cdot 365 \cdot 365 \cdot 365 = (365)^5.$$

Finally, the *probability* that none of the 5 people have the same birthday is

$$\frac{P(365, 5)}{365^5} = \frac{365 \cdot 364 \cdot 363 \cdot 362 \cdot 361}{365 \cdot 365 \cdot 365 \cdot 365 \cdot 365} \approx 0.9729.$$

The probability that at least 2 of the 5 people *do* have the same birthday is $1 - 0.9729 = 0.0271$.

Now this result can be extended to more than 5 people. Generalizing, the probability that no 2 people among n people have the same birthday is

$$\frac{P(365, n)}{365^n}.$$

The probability that at least 2 of the n people *do* have the same birthday is

$$1 - \frac{P(365, n)}{365^n}.$$

The following table shows this probability for various values of n.

Number of People, n	Probability That Two Have the Same Birthday
5	0.0271
10	0.1169
15	0.2529
20	0.4114
22	0.4757
23	0.5073
25	0.5687
30	0.7063
35	0.8144
40	0.8912
50	0.9704
366	1

The probability that 2 people among 23 have the same birthday is 0.5073, a little more than half. Many people are surprised at this result; it seems that a larger number of people should be required.

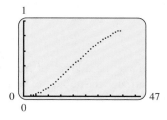

FIGURE 7

Using a graphing calculator, we can graph the probability formula in the previous example as a function of n, but care must be taken that the graphing calculator evaluates the function at integer points. Figure 7 was produced on a TI-83/84 Plus by letting $Y_1 = 1 - (365 \; nPr \; X)/365^X$ on $0 \le x \le 47$. (This domain ensures integer values for x.) Notice that the graph does not extend past $x = 39$. This is because $P(365, n)$ and 365^n are too large for the calculator when $n \ge 40$.

An alternative way of doing the calculations that does not run into such large numbers is based on the concept of conditional probability. The probability that the first person's birthday does not match any so far is $365/365$. The probability that the second person's birthday does not match the first's is $364/365$. The probability that the third person's birthday does not match the first's or the second's is $363/365$. By the product rule of probability, the probability that none of the first 3 people have matching birthdays is

$$\frac{365}{365} \cdot \frac{364}{365} \cdot \frac{363}{365}.$$

Similarly, the probability that no two people in a group of 40 have the same birthday is

$$\frac{365}{365} \cdot \frac{364}{365} \cdot \frac{363}{365} \cdot \ldots \cdot \frac{326}{365}.$$

This probability can be calculated (and then subtracted from 1 to get the probability we seek) without overflowing the calculator by multiplying each fraction times the next, rather then trying to compute the entire numerator and the entire denominator. The calculations are somewhat tedious to do by hand, but can be programmed on a graphing calculator or computer.

As we saw in Examples 1 and 4(d), probability can sometimes be calculated in more than one way. We now look at one more example of this.

EXAMPLE 7 **Fruit**

Ray and Nate are arranging a row of fruit at random on a table. They have 5 apples, 6 oranges, and 7 lemons. What is the probability that all fruit of the same kind are together?

▶**Solution**

METHOD 1
Distinguishable Permutations

Ray can't tell individual pieces of fruit of the same kind apart. All apples look the same to him, as do all oranges and all lemons. So in the denominator of the probability, he calculates the number of distinguishable ways to arrange the 18 pieces of fruit, given that all apples are indistinguishable, as are all oranges and all lemons.

$$\frac{18!}{5!\,6!\,7!} = 14{,}702{,}688$$

As for the numerator, the only choice is how to arrange the 3 kinds of fruit, for which there are $3! = 6$ ways. Thus

$$P(\text{all fruit of the same kind are together}) = \frac{6}{14{,}702{,}688} = 0.4081 \times 10^{-7}.$$

METHOD 2
Permutations

Nate has better eyesight than Ray and can tell the individual pieces of fruit apart. So in the denominator of the probability, he calculates the number of ways to arrange the 18 pieces of fruit, which is

$$18! = 6.4024 \times 10^{15}.$$

For the numerator, he first must choose how to arrange the 3 kinds of fruit, for which there are $3!$ ways. Then there are $5!$ ways to arrange the apples, $6!$ ways to arrange the oranges, and $7!$ ways to arrange the lemons, for a total number of possibilities of

$$3!\,5!\,6!\,7! = 2{,}612{,}736{,}000.$$

Therefore,

$$P(\text{all fruit of the same kind are together}) = \frac{2{,}612{,}736{,}000}{6.4024 \times 10^{15}} = 0.4081 \times 10^{-7}.$$

The results for Method 1 and Method 2 are the same. The probability does not depend on whether a person can distinguish individual pieces of the same kind of fruit.

→ 8.3 Exercises

A basket contains 7 red apples and 4 yellow apples. A sample of 3 apples is drawn. Find the probabilities that the sample contains the following.

1. All red apples

2. All yellow apples

3. 2 yellow and 1 red apple

4. More red than yellow apples

Two cards are drawn at random from an ordinary deck of 52 cards.

5. How many 2-card hands are possible?

Find the probability that the 2-card hand described above contains the following.

6. 2 aces 　　　　　　　　**7.** At least 1 ace 　　　　　　**8.** All spades

9. 2 cards of the same suit 　**10.** Only face cards 　　　　　**11.** No face cards

12. No card higher than 8 (count ace as 1)

Twenty-six slips of paper are each marked with a different letter of the alphabet and placed in a basket. A slip is pulled out, its letter recorded (in the order in which the slip was drawn), and the slip is replaced. This is done 5 times. Find the probabilities that the following "words" are formed.

13. Chuck

14. A word that starts with "p"

15. A word with no repetition of letters

16. A word that contains no "x," "y," or "z"

17. Discuss the relative merits of using tree diagrams versus combinations to solve probability problems. When would each approach be most appropriate?

18. Several examples in this section used the rule $P(E') = 1 - P(E)$. Explain the advantage (especially in Example 6) of using this rule.

For Exercises 19–22, refer to Example 6 in this section.

19. A total of 42 men have served as president through 2007.* Set up the probability that, if 42 men were selected at random, at least 2 have the same birthday.[†]

20. Set up the probability that at least 2 of the 100 U.S. senators have the same birthday.

21. What is the probability that at least 2 of the 435 members of the House of Representatives have the same birthday?

22. Argue that the probability that in a group of *n* people *exactly one pair* have the same birthday is

$$\binom{n}{2} \cdot \frac{P(365, n-1)}{365^n}.$$

*Although Bush is the 43rd President, the 22nd and 24th Presidents were the same man: Grover Cleveland.

[†]In fact, James Polk and Warren Harding were both born on November 2.

23. An elevator has 4 passengers and stops at 7 floors. It is equally likely that a person will get off at any one of the 7 floors. Find the probability that at least 2 passengers leave at the same floor. (*Hint:* Compare this with the birthday problem.)

24. On National Public Radio, the *Weekend Edition* program on Sunday, September 7, 1991, posed the following probability problem: Given a certain number of balls, of which some are blue, pick 5 at random. The probability that all 5 are blue is 1/2. Determine the original number of balls and decide how many were blue.

25. A reader wrote to the "Ask Marilyn" column* in *Parade* magazine, "You have six envelopes to pick from. Two-thirds (that is, four) are empty. One-third (that is, two) contain a $100 bill. You're told to choose 2 envelopes at random. Which is more likely: (1) that you'll get at least one $100 bill, or (2) that you'll get no $100 bill at all?" Find the two probabilities.

26. After studying all night for a final exam, a bleary-eyed student randomly grabs 2 socks from a drawer containing 9 black, 6 brown, and 2 blue socks, all mixed together. What is the probability that she grabs a matched pair?

27. Three crows, 4 blue jays, and 5 starlings sit in a random order on a section of telephone wire. Find the probability that birds of a feather flock together, that is, that all birds of the same type are sitting together.

28. If the letters l, i, t, t, l, and e are chosen at random, what is the probability that they spell the word "little"?

29. If the letters M, i, s, s, i, s, s, i, p, p, and i are chosen at random, what is the probability that they spell the word "Mississippi"?

► Applications

BUSINESS AND ECONOMICS

Quality Control   A shipment of 11 printers contains 2 that are defective. Find the probability that a sample of the following sizes, drawn from the 11, will not contain a defective printer.

30. 1   **31.** 2   **32.** 3   **33.** 4

Refer to Example 3. The managers feel that the probability of 0.5455 that a container will be shipped even though it contains 2 defective engines is too high. They decide to increase the sample size chosen. Find the probabilities that a container will be shipped even though it contains 2 defective engines, if the sample size is increased to the following.

34. 4   **35.** 5

SOCIAL SCIENCES

36. *Election Ballots* Five names are put on a ballot in a randomly selected order. What is the probability that they are not in alphabetical order?

37. *Native American Council* At the first meeting of a committee to plan a Northern California pow-wow, there were 3 women and 3 men from the Miwok tribe, 2 men and 3 women from the Hoopa tribe, and 4 women and 5 men from the Pomo tribe. If the ceremony subcouncil consists of 5 people, and is randomly selected, find the probabilities that the subcouncil contains the following:

a. 3 men and 2 women;

b. exactly 3 Miwoks and 2 Pomos;

c. 2 Miwoks, 2 Hoopas, and a Pomo;

d. 2 Miwoks, 2 Hoopas, and 2 Pomos;

e. more women than men;

f. exactly 3 Hoopas;

g. at least 2 Pomos.

38. *Education* A school in Bangkok requires that students take an entrance examination. After the examination, there is a drawing in which 5 students are randomly selected from each group of 40 for automatic acceptance into the school, regardless of their performance on the examination.

*Source: *Parade* magazine, Apr. 30, 1995, p. 8. © 1995 Marilyn vos Savant. Initially published in *Parade* magazine. All rights reserved.

The drawing consists of placing 35 red and 5 green pieces of paper into a box. Each student picks a piece of paper from the box and then does not return the piece of paper to the box. The 5 lucky students who pick the green pieces are automatically accepted into the school.*

a. What is the probability that the first person wins automatic acceptance?

b. What is the probability that the last person wins automatic acceptance?

c. If the students are chosen by the order of their seating, does this give the student who goes first a better chance of winning than the second, third, . . . person? (*Hint:* Imagine that the 40 pieces of paper have been mixed up and laid in a row so that the first student picks the first piece of paper, the second student picks the second piece of paper, and so on.)

GENERAL INTEREST

Poker Find the probabilities of the following hands at poker. Assume aces are either high or low.

39. Royal flush (5 highest cards of a single suit)

40. Straight flush (5 in a row in a single suit, but not a royal flush)

41. Four of a kind (4 cards of the same value)

42. Straight (5 cards in a row, not all of the same suit), with ace either high or low

43. Three of a kind (3 cards of one value, with the other cards of two different values)

44. Two pairs (2 cards of one value, 2 of another value, and 1 of a third value)

45. One pair (2 cards of one value, with the other cards of three different values)

Bridge A bridge hand is made up of 13 cards from a deck of 52. Find the probabilities that a hand chosen at random contains the following.

46. Only hearts

47. At least 3 aces

48. Exactly 2 aces and exactly 2 kings

49. 6 of one suit, 4 of another, and 3 of another

50. *Writers* At a conference of African American writers in Detroit, special-edition books were selected to be given away in contests. There were 9 books written by Langston Hughes, 5 books by James Baldwin, and 7 books by Toni Morrison. The judge of one contest selected 6 books at random for prizes. Find the probabilities that the selection consisted of the following.

a. 3 Hughes and 3 Morrison books

b. Exactly 4 Baldwin books

c. 2 Hughes, 3 Baldwin, and 1 Morrison book

d. At least 4 Hughes books

e. Exactly 4 books written by males (Morrison is female)

f. No more than 2 books written by Baldwin

51. *Lottery* In the previous section, we found the number of ways to pick 6 different numbers from 1 to 99 in a state lottery. Assuming order is unimportant, what is the probability of picking all 6 numbers correctly to win the big prize?

52. *Lottery* In Exercise 51, what is the probability of picking exactly 5 of the 6 numbers correctly?

53. *Lottery* An article in *The New York Times* discussing the odds of winning the lottery stated, "And who cares if a game-theory professor once calculated the odds of winning as equal to a poker player's chance of drawing four royal flushes in a row, all in spades—then getting up from the card table and meeting four strangers, all with the same birthday?"[†] Calculate this probability. Does this probability seem comparable to the odds of winning the lottery? (Ignore February 29 as a birthday, and assume that all four strangers have the same birthday as each other, not necessarily the same as the poker player.)

54. *Lottery* A reader wrote to the "Ask Marilyn" column[‡] in *Parade* magazine, "A dozen glazed doughnuts are riding on the answer to this question: Are the odds of winning in a lotto drawing higher when picking 6 numbers out of 49 or when picking 5 numbers out of 52?" Calculate each probability to answer the question.

55. *Lottery* On October 22, 2005, the Powerball Lottery had a record jackpot of $340 million. To enter the lottery, 5 numbers are picked between 1 and 55, plus a bonus number between 1 and 42. All 6 numbers must be correct to win the jackpot.

a. What is the probability of winning the jackpot with a single ticket?

b. In an article for the *Minneapolis Star Tribune*, mathematician Douglas Arnold was quoted as saying, "If you were to select a group of Powerball numbers every minute for 138 years, you would have about a 50 percent

---

*Letter to the editor, *Mathematics Teacher*, Vol. 92, No. 8, Nov. 1999.

†Gould, Lois, "Ticket to Trouble," *The New York Times Magazine,* Apr. 23, 1995, p. 39.

‡Source: *Parade* magazine, Dec. 10, 2000, p. 11. © 2000 Marilyn vos Savant. Initially published in *Parade* magazine. All rights reserved.

chance of picking the winning Powerball ticket."* Calculate the actual probability, using an estimate of 365.25 for the number of days in the year. (Arnold later told *Chance News* that this was an "off-the-top-of-my-head calculation" made when a reporter called.[†])

56. *Canadian Lottery* In June 2004, Canada introduced a change in its lottery that violated the usual convention that the smaller the probability of an event, the bigger the prize.[‡] In this lottery, participants have to guess six numbers from 1 to 49. Six numbers between 1 and 49 are then drawn at random, plus a seventh "bonus number."

a. A fifth prize of $10 goes to those who correctly guess exactly three of the six numbers, but do not guess the bonus number. Find the probability of winning fifth prize.

b. A sixth prize of $5 goes to those who correctly guess exactly two of the six numbers plus the bonus number. Find the probability of winning sixth prize, and compare this with the probability of winning fifth prize.

57. *Barbie* A controversy arose in 1992 over the Teen Talk Barbie doll, each of which was programmed with four sayings randomly picked from a set of 270 sayings. The controversy was over the saying, "Math class is tough," which some felt gave a negative message toward girls doing well in math. In an interview with *Science*, a spokeswoman for Mattel, the makers of Barbie, said that "There's a less than 1% chance you're going to get a doll that says math class is tough."[§] Is this figure correct? If not, give the correct figure.

58. *Football* During the 1988 college football season, the Big Eight Conference ended the season in a "perfect progression," as shown in the following table.[‖]

Won	Lost	Team
7	0	Nebraska (NU)
6	1	Oklahoma (OU)
5	2	Oklahoma State (OSU)
4	3	Colorado (CU)
3	4	Iowa State (ISU)
2	5	Missouri (MU)
1	6	Kansas (KU)
0	7	Kansas State (KSU)

Someone wondered what the probability of such an outcome might be.

a. How many games do the 8 teams play?

b. Assuming no ties, how many different outcomes are there for all the games together?

c. In how many ways could the 8 teams end in a perfect progression?

d. Assuming that each team had an equally likely probability of winning each game, find the probability of a perfect progression with 8 teams.

e. Find a general expression for the probability of a perfect progression in an *n*-team league with the same assumptions.

59. *Bingo* Bingo has become popular in the United States, and it is an efficient way for many organizations to raise money. The bingo card has 5 rows and 5 columns of numbers from 1 to 75, with the center given as a free cell. Balls showing one of the 75 numbers are picked at random from a container. If the drawn number appears on a player's card, then the player covers the number. In general, the winner is the person who first has a card with an entire row, column, or diagonal covered.[#]

a. Find the probability that a person will win bingo after just four numbers are called.

b. An L occurs when the first column and the bottom row are both covered. Find the probability that an L will occur in the fewest number of calls.

c. An X-out occurs when both diagonals are covered. Find the probability that an X-out occurs in the fewest number of calls.

d. If bingo cards are constructed so that column one has 5 of the numbers from 1 to 15, column two has 5 of the numbers from 16 to 30, column three has 4 of the numbers from 31 to 45, column four has 5 of the numbers from 46 to 60, and column five has 5 of the numbers from 61 to 75, how many different bingo cards could be constructed? (*Hint:* Order matters!)

*Furst, Randy, "Advice from 2 number crunchers: Don't spend that $340 million just yet," *Minneapolis Star Tribune*, Oct. 18, 2005.

[†]*Chance News 8*, Oct. 15–30, 2005.

[‡]Helman, Danny, "Reversal of Fortunes," *Chance*, Vol. 18, No. 3, Summer 2005, pp. 20–22.

[§]*Science*, Vol. 258, Oct. 16, 1992, p. 398.

[‖]Madsen, Richard, "On the Probability of a Perfect Progression," *The American Statistician*, Aug. 1991, Vol. 45, No. 3, p. 214.

[#]Bay, Jennifer M., Robert E. Reys, Ken Simms, and P. Mark Taylor, "Bingo Games: Turning Student Intuitions into Investigations in Probability and Number Sense," *Mathematics Teacher*, Vol. 93, No. 3, Mar. 2000, pp. 200–206.

8.4 Binomial Probability

? *THINK ABOUT IT*

What is the probability that 3 out of 6 randomly selected college students attend more than one institution during their college career?

This question involves an experiment that is repeated 6 times. Many probability problems are concerned with experiments in which an event is repeated many times. Other examples include finding the probability of getting 7 heads in 8 tosses of a coin, of hitting a target 6 times out of 6, and of finding 1 defective item in a sample of 15 items. Probability problems of this kind are called **Bernoulli trials** problems, or **Bernoulli processes**, named after the Swiss mathematician Jakob Bernoulli (1654–1705), who is well known for his work in probability theory. In each case, some outcome is designated a success, and any other outcome is considered a failure. This labeling is arbitrary, and does not necessarily have anything to do with real success or failure. Thus, if the probability of a success in a single trial is p, the probability of failure will be $1 - p$. A Bernoulli trials problem, or **binomial experiment**, must satisfy the following conditions.

BINOMIAL EXPERIMENT

1. The same experiment is repeated a fixed number of times.

2. There are only two possible outcomes, success and failure.

3. The repeated trials are independent, so that the probability of success remains the same for each trial.

EXAMPLE 1 | Sleep

The chance that an American falls asleep with the TV on at least three nights a week is 1/4.* Suppose a researcher selects 5 Americans at random and is interested in the probability that all 5 are "TV sleepers."

▶**Solution**   Here the experiment, selecting a person, is repeated 5 times. If selecting a TV sleeper is labeled a success, then getting a "non-TV sleeper" is labeled a failure. The 5 trials are almost independent. There is a very slight dependence; if, for example, the first person selected is a TV sleeper, then there is one less TV sleeper to choose from when we select the next person (assuming we never select the same person twice). When selecting a small sample out of a large population, however, the probability changes negligibly, so researchers consider such trials to be independent. Thus, the probability that all 5 in our sample are sleepers is

$$\frac{1}{4} \cdot \frac{1}{4} \cdot \frac{1}{4} \cdot \frac{1}{4} \cdot \frac{1}{4} = \left(\frac{1}{4}\right)^5 \approx 0.0009766.$$

Now suppose the problem in Example 1 is changed to that of finding the probability that exactly 4 of the 5 people in the sample are TV sleepers. This

---

▶FOR REVIEW

Recall that if A and B are independent events,

$$P(A \text{ and } B) = P(A)P(B).$$

Harper's Magazine, Mar. 1996, p. 13.

outcome can occur in more than one way, as shown below, where s represents a success (a TV sleeper) and f represents a failure (a non-TV sleeper).

outcome 1:	s	s	s	s	f
outcome 2:	s	s	s	f	s
outcome 3:	s	s	f	s	s
outcome 4:	s	f	s	s	s
outcome 5:	f	s	s	s	s

Keep in mind that since the probability of success is $1/4$, the probability of failure is $1 - 1/4 = 3/4$. The probability, then, of each of these 5 outcomes is

$$\left(\frac{1}{4}\right)^4\left(\frac{3}{4}\right).$$

Since the 5 outcomes represent mutually exclusive events, add the 5 identical probabilities, which is equivalent to multiplying the above probability by 5. The result is

$$P(4 \text{ of the 5 people are TV sleepers}) = 5\left(\frac{1}{4}\right)^4\left(\frac{3}{4}\right) = \frac{15}{4^5} \approx 0.01465.$$

In the same way, we can compute the probability of selecting 3 TV sleepers in our sample of 5. The probability of any one way of achieving 3 successes and 2 failures will be

$$\left(\frac{1}{4}\right)^3\left(\frac{3}{4}\right)^2.$$

Rather than list all the ways of achieving 3 successes out of 5 trials, we will count this number using combinations. The number of ways to select 3 elements out of a set of 5 is $\binom{5}{3} = 5!/(2!\,3!) = 10$, giving

$$P(3 \text{ of the 5 people are TV sleepers}) = 10\left(\frac{1}{4}\right)^3\left(\frac{3}{4}\right)^2 = \frac{90}{4^5} \approx 0.08789.$$

A similar argument works in the general case.

BINOMIAL PROBABILITY

If p is the probability of success in a single trial of a binomial experiment, the probability of x successes and $n - x$ failures in n independent repeated trials of the experiment, known as **binomial probability**, is

$$\binom{n}{x} \cdot p^x \cdot (1 - p)^{n-x}.$$

EXAMPLE 2 **College Students**

A recent survey found that 59% of college students attend more than one institution during their college career.* Suppose a sample of 6 students is chosen.

*"Education Life," *The New York Times*, April 23, 2006, p. 24.

Assuming that each student's college attendance pattern is independent of the others, find the probability of each of the following.

(a) Exactly 3 of the 6 students attend more than one institution.

▶**Solution** Think of the 6 students chosen as 6 independent trials. A success occurs if the student attends more than one institution. Then this is a binomial experiment with $n = 6$ and $p = P(\text{attend more than one institution}) = 0.59$. To find the probability that exactly 3 students attend more than one institution, let $x = 3$ and use the formula given in the box on the previous page.

$$
\begin{aligned}
P(\text{exactly } 3) &= \binom{6}{3}(0.59)^3(1 - 0.59)^{6-3} \\
&= 20(0.59)^3(0.41)^3 \\
&= 20(0.2054)(0.06892) \\
&\approx 0.2831
\end{aligned}
$$

(b) None of the 6 students attend more than one institution.

▶**Solution** Let $x = 0$.

$$
\begin{aligned}
P(\text{exactly } 0) &= \binom{6}{0}(0.59)^0(1 - 0.59)^6 \\
&= 1(1)(0.41)^6 \approx 0.00475
\end{aligned}
$$

EXAMPLE 3 **Coin Toss**

Find the probability of getting exactly 7 heads in 8 tosses of a fair coin.

▶**Solution** The probability of success (getting a head in a single toss) is $1/2$. The probability of a failure (getting a tail) is $1 - 1/2 = 1/2$. Thus,

$$
P(7 \text{ heads in 8 tosses}) = \binom{8}{7}\left(\frac{1}{2}\right)^7\left(\frac{1}{2}\right)^1 = 8\left(\frac{1}{2}\right)^8 = 0.03125.
$$

EXAMPLE 4 **Defective Items**

Assuming that selection of items for a sample can be treated as independent trials, and that the probability that any 1 item is defective is 0.01, find the following.

(a) The probability of 1 defective item in a random sample of 15 items from a production line

▶**Solution** Here, a "success" is a defective item. Since selecting each item for the sample is assumed to be an independent trial, the binomial probability formula applies. The probability of success (a defective item) is 0.01, while the probability of failure (an acceptable item) is 0.99. This makes

$$
\begin{aligned}
P(1 \text{ defective in 15 items}) &= \binom{15}{1}(0.01)^1(0.99)^{14} \\
&= 15(0.01)(0.99)^{14} \\
&\approx 0.1303.
\end{aligned}
$$

(b) The probability of at most 1 defective item in a random sample of 15 items from a production line

▶**Solution** "At most 1" means 0 defective items or 1 defective item. Since 0 defective items is equivalent to 15 acceptable items,

$$P(0 \text{ defective}) = (0.99)^{15} \approx 0.8601.$$

Use the union rule, noting that 0 defective and 1 defective are mutually exclusive events, to get

$$P(\text{at most 1 defective}) = P(0 \text{ defective}) + P(1 \text{ defective})$$
$$\approx 0.8601 + 0.1303$$
$$= 0.9904.$$

EXAMPLE 5 **Supermarket Scanners**

A survey by *Money* magazine found that supermarket scanners are overcharging customers at 30% of stores.*

(a) If you shop at 3 supermarkets that use scanners, what is the probability that you will be overcharged in at least one store?

▶**Solution** We can treat this as a binomial experiment, letting $n = 3$ and $p = 0.3$. At least 1 of 3 means 1 or 2 or 3. It will be simpler here to find the probability of being overcharged in none of the 3 stores, that is, $P(0 \text{ overcharges})$, and then find $1 - P(0 \text{ overcharges})$.

$$P(0 \text{ overcharges}) = \binom{3}{0}(0.3)^0(0.7)^3$$
$$= 1(1)(0.343) = 0.343$$
$$P(\text{at least one}) = 1 - P(0 \text{ overcharges})$$
$$= 1 - 0.343 = 0.657$$

(b) If you shop at 3 supermarkets that use scanners, what is the probability that you will be overcharged in at most one store?

▶**Solution** "At most one" means 0 or 1, so

$$P(0 \text{ or } 1) = P(0) + P(1)$$
$$= \binom{3}{0}(0.3)^0(0.7)^3 + \binom{3}{1}(0.3)^1(0.7)^2$$
$$= 1(1)(0.343) + 3(0.3)(0.49) = 0.784.$$

The triangular array of numbers shown on the next page is called **Pascal's triangle** in honor of the French mathematician Blaise Pascal (1623–1662), who was one of the first to use it extensively. The triangle was known long before Pascal's time and appears in Chinese and Islamic manuscripts from the eleventh century.

*O'Connell, Vanessa, "Don't Get Cheated by Supermarket Scanners," *Money*, Apr. 1993, pp. 132–138.

PASCAL'S TRIANGLE

$$
\begin{array}{ccccccccccc}
 & & & & & 1 & & & & & \\
 & & & & 1 & & 1 & & & & \\
 & & & 1 & & 2 & & 1 & & & \\
 & & 1 & & 3 & & 3 & & 1 & & \\
 & 1 & & 4 & & 6 & & 4 & & 1 & \\
1 & & 5 & & 10 & & 10 & & 5 & & 1
\end{array}
$$

The array provides a quick way to find binomial probabilities. The nth row of the triangle, where $n = 0, 1, 2, 3, \ldots$, gives the coefficients $\binom{n}{r}$ for $r = 0,$ 1, 2, 3, $\ldots$, n. For example, for $n = 4$, $1 = \binom{4}{0}$, $4 = \binom{4}{1}$, $6 = \binom{4}{2}$, and so on. Each number in the triangle is the sum of the two numbers directly above it. For example, in the row for $n = 4$, 1 is the sum of 1, the only number above it, 4 is the sum of 1 and 3, 6 is the sum of 3 and 3, and so on. Adding in this way gives the sixth row:

$$1 \quad 6 \quad 15 \quad 20 \quad 15 \quad 6 \quad 1.$$

Notice that Pascal's triangle tells us, for example, that $\binom{4}{1} + \binom{4}{2} = \binom{5}{2}$ (that is, $4 + 6 = 10$). Using the combinations formula, it can be shown that, in general, $\binom{n}{r} + \binom{n}{r+1} = \binom{n+1}{r+1}$. This is left as an exercise.

EXAMPLE 6 **Pascal's Triangle**
Use Pascal's triangle to find the probability in Example 5 that if you shop at 6 supermarkets, at least 3 will overcharge you.

▶**Solution** The probability of success is 0.3. Since at least 3 means 3, 4, 5, or 6,

$$P(\text{at least } 3) = P(3) + P(4) + P(5) + P(6)$$
$$= \binom{6}{3}(0.3)^3(0.7)^3 + \binom{6}{4}(0.3)^4(0.7)^2$$
$$+ \binom{6}{5}(0.3)^5(0.7)^1 + \binom{6}{6}(0.3)^6(0.7)^0.$$

Use the sixth row of Pascal's triangle for the combinations to get

$$P(\text{at least } 3) = 20(0.3)^3(0.7)^3 + 15(0.3)^4(0.7)^2$$
$$+ 6(0.3)^5(0.7)^1 + 1(0.3)^6(0.7)^0$$
$$= 0.1852 + 0.0595 + 0.0102 + 0.0007$$
$$= 0.2556.$$

| EXAMPLE 7 | **Independent Jury** |

If each member of a 9-person jury acts independently of each other and makes the correct determination of guilt or innocence with probability 0.65, find the probability that the majority of jurors will reach a correct verdict.*

▶**Solution**

METHOD 1
Calculating by Hand

Since the jurors in this particular situation act independently, we can treat this as a binomial experiment. Thus, the probability that the majority of the jurors will reach the correct verdict is given by

$$P(\text{at least } 5) = \binom{9}{5}(0.65)^5(0.35)^4 + \binom{9}{6}(0.65)^6(0.35)^3$$

$$+ \binom{9}{7}(0.65)^7(0.35)^2 + \binom{9}{8}(0.65)^8(0.35)^1 + \binom{9}{9}(0.65)^9$$

$$= 0.2194 + 0.2716 + 0.2162 + 0.1004 + 0.0207$$

$$= 0.8283.$$

METHOD 2
Graphing Calculator

Some graphing calculators provide binomial probabilities. On a TI-83/84 Plus, for example, the command `binompdf(9,.65, 5)`, found in the DISTR menu, gives 0.21939, which is the probability that $x = 5$. Alternatively, the command `binomcdf(9,.65, 4)` gives 0.17172 as the probability that 4 or fewer jurors will make the correct decision. Subtract 0.17172 from 1 to get 0.82828 as the probability that the majority of the jurors will make the correct decision. This value rounds to 0.8283, which is in agreement with Method 1. Often, Method 2 is more accurate than Method 1 due to the accumulation of rounding errors when doing successive calculations by hand.

METHOD 3
Spreadsheet

Some spreadsheets also provide binomial probabilities. In Microsoft Excel, for example, the command "`=BINOMDIST(5, 9,.65, 0)`" gives 0.21939, which is the probability that $x = 5$. Alternatively, the command "`=BINOMDIST (4, 9,.65, 1)`" gives 0.17172 as the probability that 4 or fewer jurors will make the correct decision. Subtract 0.17172 from 1 to get 0.82828 as the probability that the majority of the jurors will make the correct decision. This value agrees with the value found in Methods 1 and 2.

▶ 8.4 Exercises

Suppose that a family has 5 children. Also, suppose that the probability of having a girl is 1/2. Find the probabilities that the family has the following children.

1. Exactly 2 girls and 3 boys

2. Exactly 3 girls and 2 boys

3. No girls

*Grofman, Bernard, "A Preliminary Model of Jury Decision Making as a Function of Jury Size, Effective Jury Decision Rule, and Mean Juror Judgmental Competence," *Frontiers in Economics*, 1979, pp. 98–110.

4. No boys

5. At least 4 girls

6. At least 3 boys

7. No more than 3 boys

8. No more than 4 girls

A die is rolled 12 times. Find the probabilities of rolling the following.

9. Exactly 12 ones

10. Exactly 6 ones

11. Exactly 1 one

12. Exactly 2 ones

13. No more than 3 ones

14. No more than 1 one

A coin is tossed 6 times. Find the probabilities of getting the following.

15. All heads

16. Exactly 3 heads

17. No more than 3 heads

18. At least 3 heads

19. How do you identify a probability problem that involves a binomial experiment?

20. How is Pascal's triangle used to find probabilities?

21. Using the definition of combination in Section 8.2, prove that

$$\binom{n}{r} + \binom{n}{r+1} = \binom{n+1}{r+1}.$$

(This is the formula underlying Pascal's triangle.)

In Exercises 22 and 23, argue that the use of binomial probabilities is not applicable and thus the probabilities that are computed are not correct.

22. In England, a woman was found guilty of smothering her two infant children. Much of the Crown's case against the lady was based on the testimony from a pediatrician who indicated that the chances of two crib deaths occurring in both siblings was only about 1 in 73 million. This number was calculated by assuming that the probability of a single crib death is 1 in 8543 and the probability of two crib deaths is 1 in 8543^2 (i.e., binomial).*

23. A contemporary radio station in Boston has a contest in which a caller is asked his or her date of birth. If the caller's date of birth, including the day, month, and year of birth, matches a predetermined date, the caller wins $1 million. Assuming that there were 36,525 days in the twentieth century and the contest was run 51 times on consecutive days, the probability that the grand prize will be won is

$$1 - \left(1 - \frac{1}{36,525}\right)^{51} \approx 0.0014.^{\dagger}$$

Science, Vol. 309, July 22, 2005, p. 543. Also see Chapter 7 Review Exercise 89.
†Snell, J. Laurie, "40-Million-Dollar Thursday," *Chance News 9.04*, Mar. 7–April 5, 2000.

► Applications

Management *The survey discussed in Example 5 also found that customers overpay for* 1 *out of every* 10 *items, on average. Suppose a customer purchases* 15 *items. Find the following probabilities.*

24. A customer overpays on 3 items.

25. A customer does not overpay for any item.

26. A customer overpays on at least one item.

27. A customer overpays on at least 2 items.

28. A customer overpays on at most 2 items.

Credit Cards *A survey of consumer finance found that* 25.6% *of credit-card-holding families hardly ever pay off the balance.* Suppose a random sample of* 20 *credit-card-holding families is taken. Find the probabilities of each of the following results.*

29. Exactly 6 families hardly ever pay off the balance.

30. Exactly 9 families hardly ever pay off the balance.

31. At least 4 families hardly ever pay off the balance.

32. At most 5 families hardly ever pay off the balance.

Personnel Screening *A company gives prospective workers a 6-question, multiple-choice test. Each question has* 5 *possible answers, so that there is a* 1/5 *or* 20% *chance of answering a question correctly just by guessing. Find the probabilities of getting the following results by chance.*

33. Exactly 2 correct answers

34. No correct answers

35. At least 4 correct answers

36. No more than 3 correct answers

Quality Control *A factory tests a random sample of* 20 *transistors for defects. The probability that a particular transistor will be defective has been established by past experience as* 0.05.

37. What is the probability that there are no defective transistors in the sample?

38. What is the probability that the number of defective transistors in the sample is at most 2?

39. *Quality Control* The probability that a certain machine turns out a defective item is 0.05. Find the probabilities that in a run of 75 items, the following results are obtained.

a. Exactly 5 defective items

b. No defective items

c. At least 1 defective item

40. *Survey Results* A company is taking a survey to find out whether people like its product. Its last survey indicated that 70% of the population like the product. Based on that, in a sample of 58 people, find the probabilities of the following.

a. All 58 like the product.

b. From 28 to 30 (inclusive) like the product.

41. *Pecans* Pecan producers blow air through the pecans so that the lighter ones are blown out. The lighter-weight pecans are generally bad and the heavier ones tend to be better. These "blow outs" and "good nuts" are often sold to tourists along the highway. Suppose 60% of the "blow outs" are good, and 80% of the "good nuts" are good.[†]

a. What is the probability that if you crack and check 20 "good nuts" you will find 8 bad ones?

b. What is the probability that if you crack and check 20 "blow outs" you will find 8 bad ones?

c. If we assume that 70% of the roadside stands sell "good nuts," and that out of 20 nuts we find 8 that are bad, what is the probability that the nuts are "blow outs"?

42. *Hurricane Insurance* A company prices its hurricane insurance using the following assumptions:

(i) In any calendar year, there can be at most one hurricane.

(ii) In any calendar year, the probability of a hurricane is 0.05.

(iii) The number of hurricanes in any calendar year is independent of the number of hurricanes in any other calendar year.

Using the company's assumptions, calculate the probability that there are fewer than 3 hurricanes in a 20-year period.* (Choose one of the following.)

a. 0.06   **b.** 0.19   **c.** 0.38   **d.** 0.62   **e.** 0.92

LIFE SCIENCES

Breast Cancer A recent study found that 85% of breast-cancer cases are detectable by mammogram.[†] Suppose a random sample of 15 women with breast cancer are given mammograms. Find the probability of each of the following results, assuming that detection in the cases is independent.

43. All of the cases are detectable.

44. None of the cases are detectable.

45. Not all cases are detectable.

46. More than half of the cases are detectable.

Births of Twins The probability that a birth will result in twins is 0.012. Assuming independence (perhaps not a valid assumption), what are the probabilities that out of 100 births in a hospital, there will be the following numbers of sets of twins?

47. Exactly 2 sets of twins

48. At most 2 sets of twins

49. *Effects of Radiation* The probability of a mutation of a given gene under a dose of 1 roentgen of radiation is approximately 2.5×10^{-7}. What is the probability that in 10,000 genes, at least 1 mutation occurs?

50. *Flu Inoculations* A flu vaccine has a probability of 80% of preventing a person who is inoculated from getting the flu. A county health office inoculates 83 people. Find the probabilities of the following.

a. Exactly 10 of the people inoculated get the flu.

b. No more than 4 of the people inoculated get the flu.

c. None of the people inoculated get the flu.

51. *Color Blindness* The probability that a male will be color-blind is 0.042. Find the probabilities that in a group of 53 men, the following will be true.

a. Exactly 5 are color-blind.

b. No more than 5 are color-blind.

c. At least 1 is color-blind.

52. *Pharmacology* In placebo-controlled trials of Pravachol®, a drug that is prescribed to lower cholesterol, 7.3% of the patients who were taking the drug experienced nausea/vomiting, whereas 7.1% of the patients who were taking the placebo experienced nausea/vomiting.[‡]

a. If 100 patients who are taking Pravachol® are selected, what is the probability that 10 or more will experience nausea/vomiting?

b. If a second group of 100 patients receives a placebo, what is the probability that 10 or more will experience nausea/vomiting?

c. Since 7.3% is larger than 7.1%, do you believe that the Pravachol® causes more people to experience nausea/vomiting than a placebo? Explain.

53. *Genetic Fingerprinting* The use of DNA has become an integral part of many court cases. When DNA is extracted from cells and body fluids, genetic information is represented by bands of information, which look similar to a bar code at a grocery store. It is generally accepted that in unrelated people, the probability of a particular band matching is 1 in 4.[§]

a. If 5 bands are compared in unrelated people, what is the probability that all 5 of the bands match? (Express your answer in terms of "1 chance in ?".)

b. If 20 bands are compared in unrelated people, what is the probability that all 20 of the bands match? (Express your answer in terms of "1 chance in ?".)

c. If 20 bands are compared in unrelated people, what is the probability that 16 or more bands match? (Express your answer in terms of "1 chance in ?".)

d. If you were deciding paternity and there were 16 matches out of 20 bands compared, would you believe that the person being tested was the father? Explain.

54. *Salmonella* According to *The Salt Lake Tribune*, the Coffee Garden in Salt Lake City ran into trouble because of their four-egg quiche:[‖]

"A Salt Lake County Health Department inspector paid a visit recently and pointed out that research by the Food and Drug Administration indicates that one in four eggs

*Problem 39 from the 2005 Sample Exam P of the *Education and Examination Committee of the Society of Actuaries*. Reprinted by permission of the Society of Actuaries.

[†]*Harper's Index*, April 2006.

[‡]Advertisement in *Time*, July 17, 2000, for Pravachol®, developed and marketed by Bristol-Myers Squibb Company.

[§]"Genetic Fingerprinting Worksheet," Centre for Innovation in Mathematics Teaching, http://www.ex.ac.uk/cimt/resource/fgrprnts.htm.

[‖]Rolly, Paul and JoAnn Jacobsen-Wells, "Bureaucrat's Math Makes Dizzy Dozen," *The Salt Lake Tribune*, Oct. 11, 2002.

carries *Salmonella* bacterium, so restaurants should never use more than three eggs when preparing quiche.

The manager on duty wondered aloud if simply throwing out three eggs from each dozen and using the remaining nine in four-egg quiches would serve the same purpose.

The inspector wasn't sure, but she said she would research it."

a. Assuming that one in four eggs carries *Salmonella*, and that the event that any one egg is infected is independent of whether any other egg is infected, find the probability that at least one of the eggs in a four-egg quiche carries *Salmonella*.

b. Repeat part a for a three-egg quiche.

c. Discuss whether the assumption of independence is justified.

d. Discuss whether the inspector's reasoning makes sense.

55. *Herbal Remedies* According to Dr. Peter A.G.M. De Smet of the Netherlands, "If an herb caused an adverse reaction in 1 in 1,000 users, a traditional healer would have to treat 4,800 patients with that herb (i.e., one new patient every single working day for more than 18 years) to have a 95 percent chance of observing the reaction in more than one user."* Verify this calculation by finding the probability of observing more than one reaction in 4800 patients, given that 1 in 1000 has a reaction.

56. *Vaccines* A hospital receives 1/5 of its flu vaccine shipments from Company X and the remainder of its shipments from other companies. Each shipment contains a very large number of vaccine vials. For Company X's shipments, 10% of the vials are ineffective. For every other company, 2% of the vials are ineffective. The hospital tests 30 randomly selected vials from a shipment and finds that one vial is ineffective. What is the probability that this shipment came from Company X?† (Choose one of the following. *Hint:* Find the probability that one out of 30 vials is ineffective, given that the shipment came from Company X, and also that the shipment came from other companies. Then use Bayes' theorem.)

a. 0.10 **b.** 0.14 **c.** 0.37 **d.** 0.63 **e.** 0.86

57. *Health Study* A study is being conducted in which the health of two independent groups of ten policyholders is being monitored over a one-year period of time. Individual participants in the study drop out before the end of the study with probability 0.2 (independently of the other participants). What is the probability that at least 9 participants complete the study in one of the two groups, but not in both groups?‡ (Choose one of the following.)

a. 0.096 **b.** 0.192 **c.** 0.235 **d.** 0.376 **e.** 0.469

SOCIAL SCIENCES

58. *Women Working* A recent study found that 33% of women would prefer to work part-time rather than full-time if money were not a concern.§ Find the probability that if 10 women are selected at random, at least 3 of them would prefer to work part-time.

Volunteering A recent survey found that 83% of first-year college students were involved in volunteer work at least occasionally.‖ *Suppose a random sample of 12 college students is taken. Find the probabilities of each of the following results.*

59. Exactly 7 students volunteered at least occasionally.

60. Exactly 9 students volunteered at least occasionally.

61. At least 9 students volunteered at least occasionally.

62. At most 9 students volunteered at least occasionally.

63. *Community College Population* According to the state of California, 33% of all state community college students belong to ethnic minorities. Find the probabilities of the following results in a random sample of 10 California community college students.

a. Exactly 2 belong to an ethnic minority.

b. Three or fewer belong to an ethnic minority.

c. Exactly 5 do not belong to an ethnic minority.

d. Six or more do not belong to an ethnic minority.

64. *Cheating* According to a poll conducted by *U.S. News and World Report*, 84% of college students believe they need to cheat to get ahead in the world today.#

---

*De Smet, Peter A.G.M., "Drug Therapies: Herbal Remedies," *The New England Journal of Medicine*, Vol. 347, Dec. 19, 2002, pp. 2046–2056.

†Problem 28 from the 2005 Sample Exam P of the *Education and Examination Committee of the Society of Actuaries*. Reprinted by permission of the Society of Actuaries.

‡Problem 41 from the 2005 Sample Exam P of the *Education and Examination Committee of the Society of Actuaries*. Reprinted by permission of the Society of Actuaries.

§Ferraro, Cathleen, "Feelings of the Working Women," *The Sacramento Bee*, May 11, 1995, pp. A1, A22.

‖"Education Life," *The New York Times*, April 23, 2006, p. 7.

#Kleiner, Carolyn and Mary Lord, "The Cheating Game," *U.S. News and World Report*, Nov. 22, 1999, pp. 55–66.

a. Do the results of this poll indicate that 84% of all college students cheat? Explain.

b. If this result is accurate and 100 college students are asked if they believe that cheating is necessary to get ahead in the world, what is the probability that 90 or more of the students will answer affirmatively to the question?

65. *Education* In the "Numbers" section of a recent *Time* magazine, it was reported that 15.2% of low-birth-weight babies graduate from high school by age 19. On the other hand, it was reported that 57.5% of the normal-birth-weight siblings graduated from high school.[*]

a. If 40 low-birth-weight babies were tracked through high school, what is the probability that fewer than 15 will graduate from high school by age 19?

b. What are some of the factors that may contribute to the wide difference in high school success between these siblings? Do you believe that low birth weight is the primary cause of the difference? What other information do you need to better answer these questions?

66. *War Dead* A newspaper article questioned whether soldiers and marines from some states bear greater risks in Afghanistan and Iraq than those from others.[†] Out of 644,066 troops deployed as of the time of the article, 1174 had been killed, for a probability of being killed of $p = 1174/644{,}066$. Assume the deaths are independent.

a. Vermont had 9 deaths out of 1613 troops deployed. Find the probability of at least this many deaths.

b. Massachusetts had 28 deaths out of 7146 troops deployed. Find the probability of at least this many deaths.

c. Florida had 54 deaths out of 62,572 troops deployed. Find the probability of at most this many deaths.

d. Discuss why the assumption of independence may be questionable.

67. *Sports* In many sports championships, such as the World Series in baseball and the Stanley Cup final series in hockey, the winner is the first team to win four games. For this exercise, assume that each game is independent of the others, with a constant probability p that one specified team (say, the National League team) wins.

a. Find the probability that the series lasts for four, five, six, and seven games when $p = 0.5$. (*Hint:* Suppose the National League wins the series, so they must win the last game. Consider how the previous games might come out. Then consider the probability that the American League wins.)

b. Morrison and Schmittlein have found that the Stanley Cup finals can be described by letting $p = 0.73$ be the probability that the better team wins each game.[‡] Find the probability that the series lasts for four, five, six, and seven games.

c. Some have argued that the assumption of independence does not apply.[§] Discuss this issue.

8.5 Probability Distributions; Expected Value

? THINK ABOUT IT

What is the expected payback for someone who buys one ticket in a raffle?

In this section we shall see that the *expected value* of a probability distribution is a type of average. Probability distributions were introduced briefly in the chapter on Sets and Probability. Now we take a more complete look at probability distributions. A probability distribution depends on the idea of a *random variable*, so we begin with that.

[*]"Numbers," *Time,* July 17, 2000, p. 21.
[†]Tillman, Jodie, "The Price They Paid: By Several Measures, Vermont Bears Heavy War Burden," *Valley News,* Jan. 30, 2005. For further statistical analysis, see http://www.dartmouth.edu/~chance/ForWiki/GregComments.pdf.
[‡]Morrison, Donald G. and David C. Schmittlein, "It Takes a Hot Goalie to Raise the Stanley Cup," *Chance,* Vol. 11, No. 1, 1998, pp. 3–7.
[§]For example, see Groeneveld, Richard A. and Glen Meeden, "Seven Game Series in Sports," *Mathematics Magazine,* Vol. 48, No. 4, Sept. 1975, pp. 187–192.

Random Variables   Suppose that the shipping manager at a company receives a package of one dozen computer monitors, of which, unknown to him, three are broken. He checks four of the monitors at random to see how many are broken in his sample of 4. The answer, which we will label x, is one of the numbers 0, 1, 2, or 3. Since the value of x is random, x is called a random variable.

RANDOM VARIABLE

A **random variable** is a function that assigns a real number to each outcome of an experiment.

Probability Distribution   In the example with the shipping manager, we can calculate the probability that 0, 1, 2, or 3 monitors in his sample of 4 are broken using the methods of Section 8.3. There are 3 broken monitors and 9 unbroken monitors, so the number of ways of choosing 0 broken monitors (which implies 4 unbroken monitors) is $\binom{3}{0}\binom{9}{4}$. The number of ways of choosing a sample of 4 monitors is $\binom{12}{4}$. Therefore, the probability of choosing 0 broken monitors is

$$P(0) = \frac{\binom{3}{0}\binom{9}{4}}{\binom{12}{4}} = \frac{1\left(\dfrac{9 \cdot 8 \cdot 7 \cdot 6}{4 \cdot 3 \cdot 2 \cdot 1}\right)}{\left(\dfrac{12 \cdot 11 \cdot 10 \cdot 9}{4 \cdot 3 \cdot 2 \cdot 1}\right)} = \frac{126}{495} = \frac{14}{55}.$$

Similarly, the probability of choosing 1 broken monitor is

$$P(1) = \frac{\binom{3}{1}\binom{9}{3}}{\binom{12}{4}} = \frac{3 \cdot 84}{495} = \frac{252}{495} = \frac{28}{55}.$$

The probability of choosing 2 broken monitors is

$$P(2) = \frac{\binom{3}{2}\binom{9}{2}}{\binom{12}{4}} = \frac{3 \cdot 36}{495} = \frac{108}{495} = \frac{12}{55}.$$

The probability of choosing 3 broken monitors is

$$P(3) = \frac{\binom{3}{3}\binom{9}{1}}{\binom{12}{4}} = \frac{1 \cdot 9}{495} = \frac{9}{495} = \frac{1}{55}.$$

The results can be put in a table.

x	0	1	2	3
$P(x)$	14/55	28/55	12/55	1/55

Such a table that lists the possible values of a random variable, together with the corresponding probabilities, is called a **probability distribution**. The sum of the probabilities in a probability distribution must always equal 1. (The sum in some distributions may vary slightly from 1 because of rounding.)

Instead of writing the probability distribution as a table, we could write the same information as a set of ordered pairs:

$$\{(0, 14/55), (1, 28/55), (2, 12/55), (3, 1/55)\}.$$

There is just one probability for each value of the random variable. Thus, a probability distribution defines a function, called a **probability distribution function**, or simply a **probability function**. We shall use the terms "probability distribution" and "probability function" interchangeably.

The information in a probability distribution is often displayed graphically as a special kind of bar graph called a **histogram**. The bars of a histogram all have the same width, usually 1. (The widths might be different from 1 when the values of the random variable are not consecutive integers.) The heights of the bars are determined by the probabilities. A histogram for the data in the table above is given in Figure 8. A histogram shows important characteristics of a distribution that may not be readily apparent in tabular form, such as the relative sizes of the probabilities and any symmetry in the distribution.

The area of the bar above $x = 0$ in Figure 8 is the product of 1 and 14/55, or $1 \cdot 14/55 = 14/55$. Since each bar has a width of 1, its area is equal to the probability that corresponds to that value of x. The probability that a particular value will occur is thus given by the area of the appropriate bar of the graph. For example, the probability that one or more monitors is broken is the sum of the areas for $x = 1$, $x = 2$, and $x = 3$. This area, shown in pink in Figure 9, corresponds to 41/55 of the total area, since

$$P(x \geq 1) = P(x = 1) + P(x = 2) + P(x = 3)$$
$$= 28/55 + 12/55 + 1/55 = 41/55.$$

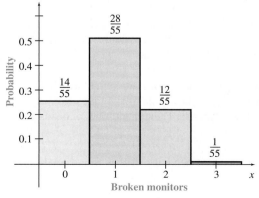

FIGURE 8

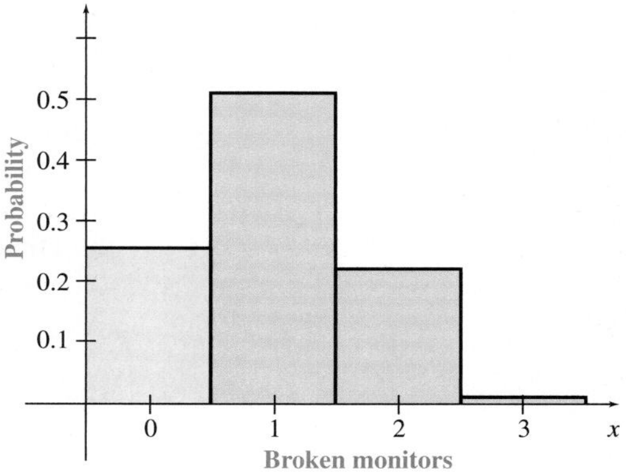

FIGURE 9

EXAMPLE 1 **Probability Distributions**

(a) Give the probability distribution for the number of heads showing when two coins are tossed.

▶**Solution** Let x represent the random variable "number of heads." Then x can take on the values 0, 1, or 2. Now find the probability of each outcome. To find the probability of 0, 1, or 2 heads, we can either use binomial probability, or notice that there are 4 outcomes in the sample space: $\{hh, ht, th, tt\}$. The results are shown in the table with Figure 10.

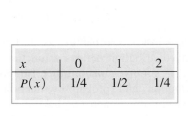

x	0	1	2
$P(x)$	1/4	1/2	1/4

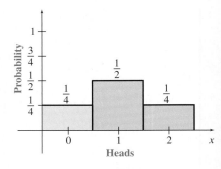

FIGURE 10

(b) Draw a histogram for the distribution in the table. Find the probability that at least one coin comes up heads.

▶**Solution** The histogram is shown in Figure 10. The portion in pink represents

$$P(x \geq 1) = P(x = 1) + P(x = 2)$$
$$= \frac{3}{4}.$$

Expected Value

In working with probability distributions, it is useful to have a concept of the typical or average value that the random variable takes on. In Example 1, for instance, it seems reasonable that, on the average, one head shows when two coins are tossed. This does not tell what will happen the next time we toss two coins; we may get two heads, or we may get none. If we tossed two coins many times, however, we would expect that, in the long run, we would average about one head for each toss of two coins.

A way to solve such problems in general is to imagine flipping two coins 4 times. Based on the probability distribution in Example 1, we would expect that 1 of the 4 times we would get 0 heads, 2 of the 4 times we would get 1 head, and 1 of the 4 times we would get 2 heads. The total number of heads we would get, then, is

$$0 \cdot 1 + 1 \cdot 2 + 2 \cdot 1 = 4.$$

The expected numbers of heads per toss is found by dividing the total number of heads by the total number of tosses, or

$$\frac{0 \cdot 1 + 1 \cdot 2 + 2 \cdot 1}{4} = 0 \cdot \frac{1}{4} + 1 \cdot \frac{1}{2} + 2 \cdot \frac{1}{4} = 1.$$

Notice that the expected number of heads turns out to be the sum of the three values of the random variable x multiplied by their corresponding probabilities. We can use this idea to define the *expected value* of a random variable as follows.

EXPECTED VALUE

Suppose the random variable x can take on the n values $x_1, x_2, x_3, \ldots, x_n$. Also, suppose the probabilities that these values occur are, respectively, $p_1, p_2, p_3, \ldots, p_n$. Then the **expected value** of the random variable is

$$E(x) = x_1 p_1 + x_2 p_2 + x_3 p_3 + \cdots + x_n p_n$$

EXAMPLE 2 **Computer Monitors**

In the example with the computer monitors, find the expected number of broken monitors that the shipping manager finds.

▶**Solution** Using the values in the first table in this section and the definition of expected value, we find that

$$E(x) = 0 \cdot \frac{14}{55} + 1 \cdot \frac{28}{55} + 2 \cdot \frac{12}{55} + 3 \cdot \frac{1}{55} = 1.$$

On the average, the shipping manager will find 1 broken monitor in the sample of 4. On reflection, this seems natural; 3 of the 12 monitors, or 1/4 of the total, are broken. We should expect, then, that 1/4 of the sample of 4 monitors are broken.

Physically, the expected value of a probability distribution represents a balance point. If we think of the histogram in Figure 8 as a series of weights with magnitudes represented by the heights of the bars, then the system would balance if supported at the point corresponding to the expected value.

EXAMPLE 3 **Symphony Orchestra**

Suppose a local symphony decides to raise money by raffling a microwave oven worth $400, a dinner for two worth $80, and 2 books worth $20 each. A total of 2000 tickets are sold at $1 each. Find the expected payback for a person who buys one ticket in the raffle.

▶**Solution**

METHOD 1
Direct Calculation

Here the random variable represents the possible amounts of payback, where payback = amount won − cost of ticket. The payback of the person winning the oven is $400 (amount won) − $1 (cost of ticket) = $399. The payback for each losing ticket is $0 − $1 = −$1.

The paybacks of the various prizes, as well as their respective probabilities, are shown in the table below. The probability of winning $19 is 2/2000 because there are 2 prizes worth $20. We have not reduced the fractions in order to keep all the denominators equal. Because there are 4 winning tickets, there are 1996 losing tickets, so the probability of winning −$1 is 1996/2000.

x	$399	$79	$19	−$1
$P(x)$	1/2000	1/2000	2/2000	1996/2000

The expected payback for a person buying one ticket is

$$399\left(\frac{1}{2000}\right) + 79\left(\frac{1}{2000}\right) + 19\left(\frac{2}{2000}\right) + (-1)\left(\frac{1996}{2000}\right) = -\frac{1480}{2000}$$
$$= -0.74.$$

On the average, a person buying one ticket in the raffle will lose $0.74, or 74¢.

It is not possible to lose 74¢ in this raffle: either you lose $1, or you win a prize worth $400, $80, or $20, minus the $1 you pay to play. But if you bought tickets in many such raffles over a long period of time, you would lose 74¢ per ticket on the average. It is important to note that the expected value of a random variable may be a number that can never occur in any one trial of the experiment.

METHOD 2
Alternate Procedure

An alternative way to compute expected value in this and other examples is to calculate the expected amount won and then subtract the cost of the ticket afterward. The amount won is either $400 (with probability 1/2000), $80 (with probability 1/2000), $20 (with probability 2/2000), or $0 (with probability 1996/2000). The expected payback for a person buying one ticket is then

$$400\left(\frac{1}{2000}\right) + 80\left(\frac{1}{2000}\right) + 20\left(\frac{2}{2000}\right) + 0\left(\frac{1996}{2000}\right) - 1 = -\frac{1480}{2000}$$
$$= -0.74.$$

EXAMPLE 4

Friendly Wager

Each day Donna and Mary toss a coin to see who buys coffee ($1.20 a cup). One tosses and the other calls the outcome. If the person who calls the outcome is correct, the other buys the coffee; otherwise the caller pays. Find Donna's expected winnings.

▶**Solution** Assume that an honest coin is used, that Mary tosses the coin, and that Donna calls the outcome. The possible results and corresponding probabilities are shown below.

Possible Results				
Result of Toss	Heads	Heads	Tails	Tails
Call	Heads	Tails	Heads	Tails
Caller Wins?	Yes	No	No	Yes
Probability	1/4	1/4	1/4	1/4

Donna wins a $1.20 cup of coffee whenever the results and calls match, and she loses a $1.20 cup when there is no match. Her expected winnings are

$$(1.20)\left(\frac{1}{4}\right) + (-1.20)\left(\frac{1}{4}\right) + (-1.20)\left(\frac{1}{4}\right) + (1.20)\left(\frac{1}{4}\right) = 0.$$

On the average, over the long run, Donna neither wins nor loses.

A game with an expected value of 0 (such as the one in Example 4) is called a **fair game**. Casinos do not offer fair games. If they did, they would win (on the average) $0, and have a hard time paying the help! Casino games have expected winnings for the house that vary from 1.5 cents per dollar to 60 cents per dollar. Exercises 47–52 at the end of the section ask you to find the expected winnings for certain games of chance.

The idea of expected value can be very useful in decision making, as shown by the next example.

EXAMPLE 5   Life Insurance

At age 50, you receive a letter from Mutual of Mauritania Insurance Company. According to the letter, you must tell the company immediately which of the following two options you will choose: take $20,000 at age 60 (if you are alive, $0 otherwise) or $30,000 at age 70 (again, if you are alive, $0 otherwise). Based *only* on the idea of expected value, which should you choose?

▶ **Solution**   Life insurance companies have constructed elaborate tables showing the probability of a person living a given number of years into the future. From a recent such table, the probability of living from age 50 to 60 is 0.88, while the probability of living from age 50 to 70 is 0.64. The expected values of the two options are given below.

$$\text{First option: } (20{,}000)(0.88) + (0)(0.12) = 17{,}600$$
$$\text{Second option: } (30{,}000)(0.64) + (0)(0.36) = 19{,}200$$

Based strictly on expected values, choose the second option.   ▬▬▬

EXAMPLE 6   Bachelor's Degrees

According to the National Center for Education Statistics, 78.5% of those earning bachelor's degrees in education in the United States in 2003–2004 were female.* Suppose 5 holders of bachelor's degrees in education from 2003 to 2004 are picked at random.

(a) Find the probability distribution for the number that are female.

▶ **Solution**   We first note that each of the 5 people in the sample is either female (with probability 0.785) or male (with probability 0.215). As in the previous section, we may assume that the probability for each member of the sample is independent of that of any other. Such a situation is described by binomial probability with $n = 5$ and $p = 0.785$, for which we use the binomial probability formula

$$\binom{n}{x} \cdot p^x \cdot (1 - p)^{n-x},$$

where x is the number of females in the sample. For example,

$$P(x = 0) = \binom{5}{0}(0.785)^0(0.215)^5 \approx 0.0005.$$

Similarly, we could calculate the probability that x is any value from 0 to 5, resulting in the probability distribution on the next page (with all probabilities rounded to four places).

*http://nces.ed.gov/programs/digest/d05/tables/dt05_280.asp.

x	0	1	2	3	4	5
$P(x)$	0.0005	0.0084	0.0612	0.2236	0.4082	0.2981

(b) Find the expected number of females in the sample of 5 people.

▶**Solution** Using the formula for expected value, we have

$$E(x) = 0(0.0005) + 1(0.0084) + 2(0.0612) + 3(0.2236)$$
$$+ 4(0.4082) + 5(0.2981) = 3.925.$$

On the average, 3.925 of the people in the sample of 5 will be female. ▬▬▬

There is another way to get the answer in part (b) of the previous example. Because 78.5% of those earning bachelor's degrees in education in the United States in 2003–2004 are female, it is reasonable to expect 78.5% of our sample to be female. Thus, 78.5% of 5 is $5(0.785) = 3.925$. Notice that what we have done is to multiply n by p. It can be shown that this method always gives the expected value for binomial probability.

EXPECTED VALUE FOR BINOMIAL PROBABILITY

For binomial probability, $E(x) = np$. In other words, the expected number of successes is the number of trials times the probability of success in each trial.

EXAMPLE 7 **Female Children**
Suppose a family has 3 children.

(a) Find the probability distribution for the number of girls.

▶**Solution** Assuming girls and boys are equally likely, the probability distribution is binomial with $n = 3$ and $p = 1/2$. Letting x be the number of girls in the formula for binomial probability, we find, for example,

$$P(x = 0) = \binom{3}{0}\left(\frac{1}{2}\right)^0\left(\frac{1}{2}\right)^3 = \frac{1}{8}.$$

The other values are found similarly, and the results are shown in the following table.

x	0	1	2	3
$P(x)$	1/8	3/8	3/8	1/8

We can verify this by noticing that in the sample space S of all 3-child families, there are eight equally likely outcomes: $S = \{ggg, ggb, gbg, gbb, bgg, bgb, bbg, bbb\}$. One of the outcomes has 0 girls, three have 1 girl, three have 2 girls, and one has 3 girls.

(b) Find the expected number of girls in a 3-child family using the distribution from part (a).

▶**Solution** Using the formula for expected value, we have

$$\text{Expected number of girls} = 0\left(\frac{1}{8}\right) + 1\left(\frac{3}{8}\right) + 2\left(\frac{3}{8}\right) + 3\left(\frac{1}{8}\right)$$

$$= \frac{12}{8} = 1.5.$$

On average, a 3-child family will have 1.5 girls. This result agrees with our intuition that, on the average, half the children born will be girls.

(c) Find the expected number of girls in a 3-child family using the formula for expected value for binomial probability.

▶**Solution** Using the formula $E(x) = np$ with $n = 3$ and $p = 1/2$, we have

$$\text{Expected number of girls} = 3\left(\frac{1}{2}\right) = 1.5.$$

This agrees with our answer from part (b), as it must.

➤ 8.5 Exercises

For each experiment described below, let x determine a random variable, and use your knowledge of probability to prepare a probability distribution.

1. Four coins are tossed, and the number of heads is noted.

2. Two dice are rolled, and the total number of points is recorded.

3. Three cards are drawn from a deck. The number of aces is counted.

4. Two balls are drawn from a bag in which there are 4 white balls and 2 black balls. The number of black balls is counted.

Draw a histogram for the following, and shade the region that gives the indicated probability.

5. Exercise 1; $P(x \le 2)$

6. Exercise 2; $P(x \ge 11)$

7. Exercise 3; $P(\text{at least one ace})$

8. Exercise 4; $P(\text{at least one black ball})$

Find the expected value for each random variable.

9.

x	2	3	4	5
$P(x)$	0.1	0.4	0.3	0.2

10.

y	4	6	8	10
$P(y)$	0.4	0.4	0.05	0.15

11.

z	9	12	15	18	21
$P(z)$	0.14	0.22	0.38	0.19	0.07

12.

x	30	32	36	38	44
$P(x)$	0.31	0.29	0.26	0.09	0.05

Find the expected value for the random variable x having the probability function shown in each graph.

13.

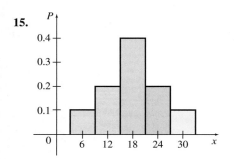

14.

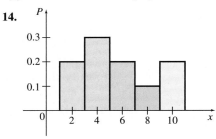

15.

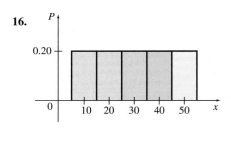

16.

17. For the game in Example 4, find Mary's expected winnings. Is it a fair game?

18. Suppose one day Mary brings a 2-headed coin and uses it to toss for the coffee. Since Mary tosses, Donna calls.

   a. Is this still a fair game?

   b. What is Donna's expected gain if she calls heads?

   c. What is Donna's expected gain if she calls tails?

Solve each exercise. Many of these exercises require the use of combinations.

19. Suppose 3 marbles are drawn from a bag containing 3 yellow and 4 white marbles.

   a. Draw a histogram for the number of yellow marbles in the sample.

   b. What is the expected number of yellow marbles in the sample?

20. Suppose 5 apples in a barrel of 25 apples are known to be rotten.

   a. Draw a histogram for the number of rotten apples in a sample of 2 apples.

   b. What is the expected number of rotten apples in a sample of 2 apples?

21. Suppose a die is rolled 4 times.

   a. Find the probability distribution for the number of times 1 is rolled.

   b. What is the expected number of times 1 is rolled?

22. A delegation of 3 is selected from a city council made up of 5 liberals and 6 conservatives.

a. What is the expected number of liberals in the delegation?

b. What is the expected number of conservatives in the delegation?

23. From a group of 3 women and 5 men, a delegation of 2 is selected. Find the expected number of women in the delegation.

24. In a club with 20 senior and 10 junior members, what is the expected number of junior members on a 4-member committee?

25. If 2 cards are drawn at one time from a deck of 52 cards, what is the expected number of diamonds?

26. Suppose someone offers to pay you $5 if you draw 2 diamonds in the game in Exercise 25. He says that you should pay 50 cents for the chance to play. Is this a fair game?

27. Your friend missed class the day probability distributions were discussed. How would you explain probability distribution to him?

28. Explain what expected value means in your own words.

29. Four slips of paper numbered 2, 3, 4, and 5 are in a hat. You draw a slip, note the result, and then draw a second slip and note the result (without replacing the first).

a. Find the probability distribution for the sum of the two slips.

b. Draw a histogram for the probability distribution in part a.

c. Find the odds that the sum is even.

d. Find the expected value of the sum.

→ Applications

BUSINESS AND ECONOMICS

30. *Complaints* A local used-car dealer gets complaints about his cars as shown in the table below.

Find the expected number of complaints per day.

Number of Complaints per Day	0	1	2	3	4	5	6
Probability	0.02	0.06	0.16	0.25	0.32	0.13	0.06

31. *Payout on Insurance Policies* An insurance company has written 100 policies for $100,000, 500 policies for $50,000,

and 1000 policies for $10,000 for people of age 20. If experience shows that the probability that a person will die at age 20 is 0.0012, how much can the company expect to pay out during the year the policies were written?

32. *Rating Sales Accounts* Levi Strauss and Company* uses expected value to help its salespeople rate their accounts. For each account, a salesperson estimates potential additional volume and the probability of getting it. The product of these figures gives the expected value of the potential, which is added to the existing volume. The totals are then classified as A, B, or C, as follows: $40,000 or below, class C; from $40,000 up to and including $55,000, class B; above $55,000, class A. Complete the table on the next page for one salesperson.

*This example was supplied by James McDonald, Levi Strauss and Company, San Francisco.

Account Number	Existing Volume	Potential Additional Volume	Probability of Getting It	Expected Value of Potential	Existing Volume + Expected Value of Potential	Class
1	$15,000	$10,000	0.25	$2500	$17,500	C
2	$40,000	$0	—	—	$40,000	C
3	$20,000	$10,000	0.20			
4	$50,000	$10,000	0.10			
5	$5000	$50,000	0.50			
6	$0	$100,000	0.60			
7	$30,000	$20,000	0.80			

33. *Pecans* Refer to Exercise 41 in Section 8.4. Suppose that 60% of the pecan "blow outs" are good, and 80% of the "good nuts" are good.

a. If you purchase 50 pecans, what is the expected number of good nuts you will find if you purchase "blow outs"?

b. If you purchase 50 pecans, what is the expected number of bad nuts you will find if you have purchased "good nuts"?

34. *Device Failure* An insurance policy on an electrical device pays a benefit of $4000 if the device fails during the first year. The amount of the benefit decreases by $1000 each successive year until it reaches 0. If the device has not failed by the beginning of any given year, the probability of failure during that year is 0.4. What is the expected benefit under this policy?* (Choose one of the following.)

a. $2234   **b.** $2400   **c.** $2500   **d.** $2667   **e.** $2694

35. *Tour Bus* A tour operator has a bus that can accommodate 20 tourists. The operator knows that tourists may not show up, so he sells 21 tickets. The probability that an individual tourist will not show up is 0.02, independent of all other tourists. Each ticket costs $50, and is non-refundable if a tourist fails to show up. If a tourist shows up and a seat is not available, the tour operator has to pay $100 (ticket cost + $50 penalty) to the tourist. What is the expected revenue of the tour operator?† (Choose one of the following.)

a. $935   **b.** $950   **c.** $967   **d.** $976   **e.** $985

LIFE SCIENCES

36. *Animal Offspring* In a certain animal species, the probability that a healthy adult female will have no offspring in a

given year is 0.29, while the probabilities of 1, 2, 3, or 4 offspring are, respectively, 0.23, 0.18, 0.16, and 0.14. Find the expected number of offspring.

37. *Ear Infections* Otitis media, or middle ear infection, is initially treated with an antibiotic. Researchers have compared two antibiotics, amoxicillin and cefaclor, for their cost effectiveness. Amoxicillin is inexpensive, safe, and effective. Cefaclor is also safe. However, it is considerably more expensive and it is generally more effective. Use the tree diagram below (where the costs are estimated as the total cost of medication, office visit, ear check, and hours of lost work) to answer the following.‡

a. Find the expected cost of using each antibiotic to treat a middle ear infection.

b. To minimize the total expected cost, which antibiotic should be chosen?

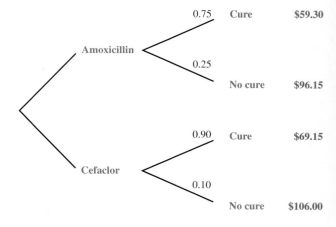

*Problem 48 from the 2005 Sample Exam P of the *Education and Examination Committee of the Society of Actuaries*. Reprinted by permission of the Society of Actuaries.
†Problem 96 from the 2005 Sample Exam P of the *Education and Examination Committee of the Society of Actuaries*. Reprinted by permission of the Society of Actuaries.
‡Weiss, Jeffrey and Shoshana Melman, based on "Cost Effectiveness in the Choice of Antibiotics for the Initial Treatment of Otitis Media in Children: A Decision Analysis Approach," *Journal of Pediatric Infectious Disease*, Vol. 7, No. 1, 1988, pp. 23–26.

38. *Hospitalization Insurance* An insurance policy pays an individual $100 per day for up to 3 days of hospitalization and $25 per day for each day of hospitalization thereafter. The number of days of hospitalization, X, is a discrete random variable with probability function

$$P(X = k) = \begin{cases} \dfrac{6 - k}{15} & \text{for } k = 1, 2, 3, 4, 5 \\ 0 & \text{otherwise.} \end{cases}$$

Calculate the expected payment for hospitalization under this policy.* (Choose one of the following.)

a. $85   **b.** $163   **c.** $168   **d.** $213   **e.** $255

SOCIAL SCIENCES

39. *Education* Recall from Exercise 65 in Section 8.4 that a *Time* magazine "Numbers" section reported that 15.2% of low-birth-weight babies graduate from high school by age 19.[†] If 250 low-birth-weight babies are followed through high school, how many would you expect to graduate from high school?

40. *Cheating* Recall from Exercise 64 in Section 8.4 that a poll conducted by *U.S. News and World Report* reported that 84% of college students believe they need to cheat to get ahead in the world today.[‡] If 500 college students were surveyed, how many would you expect to say that they need to cheat to get ahead in the world today?

41. *Samuel Alito* When Supreme Court Justice Samuel Alito was on the U.S. Court of Appeals for the 3rd Circuit, he dissented in the successful appeal of a first-degree murder case. The prosecution used its peremptory challenges to eliminate all African Americans from the jury, as it had in three other first-degree murder trials in the same county that year. According to a majority of the judges, "An amateur with a pocket calculator can calculate the number of blacks that would have served had the State used its strikes in a racially proportionate manner. In the four capital cases there was a total of 82 potential jurors on the venires who were not removed for cause, of whom eight, or 9.76%, were black. If the prosecution had used its peremptory challenges in a manner proportional to the percentage of blacks in the overall venire, then only 3 of the 34 jurors peremptorily struck (8.82%) would have been black and 5

of the 48 actual jurors (10.42%) would have been black. Instead, none of the 48 jurors were black. Admittedly, there was no statistical analysis of these figures presented by either side in the post-conviction proceeding. But is it really necessary to have a sophisticated analysis by a statistician to conclude that there is little chance of randomly selecting four consecutive all white juries?"[§]

a. Using binomial probability, calculate the probability that no African Americans would be selected out of 48 jurors if the percentage African American is 9.76%.

b. Binomial probability is not entirely accurate in this case, because the jurors were selected without replacement, so the selections were not independent. Recalculate the probability in part a using combinations.

c. In his dissent, Judge Alito wrote, "Statistics can be very revealing—and also terribly misleading in the hands of 'an amateur with a pocket calculator.' . . . Although only about 10% of the population is left-handed, left-handers have won five of the last six presidential elections. Our 'amateur with a calculator' would conclude that 'there is little chance of randomly selecting' left-handers in five out of six presidential elections. But does it follow that the voters cast their ballots based on whether a candidate was right- or left-handed?" Given the figures quoted by Judge Alito, what is the probability that at least 5 out of the last 6 presidents elected would be left-handed?

d. The majority of the judges, in disagreeing with Judge Alito, said, "The dissent has overlooked the obvious fact that there is no provision in the Constitution that protects persons from discrimination based on whether they are right-handed or left handed." Furthermore, according to *Chance News,* only 2 of the last 6 men elected president were left-handed.[||] What is the probability that at least 2 out of the last 6 presidents elected would be left-handed?

PHYSICAL SCIENCES

42. *Seeding Storms* One of the few methods that can be used in an attempt to cut the severity of a hurricane is to *seed* the storm. In this process, silver iodide crystals are dropped into the storm. Unfortunately, silver iodide crystals sometimes cause the storm to *increase* its speed. Wind speeds

---

*Problem 36 from May 2003 Course 1 Examination of the *Education and Examination Committee of the Society of Actuaries*. Reprinted by permission of the Society of Actuaries.

[†]"Numbers," *Time,* July 17, 2000, p. 21.

[‡]Kleiner, Carolyn and Mary Lord, "The Cheating Game," *U.S. News and World Report,* Nov. 22, 1999, pp. 55–66.

[§]http://caselaw.lp.findlaw.com/scripts/getcase.pl?court=3rd&navby=case&no=989009v3&exact=1.

[||]*Chance News 9,* Nov. 1–27, 2005.

may also increase or decrease even with no seeding. Use the tree diagram below to answer the following.*

a. Find the expected amount of damage under each option, "seed" and "do not seed."

b. To minimize total expected damage, what option should be chosen?

	Change in wind speed	Property damage (millions of dollars)
0.038	+32%	335.8
0.143	+16%	191.1
0.392	0	100.0
0.255	−16%	46.7
0.172	−34%	16.3
0.054	+32%	335.8
0.206	+16%	191.1
0.480	0	100.0
0.206	−16%	46.7
0.054	−34%	16.3

(Seed: 0.038, 0.143, 0.392, 0.255, 0.172)
(Do not seed: 0.054, 0.206, 0.480, 0.206, 0.054)

GENERAL INTEREST

43. *Cats* Kimberly Workman has four cats: Riley, Abby, Beastie, and Sylvester. Each cat has a 30% probability of climbing into the chair in which Kimberly is sitting, independent of how many cats are already in the chair with Kimberly.

a. Find the probability distribution for the number of cats in the chair with Kimberly.

b. Find the expected number of cats in the chair with Kimberly using the probability distribution in part a.

c. Find the expected number of cats in the chair with Kimberly using the formula for expected value of the binomial distribution.

44. *Postal Service* Mr. Statistics (a feature in *Fortune* magazine) investigated the claim of the U.S. Postal Service that 83% of first class mail in New York City arrives by the next day.[†] (The figure is 87% nationwide.) He mailed a letter to himself on 10 consecutive days; only 4 were delivered by the next day.

a. Find the probability distribution for the number of letters delivered by the next day if the overall probability of next-day delivery is 83%.

b. Using your answer to part a, find the probability that 4 or fewer out of 10 letters would be delivered by the next day.

c. Based on your answer to part b, do you think it is likely that the 83% figure is accurate? Explain.

d. Find the number of letters out of 10 that you would expect to be delivered by the next day if the 83% figure is accurate.

45. *Raffle* A raffle offers a first prize of $400 and 3 second prizes of $80 each. One ticket costs $2, and 500 tickets are sold. Find the expected payback for a person who buys 1 ticket. Is this a fair game?

46. *Raffle* A raffle offers a first prize of $1000, 2 second prizes of $300 each, and 20 third prizes of $10 each. If 10,000 tickets are sold at 50¢ each, find the expected payback for a person buying 1 ticket. Is this a fair game?

Find the expected payback for the games of chance described in Exercises 47–52.

47. *Lottery* A state lottery requires you to choose 4 cards from an ordinary deck: 1 heart, 1 club, 1 diamond, and 1 spade in that order from the 13 cards in each suit. If all four choices are selected by the lottery, you win $5000. It costs $1 to play.

48. *Lottery* If exactly 3 of the 4 choices in Exercise 47 are selected, the player wins $200. (Ignore the possibility that all 4 choices are selected. It still costs $1 to play.)

49. *Roulette* In one form of roulette, you bet $1 on "even." If 1 of the 18 even numbers comes up, you get your dollar

---

*The probabilities and amounts of property damage in the tree diagram for Exercise 42 are from Howard, R. A., J. E. Matheson, and D. W. North, "The Decision to Seed Hurricanes," *SCIENCE*, Vol. 176, No. 16, June 1972, pp. 1191–1202. Copyright © 1972 by The American Association for the Advancement of Science. Reprinted with permission from AAAS.

[†]Seligman, Daniel, "Ask Mr. Statistics," *Fortune*, July 24, 1995, pp. 170–171.

back, plus another one. If 1 of the 20 noneven (18 odd, 0, and 00) numbers comes up, you lose your dollar.

50. *Roulette* In another form of roulette, there are only 19 noneven numbers (no 00).

51. *Numbers* *Numbers* is a game in which you bet $1 on any three-digit number from 000 to 999. If your number comes up, you get $500.

52. *Keno* In one form of the game *Keno*, the house has a pot containing 80 balls, each marked with a different number from 1 to 80. You buy a ticket for $1 and mark one of the 80 numbers on it. The house then selects 20 numbers at random. If your number is among the 20, you get $3.20 (for a net winning of $2.20).

53. *Contests* A magazine distributor offers a first prize of $100,000, two second prizes of $40,000 each, and two third prizes of $10,000 each. A total of 2,000,000 entries are received in the contest. Find the expected payback if you submit one entry to the contest. If it would cost you 50¢ in time, paper, and stamps to enter, would it be worth it?

54. *Contests* A contest at a fast-food restaurant offered the following cash prizes and probabilities of winning on one visit. Suppose you spend $1 to buy a bus pass that lets you go to 25 different restaurants in the chain and pick up entry forms. Find your expected value.

Prize	Probability
$100,000	1/176,402,500
$25,000	1/39,200,556
$5000	1/17,640,250
$1000	1/1,568,022
$100	1/282,244
$5	1/7056
$1	1/588

55. *The Hog Game* In the hog game, each player states the number of dice that he or she would like to roll. The player then rolls that many dice. If a 1 comes up on any die, the player's score is 0. Otherwise, the player's score is the sum of the numbers rolled.*

a. Find the expected value of the player's score when the player rolls one die.

b. Find the expected value of the player's score when the player rolls two dice.

c. Verify that the expected nonzero score of a single die is 4, so that if a player rolls n dice that do not result in a score of 0, the expected score is $4n$.

d. Verify that if a player rolls n dice, there are 5^n possible ways to get a nonzero score, and 6^n possible ways to roll the dice. Explain why the expected value, E, of the player's score when the player rolls n dice is then

$$E = \frac{5^n(4n)}{6^n}.$$

56. *Football* After a team scores a touchdown, it can either attempt to kick an extra point or attempt a two-point conversion. During the 1999–2000 NFL season, two-point conversions were successful 37% of the time and the extra-point kicks were successful 94% of the time.[†]

a. Calculate the expected value of each strategy.

b. Which strategy, over the long run, will maximize the number of points scored?

c. Using this information, should a team always only use one strategy? Explain.

57. *Baseball* The 2005 National League batting champion was Derrek Lee, with an average of 0.335.[‡] This can be interpreted as a probability of 0.335 of getting a hit whenever he bats. Assume that each time at bat is an independent event. Suppose he goes to bat four times in a game.

a. Find the probability distribution for the number of hits.

b. What is the expected number of hits that Derrek Lee gets in a game?

*Bohan, James and John Shultz, "Revisiting and Extending the Hog Game," *Mathematics Teacher*, Vol. 89, No. 9, Dec. 1996, pp. 728–733.
[†]Leonhardt, David, "In Football, 6 + 2 Often Equals 6," *The New York Times*, Sunday, Jan. 16, 2000, pp. 4–2.
[‡]http://www.infoplease.com/ipsa/A0932329.html.

Chapter 8 Review

▶ Chapter Summary

In this chapter we continued our study of probability by introducing some elementary principles of counting. Our primary tool is the multiplication principle:

> If n choices must be made, with m_1 ways to make choice 1, and for each of these ways, m_2 ways to make choice 2, and so on, with m_n ways to make choice n, then there are $m_1 \cdot m_2 \cdot \ldots \cdot m_n$ ways to make the entire sequence of choices.

We learned two counting ideas to efficiently count the number of ways we can select a number of objects without replacement:

- permutations (when order matters), and
- combinations (when order doesn't matter).

We also considered distinguishable permutations, in which some of the objects are indistinguishable. All of these concepts were then used to calculate the numerator and denominator of various probabilities. We next explored binomial probability, in which the following conditions were satisfied:

- the same experiment is repeated a fixed number of times (n),
- there are only two possible outcomes (success and failure), and
- the trials are independent, so the probability of success remains constant (p).

We showed how to quickly calculate an entire set of combinations for binomial probability using Pascal's triangle. Finally, we introduced the following terms regarding probability distributions:

- random variable (a function assigning a real number to each outcome of an experiment),
- probability distribution (the possible values of a random variable, along with the corresponding probabilities),
- histogram (a bar graph displaying a probability distribution), and
- expected value (the average value of a random variable that we would expect in the long run).

In the next chapter, we will see how probability forms the basis of the field known as statistics.

COUNTING SUMMARY

Factorial Notation $n! = n(n-1)(n-2)\cdots(3)(2)(1)$
$0! = 1$

Permutations $P(n, r) = \dfrac{n!}{(n-r)!}$

Distinguishable Permutations If there are n_1 objects of type 1, n_2 of type 2, and so on for r different types, then the number of distinguishable permutations is

$$\frac{n!}{n_1! \, n_2! \cdots n_r!}.$$

Combinations $\dbinom{n}{r} = \dfrac{n!}{(n-r)! \, r!}$

PROBABILITY SUMMARY

Binomial Probability $P(x) = \dbinom{n}{x} p^x (1 - p)^{n-x}$

Expected Value $E(x) = x_1 p_1 + x_2 p_2 + x_3 p_3 + \cdots + x_n p_n$

For binomial probability, $E(x) = np$.

→ **Key Terms**

8.1 multiplication principle
    factorial notation
    permutations
    distinguishable
      permutations

8.2 combinations
8.4 Bernoulli trials
    binomial experiment
    binomial probability
    Pascal's triangle

8.5 random variable
    probability distribution
    probability function
    histogram
    expected value

fair game

→ **Concept Check**

Determine whether each of the following statements is true or false, and explain why.

1. Permutations provide a way of counting possibilities when order matters.

2. Combinations provide a way of counting possibilities when order doesn't matter.

3. The number of distinguishable permutations of n objects, when r are indistinguishable and the remaining $n - r$ are also indistinguishable, is the same as the number of combinations of r objects chosen from n.

4. Calculating the numerator or the denominator of a probability can involve either permutations or combinations.

5. The probability of at least 2 occurrences of an event is equal to the probability of 1 or fewer occurrences.

6. The probability of at least two people in a group having the same birthday is found by subtracting the probability of the complement of the event from 1.

7. The trials in binomial probability must be independent.

8. Binomial probability can be used when each trial has three possible outcomes.

9. A random variable can have negative values.

10. The expected value of a random variable must equal one of the values that the random variable can have.

11. The probabilities in a probability distribution must add up to 1.

12. A fair game can have an expected value that is greater than 0.

→ **Chapter 8 Review Exercises**

1. In how many ways can 6 shuttle vans line up at the airport?

2. How many variations in first-, second-, and third-place finishes are possible in a 100-yd dash with 6 runners?

3. In how many ways can a sample of 3 oranges be taken from a bag of a dozen oranges?

4. If 2 of the 12 oranges in Exercise 3 are rotten, in how many ways can the sample of 3 include

   a. 1 rotten orange?

   b. 2 rotten oranges?

   c. no rotten oranges?

   d. at most 2 rotten oranges?

5. In how many ways can 2 pictures, selected from a group of 5 different pictures, be arranged in a row on a wall?

6. In how many ways can the 5 pictures in Exercise 5 be arranged in a row if a certain one must be first?

7. In how many ways can the 5 pictures in Exercise 5 be arranged if 2 are landscapes and 3 are puppies and if

   a. like types must be kept together?

   b. landscapes and puppies are alternated?

8. In a Chinese restaurant the menu lists 8 items in column A and 6 items in column B.

   a. To order a dinner, the diner is told to select 3 items from column A and 2 from column B. How many dinners are possible?

   b. How many dinners are possible if the diner can select up to 3 from column A and up to 2 from column B? Assume at least one item must be included from either A or B.

9. A representative is to be selected from each of 3 departments in a small college. There are 7 people in the first department, 5 in the second department, and 4 in the third department.

   a. How many different groups of 3 representatives are possible?

   b. How many groups are possible if any number (at least 1) up to 3 representatives can form a group? (Each department is still restricted to at most one representative.)

10. Explain under what circumstances a permutation should be used in a probability problem, and under what circumstances a combination should be used.

11. Discuss under what circumstances the binomial probability formula should be used in a probability problem.

A basket contains 4 black, 2 blue, and 7 green balls. A sample of 3 balls is drawn. Find the probabilities that the sample contains the following.

12. All black balls

13. All blue balls

14. 2 black balls and 1 green ball

15. Exactly 2 black balls

16. Exactly 1 blue ball

17. 2 green balls and 1 blue ball

Suppose a family plans 6 children, and the probability that a particular child is a girl is 1/2. Find the probabilities that the 6-child family has the following children.

18. Exactly 3 girls

19. All girls

20. At least 4 girls

21. No more than 2 boys

Suppose 2 cards are drawn without replacement from an ordinary deck of 52. Find the probabilities of the following results.

22. Both cards are red.

23. Both cards are spades.

24. At least 1 card is a spade.

25. One is a face card and the other is not.

26. At least one is a face card.

27. At most one is a queen.

In Exercises 28 and 29, **(a)** *give a probability distribution,* **(b)** *sketch its histogram, and* **(c)** *find the expected value.*

28. A coin is tossed 3 times and the number of heads is recorded.

29. A pair of dice is rolled and the sum of the results for each roll is recorded.

In Exercises 30 and 31, give the probability that corresponds to the shaded region of each histogram.

30.

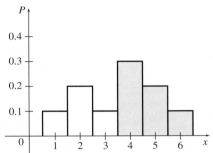

31.

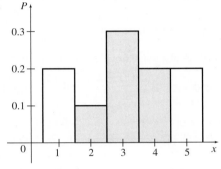

32. You pay $6 to play in a game where you will roll a die, with payoffs as follows: $8 for a 6, $7 for a 5, and $4 for any other results. What are your expected winnings? Is the game fair?

33. Find the expected number of girls in a family of 5 children.

34. Three cards are drawn from a standard deck of 52 cards.

  a. What is the expected number of aces?   **b.** What is the expected number of clubs?

35. Suppose someone offers to pay you $100 if you draw 3 cards from a standard deck of 52 cards and all the cards are clubs. What should you pay for the chance to win if it is a fair game?

36. Six students will decide which of them are on a committee by flipping a coin. Each student flips the coin, and is on the committee if he or she gets a head. What is the probability that someone is on the committee, but not all 6 students?

37. In this exercise we study the connection between sets (from Chapter 7) and combinations (from Chapter 8).

  a. Given a set with n elements, what is the number of subsets of size 0? of size 1? of size 2? of size n?

  b. Using your answer from part a, give an expression for the total number of subsets of a set with n elements.

  c. Using your answer from part b and a result from Chapter 7, explain why the following equation must be true:

$$\binom{n}{0} + \binom{n}{1} + \binom{n}{2} + \cdots + \binom{n}{n} = 2^n.$$

d. Verify the equation in part c for $n = 4$ and $n = 5$.

e. Explain what the equation in part c tells you about Pascal's triangle.

In the following exercise, find the digit (0 through 9) that belongs in each box. This exercise is from the 1990 University Entrance Center Examination, given in Japan to all applicants for public universities. *

38. The numbers 1 through 9 are written individually on nine cards. Choose three cards from the nine, letting x, y, and z denote the numbers of the cards arranged in increasing order.

a. There are $\square\square$ such x, y, and z combinations.

b. The probability of having x, y, and z all even is $\dfrac{\square}{\square\square}$.

c. The probability of having x, y, and z be consecutive numbers is $\dfrac{\square}{\square\square}$.

d. The probability of having $x = 4$ is $\dfrac{\square}{\square\square}$.

e. Possible values of x range from $\square$ to $\square$. If k is an integer such that $\square \le k \le \square$, the probability that $x = k$ is $\dfrac{(\square - k)(\square - k)}{\square\square\square}$. The expected value of x is $\dfrac{\square}{\square}$.

▶ Applications

BUSINESS AND ECONOMICS

Identity Theft *According to a survey by Javelin Strategy and Research, 1 out of 6 adults in Arizona were victims of identity theft.[†] Suppose that 12 adults are randomly selected from Arizona. Find the probabilities of each of the following results.*

39. None of the adults were victims of identity theft.

40. All of the adults were victims of identity theft.

41. Exactly 10 of the adults were victims of identity theft.

42. Exactly 2 of the adults were victims of identity theft.

43. At least 2 of the adults were victims of identity theft.

44. At most 3 of the adults were victims of identity theft.

45. Find the expected number of victims of identity theft in a sample of 12 adults in Arizona.

46. *Land Development* A developer can buy a piece of property that will produce a profit of $26,000 with probability 0.7, or a loss of $9000 with probability 0.3. What is the expected profit?

47. *Insurance Claims* An insurance company determines that N, the number of claims received in a week, is a random variable with $P(N = n) = 1/2^{n+1}$, where $n \ge 0$. The company also determines that the number of claims received in a given week is independent of the number of claims received in any other week. Determine the probability that exactly seven claims will be received during a given two-week period.[‡] (Choose one of the following.)

a. $1/256$ **b.** $1/128$ **c.** $7/512$ **d.** $1/64$ **e.** $1/32$

48. *Injury Claims* The number of injury claims per month is modeled by a random variable N with

$$P(N = n) = \frac{1}{(n + 1)(n + 2)}, \quad \text{where } n \ge 0.$$

---

*"Japanese University Entrance Examination Problems in Mathematics," by Ling-Erl Eileen T. Wu, ed., Mathematical Association of America, 1993, p. 5. Copyright © 1993 from Wu's *Japanese University Entrance Examination Problems in Mathematics*, published by The Mathematical Association of America.
[†]*The New York Times*, May 30, 2006, p. A1.
[‡]Problem 16 from the 2005 Sample Exam P of the *Education and Examination Committee of the Society of Actuaries*. Reprinted by permission of the Society of Actuaries.

Determine the probability of at least one claim during a particular month, given that there have been at most four claims during that month.* (Choose one of the following.)

a. 1/3   **b.** 2/5   **c.** 1/2   **d.** 3/5   **e.** 5/6

49. *Product Success* A company is considering the introduction of a new product that is believed to have probability 0.5 of being successful and probability 0.5 of being unsuccessful. Successful products pass quality control 80% of the time. Unsuccessful products pass quality control 25% of the time. If the product is successful, the net profit to the company will be $40 million; if unsuccessful, the net loss will be $15 million. Determine the expected net profit if the product passes quality control.[†] (Choose one of the following.)

a. $23 million   **b.** $24 million   **c.** $25 million

d. $26 million   **e.** $27 million

50. *Sampling Fruit* A merchant buys boxes of fruit from a grower and sells them. Each box of fruit is either Good or Bad. A Good box contains 80% excellent fruit and will earn $200 profit on the retail market. A Bad box contains 30% excellent fruit and will produce a loss of $1000. The a priori probability of receiving a Good box of fruit is 0.9. Before the merchant decides to put the box on the market, he can sample one piece of fruit to test whether it is excellent. Based on that sample, he has the option of rejecting the box without paying for it. Determine the expected value of the right to sample.[‡] (Choose one of the following. *Hint:* The a priori probability is the probability before sampling a piece of fruit. If the merchant samples the fruit, what are the probabilities of accepting a Good box, accepting a Bad box, and not accepting the box? What are these probabilities if he does not sample the fruit?)

a. 0   **b.** $16   **c.** $34   **d.** $72   **e.** $80

51. *Overbooking Flights* The March 1982 issue of *Mathematics Teacher* included "Overbooking Airline Flights," an article by Joe Dan Austin. In this article, Austin developed a model for the expected income for an airline flight. With appropriate assumptions, the probability that exactly x of n people with reservations show up at the airport to buy a ticket is given by the binomial probability formula. Assume the following: 6 reservations have been accepted for 3 seats, $p = 0.6$ is the probability that a person with a reservation will show up, a ticket costs $400, and the airline must pay $400 to anyone with a reservation who does not get a ticket. Complete the following table.

Number Who Show Up (x)	0	1	2	3	4	5	6
Airline's Income							
$P(x)$							

a. Use the table to find $E(I)$, the expected airline income from the 3 seats.

b. Find $E(I)$ for $n = 3$, $n = 4$, and $n = 5$. Compare these answers with $E(I)$ for $n = 6$. For these values of n, how many reservations should the airline book for the 3 seats in order to maximize the expected revenue?

LIFE SCIENCES

52. *Pharmacology* In placebo-controlled trials of Prozac[®], a drug that is prescribed to fight depression, 23% of the patients who were taking the drug experienced nausea, whereas 10% of the patients who were taking the placebo experienced nausea.[§]

a. If 50 patients who are taking Prozac[®] are selected, what is the probability that 10 or more will experience nausea?

b. Of the 50 patients in part a, what is the expected number of patients who will experience nausea?

c. If a second group of 50 patients receives a placebo, what is the probability that 10 or fewer will experience nausea?

d. If a patient from a study of 1000 people, who are equally divided into two groups (those taking a placebo and those taking Prozac[®]), is experiencing nausea, what is the probability that he/she is taking Prozac[®]?

e. Since 0.23 is more than twice as large as 0.10, do you think that people who take Prozac[®] are more likely to experience nausea than those who take a placebo? Explain.

---

*Problem 24 from the 2005 Sample Exam P of the *Education and Examination Committee of the Society of Actuaries*. Reprinted by permission of the Society of Actuaries.

[†]*Course 130 Examination*, Operations Research, Nov. 1989. Reprinted by permission of the Society of Actuaries.

[‡]Ibid.

[§]Advertisement in *The New England Journal of Medicine*, Vol. 338, No. 9, Feb. 26, 1998, for Prozac[®], developed and marketed by Eli Lilly and Company.

53. *Education* In Exercise 38 of Section 8.3, we saw that a school in Bangkok requires that students take an entrance examination. After the examination, 5 students are randomly drawn from each group of 40 for automatic acceptance into the school regardless of their performance on the examination. The drawing consists of placing 35 red and 5 green pieces of paper into a box. If the lottery is changed so that each student picks a piece of paper from the box and then returns the piece of paper to the box, find the probability that exactly 5 of the 40 students will choose a green piece of paper.*

In Exercises 54–57, **(a)** *give a probability distribution,* **(b)** *sketch its histogram, and* **(c)** *find the expected value.*

54. *Candy* According to officials of Mars, the makers of M&M Plain Chocolate Candies, 20% of the candies in each bag are orange.[†] Four candies are selected from a bag and the number of orange candies is recorded.

55. *Women Athletes* In 1992, the Big 10 collegiate sports conference moved to have women compose at least 40% of its athletes within 5 years.[‡] Suppose they exactly achieve the 40% figure, and that 5 athletes are picked at random from Big 10 universities. The number of women is recorded.

56. *Race* In the mathematics honors society at a college, 2 of the 8 members are African American. Three members are selected at random to be interviewed by the student newspaper, and the number of African Americans is noted.

57. *Homework* In a small class of 10 students, 3 did not do their homework. The professor selects half of the class to present solutions to homework problems on the board, and records how many of those selected did not do their homework.

58. *Lottery* A lottery has a first prize of $5000, two second prizes of $1000 each, and two $100 third prizes. A total of 10,000 tickets is sold, at $1 each. Find the expected payback of a person buying 1 ticket.

59. *Contests* At one time, game boards for a United Airlines contest could be obtained by sending a self-addressed, stamped envelope to a certain address. The prize was a ticket for any city to which United flies. Assume that the value of the ticket was $2000 (we might as well go first-class), and that the probability that a particular game board would win was 1/8000. If the stamps to enter the contest cost 41¢ and envelopes cost 4¢ each, find the expected payback for a person ordering 1 game board. (Notice that 2 stamps and envelopes were required to enter.)

60. *Lottery* On June 23, 2003, an interesting thing happened in the Pennsylvania Lottery's Big 4, in which a four-digit number from 0000 to 9999 is chosen twice a day.[§] On this day, the number 3199 was chosen both times.

   a. What is the probability of the same number being chosen twice in one day?

   b. What is the probability of the number 3199 being chosen twice in one day?

61. *Lottery* In the Pennsylvania Lottery's Daily Number game, a three-digit number between 000 and 999 is chosen each day.[§] The favorite number among players is 000, which on July 28, 2003, was the winning number for the tenth time since 1977. Find the number of times that 000 would be expected to win in 26 years of play. (Assume that the game is played 365 days a year, ignoring leap years and the fact that before 1990, the game was not played on Christmas or New Year's Day. Also ignore the fact that since February 2003, the game has been played twice a day.)

62. *Lottery* New York has a lottery game called Quick Draw, in which the player can pick anywhere from 1 up to 10 numbers from 1 to 80. The computer then picks 20 numbers, and how much you win is based on how many of your numbers match the computer's. For simplicity, we will only consider the two cases in which you pick 4 or 5 numbers. The payoffs for each dollar that you bet are given in the table below.

	How Many Numbers Match the Computer's Numbers					
	0	**1**	**2**	**3**	**4**	**5**
You Pick 4	0	0	1	5	55	
You Pick 5	0	0	0	2	20	300

a. According to the Quick Draw playing card, the "Overall Chances of Winning" when you pick 4 are "1:3.86," while the chances when you pick 5 are "1:10.34." Verify these figures.

b. Find the expected value when you pick 4 and when you pick 5, betting $1 each time.

c. Based on your results from parts a and b, are you better off picking 4 numbers or picking 5? Explain your reasoning.

63. *Murphy's Law* Robert Matthews wrote an article about Murphy's Law, which says that if something can go wrong, it will.* He considers Murphy's Law of Odd Socks, which says that if an odd sock can be created it will be, in a drawer of 10 loose pairs of socks.

a. Find the probability of getting a matching pair when the following numbers of socks are selected at random from the drawer.

    i. 5 socks   **ii.** 6 socks

b. Matthews says that it is necessary to rummage through 30% of the socks to get a matching pair. Using your answers from part a, explain precisely what he means by that.

c. Matthews claims that if you lose 6 socks at random from the drawer, then it is 100 times more likely that you will be left with the worst possible outcome—6 odd socks—than with a drawer free of odd socks. Verify this calculation by finding the probability that you will be left with 6 odd socks and the probability that you will have a drawer free of odd socks.

64. *Baseball* The number of runs scored in 16,456 half-innings of the 1986 National League Baseball season was analyzed by Hal Stern. Use the table in the next column to answer the following questions.[†]

a. What is the probability that a given team scored 5 or more runs in any given half-inning during the 1986 season?

b. What is the probability that a given team scored fewer than 2 runs in any given half-inning of the 1986 season?

c. What is the expected number of runs that a team scored during any given half-inning of the 1986 season? Interpret this number.

Runs	Frequency	Probability
0	12,087	0.7345
1	2451	0.1489
2	1075	0.0653
3	504	0.0306
4	225	0.0137
5	66	0.0040
6	29	0.0018
7	12	0.0007
8	5	0.0003
9	2	0.0001

65. *St. Petersburg Paradox* Suppose you play a gambling game in which you flip a coin until you get a head. If you get a head on the first toss, you win $2. You win $4 if the first head occurs on the second toss, $8 if it occurs on the the third toss, and so forth, with a prize of 2^n if the first head occurs on the nth toss. Show that the expected value of this game is infinite. Explain why this is a paradox.[‡]

66. *Pit* The card game of Pit was introduced by Parker Brothers in 1904 and is still popular. In the version owned by one of the authors of this book, there are 10 suits of 9 identical cards, plus the Bull and the Bear card, for a total of 92 cards. (Newer versions of the game have only 8 suits of cards.) For this problem, assume that all 92 cards are used, and you are dealt 9 cards.

a. What is the probability that you have one card from each of 9 different suits, but neither the Bull nor the Bear?

b. What is the probability that you have a pairs of cards from one suit and one card from each of 7 other suits, but neither the Bull nor the Bear?

c. What is the probability that you have two pair of cards from two different suits and one card from each of 5 other suits, but neither the Bull nor the Bear?

---

*Matthews, Robert, "Why Does Toast Always Land Butter-Side Down?" *Sunday Telegraph*, March 17, 1996, p. 4.

[†]J. Laurie Snell's report of Hal Stern's analysis in *Chance News 7.05*, Apr. 27–May 26, 1998.

[‡]Many articles have been written in an attempt to explain this paradox, first posed by the Swiss mathematician Daniel Bernoulli when he lived in St. Petersburg. For example, see Székely, Gábor and Donald St. P. Richards, "The St. Petersburg Paradox and the Crash of High-Tech Stocks in 2000," *The American Statistician*, Vol. 58, No. 3, Aug. 2004, pp. 225–231.

Optimal Inventory for a Service Truck

For many different items it is difficult or impossible to take the item to a central repair facility when service is required. Washing machines, large television sets, office copiers, and computers are only a few examples of such items. Service for items of this type is commonly performed by sending a repair person to the item, with the person driving to the location in a truck containing various parts that might be required in repairing the item. Ideally, the truck should contain all the parts that might be required. However, most parts would be needed only infrequently, so that inventory costs for the parts would be high.

An optimum policy for deciding on which parts to stock on a truck would require that the probability of not being able to repair an item without a trip back to the warehouse for needed parts be as low as possible, consistent with minimum inventory costs. An analysis similar to the one below was developed at the Xerox Corporation.*

To set up a mathematical model for deciding on the optimum truck-stocking policy, let us assume that a broken machine might require one of 5 different parts (we could assume any number of different parts—we use 5 to simplify the notation). Suppose also that the probability that a particular machine requires part 1 is p_1; that it requires part 2 is p_2; and so on. Assume also that failures of different part types are independent, and that at most one part of each type is used on a given job.

Suppose that, on the average, a repair person makes N service calls per time period. If the repair person is unable to make a repair because at least one of the parts is unavailable, there is a penalty cost, L, corresponding to wasted time for the repair person, an extra trip to the parts depot, customer unhappiness, and so on. For each of the parts carried on the truck, an average inventory cost is incurred. Let H_i be the average inventory cost for part i, where $1 \leq i \leq 5$.

Let M_1 represent a policy of carrying only part 1 on the repair truck, M_{24} represent a policy of carrying only parts 2 and 4, with M_{12345} and M_0 representing policies of carrying all parts and no parts, respectively.

For policy M_{35}, carrying parts 3 and 5 only, the expected cost per time period per repair person, written $C(M_{35})$, is

$$C(M_{35}) = (H_3 + H_5) + NL[1 - (1 - p_1)(1 - p_2)(1 - p_4)].$$

(The expression in brackets represents the probability of needing at least one of the parts not carried, 1, 2, or 4 here.) As further examples,

$$C(M_{125}) = (H_1 + H_2 + H_5) + NL[1 - (1 - p_3)(1 - p_4)],$$

while

$$\begin{aligned} C(M_{12345}) &= (H_1 + H_2 + H_3 + H_4 + H_5) + NL[1 - 1] \\ &= H_1 + H_2 + H_3 + H_4 + H_5, \end{aligned}$$

and

$$C(M_0) = NL[1 - (1 - p_1)(1 - p_2)(1 - p_3)(1 - p_4)(1 - p_5)].$$

To find the best policy, evaluate $C(M_0)$, $C(M_1)$, ..., $C(M_{12345})$, and choose the smallest result. (A general solution method is in the *Management Science* paper.)

EXAMPLE

Suppose that for a particular item, only 3 possible parts might need to be replaced. By studying past records of failures of the item, and finding necessary inventory costs, suppose that the following values have been found.

p_1	p_2	p_3
0.09	0.24	0.17

H_1	H_2	H_3
$15	$40	$9

*Smith, Stephen, John Chambers, and Eli Shlifer, "Optimal Inventories Based on Job Completion Rate for Repairs Requiring Multiple Items," *Management Science*, Vol. 26, No. 8, Aug. 1980. © 1980 by The Institute of Management Sciences.

Suppose $N = 3$ and L is \$54. Then, as an example,

$$C(M_1) = H_1 + NL[1 - (1 - p_2)(1 - p_3)]$$
$$= 15 + 3(54)[1 - (1 - 0.24)(1 - 0.17)]$$
$$= 15 + 3(54)[1 - (0.76)(0.83)]$$
$$\approx 15 + 59.81 = 74.81.$$

Thus, if policy M_1 is followed (carrying only part 1 on the truck), the expected cost per repair person per time period is \$74.81. Also,

$$C(M_{23}) = H_2 + H_3 + NL[1 - (1 - p_1)]$$
$$= 40 + 9 + 3(54)(0.09) = 63.58,$$

so that M_{23} is a better policy than M_1. By finding the expected values for all other possible policies (see the exercises), the optimum policy may be chosen.

EXERCISES

1. Refer to the example and find the following.

   a. $C(M_0)$ **b.** $C(M_2)$ **c.** $C(M_3)$ **d.** $C(M_{12})$

   e. $C(M_{13})$ **f.** $C(M_{123})$

2. Which policy leads to the lowest expected cost?

3. In the example, $p_1 + p_2 + p_3 = 0.09 + 0.24 + 0.17 = 0.50$. Why is it not necessary that the probabilities add up to 1?

4. Suppose an item to be repaired might need one of n different parts. How many different policies would then need to be evaluated?

DIRECTIONS FOR GROUP PROJECT

Suppose you and three others are employed as service repair persons and that you have some disagreement with your supervisor as to the quantity and type of parts to have on hand for your service calls. Use the answers to Exercises 1–4 to prepare a report with a recommendation to your boss on optimal inventory. Make sure that you describe each concept well since your boss is not mathematically minded.

9

Statistics

To understand the economics of large-scale farming, analysts look at historical data on the farming industry. In an exercise in Section 1 you will calculate basic descriptive statistics for U.S. wheat prices and production levels over a recent decade. Later sections in this chapter develop more sophisticated techniques for extracting useful information from this kind of data.

TABLE 1 Formulas from Geometry

PYTHAGOREAN THEOREM
For a right triangle with legs of lengths a and b and hypotenuse of length c, $a^2 + b^2 = c^2$.

CIRCLE
Area: $A = \pi r^2$
Circumference: $C = 2\pi r$

RECTANGLE
Area: $A = lw$
Perimeter: $P = 2l + 2w$

TRIANGLE
Area: $A = \dfrac{1}{2}bh$

SPHERE
Volume: $V = \dfrac{4}{3}\pi r^3$

Surface area: $A = 4\pi r^2$

CONE
Volume: $V = \dfrac{1}{3}\pi r^2 h$

RECTANGULAR BOX
Volume: $V = lwh$
Surface area: $A = 2lh + 2wh + 2lw$

CIRCULAR CYLINDER
Volume: $V = \pi r^2 h$
Surface area: $A = 2\pi r^2 + 2\pi rh$

TRIANGULAR CYLINDER
Volume: $V = \dfrac{1}{2}bhl$

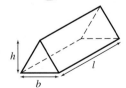

GENERAL INFORMATION ON SURFACE AREA
To find the surface area of a figure, break down the total surface area into the individual components and add up the areas of the components. For example, a rectangular box has six sides, each of which is a rectangle. A circular cylinder has two ends, each of which is a circle, plus the side, which forms a rectangle when opened up.

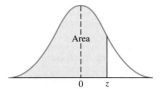

TABLE 2 Area Under a Normal Curve to the Left of z, where $z = \dfrac{x - \mu}{\sigma}$

z	0.00	0.01	0.02	0.03	0.04	0.05	0.06	0.07	0.08	0.09
-3.4	0.0003	0.0003	0.0003	0.0003	0.0003	0.0003	0.0003	0.0003	0.0003	0.0002
-3.3	0.0005	0.0005	0.0005	0.0004	0.0004	0.0004	0.0004	0.0004	0.0004	0.0003
-3.2	0.0007	0.0007	0.0006	0.0006	0.0006	0.0006	0.0006	0.0005	0.0005	0.0005
-3.1	0.0010	0.0009	0.0009	0.0009	0.0008	0.0008	0.0008	0.0008	0.0007	0.0007
-3.0	0.0013	0.0013	0.0013	0.0012	0.0012	0.0011	0.0011	0.0011	0.0010	0.0010
-2.9	0.0019	0.0018	0.0017	0.0017	0.0016	0.0016	0.0015	0.0015	0.0014	0.0014
-2.8	0.0026	0.0025	0.0024	0.0023	0.0023	0.0022	0.0021	0.0021	0.0020	0.0019
-2.7	0.0035	0.0034	0.0033	0.0032	0.0031	0.0030	0.0029	0.0028	0.0027	0.0026
-2.6	0.0047	0.0045	0.0044	0.0043	0.0041	0.0040	0.0039	0.0038	0.0037	0.0036
-2.5	0.0062	0.0060	0.0059	0.0057	0.0055	0.0054	0.0052	0.0051	0.0049	0.0048
-2.4	0.0082	0.0080	0.0078	0.0075	0.0073	0.0071	0.0069	0.0068	0.0066	0.0064
-2.3	0.0107	0.0104	0.0102	0.0099	0.0096	0.0094	0.0091	0.0089	0.0087	0.0084
-2.2	0.0139	0.0136	0.0132	0.0129	0.0125	0.0122	0.0119	0.0116	0.0113	0.0110
-2.1	0.0179	0.0174	0.0170	0.0166	0.0162	0.0158	0.0154	0.0150	0.0146	0.0143
-2.0	0.0228	0.0222	0.0217	0.0212	0.0207	0.0202	0.0197	0.0192	0.0188	0.0183
-1.9	0.0287	0.0281	0.0274	0.0268	0.0262	0.0256	0.0250	0.0244	0.0239	0.0233
-1.8	0.0359	0.0352	0.0344	0.0336	0.0329	0.0322	0.0314	0.0307	0.0301	0.0294
-1.7	0.0446	0.0436	0.0427	0.0418	0.0409	0.0401	0.0392	0.0384	0.0375	0.0367
-1.6	0.0548	0.0537	0.0526	0.0516	0.0505	0.0495	0.0485	0.0475	0.0465	0.0455
-1.5	0.0668	0.0655	0.0643	0.0630	0.0618	0.0606	0.0594	0.0582	0.0571	0.0559
-1.4	0.0808	0.0793	0.0778	0.0764	0.0749	0.0735	0.0722	0.0708	0.0694	0.0681
-1.3	0.0968	0.0951	0.0934	0.0918	0.0901	0.0885	0.0869	0.0853	0.0838	0.0823
-1.2	0.1151	0.1131	0.1112	0.1093	0.1075	0.1056	0.1038	0.1020	0.1003	0.0985
-1.1	0.1357	0.1335	0.1314	0.1292	0.1271	0.1251	0.1230	0.1210	0.1190	0.1170
-1.0	0.1587	0.1562	0.1539	0.1515	0.1492	0.1469	0.1446	0.1423	0.1401	0.1379
-0.9	0.1841	0.1814	0.1788	0.1762	0.1736	0.1711	0.1685	0.1660	0.1635	0.1611
-0.8	0.2119	0.2090	0.2061	0.2033	0.2005	0.1977	0.1949	0.1922	0.1894	0.1867
-0.7	0.2420	0.2389	0.2358	0.2327	0.2296	0.2266	0.2236	0.2206	0.2177	0.2148
-0.6	0.2743	0.2709	0.2676	0.2643	0.2611	0.2578	0.2546	0.2514	0.2483	0.2451
-0.5	0.3085	0.3050	0.3015	0.2981	0.2946	0.2912	0.2877	0.2843	0.2810	0.2776

TABLE 2 Area Under a Normal Curve (continued)

z	0.00	0.01	0.02	0.03	0.04	0.05	0.06	0.07	0.08	0.09
−0.4	0.3446	0.3409	0.3372	0.3336	0.3300	0.3264	0.3228	0.3192	0.3156	0.3121
−0.3	0.3821	0.3783	0.3745	0.3707	0.3669	0.3632	0.3594	0.3557	0.3520	0.3483
−0.2	0.4207	0.4168	0.4129	0.4090	0.4052	0.4013	0.3974	0.3936	0.3897	0.3859
−0.1	0.4602	0.4562	0.4522	0.4483	0.4443	0.4404	0.4364	0.4325	0.4286	0.4247
−0.0	0.5000	0.4960	0.4920	0.4880	0.4840	0.4801	0.4761	0.4721	0.4681	0.4641
0.0	0.5000	0.5040	0.5080	0.5120	0.5160	0.5199	0.5239	0.5279	0.5319	0.5359
0.1	0.5398	0.5438	0.5478	0.5517	0.5557	0.5596	0.5636	0.5675	0.5714	0.5753
0.2	0.5793	0.5832	0.5871	0.5910	0.5948	0.5987	0.6026	0.6064	0.6103	0.6141
0.3	0.6179	0.6217	0.6255	0.6293	0.6331	0.6368	0.6406	0.6443	0.6480	0.6517
0.4	0.6554	0.6591	0.6628	0.6664	0.6700	0.6736	0.6772	0.6808	0.6844	0.6879
0.5	0.6915	0.6950	0.6985	0.7019	0.7054	0.7088	0.7123	0.7157	0.7190	0.7224
0.6	0.7257	0.7291	0.7324	0.7357	0.7389	0.7422	0.7454	0.7486	0.7517	0.7549
0.7	0.7580	0.7611	0.7642	0.7673	0.7704	0.7734	0.7764	0.7794	0.7823	0.7852
0.8	0.7881	0.7910	0.7939	0.7967	0.7995	0.8023	0.8051	0.8078	0.8106	0.8133
0.9	0.8159	0.8186	0.8212	0.8238	0.8264	0.8289	0.8315	0.8340	0.8365	0.8389
1.0	0.8413	0.8438	0.8461	0.8485	0.8508	0.8531	0.8554	0.8577	0.8599	0.8621
1.1	0.8643	0.8665	0.8686	0.8708	0.8729	0.8749	0.8770	0.8790	0.8810	0.8830
1.2	0.8849	0.8869	0.8888	0.8907	0.8925	0.8944	0.8962	0.8980	0.8997	0.9015
1.3	0.9032	0.9049	0.9066	0.9082	0.9099	0.9115	0.9131	0.9147	0.9162	0.9177
1.4	0.9192	0.9207	0.9222	0.9236	0.9251	0.9265	0.9278	0.9292	0.9306	0.9319
1.5	0.9332	0.9345	0.9357	0.9370	0.9382	0.9394	0.9406	0.9418	0.9429	0.9441
1.6	0.9452	0.9463	0.9474	0.9484	0.9495	0.9505	0.9515	0.9525	0.9535	0.9545
1.7	0.9554	0.9564	0.9573	0.9582	0.9591	0.9599	0.9608	0.9616	0.9625	0.9633
1.8	0.9641	0.9649	0.9656	0.9664	0.9671	0.9678	0.9686	0.9693	0.9699	0.9706
1.9	0.9713	0.9719	0.9726	0.9732	0.9738	0.9744	0.9750	0.9756	0.9761	0.9767
2.0	0.9772	0.9778	0.9783	0.9788	0.9793	0.9798	0.9803	0.9808	0.9812	0.9817
2.1	0.9821	0.9826	0.9830	0.9834	0.9838	0.9842	0.9846	0.9850	0.9854	0.9857
2.2	0.9861	0.9864	0.9868	0.9871	0.9875	0.9878	0.9881	0.9884	0.9887	0.9890
2.3	0.9893	0.9896	0.9898	0.9901	0.9904	0.9906	0.9909	0.9911	0.9913	0.9916
2.4	0.9918	0.9920	0.9922	0.9925	0.9927	0.9929	0.9931	0.9932	0.9934	0.9936
2.5	0.9938	0.9940	0.9941	0.9943	0.9945	0.9946	0.9948	0.9949	0.9951	0.9952
2.6	0.9953	0.9955	0.9956	0.9957	0.9959	0.9960	0.9961	0.9962	0.9963	0.9964
2.7	0.9965	0.9966	0.9967	0.9968	0.9969	0.9970	0.9971	0.9972	0.9973	0.9974
2.8	0.9974	0.9975	0.9976	0.9977	0.9977	0.9978	0.9979	0.9979	0.9980	0.9981
2.9	0.9981	0.9982	0.9982	0.9983	0.9984	0.9984	0.9985	0.9985	0.9986	0.9986
3.0	0.9987	0.9987	0.9987	0.9988	0.9988	0.9989	0.9989	0.9989	0.9990	0.9990
3.1	0.9990	0.9991	0.9991	0.9991	0.9992	0.9992	0.9992	0.9992	0.9993	0.9993
3.2	0.9993	0.9993	0.9994	0.9994	0.9994	0.9994	0.9994	0.9995	0.9995	0.9995
3.3	0.9995	0.9995	0.9995	0.9996	0.9996	0.9996	0.9996	0.9996	0.9996	0.9997
3.4	0.9997	0.9997	0.9997	0.9997	0.9997	0.9997	0.9997	0.9997	0.9997	0.9998

TABLE 3 Integrals

(*C* is an arbitrary constant.)

1. $\displaystyle\int x^n\, dx = \frac{x^{n+1}}{n+1} + C \quad (\text{if } n \neq -1)$

2. $\displaystyle\int e^{kx}\, dx = \frac{e^{kx}}{k} + C$

3. $\displaystyle\int \frac{a}{x}\, dx = a \ln |x| + C$

4. $\displaystyle\int \ln |ax|\, dx = x(\ln |ax| - 1) + C$

5. $\displaystyle\int \frac{1}{\sqrt{x^2 + a^2}}\, dx = \ln \left| x + \sqrt{x^2 + a^2} \right| + C$

6. $\displaystyle\int \frac{1}{\sqrt{x^2 - a^2}}\, dx = \ln \left| x + \sqrt{x^2 - a^2} \right| + C$

7. $\displaystyle\int \frac{1}{a^2 - x^2}\, dx = \frac{1}{2a} \cdot \ln \left| \frac{a + x}{a - x} \right| + C \quad (a \neq 0)$

8. $\displaystyle\int \frac{1}{x^2 - a^2}\, dx = \frac{1}{2a} \cdot \ln \left| \frac{x - a}{x + a} \right| + C \quad (a \neq 0)$

9. $\displaystyle\int \frac{1}{x\sqrt{a^2 - x^2}}\, dx = -\frac{1}{a} \cdot \ln \left| \frac{a + \sqrt{a^2 - x^2}}{x} \right| + C \quad (a \neq 0)$

10. $\displaystyle\int \frac{1}{x\sqrt{a^2 + x^2}}\, dx = -\frac{1}{a} \cdot \ln \left| \frac{a + \sqrt{a^2 + x^2}}{x} \right| + C \quad (a \neq 0)$

11. $\displaystyle\int \frac{x}{ax + b}\, dx = \frac{x}{a} - \frac{b}{a^2} \cdot \ln |ax + b| + C \quad (a \neq 0)$

12. $\displaystyle\int \frac{x}{(ax + b)^2}\, dx = \frac{b}{a^2(ax + b)} + \frac{1}{a^2} \cdot \ln |ax + b| + C \quad (a \neq 0)$

13. $\displaystyle\int \frac{1}{x(ax + b)}\, dx = \frac{1}{b} \cdot \ln \left| \frac{x}{ax + b} \right| + C \quad (b \neq 0)$

14. $\displaystyle\int \frac{1}{x(ax + b)^2}\, dx = \frac{1}{b(ax + b)} + \frac{1}{b^2} \cdot \ln \left| \frac{x}{ax + b} \right| + C \quad (b \neq 0)$

15. $\displaystyle\int \sqrt{x^2 + a^2}\, dx = \frac{x}{2} \sqrt{x^2 + a^2} + \frac{a^2}{2} \cdot \ln \left| x + \sqrt{x^2 + a^2} \right| + C$

16. $\displaystyle\int x^n \cdot \ln |x|\, dx = x^{n+1} \left[\frac{\ln |x|}{n + 1} - \frac{1}{(n + 1)^2} \right] + C \quad (n \neq -1)$

17. $\displaystyle\int x^n e^{ax}\, dx = \frac{x^n e^{ax}}{a} - \frac{n}{a} \cdot \int x^{n-1} e^{ax}\, dx + C \quad (a \neq 0)$

Answers to Selected Exercises

Answers to selected writing exercises are provided.

CHAPTER R Algebra Reference

Exercises R.1 (page xxvii)

1. $-x^2 + x + 9$ **2.** $-6y^2 + 3y + 10$ **3.** $-16q^2 + 4q + 6$ **4.** $9r^2 - 4r + 19$ **5.** $-0.327x^2 - 2.805x - 1.458$
6. $0.8r^2 + 3.6r - 1.5$ **7.** $-18m^3 - 27m^2 + 9m$ **8.** $12k^2 - 20k + 3$ **9.** $9t^2 + 9ty - 10y^2$ **10.** $18k^2 - 7kq - q^2$
11. $(6/25)y^2 + (11/40)yz + (1/16)z^2$ **12.** $(15/16)r^2 - (7/12)rs - (2/9)s^2$ **13.** $4 - 9x^2$ **14.** $36m^2 - 25$ **15.** $27p^3 - 1$
16. $15p^3 + 13p^2 - 10p - 8$ **17.** $8m^3 + 1$ **18.** $12k^4 + 21k^3 - 5k^2 + 3k + 2$ **19.** $3x^2 + xy + 2xz - 2y^2 - 3yz - z^2$
20. $2r^2 + 2rs - 5rt - 4s^2 + 8st - 3t^2$ **21.** $x^3 + 6x^2 + 11x + 6$ **22.** $x^3 - 2x^2 - 5x + 6$ **23.** $x^2 + 4x + 4$
24. $4a^2 - 16ab + 16b^2$ **25.** $x^3 - 6x^2y + 12xy^2 - 8y^3$

Exercises R.2 (page xxx)

1. $7a^2(a + 2)$ **2.** $3y(y^2 + 8y + 3)$ **3.** $13p^2q(p^2q - 3p + 2q)$ **4.** $10m^2(6m^2 - 12mn + 5n^2)$ **5.** $(m + 2)(m - 7)$
6. $(x + 5)(x - 1)$ **7.** $(z + 4)(z + 5)$ **8.** $(b - 7)(b - 1)$ **9.** $(a - 5b)(a - b)$ **10.** $(s - 5t)(s + 7t)$
11. $(y - 7z)(y + 3z)$ **12.** $6(a - 10)(a + 2)$ **13.** $3m(m + 3)(m + 1)$ **14.** $(3x + 7)(x - 1)$ **15.** $(3a + 7)(a + 1)$
16. $2(2a + 3)(a + 1)$ **17.** $(5y + 2)(3y - 1)$ **18.** $(7m + 2n)(3m + n)$ **19.** $2a^2(4a - b)(3a + 2b)$
20. $12x^2(x - y)(2x + 5y)$ **21.** $(x + 8)(x - 8)$ **22.** $(3m + 5)(3m - 5)$ **23.** $10(x + 4)(x - 4)$ **24.** Prime
25. $(z + 7y)^2$ **26.** $(s - 5t)^2$ **27.** $(3p - 4)^2$ **28.** $(a - 6)(a^2 + 6a + 36)$ **29.** $(3r - 4s)(9r^2 + 12rs + 16s^2)$
30. $3(m + 5)(m^2 - 5m + 25)$ **31.** $(x - y)(x + y)(x^2 + y^2)$ **32.** $(2a - 3b)(2a + 3b)(4a^2 + 9b^2)$

Exercises R.3 (page xxxiii)

1. $v/7$ **2.** $5p/2$ **3.** $8/9$ **4.** $2/(t + 2)$ **5.** $x - 2$ **6.** $4(y + 2)$ **7.** $(m - 2)/(m + 3)$ **8.** $(r + 2)/(r + 4)$
9. $3(x - 1)/(x - 2)$ **10.** $(z - 3)/(z + 2)$ **11.** $(m^2 + 4)/4$ **12.** $(2y + 1)/(y + 1)$ **13.** $3k/5$ **14.** $25p^2/9$
15. $9/(5c)$ **16.** 2 **17.** $1/4$ **18.** $3/10$ **19.** $2(a + 4)/(a - 3)$ **20.** $2/(r + 2)$ **21.** $(k - 2)/(k + 3)$
22. $(m + 6)/(m + 3)$ **23.** $(m - 3)/(2m - 3)$ **24.** $2(2n - 1)/(3n - 5)$ **25.** 1 **26.** $(6 + p)/(2p)$
27. $(12 - 15y)/(10y)$ **28.** $137/(30m)$ **29.** $(3m - 2)/[m(m - 1)]$ **30.** $(r - 6)/[r(2n + 3)]$ **31.** $14/[3(a - 1)]$
32. $23/[20(k - 2)]$ **33.** $(7x + 1)/[(x - 2)(x + 3)(x + 1)]$ **34.** $(y^2 + 1)/[(y + 3)(y + 1)(y - 1)]$
35. $k(k - 13)/[(2k - 1)(k + 2)(k - 3)]$ **36.** $m(3m - 19)/[(3m - 2)(m + 3)(m - 4)]$ **37.** $(4a + 1)/[a(a + 2)]$
38. $(5x^2 + 4x - 4)/[x(x - 1)(x + 1)]$

Exercises R.4 (page xxxix)

1. 12 **2.** $-3/8$ **3.** -12 **4.** $3/4$ **5.** $-7/8$ **6.** $-6/11$ **7.** 4 **8.** $-10/19$ **9.** $-3, -2$ **10.** $-1, 3$ **11.** 7 **12.** $-2, 5/2$
13. $-1/4, 2/3$ **14.** $2, 5$ **15.** $-3, 3$ **16.** $-4, 1/2$ **17.** $0, 4$ **18.** $(5 + \sqrt{13})/6 \approx 1.434, (5 - \sqrt{13})/6 \approx 0.232$
19. $(2 + \sqrt{10})/2 \approx 2.581, (2 - \sqrt{10})/2 \approx -0.581$ **20.** $(-1 + \sqrt{5})/2 \approx 0.618, (-1 - \sqrt{5})/2 \approx -1.618$
21. $5 + \sqrt{5} \approx 7.236, 5 - \sqrt{5} \approx 2.764$ **22.** $(4 + \sqrt{6})/5 \approx 1.290, (4 - \sqrt{6})/5 \approx 0.310$ **23.** $1, 5/2$ **24.** No real number
solutions **25.** $(-1 + \sqrt{73})/6 \approx 1.257, (-1 - \sqrt{73})/6 \approx -1.591$ **26.** $-1, 0$ **27.** 3 **28.** 12 **29.** $-59/6$ **30.** 6
31. 3 **32.** $-5/2$ **33.** $2/3$ **34.** 1 **35.** 2 **36.** No solution **37.** No solution

Exercises R.5 (page xlv)

1. $(-\infty, 4)$ **2.** $[-3, \infty)$ **3.** $[1, 2)$
4. $[-2, 3]$ **5.** $(-\infty, -9)$ **6.** $[6, \infty)$
7. $-7 \leq x \leq -3$ **8.** $4 \leq x < 10$ **9.** $x \leq -1$ **10.** $x > 3$ **11.** $-2 \leq x < 6$ **12.** $0 < x < 8$ **13.** $x \leq -4$ or $x \geq 4$
14. $x < 0$ or $x \geq 3$ **15.** $(-\infty, 2]$ **16.** $(-\infty, 1)$
17. $(3, \infty)$ **18.** $(-\infty, 1]$ **19.** $(1/5, \infty)$
20. $(1/3, \infty)$ **21.** $(-4, 6)$ **22.** $[7/3, 4]$
23. $[-5, 3)$ **24.** $[-1, 2]$ **25.** $[-17/7, \infty)$

26. $(-\infty, 50/9]$ 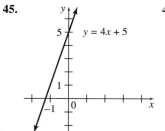 **27.** $(-5, 3)$

28. $(-\infty, -6] \cup [1, \infty)$ **29.** $(1, 2)$

30. $(-\infty, -4) \cup (1/2, \infty)$ **31.** $(-\infty, -4) \cup (4, \infty)$

32. $[-3/2, 5]$ **33.** $(-\infty, -1] \cup [5, \infty)$

34. $[-1/2, 2/5]$ **35.** $(-\infty, -1) \cup (1/3, \infty)$

36. $(-\infty, -2) \cup (5/3, \infty)$ **37.** $(-\infty, -3] \cup [3, \infty)$

38. $(-\infty, 0) \cup (16, \infty)$ **39.** $(-5, 3]$ **40.** $(-\infty, -1) \cup (1, \infty)$ **41.** $(-\infty, -2)$ **42.** $(-2, 3/2)$
43. $[-8, 5)$ **44.** $(-\infty, -3/2) \cup [-13/9, \infty)$ **45.** $[2, 3)$ **46.** $(-\infty, -1)$ **47.** $(-2, 0] \cup (3, \infty)$ **48.** $(-4, -2) \cup (0, 2)$
49. $(1, 3/2]$ **50.** $(-\infty, -2) \cup (-2, 2) \cup [4, \infty)$

Exercises R.6 (page l)

1. $1/64$ **2.** $1/81$ **3.** 1 **4.** 1 **5.** $-1/9$ **6.** $1/9$ **7.** 36 **8.** $27/64$ **9.** $1/64$ **10.** 8^5 **11.** $1/10^8$ **12.** 7 **13.** x^2 **14.** 1
15. $2^3 k^3$ **16.** $1/(3z^7)$ **17.** $x^5/(3y^3)$ **18.** $m^3/5^4$ **19.** $a^3 b^6$ **20.** $49/(c^6 d)$ **21.** x^4/y^4 **22.** b/a^3 **23.** $(a + b)/(ab)$
24. $(1 - ab^2)/b^2$ **25.** $2(m - n)/[mn(m + n^2)]$ **26.** $(3n^2 + 4m)/(mn^2)$ **27.** $xy/(y - x)$ **28.** $y^4/(xy - 1)^2$ **29.** 11
30. 3 **31.** 4 **32.** -25 **33.** $1/2$ **34.** $4/3$ **35.** $1/16$ **36.** $1/5$ **37.** $4/3$ **38.** $1000/1331$ **39.** 9 **40.** 3 **41.** 64
42. 1 **43.** r **44.** $12^3/y^8$ **45.** $3k^{3/2}/8$ **46.** $1/(2p^2)$ **47.** $a^{2/3} b^2$ **48.** $y^2/(x^{1/6} z^{5/4})$ **49.** $h^{1/3} t^{1/5}/k^{2/5}$ **50.** $m^3 p/n$
51. $3x(x^2 + 3x)^2(x^2 - 5)$ **52.** $6x(x^3 + 7)(-2x^3 - 5x + 7)$ **53.** $5x(x^2 - 1)^{-1/2}(x^2 + 1)$ **54.** $3(6x + 2)^{-1/2}(27x + 5)$
55. $(2x + 5)(x^2 - 4)^{-1/2}(4x^2 + 5x - 8)$ **56.** $(4x^2 + 1)(2x - 1)^{-1/2}(36x^2 - 16x + 1)$

Exercises R.7 (page liv)

1. 5 **2.** 6 **3.** -5 **4.** $5\sqrt{2}$ **5.** $20\sqrt{5}$ **6.** $4y^2\sqrt{2y}$ **7.** 9 **8.** 8 **9.** $7\sqrt{2}$ **10.** $9\sqrt{3}$ **11.** $9\sqrt{7}$ **12.** $-2\sqrt{7}$
13. $5\sqrt[3]{2}$ **14.** $3\sqrt[3]{5}$ **15.** $xyz^2\sqrt{2x}$ **16.** $4r^3 s^4 t^6\sqrt{10rs}$ **17.** $4xy^2 z^3\sqrt[3]{2y^2}$ **18.** $x^2 yz^2\sqrt[4]{y^3 z^3}$ **19.** $ab\sqrt{ab}(b - 2a^2 + b^3)$
20. $p^2\sqrt{pq}(pq - q^4 + p^2)$ **21.** $\sqrt[7]{a^5}$ **22.** $b^2\sqrt[4]{b}$ **23.** $5\sqrt{7}/7$ **24.** $\sqrt{10}/2$ **25.** $-\sqrt{3}/2$ **26.** $\sqrt{2}$ **27.** $-3(1 + \sqrt{2})$
28. $-5(2 + \sqrt{6})/2$ **29.** $3(2 - \sqrt{2})$ **30.** $(5 - \sqrt{10})/3$ **31.** $(\sqrt{r} + \sqrt{3})/(r - 3)$ **32.** $5(\sqrt{m} + \sqrt{5})/(m - 5)$
33. $\sqrt{y} + \sqrt{5}$ **34.** $(z + \sqrt{5z} - \sqrt{z} - \sqrt{5})/(z - 5)$ **35.** $-2x - 2\sqrt{x(x + 1)} - 1$
36. $[p^2 + p + 2\sqrt{p(p^2 - 1)} - 1]/(-p^2 + p + 1)$ **37.** $-1/[2(1 - \sqrt{2})]$ **38.** $1/(3 + \sqrt{3})$ **39.**
$-1/[2x - 2\sqrt{x(x + 1)} + 1]$ **40.** $2/[p + \sqrt{p(p - 2)}]$ **41.** $|4 - x|$ **42.** $|3y + 5|$ **43.** Cannot be simplified
44. Cannot be simplified

CHAPTER 1 Linear Functions

Exercises 1.1 (page 15)

1. $3/5$ **3.** Not defined **5.** 1 **7.** $5/9$ **9.** Not defined **11.** 0 **13.** 2 **15.** $y = -2x + 5$ **17.** $y = -7$
19. $y = -(1/3)x + 10/3$ **21.** $y = 6x - 7/2$ **23.** $x = -8$ **25.** $y = -(1/2)x - 3$ **27.** $x = -6$ **29.** $y = -(3/2)x$
31. $y = x - 7$ **33.** $y = 5x + 4$ **35.** No **39.** a **41.** -4

45.

47.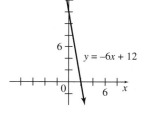

49.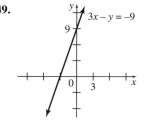

51.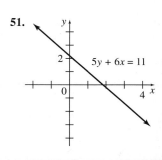

53.

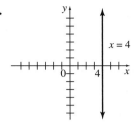

$x = 4$

55.

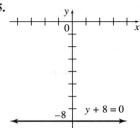

$y + 8 = 0$

57.

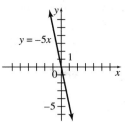

$y = -5x$

59.

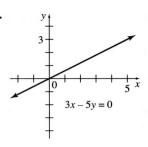

$3x - 5y = 0$

61. a.

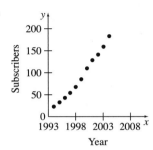

The number of subscribers is increasing and the data appear to be nearly linear.
b. $y = 17.26x - 7.75$ **c.** For 2005, the number of subscribers is 199.4, which is less than the actual number of subscribers.

63. a. $y = 4.23x + 100$ **b.** 176.14, which is more than the actual CPI.   **c.** It is increasing at a rate of 4.23 per year.

65. a. $u = 0.85(220 - x) = 187 - 0.85x, l = 0.7(220 - x) = 154 - 0.7x$ **b.** 140 to 170 beats per minute.   **c.** 126 to 153 beats per minute.   **d.** The women are 16 and 52. Their pulse is 143 beats per minute.   **67.** Approximately 86 yr

69. a. $y = 0.115x + 22.2$ **b.** $y = 0.13x + 19.95$ **c.** Women   **d.** 2028   **e.** 28.8 yr   **71. a.** $y = 0.145x + 1.59$ **b.** About 5.94 million   **73. a.** There appears to be a linear relationship.   **b.** $y = 76.9x$ **c.** About 780 megaparsecs (about 1.5×10^{22} mi)
d. About 12.4 billion yr

75.   a.

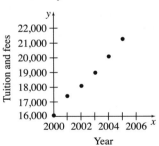

Yes, the data are approximately linear.
b. $y = 1032.6x + 16,072$; the slope 1032.6 indicates that tuition and fees have increased approximately $1033 per year.   **c.** The year 2025 is too far in the future to rely on this equation to predict costs; too many other factors may influence these costs by then.

Exercises 1.2 (page 28)

1. -3 **3.** 22   **5.** 0   **7.** -4 **9.** $7 - 5t$ **11.** True   **13.** True   **19.** If $R(x)$ is the cost of renting a snowboard for x hours, then $R(x) = 2.25x + 10$.   **21.** If $C(x)$ is the cost of parking a car for x half-hours, then $C(x) = 0.75x + 2$.
23. $C(x) = 30x + 100$ **25.** $C(x) = 75x + 550$ **27. a.** $16   **b.** $11   **c.** $6   **d.** 640 watches   **e.** 480 watches
f. 320 watches   **g.**   **h.** 0 watches   **i.** About 1333 watches   **j.** About 2667 watches

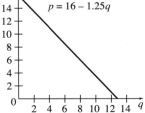

$p = 16 - 1.25q$

k.

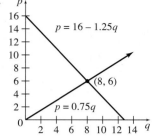

l. 800 watches, $6

29. a.

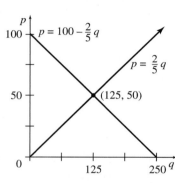

b. 125 tubs, $50

31. a. $C(x) = 3.50x + 90$ **b.** 17 shirts   **c.** 108 shirts   **33. a.** $C(x) = 0.097x + 1.32$ **b.** $1.32   **c.** $98.32   **d.** $98.417
e. 9.7¢   **f.** 9.7¢, the cost of producing one additional cup of coffee would be 9.7¢.   **35. a.** $5,100,000   **b.** (1, 100,000) and
(6, 5,100,000); $S(x) = 1,000,000x - 900,000$ **c.** 2991; sales would have to grow much faster than linearly to reach $1 billion by 2003.
d. $S(x) = 123,000,000x - 1,234,000,000$ **e.** 602,000,000; this is less than the actual sales.   **f.** 2009   **37. a.** 3 units   **b.** $3211
c. 13 units   **39.** Break-even quantity is about 41 units; produce; $P(x) = 145x - 6000$ **41.** Break-even quantity is -50 units;
impossible to make a profit when $C(x) > R(x)$ for all positive x; $P(x) = -100x - 5000$ (always a loss).   **43. a.** 98.6°F
b. 97.7°F and 99.5°F

Exercises 1.3 (page 41)

3. a.

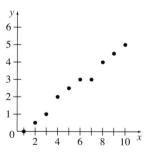

b. 0.993   **c.** $Y = 0.55x - 0.5$

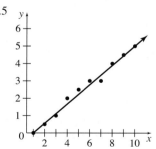

d. 5.55

7. a. $Y = -0.2519x + 33.6330$ **b.** 5924   **c.** $r = -0.977$; the line fits the data points very well.
9. a.

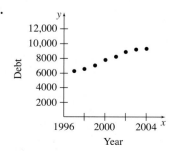

b.

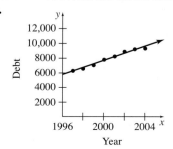

$Y = 482.25x - 40,537.5$. The least squares line
seems to be a good fit.   **c.** $r = 0.987$. This
confirms that the least squares line is a good fit.
d. 2009

11. a. 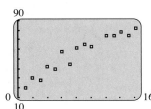   **b.** 0.959, yes   **c.** $Y = 3.98x + 22.7$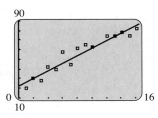

13. a. $Y = 0.212x - 0.315$ **b.** 15.2 chirps per second.   **c.** 86.4°F   **d.** 0.835

15. a. 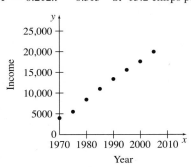   **b.** $r = 0.999$; yes   **c.** $Y = 0.467x + 3.74$ **d.** $27,090

17. a. $Y = 14.9x + 2820$ **b.** 5060, compared to actual 5000; 6990, compared to actual 7000; 9080, compared to actual 9000   **c.** 6500 BTU air conditioner

19. a. $Y = -0.1358x + 113.94$ **b.** $Y = -0.3913x + 148.98$ **c.** $x \approx 137$; the women will catch up to the men in the year 2037.
d. $r_{men} = -0.9823$; $r_{women} = -0.9487$; both sets of data points closely fit a line with negative slope.
e.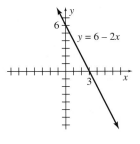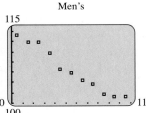

21. a. $Y = 1.121x + 34.27$ **b.** 0.8963   **c.** 3:02

Concept Check (page 49)

1. False   **2.** False **3.** True   **4.** False   **5.** True   **6.** False   **7.** True   **8.** False   **9.** False   **10.** False   **11.** False   **12.** True

Chapter 1 Review Exercises (page 50)

3. 1   **5.** $-2/11$ **7.** $-4/3$ **9.** 0   **11.** 5   **13.** $y = (2/3)x - 13/3$ **15.** $y = -x - 3$ **17.** $x = -1$
19. $y = 2x - 10$ **21.** $y = -10$ **23.** $x = -3$
25. 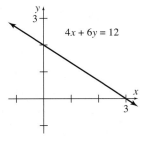   **27.**

29.

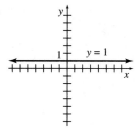

31.

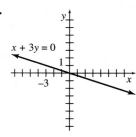

33. a. $7/6; 9/2$ **b.** $2; 2$ **c.** $5/2; 1/2$ **d.**

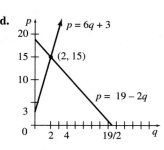

   e. $15   **f.** 2

35. $D(q) = -0.5q + 72.50$ **37.** $C(x) = 30x + 60$ **39.** $C(x) = 30x + 85$ **41. a.** 5 cartons   **b.** \$2000
43. $y = 35.25x + 66.75$ **45.** $I(x) = 180.4x + 27,384$
47. a. $r = 0.881$, yes   **b.**

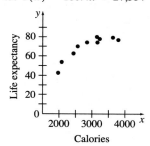

Somewhat, but there is also a nonlinear trend.   **c.** $Y = 0.0173x + 19.3$
d. $Y = 78.1$ yr   **49.** $Y = -0.797x + 201.3$

51. a. $r = 0.749$; yes, but the fit is not very good.   **b.**

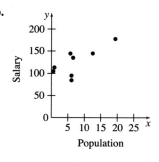

c. $Y = 3.81x + 98.24$ **d.** \$3810

CHAPTER 2   **Systems of Linear Equations and Matrices**

Exercises 2.1 (page 65)

1. $(3, 2)$ **3.** $(1, 3)$ **5.** $(-2, 0)$ **7.** $(0, 2)$ **9.** $(3, -2)$ **11.** $(2, -2)$ **13.** No solution   **15.** $((2y - 4)/3, y)$ **17.** No
19. $(4, 1)$ **21.** $(7, -2)$ **23.** $(1, 2, -1)$ **25.** $(2, 0, 3)$ **27.** $(3, 0, 1)$ **31.** $((-2z - 7)/5, (11z + 21)/5, z)$
33. $((-4z + 28)/5, (z - 7)/5, z)$ **37.** 260 skirts and 270 blouses   **39.** This situation is not possible.   **41.** 24 fives, 8 tens, and

38 twenties   **43.** Either 10 buffets, 5 chairs, and no tables, or 11 buffets, 1 chair, and 1 table   **45.** $z + 80$ long-sleeve blouses, $260 - 2z$ short-sleeve blouses, and z sleeveless blouses with $0 \le z \le 130$.   **47. a.** March 23, March 19   **b.** 1991

49. 36 field goals, 28 foul shots   **51.** One possible system is $\begin{cases} x + y = 3 \\ 3x + 2y = 8 \end{cases}$ with solution $(2, 1)$.

Exercises 2.2 (page 80)

1. $\begin{bmatrix} 3 & 1 & | & 6 \\ 2 & 5 & | & 15 \end{bmatrix}$ **3.** $\begin{bmatrix} 2 & 1 & 1 & | & 3 \\ 3 & -4 & 2 & | & -7 \\ 1 & 1 & 1 & | & 2 \end{bmatrix}$ **5.** $x = 2, y = 3$ **7.** $x = 4, y = -5, z = 1$ **9.** Row operations

11. $\begin{bmatrix} 3 & 7 & 4 & | & 10 \\ 0 & 1 & -5 & | & -8 \\ 0 & 4 & 5 & | & 11 \end{bmatrix}$ **13.** $\begin{bmatrix} 1 & 0 & 0 & | & -3 \\ 0 & 3 & 2 & | & 5 \\ 0 & 5 & 3 & | & 7 \end{bmatrix}$ **15.** $\begin{bmatrix} 1 & 0 & 0 & | & 6 \\ 0 & 5 & 0 & | & 9 \\ 0 & 0 & 4 & | & 8 \end{bmatrix}$ **17.** $(2, 3)$ **19.** $(1, 6)$ **21.** No solution

23. $((3y + 1)/6, y)$ **25.** $(4, 1, 0)$ **27.** No solution   **29.** $(-1, 23, 16)$ **31.** $((-9z + 5)/23, (10z - 3)/23, z)$

33. $((-2z + 62)/35, (3z + 5)/7, z)$ **35.** $((9 - 3y - z)/2, y, z)$ **37.** $(0, 2, -2, 1)$; the answers are given in the order x, y, z, w.

39. $(-w - 3, -4w - 19, -3w - 2, w)$ **41.** $(28.9436, 36.6326, 9.6390, 37.1036)$ **43.** row 1: 3/8, 1/6, 11/24; row 2: 5/12, 1/3, 1/4; row 3: 5/24, 1/2, 7/24   **45.** 22 units from Toronto, 56 units from Montreal, and 22 units from Ottawa   **47. a.** 15 deluxe, 10 super-deluxe, 20 ultra   **b.** None   **c.** 9   **49.** 120 vans, 60 small trucks, and 20 large trucks   **51.** Send 12 cars from I to A, 8 cars from II to A, 16 cars from I to B, and no cars from II to B.   **53.** 18,000 packages of Italian style, 15,000 packages of French style, and 54,000 packages of Oriental style   **55.** Four possibilities: no cases of A and D, 12 cases of B, 8 cases of C; or 1 case of A, 8 cases of B, 9 cases of C, 1 case of D; or 2 cases of A, 4 cases of B, 10 cases of C, 2 cases of D; or 3 cases of A, no cases of B, 11 cases of C, 3 cases of D   **57.** 2340 of the first species, 10,128 of the second species, and 224 of the third species (all are rounded)   **59. a.** No   **b.** Yes; 150 acres for honeydews, 50 acres for onions, and 20 acres for lettuce   **61. a.** $a = -0.1225, b = 2.035, c = 207.9$ **b.** 189.90   **c.** $a = 0.0002202, b = -0.1291, c = 2.079, d = 207.9$ **63. a.** $x_2 + x_3 = 700, x_3 + x_4 = 600$ **b.** $(1000 - x_4, 100 + x_4, 600 - x_4, x_4)$ **c.** $0 \le x_4 \le 600$ **d.** $400 \le x_1 \le 1000, 100 \le x_2 \le 700, 0 \le x_3 \le 600$.

65. a. 24 balls, 57 dolls, and 19 cars   **b.** None   **c.** 48   **d.** 5 balls, 95 dolls, and 0 cars   **e.** 52 balls, 1 doll, and 47 cars   **67.** 225 singles, 24 doubles, 5 triples, and 8 home runs

Exercises 2.3 (page 91)

1. False; not all corresponding elements are equal.   **3.** True   **5.** True   **7.** 2×2; square; $\begin{bmatrix} 4 & -8 \\ -2 & -3 \end{bmatrix}$

9. 3×4; $\begin{bmatrix} 6 & -8 & 0 & 0 \\ -4 & -1 & -9 & -2 \\ -3 & 5 & -7 & -1 \end{bmatrix}$ **11.** 2×1; column; $\begin{bmatrix} 7 \\ -5 \end{bmatrix}$ **13.** The $n \times m$ zero matrix   **15.** $x = 4, y = -8, z = 1$

17. $s = 10, t = 0, r = 7$ **19.** $a = 20, b = 5, c = 0, d = 4, f = 1$ **21.** $\begin{bmatrix} 10 & 4 & -5 & -6 \\ 4 & 5 & 3 & 11 \end{bmatrix}$ **23.** Not possible

25. $\begin{bmatrix} 1 & 5 & 6 & -9 \\ 5 & 7 & 2 & 1 \\ -7 & 2 & 2 & -7 \end{bmatrix}$ **27.** $\begin{bmatrix} 3 & 4 \\ 4 & 8 \end{bmatrix}$ **29.** $\begin{bmatrix} 10 & -2 \\ 10 & 9 \end{bmatrix}$ **31.** $\begin{bmatrix} -12x + 8y & -x + y \\ x & 8x - y \end{bmatrix}$ **33.** $\begin{bmatrix} -x & -y \\ -z & -w \end{bmatrix}$

39. a. Chicago: $\begin{bmatrix} 4.05 & 7.01 \\ 3.27 & 3.51 \end{bmatrix}$, Seattle: $\begin{bmatrix} 4.40 & 6.90 \\ 3.54 & 3.76 \end{bmatrix}$ **b.** $\begin{bmatrix} 4.42 & 7.43 \\ 3.38 & 3.62 \end{bmatrix}$ **41. a.** $\begin{bmatrix} 2 & 1 & 2 & 1 \\ 3 & 2 & 2 & 1 \\ 4 & 3 & 2 & 1 \end{bmatrix}$ **b.** $\begin{bmatrix} 5 & 0 & 7 \\ 0 & 10 & 1 \\ 0 & 15 & 2 \\ 10 & 12 & 8 \end{bmatrix}$ **c.** $\begin{bmatrix} 8 \\ 4 \\ 5 \end{bmatrix}$

43. a. 8   **b.** 3   **c.** $\begin{bmatrix} 85 & 15 \\ 27 & 73 \end{bmatrix}$ **d.** Yes   **45. a.** $\begin{bmatrix} 60.0 & 68.3 \\ 63.8 & 72.5 \\ 64.5 & 73.6 \\ 68.2 & 74.9 \end{bmatrix}$ **b.** $\begin{bmatrix} 68.0 & 75.6 \\ 70.7 & 78.1 \\ 72.7 & 79.4 \\ 74.8 & 80.0 \end{bmatrix}$ **c.** $\begin{bmatrix} -8.0 & -7.3 \\ -6.9 & -5.6 \\ -8.2 & -5.8 \\ -6.6 & -5.1 \end{bmatrix}$

47. a. $\begin{bmatrix} 51.4 & 7.9 \\ 59.9 & 11.1 \\ 66.2 & 11.3 \\ 73.8 & 13.3 \\ 78.9 & 16.6 \\ 80.6 & 17.6 \end{bmatrix}$ **b.** $\begin{bmatrix} 44.5 & 7.6 \\ 47.9 & 8.5 \\ 50.8 & 9.2 \\ 53.4 & 9.3 \\ 57.0 & 10.6 \\ 58.4 & 12.1 \end{bmatrix}$ **c.** $\begin{bmatrix} 6.9 & 0.3 \\ 12.0 & 2.6 \\ 15.4 & 2.1 \\ 20.4 & 4.0 \\ 21.9 & 6.0 \\ 22.2 & 5.5 \end{bmatrix}$

Exercises 2.4 (page 103)

1. $\begin{bmatrix} -4 & 8 \\ 0 & 6 \end{bmatrix}$ **3.** $\begin{bmatrix} 12 & -24 \\ 0 & -18 \end{bmatrix}$ **5.** $\begin{bmatrix} -22 & -6 \\ 20 & -12 \end{bmatrix}$ **7.** $2 \times 2; 2 \times 2$ **9.** $3 \times 4; BA$ does not exist. **11.** AB does not exist; 3×2

13. Columns: rows **15.** $\begin{bmatrix} 8 \\ -1 \end{bmatrix}$ **17.** $\begin{bmatrix} 14 \\ -23 \end{bmatrix}$ **19.** $\begin{bmatrix} -7 & 2 & 8 \\ 27 & -12 & 12 \end{bmatrix}$ **21.** $\begin{bmatrix} -2 & 10 \\ 0 & 8 \end{bmatrix}$ **23.** $\begin{bmatrix} 13 & 5 \\ 25 & 15 \end{bmatrix}$

25. $\begin{bmatrix} 13 \\ 29 \end{bmatrix}$ **27.** $\begin{bmatrix} 7 \\ -33 \\ 4 \end{bmatrix}$ **29.** $\begin{bmatrix} 22 & -8 \\ 11 & -4 \end{bmatrix}$ **31. a.** $\begin{bmatrix} 16 & 22 \\ 7 & 19 \end{bmatrix}$ **b.** $\begin{bmatrix} 5 & -5 \\ 0 & 30 \end{bmatrix}$ **c.** No **d.** No

39. a. $\begin{bmatrix} 6 & 106 & 158 & 222 & 28 \\ 120 & 139 & 64 & 75 & 115 \\ -146 & -2 & 184 & 144 & -129 \\ 106 & 94 & 24 & 116 & 110 \end{bmatrix}$ **b.** Does not exist **c.** No

41. a. $\begin{bmatrix} -1 & 5 & 9 & 13 & -1 \\ 7 & 17 & 2 & -10 & 6 \\ 18 & 9 & -12 & 12 & 22 \\ 9 & 4 & 18 & 10 & -3 \\ 1 & 6 & 10 & 28 & 5 \end{bmatrix}$ **b.** $\begin{bmatrix} -2 & -9 & 90 & 77 \\ -42 & -63 & 127 & 62 \\ 413 & 76 & 180 & -56 \\ -29 & -44 & 198 & 85 \\ 137 & 20 & 162 & 103 \end{bmatrix}$ **c.** $\begin{bmatrix} -56 & -1 & 1 & 45 \\ -156 & -119 & 76 & 122 \\ 315 & 86 & 118 & -91 \\ -17 & -17 & 116 & 51 \\ 118 & 19 & 125 & 77 \end{bmatrix}$

d. $\begin{bmatrix} 54 & -8 & 89 & 32 \\ 114 & 56 & 51 & -60 \\ 98 & -10 & 62 & 35 \\ -12 & -27 & 82 & 34 \\ 19 & 1 & 37 & 26 \end{bmatrix}$ **e.** $\begin{bmatrix} -2 & -9 & 90 & 77 \\ -42 & -63 & 127 & 62 \\ 413 & 76 & 180 & -56 \\ -29 & -44 & 198 & 85 \\ 137 & 20 & 162 & 103 \end{bmatrix}$ **f.** Yes

43. a.
$\begin{array}{c} \\ \text{Dept. 1} \\ \text{Dept. 2} \\ \text{Dept. 3} \\ \text{Dept. 4} \end{array} \begin{array}{cc} \text{A} & \text{B} \\ \begin{bmatrix} 57 & 70 \\ 41 & 54 \\ 27 & 40 \\ 39 & 40 \end{bmatrix} \end{array}$
b. Supplier A: \$164; Supplier B: \$204; Supplier A **45. a.** $\begin{bmatrix} 4.24 & 6.95 \\ 3.42 & 3.64 \end{bmatrix}$ **b.** $\begin{bmatrix} 4.41 & 7.17 \\ 3.46 & 3.69 \end{bmatrix}$

47. a. $\begin{bmatrix} 80 & 40 & 120 \\ 60 & 30 & 150 \end{bmatrix}$ **b.** $\begin{bmatrix} 1/2 & 1/5 \\ 1/4 & 1/5 \\ 1/4 & 3/5 \end{bmatrix}$ **c.** $PF = \begin{bmatrix} 80 & 96 \\ 75 & 108 \end{bmatrix}$ The rows give the average price per pair of footwear sold by each store, and the columns give the state.

49. a. $\begin{bmatrix} 20 & 52 & 27 \\ 25 & 62 & 35 \\ 30 & 72 & 43 \end{bmatrix}$; the rows give the amounts of fat, carbohydrates, and protein, respectively, in each of the daily meals.

b. $\begin{bmatrix} 75 \\ 45 \\ 70 \\ 168 \end{bmatrix}$; the rows give the number of calories in one exchange of each of the food groups.   **c.** The rows give the number of calories in each meal.

51. $\begin{bmatrix} 66.7 & 74.4 \\ 69.6 & 77.2 \\ 71.3 & 78.4 \\ 73.7 & 79.2 \end{bmatrix}$ **53. a.** $\begin{bmatrix} 0.036 & 0.014 \\ 0.019 & 0.008 \\ 0.021 & 0.006 \\ 0.014 & 0.008 \\ 0.011 & 0.011 \end{bmatrix}$; $\begin{bmatrix} 283 & 1628 & 218 & 199 & 425 \\ 361 & 2038 & 286 & 227 & 460 \\ 473 & 2494 & 362 & 252 & 484 \\ 627 & 2978 & 443 & 278 & 499 \\ 839 & 3518 & 539 & 320 & 513 \end{bmatrix}$ **b.**

	Births	Deaths
1960	53.159	24.561
1970	65.962	29.950
1980	80.868	36.086
1990	97.838	42.973
2002	118.488	51.327

Exercises 2.5 (page 116)

1. Yes   **3.** No   **5.** No   **7.** Yes   **9.** No; the row of all zeros makes it impossible to get all the 1's in the diagonal of the identity matrix, no matter what matrix is used as an inverse.

11. $\begin{bmatrix} 0 & 1/2 \\ -1 & 1/2 \end{bmatrix}$ **13.** $\begin{bmatrix} 2 & 1 \\ 5 & 3 \end{bmatrix}$ **15.** No inverse   **17.** $\begin{bmatrix} 1 & 0 & 0 \\ 0 & -1 & 0 \\ -1 & 0 & 1 \end{bmatrix}$ **19.** $\begin{bmatrix} 15 & 4 & -5 \\ -12 & -3 & 4 \\ -4 & -1 & 1 \end{bmatrix}$ **21.** No inverse

23. $\begin{bmatrix} -11/2 & -1/2 & 5/2 \\ 1/2 & 1/2 & -1/2 \\ -5/2 & 1/2 & 1/2 \end{bmatrix}$ **25.** $\begin{bmatrix} 1/2 & 1/2 & -1/4 & 1/2 \\ -1 & 4 & -1/2 & -2 \\ -1/2 & 5/2 & -1/4 & -3/2 \\ 1/2 & -1/2 & 1/4 & 1/2 \end{bmatrix}$ **27.** $(5, 1)$ **29.** $(2, 1)$ **31.** $(15, 21)$

33. No inverse, $(-8y - 12, y)$ **35.** $(-8, 6, 1)$ **37.** $(-36, 8, -8)$ **39.** No inverse, no solution for system

41. $(-7, -34, -19, 7)$

51. Entries are rounded to four places. $\begin{bmatrix} -0.0447 & -0.0230 & 0.0292 & 0.0895 & -0.0402 \\ 0.0921 & 0.0150 & 0.0321 & 0.0209 & -0.0276 \\ -0.0678 & 0.0315 & -0.0404 & 0.0326 & 0.0373 \\ 0.0171 & -0.0248 & 0.0069 & -0.0003 & 0.0246 \\ -0.0208 & 0.0740 & 0.0096 & -0.1018 & 0.0646 \end{bmatrix}$

53. Entries are rounded to four places $\begin{bmatrix} 0.0394 & 0.0880 & 0.0033 & 0.0530 & -0.1499 \\ -0.1492 & 0.0289 & 0.0187 & 0.1033 & 0.1668 \\ -0.1330 & -0.0543 & 0.0356 & 0.1768 & 0.1055 \\ 0.1407 & 0.0175 & -0.0453 & -0.1344 & 0.0655 \\ 0.0102 & -0.0653 & 0.0993 & 0.0085 & -0.0388 \end{bmatrix}$ **55.** Yes

57. $\begin{bmatrix} 1.51482 \\ 0.053479 \\ -0.637242 \\ 0.462629 \end{bmatrix}$ **59. a.** $\begin{bmatrix} 72 \\ 48 \\ 60 \end{bmatrix}$ **b.** $\begin{bmatrix} 2 & 4 & 2 \\ 2 & 1 & 2 \\ 2 & 1 & 3 \end{bmatrix} \begin{bmatrix} x_1 \\ x_2 \\ x_3 \end{bmatrix} = \begin{bmatrix} 72 \\ 48 \\ 60 \end{bmatrix}$ **c.** 8 type I, 8 type II, and 12 type III

61. a. \$10,000 at 6%, \$10,000 at 6.5%, and \$5000 at 8%   **b.** \$14,000 at 6%, \$9000 at 6.5%, and \$7000 at 8%   **c.** \$24,000 at 6%, \$4000 at 6.5%, and \$12,000 at 8%   **63. a.** 50 Super Vim, 75 Multitab, and 100 Mighty Mix   **b.** 75 Super Vim, 50 Multitab, and 60 Mighty Mix   **c.** 80 Super Vim, 100 Multitab, and 50 Mighty Mix   **65. a.** 262, −161, −12, 186, −103, −22, 264, −168, −9, 208, −134, −5, 224, −152, 5, 92, −50, −3   **b.** $\begin{bmatrix} 1.75 & 2.5 & 3 \\ -0.25 & -0.5 & 0 \\ -0.25 & -0.5 & -1 \end{bmatrix}$ **c.** happy birthday

Exercises 2.6 (page 125)

1. $\begin{bmatrix} 60 \\ 50 \end{bmatrix}$ **3.** $\begin{bmatrix} 6.43 \\ 26.12 \end{bmatrix}$ **5.** $\begin{bmatrix} 10 \\ 18 \\ 10 \end{bmatrix}$ **7.** $33:47:23$ **9.** $\begin{bmatrix} 7697 \\ 4205 \\ 6345 \\ 4106 \end{bmatrix}$ (rounded)

11. About 1440 metric tons of wheat and 1938 metric tons of oil. **13.** About 1511 units of agriculture, 1712 units of manufacturing, and 1414 units of transportation. **15.** About 3077 units of agriculture, about 2564 units of manufacturing, and about 3179 units of transportation **17. a.** 7/4 bushels of yams and $15/8 \approx 2$ pigs **b.** 167.5 bushels of yams and $153.75 \approx 154$ pigs **19.** About 848 units of agriculture, about 516 units of manufacturing, and about 2970 units of households **21.** About 195 million lb of agriculture, about 26 million lb of manufacturing, and about 13.6 million lb of energy **23.** In millions of dollars, the amounts are about 532 for natural resources, about 481 for manufacturing, about 805 for trade and services, and about 1185 for personal consumption.

25. a. $\begin{bmatrix} 1.67 & 0.56 & 0.56 \\ 0.19 & 1.17 & 0.06 \\ 3.15 & 3.27 & 4.38 \end{bmatrix}$ **b.** These multipliers imply that if the demand for one community's output increases by \$1, then the output in the other community will increase by the amount in the row and column of that matrix. For example, if the demand for Hermitage's output increases by \$1, then output from Sharon will increase by \$0.56, Farrell by \$0.06, and Hermitage by \$4.38.
27. 3 units of coal to every 4 units of steel **29.** 6 units of mining to every 8 units of manufacturing and 5 units of communication

Concept Check (page 130)

1. False **2.** False **3.** True **4.** True **5.** False **6.** True **7.** False **8.** False **9.** True **10.** False **11.** False **12.** False **13.** True **14.** True **15.** False **16.** True

Chapter 2 Review Exercises (page 131)

3. $(1, -4)$ **5.** $(-1, 2, 3)$ **7.** $(-9, 3)$ **9.** $(7, -9, -1)$ **11.** $(6 - 7z/3, 1 + z/3, z)$ **13.** $3 \times 2; a = 2, x = -1, y = 4,$
$p = 5, z = 7$ **15.** $3 \times 3 \,(\text{square}); a = -12, b = 1, k = 9/2, c = 3/4, d = 3, l = -3/4, m = -1, p = 3, q = 9$

17. $\begin{bmatrix} 0 & -16 \\ -10 & -18 \end{bmatrix}$ **19.** Not possible **21.** $\begin{bmatrix} 2 & 50 \\ 1 & -15 \\ -3 & 45 \end{bmatrix}$ **23.** $\begin{bmatrix} 6 & 18 & -24 \\ 1 & 3 & -4 \\ 0 & 0 & 0 \end{bmatrix}$ **25.** $\begin{bmatrix} 15 \\ 16 \\ 1 \end{bmatrix}$ **27.** $\begin{bmatrix} -7/19 & 4/19 \\ 3/19 & 1/19 \end{bmatrix}$

29. No inverse **31.** $\begin{bmatrix} -1/4 & 1/6 \\ 0 & 1/3 \end{bmatrix}$ **33.** No inverse **35.** $\begin{bmatrix} 1/4 & 1/2 & 1/2 \\ 1/4 & -1/2 & 1/2 \\ 1/8 & -1/4 & -1/4 \end{bmatrix}$ **37.** No inverse

39. Matrix A has no inverse. Solution: $(-2y + 5, y)$ **41.** $X = \begin{bmatrix} 6 \\ 15 \\ 16 \end{bmatrix}$ **43.** $(34, -9)$ **45.** $(1, 2, 3)$ **47.** $\begin{bmatrix} 725.7 \\ 305.9 \\ 166.7 \end{bmatrix}$

49. 8000 standard, 6000 extra large **51.** 150,000 gal were produced at Tulsa, 225,000 gal at New Orleans, and 180,000 gal at
Ardmore **53. a.** $\begin{bmatrix} 3170 \\ 2360 \\ 1800 \end{bmatrix}$ **b.** $\begin{bmatrix} x \\ y \\ z \end{bmatrix}$ **c.** $\begin{bmatrix} 10 & 5 & 8 \\ 12 & 0 & 4 \\ 0 & 10 & 5 \end{bmatrix} \begin{bmatrix} x \\ y \\ z \end{bmatrix} = \begin{bmatrix} 3170 \\ 2360 \\ 1800 \end{bmatrix}$ **d.** $\begin{bmatrix} 150 \\ 110 \\ 140 \end{bmatrix}$

55. a. $\begin{bmatrix} 1.300 & 0.045 & 0.567 & 0.012 & 0.068 & 0.020 \\ 0.204 & 1.030 & 0.183 & 0.004 & 0.022 & 0.006 \\ 0.155 & 0.038 & 1.120 & 0.020 & 0.114 & 0.034 \\ 0.018 & 0.021 & 0.028 & 1.080 & 0.016 & 0.033 \\ 0.537 & 0.525 & 0.483 & 0.279 & 1.730 & 0.419 \\ 0.537 & 0.346 & 0.497 & 0.536 & 0.087 & 1.940 \end{bmatrix}$; every \$1 of increased demand for livestock will result in an increase of

production demand of $0.204 in crops   **b.** In millions of dollars, produce $3855 in livestock, $1476 in crops, $2726 in food products, $1338 in mining and manufacturing, $8439 in households, and $10,256 in other business sectors.
57. a. $b + c$ **b.** A is tumorous, B is bone, and C is healthy   **c.** For patient X, A and C are healthy; B is tumorous. For patient Y, A and B are tumorous; C is bone. For patient Z, A could be healthy or tumorous; B and C are healthy.   **59.** About 20 head and face injuries, 12 concussions, 3 neck injuries, and 55 other injuries.   **61.** $W_1 \approx 110$ lb and $W_2 \approx 134$ lb   **63. a.** $x = 1$ and $y = 1/2$
b. $x = 1$, $y = 1$, and $z = -1$ **65.** 60 singles, 27 doubles, 3 triples, and 45 home runs

CHAPTER 3 | Linear Programming: The Graphical Method

Exercises 3.1 (page 145)

1.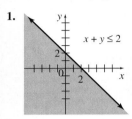

3.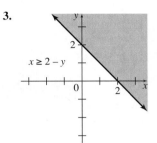

5.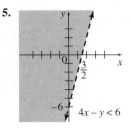

7.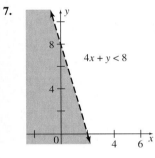

9.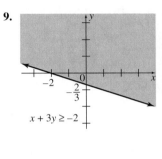

11.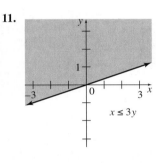

13.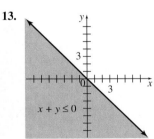

15.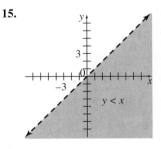

17.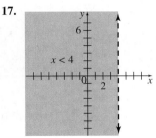

19.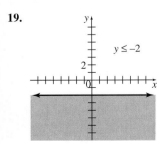

21.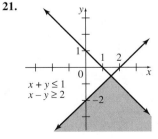

23.

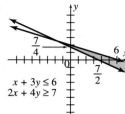

$x + 3y \leq 6$
$2x + 4y \geq 7$

25.

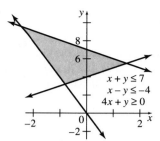

$x + y \leq 7$
$x - y \leq -4$
$4x + y \geq 0$

27.

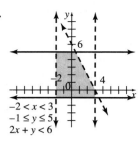

$-2 < x < 3$
$-1 \leq y \leq 5$
$2x + y < 6$

29.

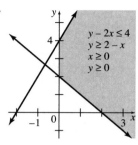

$y - 2x \leq 4$
$y \geq 2 - x$
$x \geq 0$
$y \geq 0$

31.

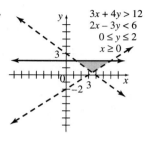

$3x + 4y > 12$
$2x - 3y < 6$
$0 \leq y \leq 2$
$x \geq 0$

33.

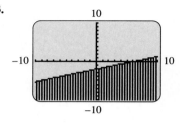

35.

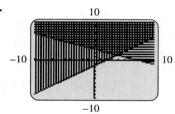

37. B: $\leq, \leq, \leq$; **C:** $\geq, \geq, \leq$; **D:** $\leq, \geq, \leq$; **E:** $\leq, \leq, \geq$; **F:** $\leq, \geq, \geq$; **G:** $\geq, \geq, \geq$

39. a.

	Shawls	**Afghans**		**Total**
Number Made	x	y		
Spinning Time	1	2	$\leq$	8
Dyeing Time	1	1	$\leq$	6
Weaving Time	1	4	$\leq$	14

b.

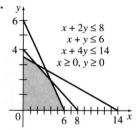

$x + 2y \leq 8$
$x + y \leq 6$
$x + 4y \leq 14$
$x \geq 0, y \geq 0$

c. Yes; no

41. a. $x \geq 4y$; $0.06x + 0.08y \geq 1.6$; $x + y \leq 30$; $x \geq 0$; $y \geq 0$ **b.**

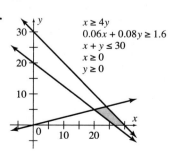

$x \geq 4y$
$0.06x + 0.08y \geq 1.6$
$x + y \leq 30$
$x \geq 0$
$y \geq 0$

43. a. $x \leq (1/2)y$; $x + y \leq 800$; $x \geq 0$; $y \geq 0$ **b.**

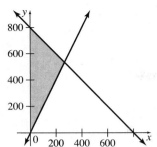

45. a. $x + y \geq 7$; $2x + y \geq 10$; $x + y \leq 9$; $x \geq 0$; $y \geq 0$ **b.**

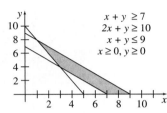

$$x + y \geq 7$$
$$2x + y \geq 10$$
$$x + y \leq 9$$
$$x \geq 0, y \geq 0$$

Exercises 3.2 (page 152)

1. a. Maximum of 29 at $(7, 4)$; minimum of 10 at $(0, 5)$ **b.** Maximum of 35 at $(3, 8)$; minimum of 8 at $(4, 1)$
3. a. Maximum of 9 at $(0, 12)$; minimum of 0 at $(0, 0)$ **b.** Maximum of 12 at $(8, 0)$; minimum of 0 at $(0, 0)$
5. a. No maximum; minimum of 16 at $(0, 8)$ **b.** No maximum; minimum of 18 at $(3, 4)$ **c.** No maximum; minimum of 21 at $(13/2, 2)$ **d.** No maximum; minimum of 12 at $(12, 0)$ **7.** Minimum of 24 when $x = 6$ and $y = 0$ **9.** Maximum of 46 when $x = 6$ and $y = 8$ **11.** Maximum of 1500 when $x = 150$ and $y = 0$, as well as when $x = 50$ and $y = 100$ and all points on the line between   **13.** No solution   **15. a.** Maximum of 204 when $x = 18$ and $y = 2$ **b.** Maximum of 588/5 when $x = 12/5$ and $y = 39/5$ **c.** Maximum of 102 when $x = 0$ and $y = 17/2$ **17.** b

Exercises 3.3 (page 160)

1. Let x be the number of product A produced and y be the number of product B. Then $3x + 5y \leq 60$.   **3.** Let x be the number of calcium carbonate supplements and y be the number of calcium citrate supplements. Then $600x + 250y \geq 1500$.   **5.** Let x be the number of pounds of $8 coffee and y be the number of $10 coffee. Then $x + y \geq 40$.   **7.** 45 to plant I and 32 to plant II, for a minimum cost of $2630   **9. a.** 6 units of policy A and 16 units of policy B, for a minimum premium cost of $940   **b.** 30 units of policy A and 0 units of policy B, for a minimum premium cost of $750   **11. a.** 500 type I and 1000 type II   **b.** Maximum revenue is $275.
c. If the price of the type I bolt exceeds 20¢, then it is more profitable to produce 1050 type I bolts and 450 type II bolts.   **13. a.** 120 kg of the half-and-half mix and 120 kg of the other mix, for a maximum revenue of $1980   **b.** 0 kg of the half-and-half mix and 200 kg of the other mix, for a maximum revenue of $2200   **15. a.** 40 gal from dairy I and 60 gal from dairy II, for a maximum butterfat of 3.4%   **b.** 10 gal from dairy I and 20 gal from dairy 2. No.   **17.** $10 million in bonds and $20 million in mutual funds, or $5 million in bonds and $22.5 million in mutual funds (or any solution on the line in between those two points), for a maximum annual interest of $2 million   **19.** a   **21. a.** Three of pill 1 and two of pill 2, for a minimum cost of $1.05 per day   **b.** 12 surplus units of vitamin A. No.   **23.** 4 ounces of fruit and 2 ounces of nuts, for a minimum of 140 calories   **25.** 0 plants and 18 animals, for a minimum of 270 hours

Concept Check (page 164)

1. False   **2.** True   **3.** False   **4.** False   **5.** False   **6.** False   **7.** True   **8.** False   **9.** False   **10.** True   **11.** True   **12.** True
13. True

Chapter 3 Review Exercises (page 165)

3.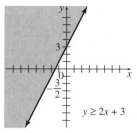

$y \geq 2x + 3$

5.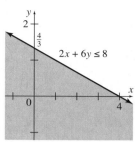

$2x + 6y \leq 8$

7.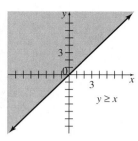

$y \geq x$

9.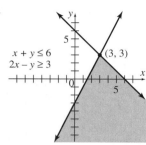

$x + y \leq 6$
$2x - y \geq 3$

(3, 3)

11.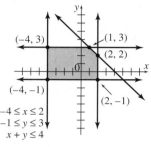

$(-4, 3)$ $(1, 3)$
$(2, 2)$
$(-4, -1)$
$(2, -1)$

$-4 \leq x \leq 2$
$-1 \leq y \leq 3$
$x + y \leq 4$

13.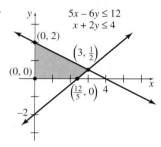

$5x - 6y \leq 12$
$x + 2y \leq 4$
$(0, 2)$
$\left(3, \frac{1}{2}\right)$
$(0, 0)$
$\left(\frac{12}{5}, 0\right)$

15. Maximum of 22 at $(3, 4)$; minimum of 0 at $(0, 0)$ **17.** Maximum of 24 at $(0, 6)$ **19.** Minimum of 40 at any point on the segment connecting $(0, 20)$ and $(10/3, 40/3)$

23. a.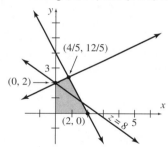

$(4/5, 12/5)$
$(0, 2)$
$(2, 0)$
$z = 8$

b.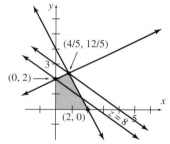

$(4/5, 12/5)$
$(0, 2)$
$(2, 0)$
$z = 8$

25. Let x = number of batches of cakes and y = number of batches of cookies. Then $x \geq 0$, $y \geq 0$, $2x + (3/2)y \leq 15$, and $3x + (2/3)y \leq 13$.

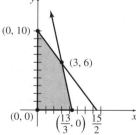

$(0, 10)$
$(3, 6)$
$(0, 0)$
$\left(\frac{13}{3}, 0\right)$ $\frac{15}{2}$

27. a. 3 batches of cakes and 6 batches of cookies, for a maximum profit of $210   **b.** If the profit per batch of cookies increases by more than $2.50 (to $22.50), then it will be more profitable to make 10 batches of cookies and no batches of cake.   **29.** 7 packages of gardening mixture and 2 packages of potting mixture, for a maximum income of $31   **31.** Produce no runs of type I and 7 runs of type II, for a minimum cost of $42,000.   **33.** 0 acres for millet and 2 acres for wheat, for a maximum harvest of 1600 lb

CHAPTER 4 Linear Programming: The Simplex Method

Exercises 4.1 (page 175)

1. $x_1 + 2x_2 + s_1 = 6$ **3.** $2.3x_1 + 5.7x_2 + 1.8x_3 + s_1 = 17$ **5. a.** 3 **b.** s_1, s_2, s_3 **c.** $2x_1 + 3x_2 + s_1 = 15$;
$4x_1 + 5x_2 + s_2 = 35$; $x_1 + 6x_2 + s_3 = 20$ **7. a.** 2 **b.** s_1, s_2 **c.** $7x_1 + 6x_2 + 8x_3 + s_1 = 118$; $4x_1 + 5x_2 + 10x_3 + s_2 = 220$
9. $x_1 = 0, x_2 = 4, x_3 = 0, s_1 = 0, s_2 = 8, z = 28$ **11.** $x_1 = 0, x_2 = 0, x_3 = 8, s_1 = 0, s_2 = 6, s_3 = 7, z = 12$ **13.** $x_1 = 0, x_2 = 20$,
$x_3 = 0, s_1 = 16, s_2 = 0, z = 60$ **15.** $x_1 = 0, x_2 = 0, x_3 = 12, s_1 = 0, s_2 = 9, s_3 = 8, z = 36$
17. $x_1 = 0, x_2 = 250, x_3 = 0, s_1 = 0, s_2 = 50, s_3 = 200, z = 1000$

19.
x_1	x_2	s_1	s_2	z	
4	2	1	0	0	5
1	2	0	1	0	4
−7	−1	0	0	1	0

21.
x_1	x_2	s_1	s_2	s_3	z	
1	1	1	0	0	0	10
5	2	0	1	0	0	20
1	2	0	0	1	0	36
−1	−3	0	0	0	1	0

23.
x_1	x_2	s_1	s_2	z	
3	1	1	0	0	12
1	1	0	1	0	15
−2	−1	0	0	1	0

25. If x_1 is the number of simple figures, x_2 is the number of figures with additions, and x_3 is the number of computer-drawn sketches, find $x_1 \geq 0, x_2 \geq 0, x_3 \geq 0, s_1 \geq 0, s_2 \geq 0, s_3 \geq 0, s_4 \geq 0$ so that $20x_1 + 35x_2 + 60x_3 + s_1 = 2200, x_1 + x_2 + x_3 + s_2 = 400$, $-x_1 - x_2 + x_3 + s_3 = 0, -x_1 + 2x_2 + s_4 = 0$, and $z = 95x_1 + 200x_2 + 325x_3$ is maximized.

x_1	x_2	x_3	s_1	s_2	s_3	s_4	z	
20	35	60	1	0	0	0	0	2200
1	1	1	0	1	0	0	0	400
−1	−1	1	0	0	1	0	0	0
−1	2	0	0	0	0	1	0	0
−95	−200	−325	0	0	0	0	1	0

27. If x_1 is the number of redwood tables made, x_2 is the number of stained Douglas fir tables made, and x_3 is the number of stained white spruce tables made, find $x_1 \geq 0, x_2 \geq 0, x_3 \geq 0, s_1 \geq 0, s_2 \geq 0$, $s_3 \geq 0$ so that $8x_1 + 7x_2 + 8x_3 + s_1 = 720, 2x_2 + 2x_3 + s_2 = 480$, $159x_1 + 138.85x_2 + 129.35x_3 + s_3 = 15,000$, and $z = x_1 + x_2 + x_3$ is maximized.

x_1	x_2	x_3	s_1	s_2	s_3	z	
8	7	8	1	0	0	0	720
0	2	2	0	1	0	0	480
159	138.85	129.35	0	0	1	0	15,000
−1	−1	−1	0	0	0	1	0

29. If x_1 is the number of newspaper ads run, x_2 is the number of Internet banner ads run, and x_3 is the number of TV ads run, find $x_1 \geq 0, x_2 \geq 0, x_3 \geq 0, s_1 \geq 0, s_2 \geq 0, s_3 \geq 0, s_4 \geq 0$ so that $400x_1 + 20x_2 + 2000x_3 + s_1 = 8000, x_1 + s_2 = 30$, $x_2 + s_3 = 60, x_3 + s_4 = 10$, and $z = 4000x_1 + 3000x_2 + 10,000x_3$ is maximized.

x_1	x_2	x_3	s_1	s_2	s_3	s_4	z	
400	20	2000	1	0	0	0	0	8000
1	0	0	0	1	0	0	0	30
0	1	0	0	0	1	0	0	60
0	0	1	0	0	0	1	0	10
−4000	−3000	−10,000	0	0	0	0	1	0

Exercises 4.2 (page 185)

1. Maximum is 30 when $x_1 = 10, x_2 = 0, x_3 = 0, s_1 = 6$, and $s_2 = 0$. **3.** Maximum is 8 when $x_1 = 4, x_2 = 0, s_1 = 8, s_2 = 2$, and $s_3 = 0$. **5.** Maximum is 264 when $x_1 = 16, x_2 = 4, x_3 = 0, s_1 = 0, s_2 = 16$, and $s_3 = 0$. **7.** Maximum is 25 when $x_1 = 0$, $x_2 = 5, s_1 = 20$, and $s_2 = 0$. **9.** Maximum is 120 when $x_1 = 0, x_2 = 10, s_1 = 0, s_2 = 40$, and $s_3 = 4$. **11.** Maximum is 944 when $x_1 = 118, x_2 = 0, x_3 = 0, s_1 = 0$, and $s_2 = 102$. **13.** Maximum is 3300 when $x_1 = 240, x_2 = 60, x_3 = 0, x_4 = 0, s_1 = 0$, and $s_2 = 0$. **15.** No maximum **17.** Maximum is 70,818.18 when $x_1 = 181.82, x_2 = 0, x_3 = 454.55, x_4 = 0, x_5 = 1363.64$, $s_1 = 0, s_2 = 0, s_3 = 0$, and $s_4 = 0$. **21.** 6 churches and 2 labor unions, for a maximum of $1000 per month **23. a.** Assemble 1000 Royal Flush poker sets, 3000 Deluxe Diamond poker sets, and 0 Full House poker sets, for a maximum profit of $104,000. **b.** $s_4 = 1000$; there are 1000 unused dealer buttons. **25. a.** No racing or touring bicycles and 2700 mountain bicycles **b.** Maximum profit is $59,400 **c.** No; there are 1500 units of aluminum left; $s_2 = 1500$. **27. a.** 17 newspaper ads, 60 Internet banner ads, and no TV ads, for a maximum exposure of 248,000 **29. a.** 3 **b.** 4 **c.** 3 **31.** $200, $66.67, $300, $100 **33.** Rachel should run 3 hours, bike 4 hours, and walk 8 hours, for a maximum calorie expenditure of 6313 calories. **35. a.** 163.6 kg of food P, none of Q, 1090.9 kg of R, 145.5 kg of S **b.** Maximum is 87,454.5. **c.** Yes; none **37.** 12 minutes to the senator, 9 minutes to the congresswoman, and 6 minutes to the governor, for a maximum of 1,050,000 viewers

Exercises 4.3 (page 199)

1. $\begin{bmatrix} 1 & 3 & 1 \\ 2 & 2 & 10 \\ 3 & 1 & 0 \end{bmatrix}$ **3.** $\begin{bmatrix} 4 & 7 & 5 \\ 5 & 14 & 0 \\ -3 & 20 & -2 \\ 15 & -8 & 23 \end{bmatrix}$

5. Minimize $w = 5y_1 + 4y_2 + 15y_3$ subject to $y_1 + y_2 + 2y_3 \geq 4$, $y_1 + y_2 + y_3 \geq 3$, $y_1 + 3y_3 \geq 2$, with $y_1 \geq 0$, $y_2 \geq 0$, and $y_3 \geq 0$.
7. Maximize $z = 150x_1 + 275x_2$ subject to $x_1 + 2x_2 \leq 3$, $x_1 + 2x_2 \leq 6$, $x_1 + 3x_2 \leq 4$, $x_1 + 4x_2 \leq 1$, with $x_1 \geq 0$ and $x_2 \geq 0$.
9. Minimum is 14 when $y_1 = 0$ and $y_2 = 7$. **11.** Minimum is 40 when $y_1 = 10$ and $y_2 = 0$. **13.** Minimum is 100 when $y_1 = 0$,
$y_2 = 100$, and $y_3 = 0$. **15. a 17. a.** 1800 small test tubes and 900 large test tubes, for a minimum cost of $459 **b.** The shadow
cost is 17 cents; total cost is $510. **19. a.** Maximize $z = x_1 + 1.5x_2$ subject to $x_1 + 2x_2 \leq 200$, $4x_1 + 3x_2 \leq 600$, $0 \leq x_2 \leq 90$,
with $x_1 \geq 0$. **b.** Make 120 bears and 40 monkeys, for a maximum profit of $180. **c.** Minimize $w = 200y_1 + 600y_2 + 90y_3$ sub-
ject to $y_1 + 4y_2 \geq 1$, $2y_1 + 3y_2 + y_3 \geq 1.5$, with $y_1 \geq 0$, $y_2 \geq 0$, and $y_3 \geq 0$. **d.** $y_1 = 0.6$, $y_2 = 0.1$, $y_3 = 0$, $w = 180$ **e.** $186
f. $179 **21. a.** 0 g of soybean meal, 8 g of meat byproducts, and 3.6 g of grain, or 0 g of soybean meal, 0 g of meat byproducts,
and 10.8 g of grain **b.** $1.08 **c.** Same as part a **23.** Make 16 large bowls, no small bowls, and 6 pots, for a minimum time of
104 hours. **25.** 3 of pill #1 and 2 of pill #2, for a minimum cost of 70¢

Exercises 4.4 (page 209)

1. $2x_1 + 3x_2 + s_1 = 8$; $x_1 + 4x_2 - s_2 = 7$ **3.** $2x_1 + x_2 + 2x_3 + s_1 = 50$; $x_1 + 3x_2 + x_3 - s_2 = 35$; $x_1 + 2x_2 - s_3 = 15$
5. Change the objective function to maximize $z = -3y_1 - 4y_2 - 5y_3$. The constraints are not changed. **7.** Change the objective
function to maximize $z = -y_1 - 2y_2 - y_3 - 5y_4$. The constraints are not changed. **9.** Maximum is 480 when $x_1 = 40$
and $x_2 = 0$. **11.** Maximum is 750 when $x_1 = 0$, $x_2 = 150$, and $x_3 = 0$. **13.** Maximum is 135 when $x_1 = 30$ and $x_2 = 5$.
15. Minimum is 108 when $y_1 = 0$, $y_2 = 9$, and $y_3 = 0$. **17.** Maximum is 400/3 when $x_1 = 100/3$ and $x_2 = 50/3$.
19. Minimum is 512 when $y_1 = 6$, $y_2 = 8$, and $y_3 = 0$. **23. a.** Ship 200 barrels of oil from supplier S_1 to distributor D_1; ship 2800
barrels of oil from supplier S_2 to distributor D_1; ship 2800 barrels of oil from supplier S_1 to distributor D_2; ship 2200 barrels of oil
from supplier S_2 to distributor D_2. Minimum cost is $180,400. **b.** $s_3 = 2000$; S_1 could furnish 2000 more barrels of oil. **25.** Make
$3,000,000 in commercial loans and $22,000,000 in home loans, for a maximum return of $2,940,000. **27.** Use 1500 lb of blue-
grass, 2700 lb of rye, and 1800 lb of Bermuda, for a mininum cost of $834. **29. a.** Ship 2 computers from W_1 to D_1, 20 computers
from W_1 to D_2, 30 computers from W_2 to D_1, and 0 computers from W_2 to D_2, for a minimum cost of $628. **b.** $s_3 = 3$; warehouse
W_1 has 3 more computers that it could ship. **31.** 5/3 oz of I, 20/3 oz of II, 5/3 oz of III, for a minimum cost of $1.55 per gal; 10 oz
of the additive should be used per gal of gasoline. **33. a.** Joe should do $5\frac{2}{3}$ hours of calisthenics, $3\frac{1}{3}$ hours of swimming, and 1
hour of playing the drums, for a maximum calorie expenditure of $4270\frac{1}{3}$ calories.

Concept Check (page 214)

1. True **2.** False **3.** True **4.** False **5.** False **6.** True **7.** True **8.** False **9.** False **10.** True **11.** False **12.** True
13. False

Chapter 4 Review Exercises (page 215)

1. When the problem has more than two variables **3. a.** $4x_1 + 6x_2 + s_1 = 60$; $3x_1 + x_2 + s_2 = 18$; $2x_1 + 5x_2 + s_3 = 20$;
$x_1 + x_2 + s_4 = 15$ **b.**

x_1	x_2	s_1	s_2	s_3	s_4	z	
4	6	1	0	0	0	0	60
3	1	0	1	0	0	0	18
2	5	0	0	1	0	0	20
1	1	0	0	0	1	0	15
-2	-7	0	0	0	0	1	0

5. a. $x_1 + x_2 + x_3 + s_1 = 90$; $2x_1 + 5x_2 + x_3 + s_2 = 120$; $x_1 + 3x_2 - s_3 = 80$ **b.**

x_1	x_2	x_3	s_1	s_2	s_3	z	
1	1	1	1	0	0	0	90
2	5	1	0	1	0	0	120
1	3	0	0	0	-1	0	80
-5	-8	-6	0	0	0	1	0

7. Maximum is 33 when $x_1 = 3$, $x_2 = 0$, $x_3 = 3$, $s_1 = 0$, and $s_2 = 0$. **9.** Maximum is 76.67 when $x_1 = 6.67$, $x_2 = 0$, $x_3 = 21.67$, $s_1 = 0$, $s_2 = 0$, and $s_3 = 35$. **11. Dual Method** Solve the dual problem: Maximize $17x_1 + 42x_2$ subject to $x_1 + 5x_2 \le 10$, $x_1 + 8x_2 \le 15$. **Method of Section 4.4** Change the objective function to maximize $z = -10y_1 - 15y_2$. The constraints are not changed. Minimum is 170 when $y_1 = 17$ and $y_2 = 0$. **13. Dual Method** Solve the dual problem: Maximize $48x_1 + 12x_2 + 10x_3 + 30x_4$ subject to $x_1 + x_2 + 3x_4 \le 7$, $x_1 + x_2 \le 2$, $2x_1 + x_3 + x_4 \le 3$. **Method of Section 4.4** Change the objective function to maximize $z = -7y_1 - 2y_2 - 3y_3$. The constraints are not changed. Minimum is 98 when $y_1 = 4$, $y_2 = 8$, and $y_3 = 18$. **15.** Minimum of 62 when $y_1 = 8$, $y_2 = 12$, $s_1 = 0$, $s_2 = 1$, $s_3 = 0$, and $s_4 = 2$ **17.** Maximum of 480 when $x_1 = 24$ and $x_2 = 0$ **19.** Maximum of 102 when $x_1 = 0$ and $x_2 = 8.5$ **21.** Problems with constraints involving "$\le$" can be solved using slack variables, while those involving "$\ge$" or "$=$" can be solved using surplus and artificial variables, respectively. **23. a.** Maximize $z = 6x_1 + 7x_2 + 5x_3$, subject to $4x_1 + 2x_2 + 3x_3 \le 9$, $5x_1 + 4x_2 + x_3 \le 10$, with $x_1 \ge 0$, $x_2 \ge 0$, $x_3 \ge 0$. **b.** The first constraint would be $4x_1 + 2x_2 + 3x_3 \ge 9$. **c.** $x_1 = 0$, $x_2 = 2.1$, $x_3 = 1.6$, and $z = 22.7$ **d.** Minimize $w = 9y_1 + 10y_2$, subject to $4y_1 + 5y_2 \ge 6$, $2y_1 + 4y_2 \ge 7$, $3y_1 + y_2 \ge 5$, with $y_1 \ge 0$, $y_2 \ge 0$. **e.** $y_1 = 1.3$, $y_2 = 1.1$, and $w = 22.7$ **25. a.** Let $x_1 =$ number of cake plates, $x_2 =$ number of bread plates, and $x_3 =$ number of dinner plates. **b.** $z = 15x_1 + 12x_2 + 5x_3$ **c.** $15x_1 + 10x_2 + 8x_3 \le 1500$; $5x_1 + 4x_2 + 4x_3 \le 2700$; $6x_1 + 5x_2 + 5x_3 \le 1200$ **27. a.** Let $x_1 =$ number of gallons of Fruity wine and $x_2 =$ number of gallons of Crystal wine to be made. **b.** $z = 12x_1 + 15x_2$ **c.** $2x_1 + x_2 \le 110$; $2x_1 + 3x_2 \le 125$; $2x_1 + x_2 \le 90$ **29.** Produce no cake plates, 150 bread plates, and no dinner plates, for a maximum profit of $1800. **31.** 36.25 gal of Fruity and 17.5 gal of Crystal, for a maximum profit of $697.50 **33. a and b** Produce 660 cases of corn, 0 cases of beans, and 340 cases of carrots, for a minimum cost of $15,100. **35.** Ginger should do $5\frac{1}{3}$ hours of tai chi, $2\frac{2}{3}$ hours of riding a unicycle, and 2 hours of fencing, for a maximum calorie expenditure of $2753\frac{1}{3}$ calories.

CHAPTER 5 Mathematics of Finance

Exercises 5.1 (page 231)

1. The interest rate and number of compounding periods **5.** $562.50 **7.** $59.79 **9.** $50.79 **11.** $3176.95; $51.95 **13.** 7.5% **17.** t is the number of years, while n is the number of compounding periods. **19.** $1593.85; $593.85 **21.** $890.82; $420.82 **23.** $12,630.55; $4130.55 **25.** $9677.13 **27.** $1246.33 **29.** $6864.08 **33.** 4.06% **35.** 7.38% **37.** $7534.80; $334.80 **39.** 6.8% **41.** $18,035.71 **43.** $30,675.11 **45. a.** 16 years old **b.** $20,516.69 **47.** $22,829.89 **49.** $1000 now **51.** 5.33% **53.** For $10,000, $48,754.39; for $149,000, $726,440.43; for $1,000,000, $4,875,439.16 **55.** 14 yr **57.** 35 yr **59.** $123,506.50 **61.** 9.31×10^{31} **63. a.** $16,288.95 **b.** $16,436.19 **c.** $16,470.09 **d.** $16,486.65 **65.** 5/4

Exercises 5.2 (page 243)

1. 48 **3.** -648 **5.** 81 **7.** 1 **9.** 15 **11.** 156/25 **13.** -208 **15.** 15.91713 **17.** 12.69593 **21.** $437.46 **23.** $2,154,099.15 **25.** $180,307.41; $128,800; $51,507.41 **27.** $28,438.21; $19,200; $9238.21 **29.** $1,145,619.96; $768,000; $377,619.96 **31.** $6294.79 **33.** $136,785.74 **35.** $26,874.97; $18,000; $8874.97 **37.** $15,662.40; $12,000; $3662.40 **39.** $628.25 **43.** $497.68 **45.** $1626.16 **47.** $282.96 **49.** $2452.47; $2400; $52.47 **51.** $189,058.14 **53.** $323,967.96 **55.** $67,940.98 **57. a.** $226.11 **b.** $245.77 **59.** $759.21 **61.** $312,232.31; $212,232.31 **63.** $432,548.65; $332,548.65 **65.** 7.397% **67. a.** $1200 **b.** $3511.58

Exercises 5.3 (page 252)

1. c **3.** 9.40267 **5.** 11.24607 **9.** $8994.25 **11.** $209,302.93 **13.** $170,275.47 **15.** $111,183.87 **17.** $438.81; $2632.86; $132.86 **19.** $10,734.93; $128,819.16; $38,819.16 **21.** $542.60; $9766.80; $2366.80 **23.** $7.61 **25.** $35.24 **27.** $6699 **29.** $1407.76; $422,328; $223,328 **31.** $1590.82; $572,695.20; $319,695.20 **33.** $1856.49; $114,168.20. The payments are $537.48 more than for the 30-yr loan, but the total interest paid is $140,675.40 less. **35. a.** $335.25 **b.** $2092 **37. a.** $571.98; $20,591.28 **b.** $358.71; $17,218.08 **39. a.** $623,110.52 **b.** $456,427.28 **c.** $563,757.78 **d.** $392,903.18 **41.** $280.46; $32,310.40

43.

Payment Number	Amount of Payment	Interest for Period	Portion to Principal	Principal at End of Period
0	—	—	—	$110,000.00
1	$14,794.23	$4400.00	$10,394.23	$99,605.77
2	$14,794.23	$3984.23	$10,810.00	$88,795.77
3	$14,794.23	$3551.83	$11,242.40	$77,553.37
4	$14,794.23	$3102.13	$11,692.10	$65,861.27

45. a. $32.49 **b.** $195.52; $10.97 **47. a.** $1959.99; $127,798.20 **b.** $1677.54; $177,609.60 **c.** $1519.22; $230,766.00
d. After 157 payments **49. a.** $1121.63; $403,786.80; $253,786.80 **b.** $115,962.66; $201,893.40 **c.** $732.96; $267,265.60
d. $1010.16; $186,328.80 **51. a.** $17,584.58 **b.** $15,069.31
53.

Payment Number	Amount of Payment	Interest for Period	Portion to Principal	Principal at End of Period
0				$4836.00
1	$585.16	$175.31	$409.85	$4426.15
2	$585.16	$160.45	$424.71	$4001.43
3	$585.16	$145.05	$440.11	$3561.32
4	$585.16	$129.10	$456.06	$3105.26
5	$585.16	$112.57	$472.59	$2632.67
6	$585.16	$95.43	$489.73	$2142.94
7	$585.16	$77.68	$507.48	$1635.46
8	$585.16	$59.29	$525.87	$1109.59
9	$585.16	$40.22	$544.94	$564.65
10	$585.12	$20.47	$564.65	$0.00

55. a. $25,000 **b.** $40,000

Concept Check (page 258)

1. True **2.** False **3.** True **4.** False **5.** True **6.** True **7.** True **8.** False **9.** False **10.** True

Chapter 5 Review Exercises (page 259)

1. $636.12 **3.** $1290.11 **5.** Compound interest **7.** $33,691.69 **9.** $77,860.80 **11.** $5244.50 **13.** $4725.22
15. $27,624.86 **17.** $1067.71 **19.** 2, 6, 18, 54, 162 **21.** −96 **23.** −120 **25.** 40.56808 **29.** $23,559.98; $5527.98
31. $12,302.78; $1118.78 **33.** $160,224.29; $5524.29 **35.** $955.61 **37.** $6156.14 **39.** $2945.34 **41.** $56,711.93 **43.** A
home loan and an auto loan **45.** $302.59; $431.08 **47.** $1796.20; $5871.40 **49.** $1140.50; $410,580; $233,470 **51.** $132.99
53. $1535.61 **55.** $10,203.80; $383.80 **57.** 8.21% **59.** $2298.58 **61.** $107,892.82; $32,892.82 **63.** $8751.91; $13,263.37
65. 5.250% and 5.252%; UFB Direct.com **67. a.** $555.56; $20,000 **b.** 1.9%: $433.03, $20,785.44; 2.9%: $358.49, $21,509.40
c. $425.62; $20,429.76 **69. a.** $954.42 **b.** $817.92 **c.** Method 1: $109,563.99; Method 2: $109,565.13 **d.** $9650
e. Method 1: $118,786.01; Method 2: $118,784.87 **71. a.** 9.569% **b.** $896.44 **c.** $626,200.88 **d.** $1200.39
e. $478,134.14 **f.** Sue is ahead by $148,066.74.

CHAPTER 6 | Logic

Exercises 6.1 (page 273)

1. Statement, not compound **3.** Not a statement **5.** Statement, compound **7.** Not a statement **9.** Statement, compound
11. Statement, not compound **13.** Statement, compound **15.** My favorite flavor is not chocolate. **17.** $y \leq 12$ **19.** $q < 5$

23. I'm not getting better.   **25.** I'm not getting better or my parrot is dead.   **27.** It is not the case that both I'm getting better and my parrot is not dead.   **29.** False   **31.** True   **33.** Both components are false.   **35.** True   **37.** True   **39.** False   **41.** True   **43.** True   **45.** True   **47.** Disjunction   **49.** True   **51.** False   **53.** True   **55.** True   **57.** False   **59.** True   **61.** True   **63.** True   **65.** a, c, d   **67.** We may not charge a fee of $35 in each billing period if the New Balance on your statement exceeds your credit line.   **69.** c, d   **71.** $p \wedge q$ where p is the statement, "Tax rates are lower for a head of household than for a person filing as single," and q is the statement, "The standard deduction is higher."   **73.** b, c, d   **75.** c, d, e   **77.** Most legal problems are not matters of civil law.   **81.** $\sim n \vee \sim b$ **83.** $\sim n \wedge b$ **85.** $(n \vee b) \wedge [\sim (n \wedge b)]$ **87.** 81, 82, and 84

Exercises 6.2 (page 283)

1. 4   **3.** 16   **5.** 128   **7.** 6

9.

p	q	$\sim p$	$\sim p \wedge q$
T	T	F	F
T	F	F	F
F	T	T	T
F	F	T	F

11.

p	q	$p \wedge q$	$\sim (p \wedge q)$
T	T	T	F
T	F	F	T
F	T	F	T
F	F	F	T

13.

p	q	$\sim p$	$\sim q$	$q \vee \sim p$	$(q \vee \sim p) \vee \sim q$
T	T	F	F	T	T
T	F	F	T	F	T
F	T	T	F	T	T
F	F	T	T	T	T

In Exercises 15–23, we are using the alternate method to save space.

15.

p	q	$\sim q$	$\wedge$	$(\sim p \vee q)$
T	T	F	F	F T T
T	F	T	F	F F F
F	T	F	F	T T T
F	F	T	T	T T F
		①	④	② ③ ②

17.

p	q	$(p \vee \sim q)$	$\wedge$	$(p \wedge q)$
T	T	T T F	T	T T T
T	F	T T T	F	T F F
F	T	F F F	F	F F T
F	F	F T T	F	F F F
		① ② ①	⑤	③ ④ ③

19.

p	q	r	$(\sim p \wedge q)$	$\wedge$	r
T	T	T	F F T	F	T
T	T	F	F F T	F	F
T	F	T	F F F	F	T
T	F	F	F F F	F	F
F	T	T	T T T	T	T
F	T	F	T T T	F	F
F	F	T	T F F	F	T
F	F	F	T F F	F	F
			① ② ①	④	③

21.

p	q	r	$(\sim p \wedge \sim q)$	$\vee$	$(\sim r \vee \sim p)$
T	T	T	F F F	F	F F F
T	T	F	F F F	T	T T F
T	F	T	F F T	F	F F F
T	F	F	F F T	T	T T F
F	T	T	T F F	T	F T T
F	T	F	T F F	T	T T T
F	F	T	T T T	T	F T T
F	F	F	T T T	T	T T T
			① ② ①	⑤	③ ④ ③

23.

p	q	r	s	~	(~p	∧	~q)	∨	(~r	∨	~s)
T	T	T	T	T	F	F	F	T	F	F	F
T	T	T	F	T	F	F	F	T	F	T	T
T	T	F	T	T	F	F	F	T	T	T	F
T	T	F	F	T	F	F	F	T	T	T	T
T	F	T	T	T	F	F	T	T	F	F	F
T	F	T	F	T	F	F	T	T	F	T	T
T	F	F	T	T	F	F	T	T	T	T	F
T	F	F	F	T	F	F	T	T	T	T	T
F	T	T	T	T	T	F	F	T	F	F	F
F	T	T	F	T	T	F	F	T	F	T	T
F	T	F	T	T	T	F	F	T	T	T	F
F	T	F	F	T	T	F	F	T	T	T	T
F	F	T	T	F	T	T	T	F	F	F	F
F	F	T	F	F	T	T	T	T	F	T	T
F	F	F	T	F	T	T	T	T	T	T	F
F	F	F	F	F	T	T	T	T	T	T	T
				③	①	②	①	⑥	④	⑤	④

25. It's not summertime, or the living is not easy.

27. The door was locked and the thief didn't break a window.

29. I'm not ready to go, or Emily Portwood is.

31. $12 \le 4$ and $8 \ne 9$

33. Neither Larry nor Moe is out sick today.

35.

p	q	$p \vee q$
T	T	F
T	F	T
F	T	T
F	F	F

37. True   **39. a.** False   **b.** True   **c.** False   **d.** True

43. $s \vee (r \wedge {\sim}q)$

s	r	q	s	∨	(r	∧	~q)
T	T	T	T	T	T	F	F
T	T	F	T	T	T	T	T
T	F	T	T	T	F	F	F
T	F	F	T	T	F	F	T
F	T	T	F	F	T	F	F
F	T	F	F	T	T	T	T
F	F	T	F	F	F	F	F
F	F	F	F	F	F	F	T
			①	④	②	③	②

The guarantee would be false if you are not completely satisfied, and they either don't refund your money or ask you questions.

45. *p*: The Pennsylvania Fish and Boat Commission is sensitive to the needs of the physically challenged. *q*: The Pennsylvania Fish and Boat Commission works to make our facilities accessible. *Negation*: Either the Pennsylvania Fish and Boat Commission is not sensitive to the needs of the physically challenged or it does not work to make our facilities accessible.   **47.** *p*: The court won't do it for you. *q*: Hiring an attorney is usually not cost effective. *Negation*: Either the court will do it for you or it is cost effective to hire an attorney.

49. $(c \wedge e) \vee \sim r$

c	e	r	(c ∧ e)	∨	~r
T	T	T	T T T	T	F
T	T	F	T T T	T	T
T	F	T	T F F	F	F
T	F	F	T F F	T	T
F	T	T	F F T	F	F
F	T	F	F F T	T	T
F	F	T	F F F	F	F
F	F	F	F F F	T	T
			① ② ①	④	③

The promise would be false if the senator runs for reelection and either doesn't cut taxes or eliminate the deficit.

51. The lady is behind Door 2 and the tiger is behind Door 1.

Exercises 6.3 (page 295)

1. True   **3.** True   **5.** True   **9.** True   **11.** True   **13.** If she dances tonight, then I'm leaving early and he sings loudly.
15. If he doesn't sing loudly, then she dances tonight or I'm not leaving early.   **17.** $d \vee (f \to g)$ **19.** $\sim f \to g$ **21.** True
23. False   **25.** False   **27.** True   **29.** True

35.

p	q	p	→	~q
T	T	T	F	F
T	F	T	T	T
F	T	F	T	F
F	F	F	T	T
		①	②	①

37.

p	q	(~q → ~p)	→	~q
T	T	F T F	F	F
T	F	T F F	T	T
F	T	F T T	F	F
F	F	T T T	T	T
		① ② ①	④	③

39.

p	q	(p ∧ ~q)	∧	(p → q)
T	T	T F F	F	T T T
T	F	T T T	F	T F F
F	T	F F F	F	F T T
F	F	F F T	F	F T F
		① ② ①	⑤	③ ④ ③

It is a contradiction.   **41.**

p	q	r	r	→	(p ∧ ~q)
T	T	T	T	F	T F F
T	T	F	F	T	T F F
T	F	T	T	T	T T T
T	F	F	F	T	T T T
F	T	T	T	F	F F F
F	T	F	F	T	F F F
F	F	T	T	F	F F T
F	F	F	F	T	F F T
			①	④	② ③ ②

43.

p	q	r	s	(~r → s)	V	(p → ~q)
T	T	T	T	F T T	T	T F F
T	T	T	F	F T F	T	T F F
T	T	F	T	T T T	T	T F F
T	T	F	F	T F F	F	T F F
T	F	T	T	F T T	T	T T T
T	F	T	F	F T F	T	T T T
T	F	F	T	T T T	T	T T T
T	F	F	F	T F F	T	T T T
F	T	T	T	F T T	T	F T F
F	T	T	F	F T F	T	F T F
F	T	F	T	T T T	T	F T F
F	T	F	F	T F F	T	F T F
F	F	T	T	F T T	T	F T T
F	F	T	F	F T F	T	F T T
F	F	F	T	T T T	T	F T T
F	F	F	F	T F F	T	F T T
				① ② ①	⑤	③ ④ ③

45. one   **47.** They cannot see me now or they'd never believe it.   **49.** I am not you or I would watch out.   **51.** I can make it there and I won't make it anywhere.   **53.** He's my brother and he's heavy.   **55.** Equivalent   **57.** Equivalent   **59.** Equivalent
61. Not equivalent

63.

p	q	p ∨ q	~p → q
T	T	T T T	F T T
T	F	T T F	F T F
F	T	F T T	T T T
F	F	F F F	T F F
		① ② ①	③ ④ ③

The columns labeled 2 and 4 are identical.

65.

p	q	p ∧ q	q ∧ p
T	T	T T T	T T T
T	F	T F F	F F T
F	T	F F T	T F F
F	F	F F F	F F F
		① ② ①	③ ④ ③

The columns labeled 2 and 4 are identical.

67.

p	q	r	(p ∧ q) ∧ r	p ∧ (q ∧ r)
T	T	T	T T T T T	T T T T T
T	T	F	T T T F F	T F T F F
T	F	T	T F F F T	T F F F T
T	F	F	T F F F F	T F F F F
F	T	T	F F T F T	F F T T T
F	T	F	F F T F F	F F T F F
F	F	T	F F F F T	F F F F T
F	F	F	F F F F F	F F F F F
			① ② ① ④ ③	⑤ ⑧ ⑥ ⑦ ⑥

The columns labeled 4 and 8 are identical.

69.

The columns labeled 4 and 9 are identical.

p	q	r	p ∧ (q ∨ r)	(p ∧ q) ∨ (p ∧ r)
T	T	T	T T T T T	T T T T T T T
T	T	F	T T T T F	T T T T T F F
T	F	T	T T F T T	T F F T T T T
T	F	F	T F F F F	T F F F T F F
F	T	T	F F T T T	F F T F F F T
F	T	F	F F T T F	F F T F F F F
F	F	T	F F F T T	F F F F F F T
F	F	F	F F F F F	F F F F F F F
			① ④ ② ③ ②	⑤ ⑥ ⑤ ⑨ ⑦ ⑧ ⑦

71.

The *p* column and the column labeled 4 are identical.

p	q	(p ∨ q) ∧ p
T	T	T T T T T
T	F	T T F T T
F	T	F T T F F
F	F	F F F F F
		① ② ① ④ ③

73. $p \wedge (r \vee q)$ **75.** $q \vee [p \wedge (q \vee \sim p)] \equiv q$ **77.** $(\sim p \vee q) \vee (\sim p \vee \sim q) \equiv T$

79. $\{[(\sim p \wedge \sim q) \vee (p \vee q)] \wedge (p \vee q)\} \wedge p \equiv p$

81. 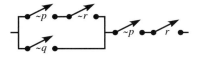   **83.** $(\sim q \wedge \sim p) \vee (\sim p \vee q) \equiv \sim p \vee q$

85. $[(\sim p \wedge \sim r) \vee \sim q] \wedge (\sim p \wedge r) \equiv (\sim p \wedge r) \wedge \sim q$ **87.** $\sim p \rightarrow (\sim p \vee \sim q) \equiv T$

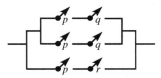

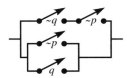

89. $[(p \wedge q) \vee (p \wedge q)] \vee (p \wedge r) \equiv p \wedge (q \vee r)$

91. $262.80   **93.** You are not wheezing persistently or you should see your doctor. *Negation*: You are wheezing persistently and you should not see your doctor.

Exercises 6.4 (page 303)

1. a. *Converse:* If I don't see it, then the exit is ahead.   **b.** *Inverse:* If the exit is not ahead, then I see it.   **c.** *Contrapositive:* If I see it, then the exit is not ahead.   **3. a.** *Converse:* If I baked a cake, then I knew you were coming.   **b.** *Inverse:* If I didn't know you were coming, I wouldn't have baked a cake.   **c.** *Contrapositive:* If I didn't bake a cake, then I didn't know you were coming.

5. a. *Converse:* If a man doesn't wear plaid, then he's dead.   **b.** *Inverse:* If a man is not dead, then he wears plaid.
c. *Contrapositive:* If a man wears plaid, then he's not dead.   **7. a.** *Converse:* $\sim q \to p$.   **b.** *Inverse:* $\sim p \to q$.
c. *Contrapositive:* $q \to \sim p$.   **9. a.** *Converse:* $(q \lor r) \to p$.   **b.** *Inverse:* $\sim p \to \sim(q \lor r)$ or $\sim p \to (\sim q \land \sim r)$.
c. *Contrapositive:* $(\sim q \land \sim r) \to \sim p$.   **13.** If you sign, then you accept the conditions.   **15.** If you can take this course pass/fail, then you have prior permission.   **17.** If the temperature is below $10°$, then you can skate on the pond.   **19.** If someone eats 10 hot dogs, then he or she will get sick.   **21.** If you travel to France, then you have a valid passport.   **23.** If a number has a real square root, then it is nonnegative.   **25.** If someone is a bride, then she is beautiful.   **27.** If the sum of a number's digits is divisible by 3, then it is divisible by 3.   **29.** d   **33.** True   **35.** False   **37.** False
39.

p	q	$(\sim p \land q)$	$\leftrightarrow$	$(p \to q)$
T	T	F F T	F	T T T
T	F	F F F	T	T F F
F	T	T T T	T	F T T
F	F	T F F	F	F T F
		① ② ①	⑤	③ ④ ③

41. a. If the award qualifies for full or partial tax-free treatment, then your employer must tell you.   **b.** If medical expenses are "qualified," then they are incurred *after* the HSA has been established.   **c.** If you elect to report the market discount annually as interest income, you can avoid this interest deduction limitation.   **43.** *Converse:* If you may avoid paying the annual fee billed on this statement, then you close your account within 30 days from the date this statement was mailed. *Inverse:* If you do not close your account within 30 days from the date this statement was mailed, you may not avoid paying the annual fee billed on this statement. *Contrapositive:* If you may not avoid paying the annual fee billed on this statement, then you do not close your account within 30 days from the date this statement was mailed. The converse and the inverse are equivalent, and the contrapositive and the original statement are equivalent.   **45. a.** $p \to (q \land r)$ **b.** If the most persistent does not stand to gain an extra meal or it does not eat at the expense of another, then there are not triplets.   **47.** If liberty and equality are not best attained when all persons share alike in the government to the utmost, then they are not, as is thought by some, chiefly to be found in democracy.
49. $(d \to l) \land \sim(l \to d)$ **51.** If there is an R.P.F. alliance, there there is a Modéré incumbent. *Converse:* If there is a Modéré incumbent, then there is an R.P.F. alliance. *Inverse:* If there is not an R.P.F. alliance, then there is not a Modéré incumbent. *Contrapositive:* If there is not a Modéré incumbent, then there is not an R.P.F. alliance. The contrapositive is equivalent to the original.
53. "Worked on the weekend": Must be turned over to see whether the employee got a day off. "Did not work on the weekend": Need not be turned over, since it does not describe an employee who worked on the weekend. "Did get a day off": Need not be turned over, since it cannot describe an employee who worked on the weekend without getting a day off. "Did not get a day off": Must be turned over to see whether the other side says "worked on the weekend."

Exercises 6.5 (page 316)

1. Valid; Reasoning by Transitivity   **3.** Valid; Modus Ponens   **5.** Invalid; Fallacy of the Converse   **7.** Valid; Modus Tollens
9. Invalid; Fallacy of the Inverse   **11.** Valid; Disjunctive Syllogism   **13.** Invalid; $p = $ T, $q = $ T   **15.** Invalid; $p = $ F, $q = $ F
17. Valid.

1.	$\sim p \to \sim q$	Premise
2.	q	Premise
3.	p	1, 2, Modus Tollens

19. Valid.

1.	$p \to q$	Premise
2.	$\sim q$	Premise
3.	$\sim p \to r$	Premise
4.	$\sim p$	1, 2, Modus Tollens
5.	r	3, 4, Modus Ponens

21. Valid.

1.	$p \to q$	Premise
2.	$q \to r$	Premise
3.	$\sim r$	Premise
4.	$p \to r$	1, 2, Transitivity
5.	$\sim p$	3, 4, Modus Tollens

23. Valid.

1.	$p \to q$	Premise
2.	$q \to \sim r$	Premise
3.	p	Premise
4.	$r \lor s$	Premise
5.	q	1, 3, Modus Ponens
6.	$\sim r$	2, 5, Modus Ponens
7.	s	4, 6, Disjunctive Syllogism

25.

p	q	$(p \wedge q) \rightarrow p$
T	T	T T T T
T	F	T F F T T
F	T	F F T T F
F	F	F F F T F
		① ② ① ③ ②

27.

p	q	$(p \wedge q) \rightarrow (p \wedge q)$
T	T	T T T T T T T
T	F	T F F T T F F
F	T	F F T T F F F
F	F	F F F T F F F
		① ② ① ⑤ ③ ④ ③

29. Valid.
1. c — Premise
2. $f \rightarrow \sim c$ — Premise
3. $\sim f \rightarrow s$ — Premise
4. $\sim f$ — 1, 2, Modus Tollens
5. s — 3, 4, Modus Ponens

31. Invalid; s = "you have strep throat" = T, f = "you have a fever" = T, c = "you have a serious cough" = F

33. Valid.
1. $y \vee \sim m$ — Premise
2. $\sim m \rightarrow \sim n$ — Premise
3. n — Premise
4. m — 2, 3, Modus Tollens
5. y — 1, 4, Disjunctive Syllogism

35. Valid.
1. $(p \wedge q) \rightarrow \sim r$ — Premise
2. r — Premise
3. $\sim(p \wedge q)$ — 1, 2, Modus Tollens
4. $\sim p \vee \sim q$ — 3, De Morgan's Law

37. *Conclusion:* If I tell you the time, then my life will be miserable. **39. a.** $s \rightarrow l$ or $\sim l \rightarrow \sim s$ **b.** $\sim s \rightarrow \sim j$ **c.** $y \rightarrow \sim l$
d. $y \rightarrow \sim j$, *Conclusion:* If he is your son, then he is not fit to serve on a jury. In Lewis Carroll's words, "None of your sons are fit to serve on a jury." **41. a.** $a \rightarrow s$ or $\sim s \rightarrow \sim a$ **b.** $g \rightarrow i$ **c.** $i \rightarrow \sim s$ **d.** $g \rightarrow \sim a$, *Conclusion:* If it is a guinea pig, then it does not appreciate Beethoven. In Lewis Carroll's words, "Guinea pigs never really appreciate Beethoven."
43. a. $p \rightarrow b$ or $\sim b \rightarrow \sim p$ **b.** $\sim t \rightarrow \sim l$ **c.** $o \rightarrow \sim s$ **d.** $b \rightarrow l$ **e.** $w \rightarrow p$ **f.** $\sim s \rightarrow \sim t$ **g.** $o \rightarrow \sim w$, *Conclusion:* If he is an opium eater, then he doesn't wear white kid gloves. In Lewis Carroll's words, "Opium eaters never wear white kid gloves."

Exercises 6.6 (page 326)

1. a. $\exists x \, [b(x) \wedge s(x)]$ **b.** $\forall x \, [b(x) \rightarrow \sim s(x)]$ **c.** No books are bestsellers. **3. a.** $\forall x \, [c(x) \rightarrow \sim s(x)]$ **b.** $\exists x \, [c(x) \wedge s(x)]$
c. There is a CEO who sleeps well at night. **5. a.** $\forall x \, [l(x) \rightarrow b(x)]$ **b.** $\exists x \, [l(x) \wedge \sim b(x)]$ **c.** There is a leaf that's not brown.

7. a. $\forall x [g(x) \rightarrow f(x)]$ **b.**

Valid

9. a. $\forall x [p(x) \rightarrow c(x)]$ **b.**

Invalid

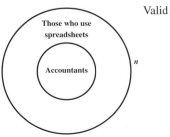

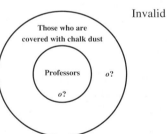

11. $\forall x \, [c(x) \rightarrow p(x)]$ **b.**

Valid

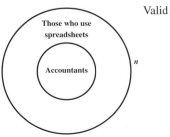

13. a. $\exists x\,[t(x) \land s(x)]$ **b.**
$\dfrac{\forall x\,[t(x) \rightarrow b(x)]}{\exists x\,[s(x) \land b(x)]}$

Valid

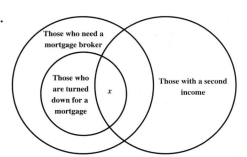

15. a. $\exists x\,[w(x) \land l(x)]$ **b.**
$\dfrac{w(m)}{l(m)}$

Invalid

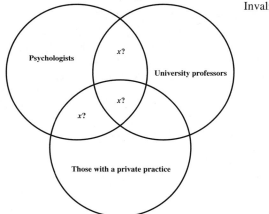

17. a. $\exists x\,[p(x) \land u(x)]$ **b.**
$\dfrac{\exists x\,[p(x) \land r(x)]}{\exists x\,[u(x) \land r(x)]}$

Invalid

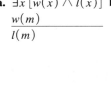

Psychologists

University professors

Those with a private practice

19. a. $\forall x\,[a(x) \lor i(x)]$ **b.**
$\dfrac{\exists x\,[\sim a(x)]}{\exists x\,[i(x)]}$

Valid

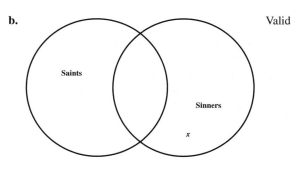

Saints

Sinners

21. Yes
23. All major league baseball players earn at least $300,000 a year.
Ryan Howard is a major league baseball player.
Ryan Howard earns at least $300,000 a year.

25. Valid   **27.** Invalid   **29.** Invalid   **31.** Invalid
37. a. $\forall x\,[l(x) \rightarrow g(x)]$ **b.** The power to collect taxes shall be vested in a Congress of the United States.
c.

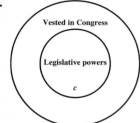

39. a. $\forall x\,\{[b(x) \lor e(x)] \rightarrow \sim p(x)\}$ **b.** The law forbidding members of the Communist Party to serve as an officer or as an employee of a labor union shall not be passed.
c.

41. a, c, d   **43.** Invalid   **45.** Invalid   **47.** Valid

Concept Check (page 331)

1. True   **2.** False   **3.** False   **4.** False   **5.** False   **6.** True   **7.** False   **8.** True   **9.** False   **10.** False   **11.** True   **12.** True

Chapter 6 Review Exercises (page 331)

1. She pays me and I have enough cash.   **3.** $l \land w$ **5.** $l \rightarrow \sim w$ **7.** He doesn't lose the election and he wins the hearts of the voters.   **9.** True   **11.** True
15.

p	q	p	$\land$	$(\sim p \lor q)$
T	T	T	T	F T T
T	F	T	F	F F F
F	T	F	F	T T T
F	F	F	F	T T F
		①	④	② ③ ②

The statement is not a tautology.

17. If someone is a mathematician, then that person is loveable.   **19.** If a system has a unique solution, then it has at least as many equations as unknowns.   **21. a.** If we need to change the way we do business, then the proposed regulations have been approved. **b.** If the proposed regulations have not been approved, then we do not need to change the way we do business.   **c.** If we do not need to change the way we do business, then the proposed regulations have not been approved.
23. $(p \land p) \land (\sim p \lor q) \equiv p \land q$ **25.**

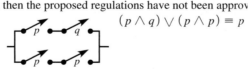

$(p \land q) \lor (p \land p) \equiv p$

27.

p	q	$p \vee q$			$(p \vee q) \wedge \sim(p \wedge q)$							
T	T	T	F	T	T	T	T	F	F	T	T	T
T	F	T	T	F	T	T	F	T	T	T	F	F
F	T	F	T	T	F	T	T	T	T	F	F	T
F	F	F	F	F	F	F	F	F	T	F	F	F
		①	②	①	③	④	③	⑧	⑦	⑤	⑥	⑤

The columns labeled 2 and 8 are identical.

29. a. Yes **b.** No   **31.** Valid; Modus Ponens   **33.** Valid; Disjunctive Syllogism   **35.** Invalid; Fallacy of the Converse

37. Valid.
1. $h \rightarrow t$		Premise
2. $r \rightarrow \sim t$		Premise
3. r		Premise
4. $\sim t$		2, 3, Modus Ponens
5. $\sim h$		1, 4, Modus Tollens

39. Invalid; $p = $ F, $q = $ F

41. a. $\forall x\,[d(x) \rightarrow h(x)]$ **b.** $\exists x\,[d(x) \wedge \sim h(x)]$ **c.** There is a dog that doesn't go to heaven.

43. a. $\forall x\,[f(x) \rightarrow w(x)]$ **b.**   Valid

$$\frac{f(j)}{w(j)}$$

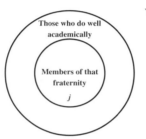

45.   No

p	q	r	$p \rightarrow$		$(q \rightarrow r)$			$(p \rightarrow q) \rightarrow r$				
T	T	T	T	T	T	T	T	T	T	T	T	T
T	T	F	T	F	T	F	F	T	T	T	F	F
T	F	T	T	T	F	T	T	T	F	F	T	T
T	F	F	T	T	F	T	F	T	F	F	T	F
F	T	T	F	T	T	T	T	F	T	T	T	T
F	T	F	F	T	T	F	F	F	T	T	F	F
F	F	T	F	T	F	T	T	F	T	F	T	T
F	F	F	F	T	F	T	F	F	T	F	F	F
			①	④	②	③	②	⑤	⑥	⑤	⑧	⑦

47. a.

p	q	$(p \wedge \sim p)$			$\rightarrow q$	
T	T	T	F	F	T	T
T	F	T	F	F	T	F
F	T	F	F	T	T	T
F	F	F	F	T	T	F
		①	②	①	④	③

49. a, b, c

51. If you do not have a net 28% rate gain or unrecaptured Section 1250 gain, then the Schedule D Tax Worksheet in the Schedule D instructions is not used.   **53. a.** Regulations do not have both costs and benefits, or rules that are passed to solve a problem cannot make it worse.   **b.** Shooters do not overwhelmingly have problems with alcoholism, or they do not have long criminal histories, particularly arrests for violent acts.   **c.** They are not disproportionately involved in automobile crashes, or they are not much more likely to have their driver's license suspended or revoked.   **55. a.**

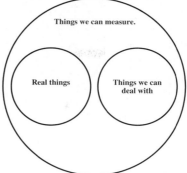

57. c   **59. a.** $h \rightarrow o$ **b.** $a \rightarrow m$ **c.** $p \rightarrow \sim o \equiv o \rightarrow \sim p$ **d.** $m \rightarrow h$ **e.** If the bird is in this aviary, it does not live on mince pies. In Lewis Carroll's words, "No bird in this aviary lives on mince pies."   **61. a.** $u \rightarrow c$ **b.** $p \rightarrow r$ **c.** $s \rightarrow h$
d. $\sim u \rightarrow \sim r \equiv r \rightarrow u$ **e.** $h \rightarrow p$ **f.** If the writer is Shakespeare, the writer is clever. In Lewis Carroll's words, "Shakespeare was clever."

CHAPTER 7 | Sets and Probability

Exercises 7.1 (page 349)

1. False   **3.** True   **5.** True   **7.** True   **9.** False   **11.** $\subseteq$ **13.** $\not\subseteq$ **15.** $\subseteq$ **17.** $\subseteq$ **19.** $\subset; \subset; \not\subset; \not\subset; \subset; \not\subset; \subset; \not\subset$ **21.** 16
23. 4   **25.** $\cap$ **27.** $\cap$ **29.** $\cap$ **31.** $\cup$ or $\cap$ **33.** $\{2, 4, 6\}$ **35.** $\{1, 3, 5, 7, 9\}$ **37.** $\{1, 7, 9\}$ **39.** $\{2, 3, 4, 6\}$ **41.** $\{4, 5, 6, 7, 8\}$ **43.** All students in this school not taking this course   **45.** All students in this school taking accounting and zoology   **47.** C
and D, B and E, C and E, D and E **49.** B' is the set of all stocks on the list with a closing price below \$26 or above \$30; $B' = \{$AT&T, CocaCola, Office Max Inc., Texas Instruments$\}$.   **51.** $(A \cap B)'$ is the set of all stocks on the list that do not have both a high price greater than \$34 and a closing price between \$26 and \$30; $(A \cap B)' = \{$AT&T, CocaCola, Disney, Office Max Inc., Texas Instruments$\}$.   **53. a.** True   **b.** True   **c.** False   **d.** False   **e.** True   **f.** True   **g.** False   **55.** $\{$Microsoft Corp., Proctor & Gamble$\}$ **57.** $\{$ExxonMobil Corp., Citigroup, Inc., American International Group$\}$ **59.** $\{s, d, c\}$ **61.** $\{g\}$ **63.** $\{s, d, c\}$
65. 11   **67.** $\{$The Disney Channel, Showtime, HBO, Encore$\}$ **69.** $\{$Encore, Starz$\}$ **71.** $\{$Showtime, HBO, Encore, Starz$\}$
75. a. The set of states who are not among those whose name contains the letter "e" or who are more than 4 million in population, and who also have an area of more than 40,000 square miles.   **b.** $\{$Alaska$\}$

Exercises 7.2 (page 360)

1.
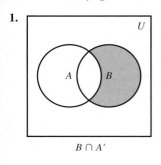
$B \cap A'$

3.
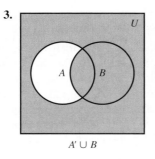
$A' \cup B$

5.
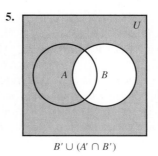
$B' \cup (A' \cap B')$

7.
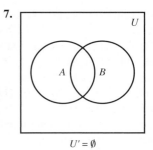
$U' = \emptyset$

9. 8

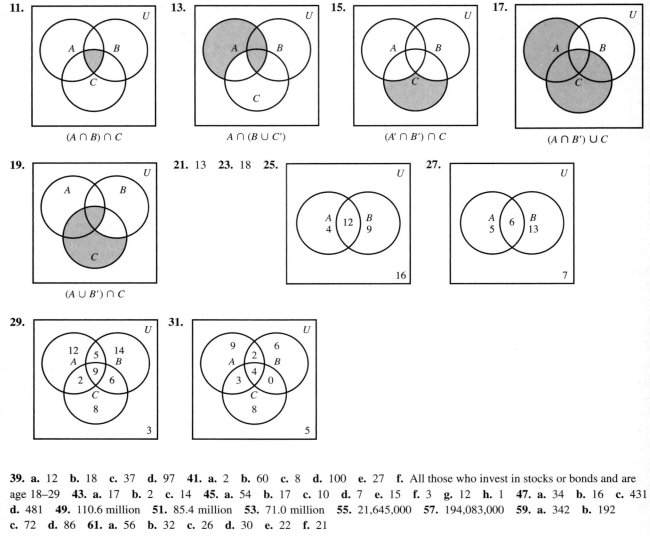

11. $(A \cap B) \cap C$

13. $A \cap (B \cup C')$

15. $(A' \cap B') \cap C$

17. $(A \cap B') \cup C$

19. $(A \cup B') \cap C$ **21.** 13   **23.** 18   **25.**   **27.**

29.   **31.**

39. a. 12   **b.** 18   **c.** 37   **d.** 97   **41. a.** 2   **b.** 60   **c.** 8   **d.** 100   **e.** 27   **f.** All those who invest in stocks or bonds and are age 18–29   **43. a.** 17   **b.** 2   **c.** 14   **45. a.** 54   **b.** 17   **c.** 10   **d.** 7   **e.** 15   **f.** 3   **g.** 12   **h.** 1   **47. a.** 34   **b.** 16   **c.** 431 **d.** 481   **49.** 110.6 million   **51.** 85.4 million   **53.** 71.0 million   **55.** 21,645,000   **57.** 194,083,000   **59. a.** 342   **b.** 192 **c.** 72   **d.** 86   **61. a.** 56   **b.** 32   **c.** 26   **d.** 30   **e.** 22   **f.** 21

Exercises 7.3 (page 371)

3. {January, February, March, …, December}   **5.** {0, 1, 2, 3, …, 79, 80}   **7.** {go ahead, cancel}
9. {$(h, 1), (h, 2), (h, 3), (h, 4), (h, 5), (h, 6), (t, 1), (t, 2), (t, 3), (t, 4), (t, 5), (t, 6)$}   **13.** {AB, AC, AD, AE, BC, BD, BE, CD, CE, DE}, 10, yes   **a.** {AC, BC, CD, CE}   **b.** {AB, AC, AD, AE, BC, BD, BE, CD, CE}   **c.** {AC}
15. {$(1, 2), (1, 3), (1, 4), (1, 5), (2, 3), (2, 4), (2, 5), (3, 4), (3, 5), (4, 5)$}, 10, yes   **a.** {$(2, 4)$}   **b.** {$(1, 2), (1, 4), (2, 3), (2, 5), (3, 4), (4, 5)$}   **c.** ∅   **17.** {$hh, thh, hth, tthh, thth, htth, ttth, ttht, thtt, httt, tttt$}, 11, no   **a.** {$tthh, thth, htth, ttth, ttht, thtt, httt, tttt$}   **b.** {$hh, thh, hth, tthh, thth, htth$}   **c.** {$tttt$}   **19.** 1/6   **21.** 2/3   **23.** 1/3   **25.** 1/13   **27.** 1/26
29. 1/52   **31.** 2/13   **33.** 7/13   **35.** 3/20   **37.** 1/4   **39.** 3/5   **41.** The outcomes are not equally likely.   **43. a.** Worker is male.   **b.** Worker is female and has worked less than 5 years.   **c.** Worker is female or does not contribute to a voluntary retirement plan.   **d.** Worker has worked 5 years or more.   **e.** Worker has worked less than 5 years or has contributed to a voluntary retirement plan.   **f.** Worker has worked 5 years or more and does not contribute to a voluntary retirement plan.   **45. a.** 8/15   **b.** 8/15

47. a. Person smokes or has a family history of heart disease, or both.   **b.** Person does not smoke and has a family history of heart disease.   **c.** Person does not have a family history of heart disease or is not overweight, or both.   **49. a.** 0.1631   **b.** 0.2450   **c.** 0.1287   **d.** 0.1360   **51. a.** 0.3151   **b.** 0.3219   **c.** 0.3670   **d.** Calvary   **e.** I Corps

Exercises 7.4 (page 382)

3. No   **5.** Yes   **7.** No   **9. a.** 5/36   **b.** 1/9   **c.** 1/12   **d.** 0   **11. a.** 5/18   **b.** 5/12   **c.** 1/3   **13.** 2/9   **15. a.** 2/13   **b.** 7/13   **c.** 3/26   **d.** 3/4   **e.** 11/26   **17. a.** 5/13   **b.** 7/13   **c.** 3/13   **19. a.** 1/10   **b.** 2/5   **c.** 7/20   **21. a.** 0.51   **b.** 0.25   **c.** 0.10   **d.** 0.84   **25.** 1 to 1   **27.** 5 to 1   **29.** 7 to 2   **31.** No. The probability the reader wins is 5/12, while the probability his opponent wins is 7/12.   **33.** 1/3; 1/5; 1/9001; 1/10; 9/19   **35.** Empirical   **37.** Not empirical   **39.** Empirical   **41.** Empirical   **43.** Possible   **45.** Not possible; the sum of the probabilities is less than 1.   **47.** Not possible; a probability cannot be negative. (*Note:* For 49 and 51, theoretical answers are given; actual answers will vary.)   **49. a.** 0.2778   **b.** 0.4167   **51. a.** 0.0463   **b.** 0.2963   **55.** 0.84   **57. a.** 0.07   **b.** 0.93   **c.** 0.49   **59.** 13 to 37   **61. a.** 0.961   **b.** 0.487   **c.** 0.513   **d.** 0.509   **e.** 0.004   **f.** 0.548   **63. a.** 1/4   **b.** 1/2   **c.** 1/4   **65.** a   **67.** c   **69. a.** 0.4   **b.** 0.1   **c.** 0.6   **d.** 0.9   **71.** 0   **73.** 2/5   **75. a.** 0.866   **b.** 0.478   **77.** 4/11

Exercises 7.5 (page 401)

1. 0   **3.** 1   **5.** 1/6   **7.** 4/17   **9.** 11/51   **11.** 8/663   **13.** 25/102   **17.** Dependent   **19.** Independent   **21. a.** 1/4   **b.** 0   **27. a.** It is better to switch, for a probability of winning of 1/6, as opposed to a probability of 1/7 of winning if you don't switch.   **29.** No; yes   **31. a.** 0.2   **b.** 0.4   **33.** The probability of a customer cashing a check, given that the customer made a deposit, is 3/4.   **35.** The probability of a customer not cashing a check, given that the customer did not make a deposit, is 1/4.   **37.** The probability of a customer not both cashing a check and making a deposit is 1/2.   **39.** 0.999985; fairly realistic   **41.** 0.03   **43.** 0.09   **45.** 1/4   **47.** 1/4   **49.** 1/7   **51.** They are independent.   **53.** 0.039   **55.** 0.491   **57.** 0.072   **59.** Yes   **61. a.** 0.323   **b.** 0.582   **c.** No   **63.** e   **65. a.** 0.0005   **b.** 0.9995   **c.** $(1999/2000)^a$ **d.** $1 - (1999/2000)^a$ **e.** $(1999/2000)^{Nc}$ **f.** $1 - (1999/2000)^{Nc}$ **67.** 7/229   **69.** 191/229   **71. a.** 0.7456   **b.** 0.1872   **73. a.** 0.58   **75. a.** 0.2713   **b.** 0.3792   **c.** 0.6246   **d.** 0.3418   **e.** 0.6897   **f.** 0.5137   **g.** Not independent   **77. a.** 0.052   **b.** 0.476   **79. a.** 7/10   **b.** 2/15   **81.** 10^{-12} **83.** No   **85. c.** They are the same.   **d.** The 2-point first strategy has a smaller probability of losing.

Exercises 7.6 (page 413)

1. 1/3   **3.** 3/19   **5.** 21/38   **7.** 8/17   **9.** 85%   **11.** 0.0727   **13.** 0.1765   **15.** 0.3636   **17.** 2/7   **19.** d   **21.** c   **23.** 0.0478   **25. a.** About 0.16   **b.** About 0.99   **c.** About 59   **27.** d   **29.** b   **31. a.** 0.53   **b.** 0.1623   **33.** 0.1457   **35.** 0.1118   **37.** 0.2441   **39.** 9.9×10^{-5}

Concept Check (page 420)

1. True   **2.** True   **3.** False   **4.** False   **5.** False   **6.** True   **7.** False   **8.** False   **9.** False   **10.** True   **11.** False   **12.** True

Chapter 7 Review Exercises (page 421)

1. False   **3.** False   **5.** True   **7.** False   **9.** False   **11.** 32   **13.** {a, b, g}   **15.** {c, d}   **17.** {a, b, e, f, g, h}   **19.** *U*   **21.** All female employees in the accounting department   All employees who are in the accounting department or who have MBA degrees   **25.** All male employees who are not in the sales department

27.
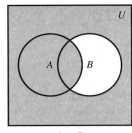

$A \cup B'$

29.
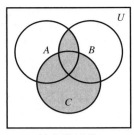

$(A \cap B) \cup C$

31. $\{1, 2, 3, 4, 5, 6\}$ **33.** $\{0, 0.5, 1, 1.5, 2, \ldots, 299.5, 300\}$ **35.** $\{(3, r), (3, g), (5, r), (5, g), (7, r), (7, g), (9, r), (9, g), (11, r), (11, g)\}$ **37.** $\{(3, g), (5, g), (7, g), (9, g), (11, g)\}$ **39.** 1/4   **41.** 3/13   **43.** 1/2   **45.** 1   **51.** The probability is 2/3 if you switch and 1/3 if you don't switch. The contestant should switch doors.   **53.** 1 to 25   **55.** 5/36   **57.** 1/6   **59.** 1/6
61. 2/11   **63. a.** 0.66   **b.** 0.29   **c.** 0.71   **d.** 0.34   **65.** 4/9   **67.** 0.8736   **69.** 0.3077   **71.** 0.87   **73. a.** $(E \cup F)'$ or $E' \cap F'$ **b.** $E \cup F$ **75. a.** 0.0297   **b.** 0.0909   **c.** 0.2626   **d.** No   **77.** b   **79.** b   **81. a.**
b. 1/4

	N_2	T_2
N_1	$N_1 N_2$	$N_1 T_2$
T_1	$T_1 N_2$	$T_1 T_2$

c. 1/2   **d.** 1/4   **83.** b   **85. a.** 0.4614   **b.** 0.5497   **c.** 0.4708   **87. b.** 7/10
89. Independence   **91.** 0.7145; 0.5688; 0.4101; 0.3212; 0.2708   **93. a.** 51   **b.** 31
c. 18   **d.** 15   **e.** 33   **f.** 23   **95. a.** 0.0025   **b.** 0.9975   **c.** 0.9753   **d.** 0.0247; no
e. Independence

CHAPTER 8 | Counting Principles; Further Probability Topics

Exercises 8.1 (page 439)

1. 720   **3.** 1.308×10^{12} **5.** 156   **7.** 1.024×10^{25} **9.** 1   **11.** n **13.** 36   **15.** 20   **19.** 3   **21.** 540,540
23. a. 8.718×10^{10} **b.** 4,354,560   **c.** 120,120   **d.** 84   **e.** 504   **25.** Multiply by 10   **27. a.** 2   **b.** 6   **c.** 18   **29.** 1120
31. No; use at least 4 initials   **33.** 720   **35.** 120   **37.** 3.352×10^{10} **39. a.** 120   **b.** 48   **41.** 280   **43. a.** 78,125
b. 900,000   **c.** 90,000   **d.** 10,000   **e.** 544,320   **45.** 800   **47.** 1,000,000,000; yes   **49.** 1,000,000,000   **51.** 4.096×10^{15}
53. a. 362,880   **b.** 181,440   **c.** No

Exercises 8.2 (page 449)

3. 792   **5.** 1.134×10^{11} **7.** 1   **9.** n **11. a.** 10   **b.** 7   **13. a.** 9   **b.** 6   **c.** 3; yes, from both   **17.** Combinations;   **a.** 126
b. 462   **c.** 4620   **19.** Permutations; 479,001,600   **21.** Combinations;   **a.** 120   **b.** 1820   **c.** 36   **23.** Combinations;   **a.** 10
b. 0   **c.** 1   **d.** 10   **e.** 30   **f.** 15   **g.** 0   **27.** 28   **29. a.** 720   **b.** 360   **31. a.** 40   **b.** 20   **c.** 7   **33.** 4,115,439,900
35. a. 84   **b.** 10   **c.** 40   **d.** 74   **37.** No; 14,190   **39. a.** 48   **b.** 658,008   **c.** 652,080   **d.** 844,272   **e.** 79,092   **41.** 50
43. a. 15,504   **b.** 816   **45. a.** 1,120,529,256   **b.** 806,781,064,320   **47. a.** 1,048,576   **b.** 524,800   **49. a.** 255   **b.** 16
c. 24   **d.** 225   **e.** 128   **51. a.** 6.402×10^{15} **b.** 3.135×10^{10} **53.** a and b. 26

Exercises 8.3 (page 463)

1. 7/33   **3.** 14/55   **5.** 1326   **7.** 33/221   **9.** 52/221   **11.** 130/221   **13.** 8.417×10^{-8} **15.** 18,975/28,561
19. $1 - P(365, 42)/365^{42}$ **21.** 1   **23.** 0.6501   **25.** 3/5 and 2/5   **27.** 2.165×10^{-4} **29.** 0.0000289   **31.** 36/55   **33.** 21/55
35. 7/22   **37. a.** 225/646   **b.** 15/323   **c.** 225/2584   **d.** 0   **e.** 1/2   **f.** 175/2584   **g.** 503/646   **39.** 1.539×10^{-6}
41. 2.401×10^{-4} **43.** 0.0211   **45.** 0.4226   **47.** 0.0438   **49.** 0.0133   **51.** 8.924×10^{-10} **53.** 4.507×10^{-34}; no
55. a. 1/146,107,962   **b.** 0.3915   **57.** No, 1.48%   **59. a.** 3.291×10^{-6} **b.** 7.962×10^{-12} **c.** 5.927×10^{-11}
d. 5.524×10^{26}

Exercises 8.4 (page 472)

1. 5/16   **3.** 1/32   **5.** 3/16   **7.** 13/16   **9.** 4.594×10^{-10} **11.** 0.2692   **13.** 0.8748   **15.** 1/64   **17.** 21/32   **23.** The potential callers are not likely to have birthdates that are evenly distributed throughout the twentieth century.   **25.** 0.2059   **27.** 0.4510

29. 0.1737   **31.** 0.7925   **33.** 0.2458   **35.** 0.0170   **37.** 0.3585   **39. a.** 0.1488   **b.** 0.0213   **c.** 0.9787   **41. a.** 0.0222
b. 0.1797   **c.** 0.7766   **43.** 0.0874   **45.** 0.9126   **47.** 0.2183   **49.** 0.0025   **51. a.** 0.0478   **b.** 0.9767   **c.** 0.8971   **53. a.** 1
chance in 1024   **b.** About 1 chance in 1.1×10^{12} **c.** About 1 chance in 2.587×10^{6} **55.** 0.9523   **57.** e   **59.** 0.0305
61. 0.8676   **63. a.** 0.1990   **b.** 0.5684   **c.** 0.1332   **d.** 0.7936   **65. a.** 0.9995   **67. a.** 0.125, 0.25, 0.3125, 0.3125
b. 0.2893, 0.3222, 0.2353, 0.1531

Exercises 8.5 (page 485)

1.

Number of Heads	0	1	2	3	4
Probability	1/16	1/4	3/8	1/4	1/16

3.

Number of Aces	0	1	2	3
Probability	0.7826	0.2042	0.0130	0.0002

5.   **7.**

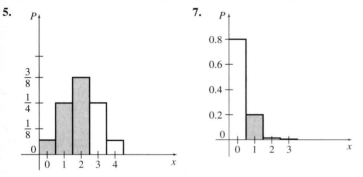

9. 3.6   **11.** 14.49   **13.** 2.7   **15.** 18   **17.** 0; yes

19. a.   **b.** 9/7

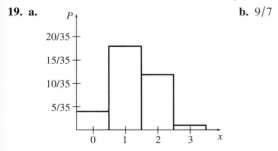

21. a.

x	0	1	2	3	4
P(x)	625/1296	125/324	25/216	5/324	1/1296

b. 2/3

23. 3/4   **25.** 1/2

29. a.

Sum	5	6	7	8	9
Probability	1/6	1/6	1/3	1/6	1/6

b.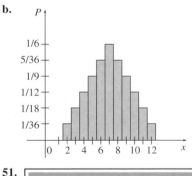

c. 1 to 2   **d.** 7

31. $54,000   **33. a.** 30   **b.** 10
35. e   **37. a.** $68.51; $72.84   **b.** Amoxicillin   **39.** 38   **41. a.** 0.007230   **b.** 5.094×10^{-4} **c.** 5.5×10^{-5} **d.** 0.1143
43. a.

Number of Cats	0	1	2	3	4
Probability	0.2401	0.4116	0.2646	0.0756	0.0081

b. 1.2   **c.** 1.2

45. $-$0.72; no   **47.** $-$0.82   **49.** $-$0.053   **51.** $-$0.50   **53.** $0.10; no   **55. a.** 10/3   **b.** 50/9
57. a.

x	0	1	2	3	4
P(x)	0.1956	0.3941	0.2978	0.1000	0.0126

b. 1.34

Concept Check (page 493)

1. True   **2.** True   **3.** True   **4.** True   **5.** False   **6.** True   **7.** True   **8.** False   **9.** True   **10.** False   **11.** True   **12.** False

Chapter 8 Review Exercises (page 493)

1. 720   **3.** 220   **5.** 20   **7. a.** 24   **b.** 12   **9. a.** 140   **b.** 239   **13.** 0   **15.** 27/143   **17.** 21/143   **19.** 1/64   **21.** 11/32
23. 1/17   **25.** 80/221   **27.** 220/221
29. a.

Number	2	3	4	5	6	7	8	9	10	11	12
Probability	1/36	1/18	1/12	1/9	5/36	1/6	5/36	1/9	1/12	1/18	1/36

b.

c. 7   **31.** 0.6   **33.** 2.5   **35.** $1.29   **37. a.** $\binom{n}{0}$, or 1; $\binom{n}{1}$, or n; $\binom{n}{2}$; $\binom{n}{n}$, or 1
b. $\binom{n}{0} + \binom{n}{1} + \binom{n}{2} + \cdots + \binom{n}{n}$ **e.** The sum of the elements in row n of Pascal's triangle is 2^n.   **39.** 0.1122   **41.** 7.580×10^{-7} **43.** 0.6187   **45.** 2   **47.** d   **49.** e

51.

x	0	1	2	3	4	5	6
Income	0	400	800	1200	800	400	0
P(x)	0.0041	0.0369	0.1382	0.2765	0.3110	0.1866	0.0467

a. $780.60   **b.** $720; $856.32; $868.22; 5
53. 0.1875

55. a.

Number of Women	0	1	2	3	4	5
Probability	0.0778	0.2592	0.3456	0.2304	0.0768	0.0102

b.

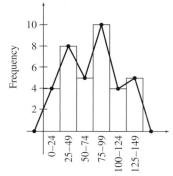

c. 2

57. a.

Number Who Did Not Do Homework	0	1	2	3
Probability	1/12	5/12	5/12	1/12

b.

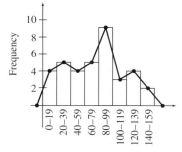

c. 3/2

59. $-\$0.65$ **61.** 9.5   **63. a.** 0.4799; 0.6533   **c.** 0.3467; 0.003096

CHAPTER 9 Statistics

Exercises 9.1 (page 511)

1. a.–b.

Interval	Frequency
0–24	4
25–49	8
50–74	5
75–99	10
100–124	4
125–149	5

c.–d.

3. a.–b.

Interval	Frequency
0–19	4
20–39	5
40–59	4
60–79	5
80–99	9
100–119	3
120–139	4
140–159	2

c.–d.

7. 16   **9.** 28,620   **11.** 7.68   **13.** 7.25   **15.** 42   **17.** 130   **19.** 29.1   **21.** 73.86, 80.5   **23.** 9   **25.** 55 and 62   **27.** 6.3
31. 73.81, 75–99   **35.** 2199 million bushels, 2252.5 million bushels   **37.** $39,696.74   **39. a.** 219.92, 152   **b.** All airlines did
not carry the same number of passengers.   **c.** 0.84, 0.875   **41.** 7.38; 7; 7, 5, 4   **43. a.** 12%   **b.** 13%   **c.** 50–59   **d.** It's
becoming uniform for all age groups.   **45. a.** 55.5°F; 50.5°F   **b.** 28.9°F; 28.5°F   **47. a.** $71,349   **49. a.** $3,573,627;
$1,750,000; $345,000 and $7,000,000   **b.** Median

Exercises 9.2 (page 524)

1. The standard deviation is the square root of the variance.   **3.** 33; 12.6   **5.** 46; 16.1   **7.** 24; 8.1   **9.** 40.05   **11.** 39.4
13. 8/9   **15.** 24/25   **17.** At least 5/9   **19.** No more than 4/9   **23. a.** Mean $= 25.5$ hr; standard deviation $= 7.2$ hr
b. Forever Power   **c.** Forever Power   **25. a.** 1/3; 2; −1/3; 0; 5/3; 7/3; 1; 4/3; 7/3; 2/3   **b.** 2.1; 2.6; 1.5; 2.6; 2.5; 0.6; 1.0;
2.1; 0.6; 1.2   **c.** 1.13   **d.** 1.68   **e.** 4.41; −2.15   **f.** 4.31; 0   **27.** Mean $= 1.8158$ mm; standard deviation $= 0.4451$ mm.
29. a. Mean $= 7.3571$; standard deviation $= 0.1326$ **b.** 100%   **31. a.** 127.7 days; 30.16 days   **b.** Seven   **33. a.** $4,233,387
b. About 4%

Exercises 9.3 (page 537)

1. The mean   **3.** z-scores are found with the formula $z = (x - \mu)/\sigma$ **5.** 45.54%   **7.** 48.96%   **9.** 37.38%   **11.** 14.78%
13. 97.72%   **15.** −1.64 or −1.65   **17.** 1.28   **19.** 0.5; 0.5   **21.** 0.8889; 0.9974   **23.** 5000   **25.** 6247   **27.** 7257   **29.** 0.1587
31. 0.0062   **33.** 84.13%   **35.** 37.79%   **37.** 7.03%   **39.** 0.0062   **41.** $90.78 and $58.22   **43.** 99.38%   **45.** 189 units
47. 0.8887   **49.** 60.32 mph   **51.** 6.68%   **53.** 38.3%   **55.** 87   **57.** 71   **59. b.** 55%   **61. a.** About 0.01; yes   **b.** Essentially
0; yes   **63. a.** 0.5596; 0.0188   **b.** Essentially 0; essentially 0   **c.** 0.9265; 0.9554   **d.** Essentially 0; essentially 0   **e.** Essentially
0; essentially 0

Exercises 9.4 (page 546)

1. The number of trials and the probability of success on each trial   **3. a.** 0.0278   **b.** 0.0279   **5. a.** 0.0106   **b.** 0.0122
7. 0.0240   **9.** 0.9463   **11.** 0.0956   **13.** 0.8643   **15.** 0.1841   **17. a.** 0.1684   **b.** 0.0305   **c.** 0.9573   **19.** 0.0038
21. a. 0.0237   **b.** 0.6808   **23. a.** 0.1974   **b.** 0.0092   **c.** Essentially 0   **d.** 0.0001   **25. a.** 0.0764   **b.** 0.1210   **c.** 0.0051;
very unlikely   **27.** 0.8643   **29.** 0.9245   **31.** 0.7357   **33. a.** 1.214×10^{-7} **b.** Essentially 0   **c.** 0.7910

Concept Check (page 550)

1. True   **2.** False   **3.** False   **4.** True   **5.** False   **6.** False   **7.** False   **8.** True   **9.** True   **10.** True   **11.** False   **12.** True

Chapter 9 Review Exercises (page 550)

3. a.

Sales	Frequency
450–474	5
475–499	6
500–524	5
525–549	2
550–574	2

b.–c.

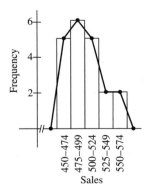

5. 29.25   **7.** 34.9   **11.** 38; 36 and 38   **13.** 55–59   **17.** 67; 23.9   **19.** 6.4   **21.** A skewed distribution has the largest frequency
at one end.   **23.** 0.7995   **25.** 0.0606   **27.** Because the histogram is skewed, not close to the shape of a normal distribution
29. a. 2.1; 1.07   **b.** 2; 1   **c.** Answers to parts a and b should be close to each other.   **31. a.** Stock I: 8%, 7.9%; Stock II: 8%,
2.6%   **b.** Stock II   **33. a.** 0.8924; 0.8962   **b.** 0.0446; 0.0477   **c.** 0.0196; 0.0150   **35.** Diet A: $\bar{x} = 2.7$, $s = 2.26$; Diet B:
$\bar{x} = 1.3$, $s = 0.95$ **a.** Diet A   **b.** Diet B   **37.** 0.9292   **39.** 0.9534   **41.** 43.25%   **43.** 56.25%   **45. a.** 137.25; 130.5; no mode
b. 46.9   **c.** 58.3%   **d.** 100%   **47. a.** 0.1020   **b.** 0.3707   **d.** 0.9987   **e.** 0.1336

CHAPTER 10 Nonlinear Functions

Exercises 10.1 (page 568)

1. Not a function   **3.** Function   **5.** Function   **7.** Not a function

9. $(-2, -1), (-1, 1), (0, 3), (1, 5), (2, 7), (3, 9)$; range: $\{-1, 1, 3, 5, 7, 9\}$

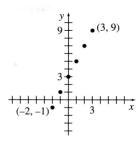

11. $(-2, 3/2), (-1, 2), (0, 5/2), (1, 3), (2, 7/2), (3, 4)$; range: $\{3/2, 2, 5/2, 3, 7/2, 4\}$

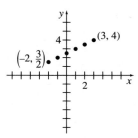

13. $(-2, 0), (-1, -1), (0, 0), (1, 3), (2, 8), (3, 15)$; range: $\{-1, 0, 3, 8, 15\}$

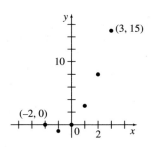

15. $(-2, 4), (-1, 1), (0, 0), (1, 1), (2, 4), (3, 9)$; range: $\{0, 1, 4, 9\}$

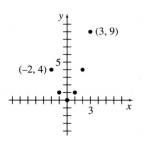

17. $(-2, 1), (-1, 1/2), (0, 1/3), (1, 1/4), (2, 1/5), (3, 1/6)$; range: $\{1, 1/2, 1/3, 1/4, 1/5, 1/6\}$

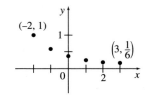

19. $(-2, -3), (-1, -4/3), (0, -1/2), (1, 0), (2, 1/3), (3, 4/7)$; range: $\{-3, -4/3, -1/2, 0, 1/3, 4/7\}$

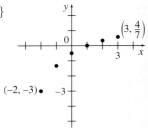

21. $(-\infty, \infty)$ **23.** $(-\infty, \infty)$ **25.** $[-2, 2]$ **27.** $[3, \infty)$ **29.** $(-\infty, -1) \cup (-1, 1) \cup (1, \infty)$ **31.** $(-\infty, -4) \cup (4, \infty)$
33. $(-\infty, -1] \cup [5, \infty)$ **35.** $(-\infty, -1) \cup (1/3, \infty)$ **37.** Domain: $[-5, 4)$; range: $[-2, 6]$ **39.** Domain: $(-\infty, \infty)$; range:
$(-\infty, 12]$ **41. a.** 33 **b.** 15/4 **c.** $3a^2 - 4a + 1$ **d.** $12/m^2 - 8/m + 1$ or $(12 - 8m + m^2)/m^2$ **e.** 0, 4/3 **43. a.** 9/2
b. 0 **c.** $(2a + 1)/(a - 2)$ **d.** $(4 + m)/(2 - 2m)$ **e.** -3 **45.** Domain: $[-2, 4]$; range: $[0, 4]$ **a.** 0 **b.** 4 **c.** 3
d. $-1.5, 1.5, 2.5$ **47.** Domain: $[-2, 4]$; range: $[-3, 2]$ **a.** -3 **b.** -2 **c.** -1 **d.** 2.5 **49.** $6t^2 + 12t + 4$
51. $r^2 + 2rh + h^2 - 2r - 2h + 5$ **53.** $9/q^2 - 6/q + 5$ or $(9 - 6q + 5q^2)/q^2$ **55.** Function **57.** Not a Function
59. Function **61. a.** $2x + 2h + 1$ **b.** $2h$ **c.** 2 **63. a.** $2x^2 + 4xh + 2h^2 - 4x - 4h - 5$ **b.** $4xh + 2h^2 - 4h$
c. $4x + 2h - 4$ **65. a.** $1/(x + h)$ **b.** $-h/[x(x + h)]$ **c.** $-1/[x(x + h)]$ **67.** Odd **69.** Even **71.** Even **73.** Odd
75. a. The years **b.** The number of Internet users **c.** 719 million **d.** Domain: $1995 \le x \le 2006$; range:
$16,000,000 \le y \le 1,043,000,000$
77. a. \$98 **b.** \$98 **c.** \$98 **d.** \$152 **e.** \$206 **f.**
g. Yes **h.** No **79. a. i.** 66 kcal/day
ii. 222 kcal/day **b.** $g(z) = 0.454z$
81. a. 1880; 50% **b.** 1965; 35%

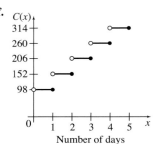

83. a. $A = (3000 - w)w$ **b.** $0 \le w \le 3000$ **c.**

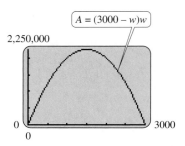

Exercises 10.2 (page 581)

3. D **5.** A **7.** C
9. Vertex is $(-5/2, -1/4)$; axis is $x = -5/2$; x-intercepts are -3 and -2; y-intercept is 6.

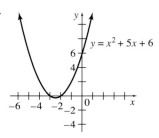

11. Vertex is $(-3, 2)$; axis is $x = -3$; x-intercepts are -4 and -2; y-intercept is -16.

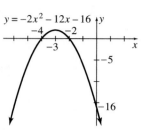

13. Vertex is $(-2, -16)$; axis is $x = -2$; x-intercepts are $-2 \pm 2\sqrt{2} \approx 0.83$ or -4.83; y-intercept is -8.

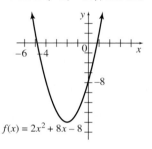

15. Vertex is $(1, 3)$; axis is $x = 1$; no x-intercepts; y-intercept is 5.

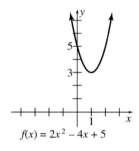

17. Vertex is $(4, 11)$; axis is $x = 4$; x-intercepts are $4 \pm \sqrt{22}/2 \approx 6.35$ or 1.65; y-intercept is -21.

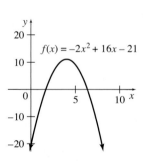

19. Vertex is $(4, -5)$; axis is $x = 4$; x-intercepts are $4 \pm \sqrt{15} \approx 7.87$ or 0.13; y-intercept is $1/3$.

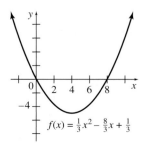

21. D **23.** C **25.** E **27.**

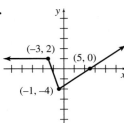

29.

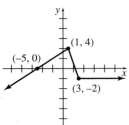

31.

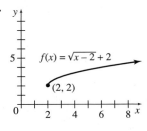

33.

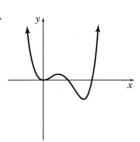

35.

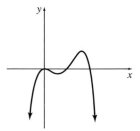

37.

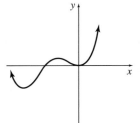

39.

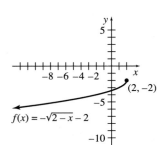

41.

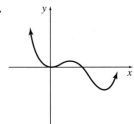

43. a. r **b.** $-r$ **c.** $-r$ **45. a.**

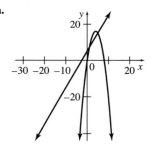

b. 1 **c.** 16 **d.** 4

47. a.

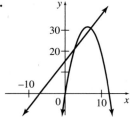

b. 2.5 **c.** 31.25 **d.** 5

49. Maximum revenue is $9225; 35 seats are unsold.

51. a. $R(x) = x(500 - x) = 500x - x^2$ **b.**

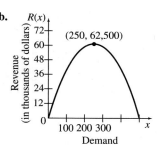

c. $250 **d.** $62,500

53. a. $800 + 25x$ **b.** $80 - x$ **c.** $R(x) = 64,000 + 1200x - 25x^2$ **d.** 24 **e.** $78,400 **55. a.** 87 yr **b.** 98 yr
57. a. 28.5 weeks **b.** 0.81 **c.** 0 weeks or 57 weeks of gestation; no **59. a.**

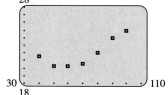

b. Quadratic

c. $y = 0.002726x^2 - 0.3113x + 29.33$;

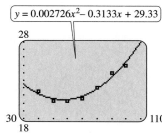

d. $f(x) = 0.003(x - 60)^2 + 20.3$

e.

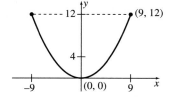

61. 49 yr; 3.98 **b.** 2 sec **63. a.** 61.70 ft **b.** 43.08 mph **65.** 9025 ft^2

67. $y = (4/27)x^2$; $6\sqrt{3}$ ft ≈ 10.39 ft

Exercises 10.3 (page 593)

3.

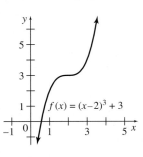

5.

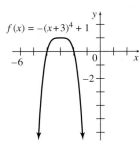

7. D **9.** E **11.** I **13.** G **15.** A **17.** D
19. E **21.** 4, 6, etc. (true degree $= 4$); $+$ **23.** 5, 7, etc.
(true degree $= 5$); $+$ **25.** 7, 9, etc. (true degree $= 7$); $-$

27. Horizontal asymptote: $y = 0$; vertical asymptote: $x = -2$; no x-intercept; y-intercept $= -2$

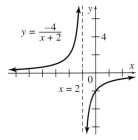

29. Horizontal asymptote: $y = 0$; vertical asymptote: $x = -3/2$; no x-intercept; y-intercept $= 2/3$

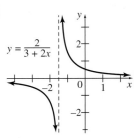

31. Horizontal asymptote: $y = 2$; vertical asymptote: $x = 3$; x-intercept $= 0$; y-intercept $= 0$

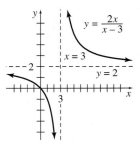

33. Horizontal asymptote: $y = 1$; vertical asymptote: $x = 4$; x-intercept $= -1$; y-intercept $= -1/4$

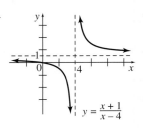

35. Horizontal asymptote: $y = -1/2$; vertical asymptote: $x = -5$; x-intercept $= 3/2$; y-intercept $= 3/20$

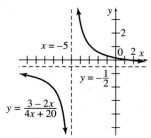

37. Horizontal asymptote: $y = -1/3$; vertical asymptote: $x = -2$; x-intercept $= -4$; y-intercept $= -2/3$

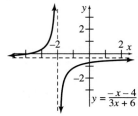

39. No asymptotes; hole at $x = -4$; x-intercept $= -3$; y-intercept $= 3$

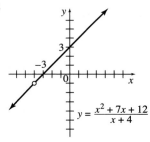

41. One possible answer is $y = 2x/(x - 1)$. **43. a.** 0 **b.** 2, −3 **d.** $(x + 1)(x - 1)(x + 2)$ **e.** $3(x + 1)(x - 1)(x + 2)$
f. $(x - a)$ **45. a.** Two; one at $x = -1.4$ and one at $x = 1.4$ **b.** Three; one at $x = -1.414$, one at $x = 1.414$, and one at $x = 1.442$
47. a. \$440; \$419; \$383; \$326; \$284; \$251 **b.** Vertical asymptote at $x = -475$; horizontal asymptote at $y = 0$ **c.** $y = 463.2$ **d.**

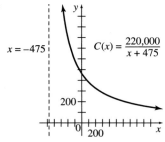

49. $f_1(x) = x(100 - x)/25,$
$f_2(x) = x(100 - x)/10,$
$f(x) = x^2(100 - x)^2/250$

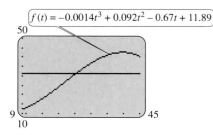

$$f(x) = \frac{x^2(100-x)^2}{250}$$

51. a. $6700; $15,600; $26,800; $60,300; $127,300; $328,300; $663,300 **b.** No **c.**

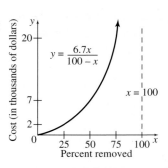

53. a. $a = 337/d$ **b.** 8.32 (using $k = 337$) **55. a.**

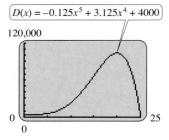

b. 1905 to 1925; 1905 to 1910; 1925 to 1930

57. a.

b. 1985

59. a. $[0, \infty)$ **b.**

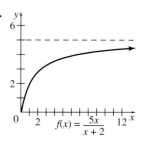

d. Maximum growth rate

61. a.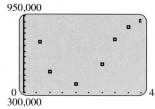

b. $y = 890.37x^2 - 36,370x + 830,144;$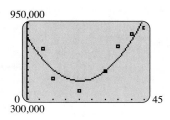

c. $y = -52.954x^3 + 5017.88x^2 - 127,714x + 1,322,606;$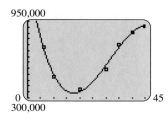

63. a.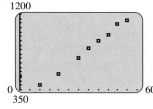

b. $y = 0.19327x^2 + 3.0039x + 431.30$

c.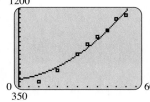

d. $y = -0.010883x^3 + 1.1079x^2 - 16.432x + 485.45$

e.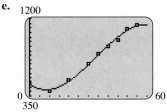

Exercises 10.4 (page 608)

1. $2, 4, 8, 16, 32, \ldots, 1024;$ $1.125899907 \times 10^{15}$ **3.** E **5.** C **7.** F **9.** A **11.** C **13.** 5 **15.** -4 **17.** -3 **19.** $21/4$
21. $-12/5$ **23.** $2, -2$ **25.** $0, -1$ **27.** $0, 1/2$ **33. a.** \$2166.53 **b.** \$2189.94 **c.** \$2201.90 **d.** \$2209.97 **35.** He should
choose the 5.9% investment, which would yield \$23.74 additional interest. **b.** 8.2% **37. a.** \$10.94 **b.** \$11.27 **c.** \$11.62
39. 6.30% **40. a.** 8.84% **b.** 8.75% **41. a.** 1, 0.92, 0.85, 0.78, 0.72, 0.66, 0.61, 0.56, 0.51, 0.47, 0.43
b.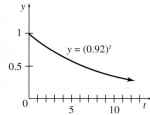

c. About \$384,000

d. About \$98

43. a **45. a.** 4000 bacteria   **b.** 500 bacteria   **c.** Every 1/3 hr or 20 min   **d.** In 2 hr

47. a. 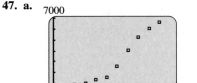 exponentially   **b.** $f(x) = 534(1.026)^x$ **c.** 2.6%

d. 2026

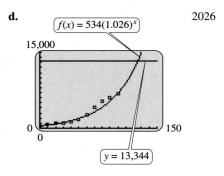

$f(x) = 534(1.026)^x$

$y = 13,344$

49. a. $P = 1013e^{-1.34 \times 10^{-4}x}$; $P = -0.0748x + 1013$; $P = 1/(2.79 \times 10^{-7}x + 9.87 \times 10^{-4})$
b. $P = 1013e^{-1.34 \times 10^{-4}x}$ is the best fit.

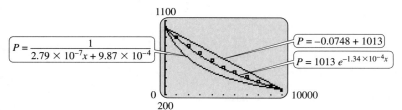

$P = \dfrac{1}{2.79 \times 10^{-7}x + 9.87 \times 10^{-4}}$

$P = -0.0748 + 1013$

$P = 1013 \, e^{-1.34 \times 10^{-4}x}$

c. 829 millibars, 232 millibars
d. $P = 1038(0.99998661)^x$. This is slightly different from the function found in part b, which can be rewritten as $P = 1013(0.99998660)^x$.

Exercises 10.5 (page 623)

1. $\log_5 125 = 3$ **3.** $\log_3 81 = 4$ **5.** $\log_3(1/9) = -2$ **7.** $2^5 = 32$ **9.** $e^{-1} = 1/e$ **11.** $10^5 = 100,000$ **13.** 2   **15.** 3
17. -4 **19.** $-2/3$ **21.** 1   **23.** 5/3   **25.** $\log_3 4$ **27.** $\log_5 3 + \log_5 k$ **29.** $1 + \log_3 p - \log_3 5 - \log_3 k$
31. $\ln 3 + (1/2) \ln 5 - (1/3) \ln 6$ **33.** $5a$ **35.** $2c + 3a + 1$ **37.** 2.113   **39.** -0.281 **41.** $x = 1/6$ **43.** $z = 4/3$
45. $r = 25$ **47.** $x = 1$ **49.** No solution   **51.** $x = 3$ **53.** $x = 5$ **55.** $x = 1.544$ **57.** $y = 1.354$ **59.** $z = 3.101$
61. $x = 7.407$ **63.** $x < -3$ or $x > 3$ **67. a.** 23.4 yr   **b.** 11.9 yr   **c.** 9.0 yr   **d.** 23.3 yr; 12 yr; 9 yr   **69.** 6.25%   **71.** 2031
73. a. About 0.693   **b.** $\ln 2$ **c.** Yes   **75. a.** About 1.099   **b.** About 1.386   **77.** About every 7 hr, $T = 3 \ln 5/\ln 2$ **79. a.**
2039   **b.** 2036   **b.** 3500   **c.** 6000   **d.** 1800   **e.** $e^{-1/5} \approx 0.8$ **81.** $s/n = 2^{C/B} - 1$ **83.** No; 1/10   **85. a.** 1000 times greater
b. 1,000,000 times greater

Exercises 10.6 (page 635)

7. 4.06%   **9.** 8.33%   **11.** $6209.93   **13.** $6283.17   **15.** 9.20%   **17.** 6.17%   **19. a.** $257,107.67   **b.** $49,892.33   **c.**
$68,189.54   **21. a.** The 8% investment compounded quarterly.   **b.** $759.26   **c.** 8.24% and 8.06%   **d.** 3.71 yr   **e.** 3.75 yr   **23.**
No; 25.96%   **25. a.** 200   **b.** About 1/2 year   **c.** No   **d.** Yes; 1000   **27. a.** $P(t) = 0.002427e^{0.007378t}$ **b.** 2445   **c.** No; it is
too small. Exponential growth does not accurately describe population growth for the world over a long period of time.   **29.** 7.46%
b. About 18.6 hours   **31. a.** $y = 50,000e^{-0.102t}$ **b.** About 6.8 hours   **35.** About 4100 years old   **37.** About 1600 years   **39. a.**
3.8 g   **b.** Approximately 8600 years   **41. a.** $y = 25.0e^{-0.00497t}$ **b.** 139 days   **43.** 0.5%   **b.** 37%   **c.** 23 days   **d.** 46 days   **45.**
a. $y = 10e^{0.0095t}$ **b.** 42.7°C   **47.** About 30 minutes

Concept Check (page 641)

1. True **2.** False **3.** True **4.** True **5.** False **6.** False **7.** True **8.** False **9.** False **10.** False **11.** False
12. False **13.** False **14.** True **15.** False **16.** False **17.** True

Chapter 10 Review Exercises (page 642)

5. $(-3, 14), (-2, 5), (-1, 0), (0, -1), (1, 2), (2, 9), (3, 20)$; range: $\{-1, 0, 2, 5, 9, 14, 20\}$

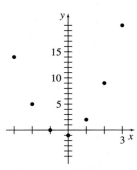

7. a. 17 **b.** 4 **c.** $5k^2 - 3$ **d.** $-9m^2 + 12m + 1$ **e.** $5x^2 + 10xh + 5h^2 - 3$ **f.** $-x^2 - 2xh - h^2 + 4x + 4h + 1$
g. $10x + 5h$ **h.** $-2x - h + 4$ **9.** $(-7, \infty)$ **11.** $(-\infty, 0) \cup (0, \infty)$

13.

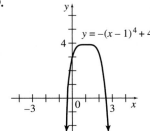

15.

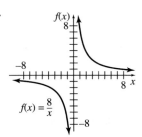

17.

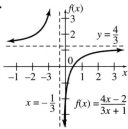

19.

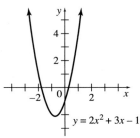

21.

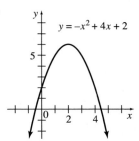

23.

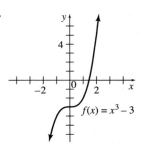

25.

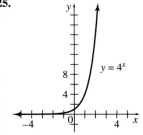

27.

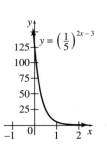

29.

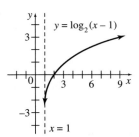

31.

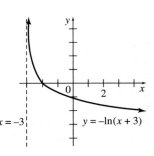

33. -5 **35.** -6 **37.** $\log_3 243 = 5$ **39.** $\ln 2.22554 = 0.8$ **41.** $2^5 = 32$ **43.** $e^{4.41763} = 82.9$ **45.** 4 **47.** 3/2
49. $\log_5(21k^4)$ **51.** $\log_3(y^4/x^2)$ **53.** $p = 1.581$ **55.** $m = -1.807$ **57.** $x = -3.305$ **59.** $m = 2.156$ **61.** $k = 2$
63. $p = 3/4$ **65. a.** $(-\infty, \infty)$ **b.** $(0, \infty)$ **c.** 1 **d.** None **e.** $y = 0$ **f.** Greater than 1 **g.** Between 0 and 1 **b.** $(-\infty, \infty)$
c. 1 **d.** None **e.** $x = 0$ is a vertical asymptote. **f.** Greater than one **g.** $0 < a < 1$
69. a. $28,000 **b.** $7000 **c.** $63,000 **d.** **e.** No. **71.** $921.95

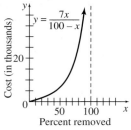

73. 70 quarters or 17.5 years; 111 quarters or 27.75 years **75.** $15,510.79 **77.** $17,901.90 **79.** 6.17% **81.** $1494.52 **83.**
$17,339.86 **85.** About 9.59% **87. a.** $n = 1500 - 10p$ **b.** $R = p(1500 - 10p)$ **c.** $50 \le p \le 150$
d. $R = (1500n - n^2)/10$ **e.** $0 \le n \le 1000$ **f.** $75 **g.** 750 **h.** $56,250

i.

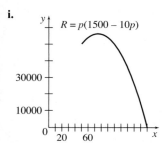

j. The revenue starts at $50,000 when the price is $50, rises to a maximum of $56,250 when the price is $75, and falls to 0 when the price is $150.

89. a.

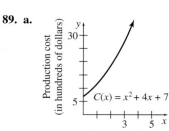

b. $2x + 5$ **c.** $A(x) = x + 4 + 7/x$ **d.** $1 - 7/[x(x+1)]$

91. The third day; 104.2°F
93. a.

b. $y = 846.061x^2 - 10,579.2x + 46,970.6$;
$y = -194.777x^3 + 3475.56x^2 - 19,558.4x + 51,879$;
$y = 8.89685x^4 - 354.921x^3 + 4374.14x^2$
$\qquad -21,159.8x + 52,263.4$

c.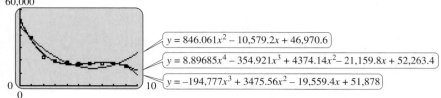

The cubic or quartic function

$y = 846.061x^2 - 10{,}579.2x + 46{,}970.6$

$y = 8.89685x^4 - 354.921x^3 + 4374.14x^2 - 21{,}159.8x + 52{,}263.4$

$y = -194{,}777x^3 + 3475.56x^2 - 19{,}559.4x + 51{,}878$

d. (Using answers from part b) quadratic: 32,973; cubic: −1969; quartic: 6635

95. 187.9 cm; 345 kg **97. a.** 8.441 billion; this is about 1.990 billion more than the estimate of 6.451 billion. **b.** 26.56 billion; 96.32 billion **99.** 0.25; 0.69 minutes **101. a.** $y = 100{,}000e^{-0.05t}$ **b.** 7.1 years **103. d.** $w = 0$ **105. a.** $P = 5.48D$; $P = 1.00D^{1.5}$; $P = 0.182D^2$ **b.** $P = 1.00D^{1.5}$ is the best fit. **c.** 248.3 yr **d.** $P = 1.00D^{1.5}$, the same as the function found in part b.

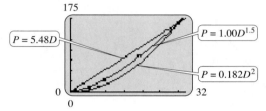

CHAPTER 11 The Derivative

Exercises 11.1 (page 665)

1. c **3.** b **5. a.** 3 **b.** 1 **7. a.** 0 **b.** Does not exist **9. a. i.** −1; **ii.** − 1/2 **iii.** Does not exist; **iv.** Does not exist **b. i.** −1/2 **ii.** − 1/2 **iii.** − 1/2 **iv.** − 1/2 **11.** 3 **15.** 4 **17.** 10 **19.** Does not exist **21.** −18 **23.** 1/3 **25.** 3 **27.** 512 **29.** 2/3 **31.** 6 **33.** 3/2 **35.** −5 **37.** −1/9 **39.** 1/10 **41.** $2x$ **43.** 3/7 **45.** 3/2 **47.** 0 **49.** ∞ (does not exist) **51.** −∞ (does not exist) **53.** 6 **54.** −4 **55.** 1.5 **56.** 1.2 **57. a.** Does not exist **b.** $x = -2$ **c.** If $x = a$ is a vertical asymptote for the graph of $f(x)$, then $\lim\limits_{x \to a} f(x)$ does not exist. **61. a.** 0 **b.** $y = 0$ **63. a.** −∞ (does not exist) **b.** $x = 0$ **67.** 5 **69.** 0.3333 or 1/3 **71. a.** 1.5 **73.** **a.** −2 **75. a.** 8 **81.** 0.0738; the average cost approaches $0.0738 per mile as the number of miles becomes very large. **83.** R/i **85. a.** 65 teeth **b.** 72 teeth **87.** 0; the concentration of the drug in the bloodstream approaches 0 as the number of hours after injection increases.

Exercises 11.2 (page 677)

1. $a = -1$: **a.** 1/2 **b.** 1/2 **c.** 1/2 **d.** $f(-1)$ does not exist. **e.** $f(-1)$ does not exist. **3.** $a = 1$: **a.** −2 **b.** −2 **c.** −2 **d.** 2 **e.** $f(1)$ does not equal the limit. **5.** $a = -5$: **a.** ∞ (does not exist) **b.** −∞ (does not exist) **c.** Limit does not exist. **d.** $f(-5)$ does not exist **e.** $f(-5)$ does not exist and the limit does not exist; $a = 0$: **a.** 0 **b.** 0 **c.** 0 **d.** $f(0)$ does not exist. **e.** $f(0)$ does not exist. **7.** $a = 0$, limit does not exist; $a = 2$, limit does not exist. **9.** $a = 2, 4$ **11.** Nowhere **13.** $a = -2$, limit does not exist. **15.** $a < 1$, limit does not exist. **17.** $a = 0$, −∞ (limit does not exist); $a = 1$, ∞ (limit does not exist).

19. a. 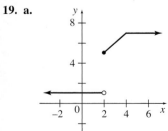 **b.** 2 **c.** 1, 5 **21. a.** 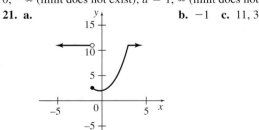 **b.** −1 **c.** 11, 3

23. a.

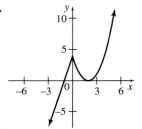

b. None

25. 2/3 **27.** 4 **31. a.** Discontinuous at $x = 1.2$ **33.** a **35. a.** $520 **b.** $600 **c.** $630 **d.** $1200 **e.** $1250 **f.** $150 and 400 **37. a.** $36 **b.** $36 **c.** $30 **d.** $25.71 **e.** $27 **f.** 36 **g.** 30 **h.** $t = 1, 2, 3, 4, 7, 8, 9, 10, 11$

39. a.

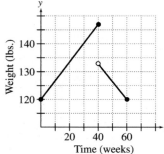

b. 40 weeks

Exercises 11.3 (page 691)

1. 6 **3.** −15 **5.** 1/3 0.4323 **9.** 17 **11.** 18 **13.** 5 **15.** 2 **17.** 2 **19.** 6.773 **21.** 1.121 **25. a.** Approximately −$6.75 billion **b.** Approximately $14.58 billion **c.** Approximately $0 billion **27. a.** −15,167 per month **b.** −24,500 per month **c.** −19,833 per month **d.** They are equal; no. **29. a.** $700 per item **b.** $500 per item **c.** $300 per item **d.** $1100 per item **31. a.** −25 boxes per dollar **b.** −20 boxes per dollar **c.** −30 boxes per dollar **d.** Demand is decreasing. Yes, a higher price usually reduces demand. **33.** All numbers are approximations. **a.** Replacement level by 2050: 75 million people per year; replacement level by 2030: 65 million people per year; replacement level by 2010: 55 million people per year. The projection for replacement-level fertility by 2010 predicts the smallest growth in world population. **b.** Replacement level by 2050: 10 million people per year; replacement level by 2030: 7.5 million people per year; replacement level by 2010: 7.5 million people per year. By 2050 the three projections show almost the same rate of change in world population.

35. a. 0.288 mm per wk **b.** 0.348 mm per wk **c.**

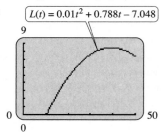

$L(t) = 0.01t^2 + 0.788t - 7.048$

37. a. 0.08 kg per day   **b.** 0.09 kg per day   **c.**

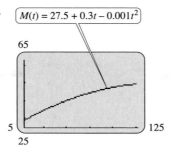

$$M(t) = 27.5 + 0.3t - 0.001t^2$$

39. a. −0.73 percent per year, −1.03 percent per year   **b.** 0.23 percent per year, −2.13 percent per year   **c.** −0.07 percent per year, −0.87 percent per year   **41. a.** 5 ft per sec   **b.** 2 ft per sec   **c.** 3 ft per sec   **d.** 5 ft per sec   **e. (i)** 2.5 ft per sec;   **(ii)** 2.5 ft per sec   **f. (i)** 4 ft per sec;   **(ii)** 4 ft per sec

Exercises 11.4 (page 712)

1. a. 0   **b.** 1   **c.** −1   **d.** Does not exist   **e.** m **3.** At $x = -2$ **5.** 2   **9.** 0   **11.** $-8x + 9$; 25; 9; −15   **13.** $-12/x^2$; −3; does not exist; −4/3   **15.** $1/(2\sqrt{x})$; does not exist; does not exist; $1/(2\sqrt{3})$ **17.** $6x^2$; 24; 0; 54   **19. a.** $y = 10x - 15$ **b.** $y = 8x - 9$ **21. a.** $y = -(1/2)x + 7/2$ **b.** $y = -(5/4)x + 5$ **23. a.** $y = (4/7)x + 48/7$ **b.** $y = (2/3)x + 6$ **25.** −5; −117; 35   **27.** 7.389; 8,886,111; 0.0498   **29.** 1/2; 1/128; 2/9   **31.** $1/(2\sqrt{2})$; 1/8; does not exist   **33.** 0   **35.** −3; −1; 0; 2; 3; 5   **37. a.** $(a, 0)$ and (b, c) **b.** $(0, b)$ **c.** $x = 0$ and $x = b$ **39. a.** Distance   **b.** Velocity   **41.** 56.66   **43.** −0.0158   **47. a.** $-4p - 4$ **b.** −44; demand is decreasing at a rate of about 44 items for each increase in price of $1.   **49. a.** $16 per table   **b.** $16   **c.** $15.998 (or $16)   **d.** The marginal revenue gives a good approximation of the actual revenue from the sale of the 1001st table.   **51.** Answers are in billions of dollars.   **a.** 961; 2526; 3806   **b.** 106; 189; −8; −318   **53.** 1000; the population is increasing at a rate of 1000 shellfish per time unit. 570; the population is increasing more slowly at 570 shellfish per time unit. 250; the population is increasing at a much slower rate of 250 shellfish per time unit.   **55. a.** 1690 m per sec   **b.** 4.84 days per m per sec; an increase in velocity from 1700 m per sec to 1701 m per sec indicates an approximate increase in the age of the cheese of 4.84 days.   **57. a.** 0.75, 3   **b.** 1033; the oven temperature is increasing at 1033° per hour.   **c.** 0; the oven temperature is not changing.   **d.** −1033; the oven temperature is decreasing at 1033° per hour.   **59.** About 0 mph per second for the hands and 640 mph per second for the bat. This represents the acceleration of the hands and the bat at the moment when the velocities are equal.

Exercises 11.5 (page 722)

3. $f:Y_2; f':Y_1$ **5.** $f:Y_1; f':Y_2$

7.

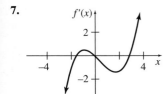

9.

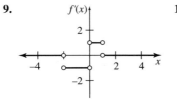

11.

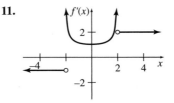

13.

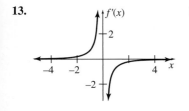

15.

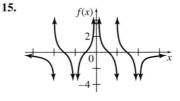

17.

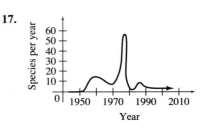

19.

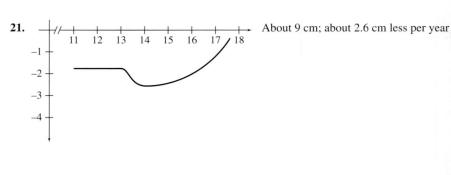

21. About 9 cm; about 2.6 cm less per year

Concept Check (page 727)

1. True   **2.** True   **3.** True   **4.** False   **5.** True   **6.** False   **7.** False   **8.** True   **9.** True   **10.** True   **11.** False   **12.** False

Chapter 11 Review Exercises (page 728)

5. a. 4   **b.** 4   **c.** 4   **d.** 4   **7. a.** ∞ **b.** $-\infty$ **c.** Does not exist   **d.** Does not exist   **9.** ∞ **11.** 19/9   **13.** 8   **15.** -13
17. 1/6   **19.** 2/5   **21.** 3/8   **23.** Discontinuous at x_2 and x_4 **25.** 0, does not exist, does not exist; $-1/3$, does not exist, does not
exist   **27.** -5, does not exist, does not exist   **29.** Continuous everywhere   **31. a.** 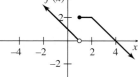   **b.** 1   **c.** 0, 2

33. 2   **35.** 126; 18   **37.** 9/77; 18/49   **39. a.** $y = 13x - 17$ **b.** $y = 7x - 5$ **41. a.** $y = -x + 9$ **b.** $y = -3x + 15$ **43.**
$8x + 3$ **45.** 1.332
47.

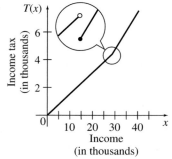

49. e

51. a. $R'(x) = 16 - 6x$ **b.** -44; an increase of \$100 spent on advertising when advertising expenditures are \$1000 will result in
the revenue decreasing by \$44.
53. a. \$3.40   **b.** \$3.28   **c.** \$3.18   **d.** \$3.15   **e.** \$10.15   **f.** \$15.15   **g.** $[0, \infty)$ **h.** No   **i.** $\overline{P}(x) = 15 + 25x$ **j.** $\overline{P}'(x) = 25$
k. No, the profit per pound never changes, no matter now many pounds are sold.
55. a. \$4395   **b.** \$4350   **c.** Does not exist   **d.**   **e.** 29,300

f. $A(x) = \begin{cases} 0.15 \text{ for } 0 \le x \le 29{,}300 \\ 0.27 - 3561/x \text{ for } x > 29{,}300 \end{cases}$ **g.** 0.15 **h.** 0.1485 **i.** Does not exist **j.** 0.27 **k.**

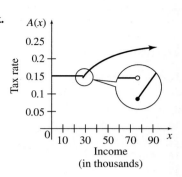

57. a. **b.** $[0.8, 5.2]$ **c.** 3 weeks; 500 cases **d.** $V'(t) = -2t + 6$ **e.** 0 **f.** $+; -$

$V(t) = -t^2 + 6t - 4$

59. a. **b.**

61. a. 1; the ball is rising 1 ft for each foot it travels horizontally. **b.** -2.7; the ball is dropping 2.7 ft for each foot it travels horizontally.

CHAPTER 12 **Calculating the Derivative**

Exercises 12.1 (page 750)

1. $dy/dx = 36x^2 - 16x + 7$ **3.** $dy/dx = 12x^3 - 18x^2 + (1/4)x$ **5.** $f'(x) = 21x^{2.5} - 5x^{-0.5}$ or $21x^{2.5} - 5/x^{0.5}$
7. $dy/dx = 4x^{-1/2} + (9/2)x^{-1/4}$ or $4/x^{1/2} + 9/(2x^{1/4})$ **9.** $g'(x) = -30x^{-6} + x^{-2}$ or $-30/x^6 + 1/x^2$
11. $dy/dx = -25x^{-6} + 12x^{-3} - 13x^{-2}$ or $-25/x^6 + 12/x^3 - 13/x^2$ **13.** $f'(t) = -14t^{-2} - 48t^{-5}$ or $-14/t^2 - 48/t^5$
15. $dy/dx = -18x^{-7} - 5x^{-6} + 14x^{-3}$ or $-18/x^7 - 5/x^6 + 14/x^3$ **17.** $h'(x) = -x^{-3/2}/2 + 21x^{-5/2}$ or $-1/(2x^{3/2}) + 21/x^{5/2}$
19. $dy/dx = 2x^{-4/3}/3$ or $2/(3x^{4/3})$ **21.** $g'(x) = (5/2)x^{1.5} - 2/\sqrt{x}$ **23.** $h'(x) = 6x^5 - 12x^3 + 6x$
27. $-(9/2)x^{-3/2} - 3x^{-5/2}$ or $-9/(2x^{3/2}) - 3/x^{5/2}$ **29.** $-25/3$ **31.** -28; $y = -28x + 34$ **33.** $25/6$ **35.** $(4/9, 20/9)$
37. $-5, 2$ **38.** $-3, -7$ **39.** $(4 \pm \sqrt{37})/3$ **41.** $(-1/2, -19/2)$ **43.** $(-2, -24)$ **45.** 7 **51. a.** 30 **b.** 0 **c.** -10
53. a. 100 **b.** 1 **55.** \$980 **57. a.** 17.9¢, 36.7¢ **b.** 0.767¢/yr, 1.12¢/yr
c. $C(t) = -1.790 \times 10^{-4}t^3 + 0.02947t^2 - 0.7105t + 3.291$, 0.894¢/yr, 0.784¢/yr **59. a.** 0.4824 **b.** 2.216 **61. a.** 1232.62
cm^3 **b.** 948.08 cm^3/yr **63.** $5.00l^{0.86}$ **65. a.** 3 minutes, 58.1 seconds **b.** 0.118 sec/m; at 100 meters, the fastest possible time
increases by 0.118 seconds for each additional meter. **c.** Yes **67. a.** 28 **b.** 26 pounds **c.** $-175{,}750/h^3$ **d.** -0.64; for a 125-
lb female with a height of 65 in. (5'5"), the BMI decreases by 0.64 for each additional inch of height. **69. a.** $v(t) = 36t - 13$
b. -13; 167; 347 **70. a.** $v(t) = 12t^2 + 16t + 1$ **b.** 1; 381; 1361 **71. a.** $v(t) = -9t^2 + 8t - 10$ **b.** -10; -195; -830
73. 0 ft/sec; -32 ft/sec **b.** 2 seconds **c.** 64 ft **75. a.** 35, 36 **b.** When $x = 5$, $dy_1/dx = 4.13$ and $dy_2/dx \approx 4.32$. These val-

ues are fairly close and represent the rate of change of four years for a dog for one year of a human, for a dog that is actually 5 years old.   **c.** $y = 4x + 16$

Exercises 12.2 (page 761)

1. $dy/dx = 18x^2 - 6x + 4$ **2.** $dy/dx = 60x^2 + 30x - 4$ **3.** $dy/dx = 8x - 20$ **4.** $dy/dx = 98x - 84$
5. $k'(t) = 4t^3 - 4t$ **6.** $g'(t) = 36t^3 + 24t$ **7.** $dy/dx = (3/2)x^{1/2} + (1/2)x^{-1/2} + 2$ or $3x^{1/2}/2 + 1/(2x^{1/2}) + 2$
8. $dy/dx = 3x^{1/2} - 3x^{-1/2}/2 - 2$ or $3x^{1/2} - 3/(2x^{1/2}) - 2$ **9.** $p'(y) = -8y^{-5} + 15y^{-6} + 30y^{-7}$
10. $q'(x) = -9x^{-4} + 12x^{-5} - 24x^{-7} + 28x^{-8}$ **11.** $f'(x) = 57/(3x + 10)^2$ **12.** $f'(x) = 101/(7x + 3)^2$
13. $dy/dx = -17/(4 + t)^2$ **14.** $dy/dx = 2/(1 - t)^2$ **15.** $dy/dx = (x^2 - 2x - 1)/(x - 1)^2$
16. $dy/dx = (x^2 + 6x - 12)/(x + 3)^2$ **17.** $f'(t) = 2t/(t^2 + 3)^2$ **18.** $dy/dx = (-32x^2 + 10x - 40)/(4x^2 - 5)^2$
19. $g'(x) = (4x^2 + 2x - 12)/(x^2 + 3)^2$ **20.** $k'(x) = (-7x^2 - 14)/(x^2 - 2)^2$
21. $p'(t) = [-\sqrt{t}/2 - 1/(2\sqrt{t})]/(t - 1)^2$ or $(-t - 1)/[2\sqrt{t}(t - 1)^2]$ **22.** $r'(t) = [-\sqrt{t} + 3/(2\sqrt{t})]/(2t + 3)^2$ or
$(-2t + 3)/[2\sqrt{t}(2t + 3)^2]$ **23.** $dy/dx = (5\sqrt{x}/2 - 3/\sqrt{x})/x$ or $(5x - 6)/(2x\sqrt{x})$
24. $h'(z) = (-z^{4.4} + 11z^{1.2})/(z^{3.2} + 5)^2$ **25.** $g'(y) = (-1.1y^{2.9} - 2.5y^{1.5} + 2.8y^{0.4})/(y^{2.5} + 2)^2$
26. $f'(x) = (60x^3 + 57x^2 - 24x + 13)/(5x + 4)^2$ **27.** $g'(x) = (120x^3 - 186x^2 - 56x - 141)/(6x - 7)^2$ **28.** 77
29. $-13/16$ **30.** In the first step, the numerator should be $(x^2 - 1)2 - (2x + 5)(2x)$.   **31.** In the first step, the denominator,
$(x^3)^2 = x^6$, was omitted.   **32.** $y = -2x + 9$ **33. a.** $f'(x) = (7x^3 - 4)/x^{5/3}$ **b.** $f'(x) = 7x^{4/3} - 4x^{-5/3}$
34. $f'(x) = kg'(x)$ **37.** $0, -1.307$, and 1.307   **38.** $x = -0.828, 4.828$ **39. a.** \$22.86 per unit   **b.** \$12.92 per unit
c. $(3x + 2)/(x^2 + 4x)$ per unit   **d.** $\overline{C}'(x) = (-3x^2 - 4x - 8)/(x^2 + 4x)^2$ **40. a.** \$2.24 per book   **b.** \$1.39 per book
c. $(5x - 6)/(2x^2 + 3x)$ per book   **d.** $\overline{P}'(x) = (-10x^2 + 24x + 18)/(2x^2 + 3x)^2$
41. a. $M'(d) = 2000d/(3d^2 + 10)^2$ **b.** 8.3; the new employee can assemble about 8.3 additional bicycles per day after 2 days of
training. 1.4; the new employee can assemble about 1.4 additional bicycles per day after 5 days of training.
44. \$700/month   **45.** Increasing at a rate of \$0.03552 per gallon per month   **46. a.** $s'(x) = m/(m + nx)^2$
b. $1/2560 \approx 0.000391$ mm per ml   **47. a.** $AK/(A + x)^2$ **b.** $K/(4A)$ **48. a.** $N'(t) = 9t^2 - 120t + 300$ **b.**
-84 million per hr   **c.** 69 million per hr   **d.** The population first declines, and then increases.   **49. a.** 8.57 min   **b.** 16.36 min
c. 6.12 min²/kcal; 2.48 min²/kcal   **50. a.** $dW/dH = (H^2 - 1.86H - 17.7351)/(H - 0.93)^2$ **b.** 5.24 m   **c.** Crows apply optimal foraging techniques.   **51. a.** -100 **b.** -0.01 **52. a.** 0.1173   **b.** 2.625

Exercises 12.3 (page 771)

1. 1767   **2.** 6919   **3.** 131   **4.** 1083   **5.** $320k^2 + 224k + 39$ **6.** $1000z^2 - 80z + 3$ **7.** $(6x + 55)/8; (3x + 164)/4$
8. $(-8x - 115)/5; (-8x + 29)/5$ **9.** $1/x^2; 1/x^2$ **10.** $2/(2 - x)^4; 2 - 2/x^4$ **11.** $\sqrt{8x^2 - 4}; 8x + 10$
12. $36x + 72 - 22\sqrt{x + 2}; 2\sqrt{9x^2 - 11x + 2}$ **13.** $\sqrt{(x - 1)/x}; -1/\sqrt{x + 1}$ **14.** $8\sqrt{3 - x}/(3 - x); \sqrt{3x^2 - 8x}/x$
16. If $f(x) = x^{2/3}$ and $g(x) = 3x^2 - 7$, then $y = f[g(x)]$.   **17.** If $f(x) = x^{3/5}$ and $g(x) = 5 - x^2$, then $y = f[g(x)]$.
18. If $f(x) = \sqrt{x}$ and $g(x) = 9 - 4x$, then $y = f[g(x)]$.   **19.** If $f(x) = -\sqrt{x}$ and $g(x) = 13 + 7x$, then $y = f[g(x)]$.
20. If $f(x) = x^2 + x + 5$ and $g(x) = x^{1/2} - 3$, then $y = f[g(x)]$.   **21.** If $f(x) = x^{1/3} - 2x^{2/3} + 7$ and $g(x) = x^2 + 5x$, then
$y = f[g(x)]$.   **22.** $dy/dx = 5(2x^3 + 9x)^4 (6x^2 + 9)$ **23.** $dy/dx = 4(8x^4 - 5x^2 + 1)^3(32x^3 - 10x)$
24. $f'(x) = 336x^3 (3x^4 + 2)^{-5}$ **25.** $k'(x) = 288x(12x^2 + 5)^{-7}$ **26.** $s'(t) = 144t^3 (2t^4 + 5)^{1/2}$
27. $s'(t) = (1215/2)t^2(3t^3 - 8)^{1/2}$ **28.** $f'(t) = 32t/\sqrt{4t^2 + 7}$ **29.** $g'(t) = -63t^2/(2\sqrt{7t^3 - 1})$
30. $r'(t) = 4(2t^5 + 3)^3 (42t^5 + 3)$ **31.** $m'(t) = -6(5t^4 - 1)^3(85t^4 - 1)$ **32.** $dy/dx = x(x^2 - 1)^3 (11x^3 - 3x + 16)$
33. $dy/dx = 3x^2(3x^4 + 1)^3(19x^4 + 64x + 1)$ **34.** $p'(z) = (6z + 1)^{1/3}(14z + 1)$ **35.** $q'(y) = 2y(y^2 + 1)^{1/4}(9y^2 + 4)$
36. $dy/dx = -30x/(3x^2 - 4)^6$ **37.** $dy/dx = 60x^2/(2x^3 + 1)^3$ **38.** $p'(t) = [2(2t + 3)^2 (4t^2 - 12t - 3)]/(4t^2 - 1)^2$
39. $r'(t) = 2(5t - 6)^3(15t^2 + 18t + 40)/(3t^2 + 4)^2$ **40.** $dy/dx = (-30x^4 - 132x^3 + 4x + 8)/(3x^3 + 2)^5$
41. $dy/dx = (-18x^2 + 2x + 1)/(2x - 1)^6$ **43. a.** -2 **b.** $-24/7$ **44. a.** $-18/7$ **b.** -5
45. $y = (3/5)x + 16/5$ **46.** $y = x + 3$ **47.** $y = x$ **48.** $y = 40x - 72$ **49.** 1, 3   **50.** $\pm 2/\sqrt{7}$
53. $D(c) = (-c^2 + 10c + 12,475)/25$ **54. a.** \$148.78   **b.** \$187.29   **c.** \$214.34   **d.** $\overline{R}(x) = 24(x^2 + x)^{2/3}/x$
e. $\overline{R}'(x) = 8(x - 1)/[x(x^2 + x)^{1/3}]$ **55. a.** \$101.22   **b.** \$111.86   **c.** \$117.59   **56.** $-30/(p^2 + 1)^{3/2}$ **57. a.** $-\$10,500$
b. $-\$4570.64$ **58. a.** $R(q) = (30,000q - 2q^3)/3$ **b.** $P(q) = 8000q - 2q^3/3 - 3500$ **c.** $dP/dq = 8000 - 2q^2$

d. −$7000   **59.** $P[f(a)] = 18a^2 + 24a + 9$ **61. a.** $A[r(t)] = A(t) = 4\pi t^2$; this function gives the area of the pollution in terms of the time since the pollutants were first emitted.   **b.** 32π; at 12 P.M. the area of pollution is changing at the rate of 32π mi^2 per hour   **63. a.** −0.5   **b.** −1/54 ≈ −0.02   **c.** −1/128 ≈ −0.008   **d.** Always decreasing; the derivative is negative for all $t \geq 0$.
65. a. 34 minutes   **b.** −(108/17)π mm^3 per minute, −(72/17)π mm^2 per minute

Exercises 12.4 (page 781)

1. $dy/dx = 4e^{4x}$ **3.** $dy/dx = -24e^{3x}$ **5.** $dy/dx = -32e^{2x+1}$ **7.** $dy/dx = 2xe^{x^2}$ **9.** $dy/dx = 12xe^{2x^2}$
11. $dy/dx = 16xe^{2x^2-4}$ **13.** $dy/dx = xe^x + e^x = e^x(x+1)$ **15.** $dy/dx = 2(x+3)(2x+7)e^{4x}$
17. $dy/dx = (2xe^x - x^2e^x)/e^{2x} = x(2-x)/e^x$ **19.** $dy/dx = [x(e^x - e^{-x}) - (e^x + e^{-x})]/x^2$
21. $dp/dx = 8000e^{-0.2t}/(9 + 4e^{-0.2t})^2$ **23.** $f'(z) = 4(2z + e^{-z^2})(1 - ze^{-z^2})$ **25.** $dy/dx = -5(\ln 4)\, 4^{-5x+2}$
27. $dy/dx = -6x(10^{3x^2-4})\ln 10$ **29.** $ds/dt = (5\ln 2)2^{\sqrt{t-2}}/(2\sqrt{t-2})$
31. $dy/dt = [(2t^3 + t^2)e^{2t} + (2t - t^2)e^{5t}]/(t + e^{3t})^2$ **33.** $f'(x) = x(4 - x^3)e^{x^2/(x^3+2)}/(x^3 + 2)^2$

35.

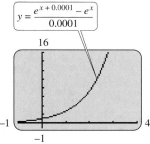

$y = \dfrac{e^{x+0.0001} - e^x}{0.0001}$

37. a. 20   **b.** 6   **c.** The rate of change of sales is decreasing.   **d.** No, but it gets closer and closer to 0 as t increases.   **39. a.** 3.07   **b.** −1.93   **c.** Public awareness increased at first and then decreased.   **41. a.** 100%   **b.** 94%   **c.** 89%   **d.** 83%   **e.** −3.045
f. −2.865   **g.** The percent of these cars on the road is decreasing, but at a slower rate as they age.   **43. a.** $G(t) = 10.3/(1 + 13.71e^{-0.3127t})$ **b.** 2.66 million, 0.617 million/year
c. 6.43 million, 0.755 million/year   **d.** 9.15 million, 0.320 million/year   **e.** It increases for a while and then gradually decreases to 0.   **45 a.** 380,000 people/yr   **b.** 463,000 people/yr   **47. a.** $5200/(1 + 12e^{-0.52t})$ **b.** 639, 292   **c.** 2081, 649   **d.** 4877, 167
e. It increases for a while and then gradually decreases to 0.   **49. a.** 3.857 cm^3
b. 0.973 cm   **c.** 18 years   **d.** 1100 cm^3 **e.** 0.282; at 240 months old, the tumor is increasing in volume at the instantaneous rate of 0.282 cm^3/month.   **51. a.** 0.589, no
b. 0.690, yes   **c.** 0.001

53. a. 2974.15 grams   **b.** 3102 grams   **c.** 124 days
d. 2.75 g/day   **e.** 3200

Growth is initially rapid, then tapers off.

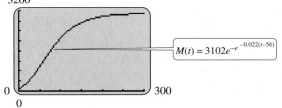

$M(t) = 3102e^{-e^{-0.022(t-56)}}$

f.

Day	Weight	Rate
50	991	24.88
100	2122	17.73
150	2734	7.60
200	2974	2.75
250	3059	0.94
300	3088	0.32

55. a. 509.7 kg, 498.4 kg   **b.** 1239 days, 1095 days   **c.** 0.22 kg/day, 0.22 kg/day
d. The growth patterns of the two functions are very similar.   525

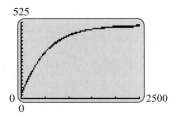

e. The graphs of the rates of change of the two functions are also very similar.   1

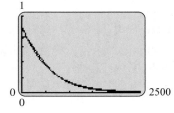

57. a. $G(t) = 1/(1 + 270e^{-3.5t})$ **b.** 0.109, 0.341 per century   **c.** 0.802, 0.555 per century   **d.** 0.993, 0.0256 per century
e. It increases for a while and then gradually decreases to 0.   **59. a.** 46,500,000   **b.** 0.967 million/year   **61. a.** $(V/R)e^{-t/RC}$
b. 1.35×10^{-7} amps   **63.** 3.90 degrees/hr

Exercises 12.5 (page 791)

1. $dy/dx = 1/x$ **3.** $dy/dx = -3/(8 - 3x)$ or $3/(3x - 8)$ **5.** $dy/dx = (8x - 9)/(4x^2 - 9x)$
9. $dy/dx = 3(2x^2 + 5)/[x(x^2 + 5)]$ **11.** $dy/dx = -15x/(3x + 2) - 5\ln(3x + 2)$ **13.** $ds/dt = t + 2t \ln|t|$
15. $dy/dx = [2x - 4(x + 3)\ln(x + 3)]/[x^3(x + 3)]$ **17.** $dy/dx = (4x + 7 - 4x \ln x)/[x(4x + 7)^2]$
19. $dy/dx = (6x \ln x - 3x)/(\ln x)^2$ **21.** $dy/dx = 4(\ln|x + 1|)^3/(x + 1)$ **23.** $dy/dx = 1/(x \ln x)$ **25.** $dy/dx = e^{x^2}/x + 2xe^{x^2} \ln x$
27. $dy/dx = (xe^x \ln x - e^x)/[x(\ln x)^2]$ **29.** $g'(z) = 3(e^{2z} + \ln z)^2(2ze^{2z} + 1)/z$ **31.** $dy/dx = 4/[(\ln 10)(4x - 3)]$
33. $dy/dx = 1/(x \ln 10)$ **35.** $dy/dx = 2/[(\ln 7)(4x - 3)]$ **37.** $dy/dx = 5(4x - 1)/[(2 \ln 2)(2x^2 - x)]$
39. $dz/dy = 10^y/[(\ln 10)y] + (\log y)(\ln 10)10^y$ **41.** $f'(x) = e^{\sqrt{x}}(\sqrt{x} + 2)/[2(xe^{\sqrt{x}} + 2)]$
43. $f'(t) = [(6t^2 + 3t^{1/2}) \ln(2t^{3/2} + 1) - 6t^2]/\{(2t^{3/2} + 1)[\ln(2t^{3/2} + 1)]^2\}$
47.

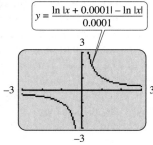

$$y = \frac{\ln |x + 0.0001| - \ln |x|}{0.0001}$$

53. $h(x) = x^x(1 + \ln x)$ **55.** 59 or 60 items are manufactured. **57. a.** 100   **b.** $P(q) = 50q/(\ln q) - 100$ **c.** $12.48
59. a. 2590 cm^2 **b.** 0.46 g/cm^2; when the infant weighs 4000 g, it is gaining 0.46 square centimeters per gram of weight increase.
c.

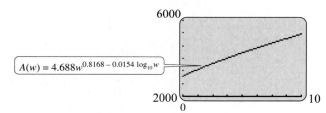

$$A(w) = 4.688w^{0.8168 - 0.0154 \log_{10} w}$$

61. a. 4 kJ/day   **b.** 1.3×10^{-5}; when a fawn is 25 kg in size, the rate of change of the energy expenditure of the fawn is about 1.3×10^{-5} kJ/day per gram.   **c.**

$$F(x) = 0.774 + 0.727 \log x$$

63. a. About 3   **b.** About 6   **c.** 0.22   **65. a.** 1.567×10^{11} kWh   **b.** 63.4 months   **c.** 4.14×10^{-6} **d.** dM/dE decreases and approaches zero.

Concept Check (page 796)

1. False   **2.** True   **3.** False   **4.** True   **5.** False   **6.** False   **7.** False   **8.** True   **9.** True   **10.** False

Chapter 12 Review Exercises (page 796)

1. $dy/dx = 15x^2 - 14x - 9$ **3.** $dy/dx = 24x^{5/3}$ **5.** $f'(x) = -12x^{-5} + 3x^{-1/2}$ or $-12/x^5 + 3/x^{1/2}$ **7.** $k'(x) = 21/(4x + 7)^2$
9. $dy/dx = (x^2 - 2x)/(x - 1)^2$ **11.** $f'(x) = 24x(3x^2 - 2)^3$ **13.** $dy/dx = 7t^6/(2t^7 - 5)^{1/2}$ **15.**
$dy/dx = 3(2x + 1)^2(8x + 1)$ **17.** $r'(t) = (-15t^2 + 52t - 7)/(3t + 1)^4$ **19.** $p'(t) = t(t^2 + 1)^{3/2}(7t^2 + 2)$ **21.**
$dy/dx = -12e^{2x}$ **23.** $dy/dx = -6x^2e^{-2x^3}$
25. $dy/dx = 10xe^{2x} + 5e^{2x} = 5e^{2x}(2x + 1)$ **27.** $dy/dx = 2x/(2 + x^2)$ **29.** $dy/dx = (x - 3 - x \ln |3x|)/[x(x - 3)^2]$
31. $dy/dx = [e^x(x + 1)(x^2 - 1) \ln(x^2 - 1) - 2x^2e^x]/[(x^2 - 1)[\ln(x^2 - 1)]^2]$ **33.** $ds/dt = 2(t^2 + e^t)(2t + e^t)$
35. $dy/dx = -6x(\ln 10) \cdot 10^{-x^2}$ **37.** $g'(z) = (3z^2 + 1)/[(\ln 2)(z^3 + z + 1)]$
39. $f'(x) = (x + 1)e^{3x}/(xe^x + 1) + 2e^{2x} \ln(xe^x + 1)$
41. a. $-3/2$ **b.** $-24/11$ **45.** $-2; y = -2x + 9$ **47.** $-5/9; y = -(5/9)x + 16/9$ **49.** $-4/5; y = -(4/5)x - 13/5$
51. $2e; y = 2ex - e$ **53.** $2; y = 2x - e$ **57.** $\overline{C}'(x) = (-x - 2)/[2x^2(x + 1)^{1/2}]$ **59.** $\overline{C}'(x) = (x^2 + 3)^2(5x^2 - 3)/x^2$
61. $\overline{C}'(x) = [e^{-x}(x + 1) - 10]/x^2$ **63. a.** 22; sales will increase by $22 million when $1000 more is spent on research.   **b.**
19.5; sales will increase by $19.5 million when $1000 more is spent on research.   **c.** 18; sales will increase by $18 million when
$1000 more is spent on research.   **d.** As more is spent on research, the increase in sales is decreasing.   **65. a.** -2.201; costs will
decrease by $2201 for the next $100 spent on training.   **b.** -0.564; costs will decrease by $564 for the next $100 spent on training.
c. Decreasing   **67.** $218.65. The balance increases by roughly $218.65 for every 1% increase in the interest rate when the rate is
5%.
69. $156/mo/yr   **71. a.** $y = 2.458 \times 10^{-5}t^3 - 6.767 \times 10^{-4}t^2 - 0.02561t +$
$2.031, y = -1.314 \times 10^{-6}t^4 + 3.363 \times 10^{-4}t^3 - 0.02565t^2 + 0.7410t - 5.070$ **b.** $0.51/yr, $0.47/yr
73. a. $G(t) = 30,000/(1 + 14e^{-0.15t})$ **b.** 4483; 572   **75. a.** 3493.76 grams   **b.** 3583 grams   **c.** 84 days   **d.** 1.76 g/day
e. 3600

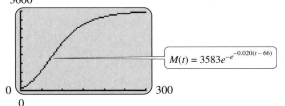

$M(t) = 3583e^{-e^{-0.020(t - 66)}}$

Growth is initially rapid, then tapers off.

f.

Day	Weight	Rate
50	904	24.90
100	2159	21.87
150	2974	11.08
200	3346	4.59
250	3494	1.76
300	3550	0.66

77. a. -5 ft/sec   **b.** -1.7 ft/sec   **79. a.** 169; 167   **b.** 136 words   **c.** -30; in the year 2050 the number of words in use will be
decreasing by 30 words per millenium.

CHAPTER 13   Graphs and the Derivative

Exercises 13.1 (page 815)

1. a. $(1, \infty)$ **b.** $(-\infty, 1)$ **3. a.** $(-\infty, -2)$ **b.** $(-2, \infty)$ **5. a.** $(-\infty, -4), -2, \infty$ **b.** $(-4, -2)$ **7. a.** $(-7, -4)$,
$(-2, \infty)$ **b.** $(-\infty, -7), (-4, -2)$ **9. a.** $(-\infty, -1), (3, \infty)$ **b.** $(-1, 3)$ **11. a.** $(-\infty, -8), (-6, -2.5), (-1.5, \infty)$
b. $(-8, -6), (-2.5, -1.5)$ **13. a.** $17/12$ **b.** $(-\infty, 17/12)$ **c.** $(17/12, \infty)$ **15. a.** $-3, 4$ **b.** $(-\infty, -3), (4, \infty)$ **c.**
$(-3, 4)$ **17. a.** $-3/2, 4$ **b.** $(-\infty, -3/2), (4, \infty)$ **c.** $(-3/2, 4)$ **19. a.** $-2, -1, 0$ **b.** $(-2, -1), (0, \infty)$ **c.** $(-\infty, -2)$,
$(-1, 0)$ **21. a.** None   **b.** None   **c.** $(-\infty, \infty)$ **23. a.** None   **b.** None   **c.** $(-\infty, -1), (-1, \infty)$ **25. a.** 0   **b.** $(0, \infty)$ **c.**
$(-\infty, 0)$
27. a. 0   **b.** $(0, \infty)$ **c.** $(-\infty, 0)$ **29. a.** 7   **b.** $(7, \infty)$ **c.** $(3, 7)$ **31. a.** $1/3$ **b.** $(-\infty, 1/3)$ **c.** $(1/3, \infty)$ **33. a.**
$0, 2/\ln 2$ **b.** $(0, 2/\ln 2)$ **c.** $(-\infty, 0), (2/\ln 2, \infty)$ **35. a.** $0, 2/5$ **b.** $(0, 2/5)$ **c.** $(-\infty, 0), (2/5, \infty)$ **39.** Vertex:
$(-b/(2a), (4ac - b^2)/(4a))$; increasing on $(-\infty, -b/(2a))$, decreasing on $(-b/(2a), \infty)$ **41.** On $(0, \infty)$; nowhere; nowhere
43. a. About $(567, \infty)$ **b.** About $(0, 567)$ **45. a.** Nowhere   **b.** $(0, \infty)$ **47.** $(0, 2200)$ **49. a.** Yes   **b.** April to July; July to
November; January to April and November to December   **c.** January to April and November to December   **51. a.** $(0, 1.85)$
b. $(1.85, 5)$ **53. a.** $(0, 1)$ **b.** $(1, \infty)$ **55. a.** $F'(t) = 175.9e^{-t/1.3}(1 - 0.769t)$ **b.** $(0, 1.3); (1.3, \infty)$ **57.** $(-\infty, 0); (0, \infty)$
59. a. $(1500, 6250)$ **b.** $(6250, 7200)$ **c.** $(1500, 2500)$ and $(3500, 4400)$ **d.** $(3000, 3500)$ and $(6000, 7200)$

Exercises 13.2 (page 829)

1. Relative minimum of -4 at 1 **3.** Relative maximum of 3 at -2 **5.** Relative maximum of 3 at -4; relative minimum of 1 at -2 **7.** Relative maximum of 3 at -4; relative minimum of -2 at -7 and -2 **9.** Relative maximum at -1; relative minimum at 3 **11.** Relative maxima at -8 and -2.5; relative minimum at -6 and -1.5 **13.** Relative minimum of 8 at 5 **15.** Relative maximum of -8 at -3; relative minimum of -12 at -1 **17.** Relative maximum of $827/96$ at $-1/4$; relative minimum of $-377/6$ at -5 **19.** Relative maximum of -4 at 0; relative minimum of -85 at 3 and -3 **21.** Relative maximum of 3 at $-8/3$ **23.** Relative maximum of 1 at -1; relative minimum of 0 at 0 **25.** No relative extrema **27.** Relative maximum of 0 at 1; relative minimum of 8 at 5 **29.** Relative maximum of -2.46 at -2; relative minimum of -3 at 0 **31.** No relative extrema **33.** Relative minimum of $e \ln 2$ at $1/\ln 2$ **35.** $(3, 13)$ **37.** Relative maximum of 6.211 at 0.085; relative minimum of -57.61 at 2.161 **39.** Relative minimum at $x = 5$

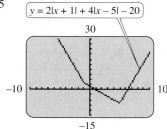

$$y = 2|x + 1| + 4|x - 5| - 20$$

41. a. 13 **b.** $\$44$ **c.** $\$258$ **43. a.** 100 **b.** $\$14.72$ **c.** $\$635.76$ **45.** Relative maximum of $23{,}410$ megawatts at midnight; relative minimum of $19{,}767$ megawatts at $3{:}30$ A.M.; relative maximum of $30{,}685$ at $3{:}00$ P.M.; relative minimum of $28{,}092$ at $6{:}00$ P.M. **47.** $q = 10$; $p \approx \$73.58$ **49.** 120 units **51. a.** 9.68 weeks; 8.54 kg **b.** b/c; $a(b/c)^b e^{-b}$ **53.** 1.3 hr **55.** 10 minutes

Exercises 13.3 (page 843)

1. $f''(x) = 30x - 14$; -14; 46 **3.** $f''(x) = 48x^2 - 18x - 4$; -4; 152 **5.** $f''(x) = 6$; 6; 6 **7.** $f''(x) = 2/(1 + x)^3$; 2; $2/27$ **9.** $f''(x) = 4/(x^2 + 4)^{3/2}$; $1/2$; $1/(4\sqrt{2})$ **11.** $f''(x) = -6x^{-5/4}$ or $-6/x^{5/4}$; $f''(0)$ does not exist; $-3/2^{1/4}$ **13.** $f''(x) = 20x^2 e^{-x^2} - 10e^{-x^2}$; -10; $70e^{-4} \approx 1.282$ **15.** $f''(x) = (-3 + 2 \ln x)/(4x^3)$; does not exist; -0.050 **17.** $f'''(x) = 168x + 36$; $f^{(4)}(x) = 168$ **19.** $f'''(x) = 300x^2 - 72x + 12$; $f^{(4)}(x) = 600x - 72$ **21.** $f'''(x) = 18(x + 2)^{-4}$ or $18/(x + 2)^4$; $f^{(4)}(x) = -72(x + 2)^{-5}$ or $-72/(x + 2)^5$ **23.** $f'''(x) = -36(x - 2)^{-4}$ or $-36/(x - 2)^4$; $f^{(4)}(x) = 144(x - 2)^{-5}$ or $144/(x - 2)^5$ **25. a.** $f'(x) = 1/x$; $f''(x) = -1/x^2$; $f'''(x) = 2/x^3$; $f^{(4)}(x) = -6/x^4$; $f^{(5)}(x) = 24/x^5$ **b.** $f^{(n)}(x) = (-1)^{n-1}[1 \cdot 2 \cdot 3 \cdots (n - 1)]/x^n$ or, using factorial notation, $f^{(n)}(x) = (-1)^{n-1}(n - 1)!/x^n$ **27.** Concave upward on $(2, \infty)$; concave downward on $(-\infty, 2)$; inflection point at $(2, 3)$ **29.** Concave upward on $(-\infty, -1)$ and $(8, \infty)$; concave downward on $(-1, 8)$; inflection points at $(-1, 7)$ and $(8, 6)$ **31.** Concave upward on $(2, \infty)$; concave downward on $(-\infty, 2)$; no inflection points **33.** Always concave upward; no inflection points **35.** Concave upward on $(-\infty, 3/2)$; concave downward on $(3/2, \infty)$; inflection point at $(3/2, 525/2)$ **37.** Concave upward on $(5, \infty)$; concave downward on $(-\infty, 5)$; no inflection points **39.** Concave upward on $(-10/3, \infty)$; concave downward on $(-\infty, -10/3)$; inflection point at $(-10/3, -250/27)$ **41.** Never concave upward; always concave downward; no inflection points **43.** Concave upward on $(-\infty, 0)$ and $(1, \infty)$; concave downward on $(0, 1)$; inflection points at $(0, 0)$ and $(1, -3)$ **45.** Concave upward on $(-1, 1)$; concave downward on $(-\infty, -1)$ and $(1, \infty)$; inflection points at $(-1, \ln 2)$ and $(1, \ln 2)$ **47.** Concave upward on $(-\infty, -e^{-3/2})$ and $(e^{-3/2}, \infty)$; concave downward on $(-e^{-3/2}, 0)$ and $(0, e^{-3/2})$; inflection points at $(-e^{-3/2}, -3e^{-3}/(2 \ln 10))$ and $(e^{-3/2}, -3e^{-3}/(2 \ln 10))$ **49.** Concave upward on $(-\infty, 0)$ and $(4, \infty)$; concave downward on $(0, 4)$; inflection points at 0 and 4 **51.** Concave upward on $(-7, 3)$ and $(12, \infty)$; concave downward on $(-\infty, -7)$ and $(3, 12)$; inflection points at -7, 3, and 12 **53.** Choose $f(x) = x^k$ where $1 < k < 2$. For example, $f(x) = x^{4/3}$ has a relative minimum at $x = 0$, and $f(x) = x^{5/3}$ has an inflection point at $x = 0$. **55. a.** Close to 0 **b.** Close to 1 **57.** Relative maximum at -5. **59.** Relative maximum at 0; relative minimum at $2/3$. **61.** Relative minimum at -3 **63.** Relative maximum at $-4/7$; relative minimum at 0 **67. a.** Minimum at 1; maximum at 0.6 **b.** Increasing on $(-\infty, 0.6)$ and $(1, \infty)$ and decreasing on $(0.6, 1)$ **c.** 0, about 0.36, and about 0.85 **d.** Concave upward on $(0, 0.36)$ and $(0.85, \infty)$; concave downward on $-\infty, 0$ and $(0.36, 0.85)$ **69. a.** Minimum at about 0.5671 **b.** Increasing on about $(0.5671, \infty)$; decreasing on about $(0, 0.5671)$ **c.** About 0.2315 **d.** Concave upward on about $(0.2315, \infty)$; concave downward on about $(0, 0.2315)$ **71.** 1.409; mid 1999 **73.** $(22, 6517.9)$ **75.** $(2.06, 20.8)$ **79. a.** 4 hours **b.** 1160 million **80.** $c(t)$ is increasing and concave downward, $c'(t) > 0$, $c''(t) < 0$. **81. a.** After 2 hours **b.** $3/4\%$ **83.** $(38.92, 5000)$ **85.** Inflection point at $t = (\ln c)/k \approx 2.96$ years; this signifies the time when the rate of growth begins to slow down, since L changes from concave up to concave down at this inflection point. **87.** Always concave down **89.** $f(t)$ is decreasing and concave up; $f'(t) < 0$, $f''(t) > 0$. **91. a.** -96 ft/sec **b.** -160 ft/sec **c.** -256 ft/sec **d.** -32 ft/sec^2 **93.** $v(t) = 256 - 32t$; $a(t) = -32$; 1024 ft; 16 seconds after being thrown **95.** $t = 6$

Exercises 13.4 (page 856)

1. 0   **3.**

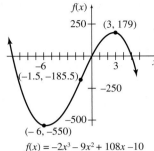

$$f(x) = -2x^3 - 9x^2 + 108x - 10$$

5.

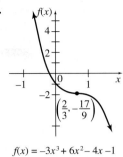

$$f(x) = -3x^3 + 6x^2 - 4x - 1$$

7.

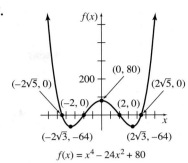

$$f(x) = x^4 - 24x^2 + 80$$

9.

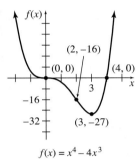

$$f(x) = x^4 - 4x^3$$

11.

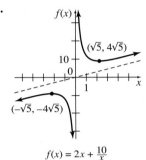

$$f(x) = 2x + \frac{10}{x}$$

13.

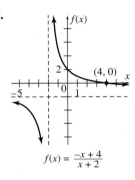

$$f(x) = \frac{-x + 4}{x + 2}$$

15.

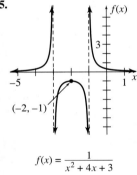

$$f(x) = \frac{1}{x^2 + 4x + 3}$$

17.

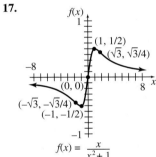

$$f(x) = \frac{x}{x^2 + 1}$$

19.

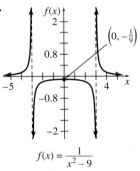

$$f(x) = \frac{1}{x^2 - 9}$$

21.

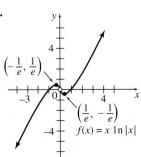

$$f(x) = x \ln |x|$$

23.

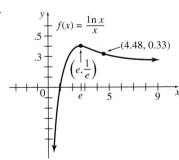

25.

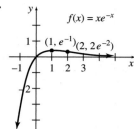

27.

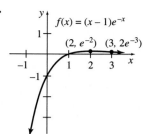

29.

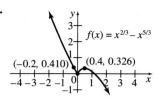

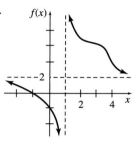

31. 3, 7, 9, 11, 15   **33.** 17, 19, 23, 25, 27   **35.** In Exercises 35–39, other answers are possible.

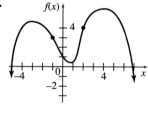

37.

39.

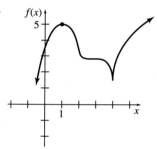

Concept Check (page 860)

1. True   **2.** False   **3.** False   **4.** False   **5.** True   **6.** False   **7.** True   **8.** False   **9.** False   **10.** False
11. False   **12.** True   **13.** False

Chapter 13 Review Exercises (page 861)

5. Increasing on $(-9/2, \infty)$; decreasing on $(-\infty, -9/2)$ **7.** Increasing on $(-5/3, 3)$; decreasing on $(-\infty, -5/3)$ and $(3, \infty)$
9. Never decreasing; increasing on $(-\infty, 3)$ and $(3, \infty)$ **11.** Decreasing on $(-\infty, -1)$ and $(0, 1)$; increasing on $(-1, 0)$ and
$(1, \infty)$ **13.** Relative maximum of -4 at 2   **15.** Relative minimum of -7 at 2   **17.** Relative maximum of 101 at -3; relative
minimum of -24 at 2   **19.** Relative maximum at $(-0.618, 0.206)$; relative minimum at $(1.618, 13.203)$
21. $f''(x) = 36x^2 - 10$; 26; 314   **23.** $f''(x) = 180(3x - 6)^{-3}$ or $180/(3x - 6)^3$; $-20/3$; $-4/75$
25. $f''(t) = (t^2 + 1)^{-3/2}$ or $1/(t^2 + 1)^{3/2}$; $1/2^{3/2} \approx 0.354$; $1/10^{3/2} \approx 0.032$

27.

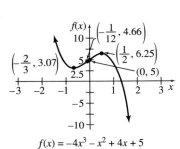

$\left(-\dfrac{1}{2}, -3.375\right)$

$\left(-\dfrac{1}{12}, -3.09\right)$

$\left(\dfrac{1}{3}, -2.80\right)$

$(0, -3)$

$f(x) = -2x^3 - \dfrac{1}{2}x^2 + x - 3$

29.

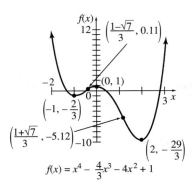

$\left(\dfrac{1-\sqrt{7}}{3}, 0.11\right)$

$(0, 1)$

$\left(-1, -\dfrac{2}{3}\right)$

$\left(\dfrac{1+\sqrt{7}}{3}, -5.12\right)$

$\left(2, -\dfrac{29}{3}\right)$

$f(x) = x^4 - \dfrac{4}{3}x^3 - 4x^2 + 1$

31.

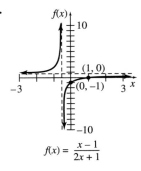

$(1, 0)$

$(0, -1)$

$f(x) = \dfrac{x-1}{2x+1}$

33.

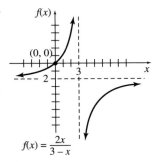

$\left(-\dfrac{1}{12}, 4.66\right)$

$\left(\dfrac{1}{2}, 6.25\right)$

$\left(-\dfrac{2}{3}, 3.07\right)$

$(0, 5)$

$f(x) = -4x^3 - x^2 + 4x + 5$

35.

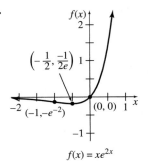

$(0, 0)$

$f(x) = x^4 + 2x^2$

37.

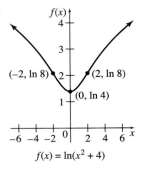

$(2, 4)$

$(-2, -4)$

$f(x) = \dfrac{x^2 + 4}{x}$

39.

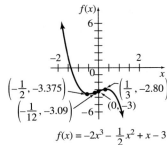

$(0, 0)$

$f(x) = \dfrac{2x}{3-x}$

41.

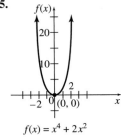

$\left(-\dfrac{1}{2}, \dfrac{-1}{2e}\right)$

$(-1, -e^{-2})$

$(0, 0)$

$f(x) = xe^{2x}$

43.

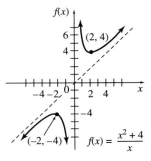

$(-2, \ln 8)$

$(2, \ln 8)$

$(0, \ln 4)$

$f(x) = \ln(x^2 + 4)$

45.

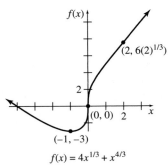

$(2, 6(2)^{1/3})$

$(0, 0)$

$(-1, -3)$

$f(x) = 4x^{1/3} + x^{4/3}$

47.

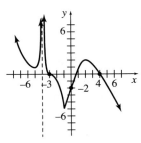

In Exercise 47, other answers are possible.

49. a. Both are negative. **51. a.** $P(q) = -q^3 + 7q^2 + 49x$ **b.** 7 brushes **c.** $229 **d.** $343 **e.** $q = 7/3$; between 2 and 3 brushes **53. a.** Metabolic rate and life span are increasing and concave downward. Heartbeat is decreasing and concave upward.

55.

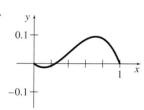

57. a. 1486 ml per square meter; for males with 1.88 m² of surface area, the red cell volume increases approximately 1486 ml for each additional square meter of surface area. **b.** 1.57 m²; 2593 ml (Hurley); 2484 ml (Pearson et al.) **c.** 1578 ml per m²; for males with 1.57 m² of surface area, the red cell volume increases approximately 1578 ml for each additional square meter of surface area. **59. a.** 2010, 380 million **b.** 2030 **c.** 325 million **61. a.** $v(t) = 512 - 32t; a(t) = -32$ **b.** 4096 ft **c.** After 32 sec; -512 ft per sec

CHAPTER 14 Applications of the Derivative

Exercises 14.1 (page 874)

1. Absolute maximum at x_3; no absolute minimum **3.** No absolute extrema **5.** Absolute minimum at x_1; no absolute maximum **7.** Absolute maximum at x_1; absolute minimum at x_2 **11.** Absolute maximum of 12 at $x = 5$; absolute minimum of -8 at $x = 0$ and $x = 3$ **13.** Absolute maximum of 19.67 at $x = -4$; absolute minimum of -1.17 at $x = 1$ **15.** Absolute maximum of 1 at $x = 0$; absolute minimum of -80 at $x = -3$ and $x = 3$ **17.** Absolute maximum of 1/3 at $x = 0$; absolute minimum of $-1/3$ at $x = 3$ **19.** Absolute maximum of 0.21 at $x = 1 + \sqrt{2} \approx 2.4$; absolute minimum of 0 at $x = 1$ **21.** Absolute maximum of 1.710 at $x = 3$; absolute minimum of -1.587 at $x = 0$ **23.** Absolute maximum of 7 at $x = 1$; absolute minimum of 0 at $x = 0$ **25.** Absolute maximum of 4.910 at $x = 4$; absolute minimum of -1.545 at $x = 2$ **27.** Absolute maximum of 19.09 at $x = -1$; absolute minimum of 0.6995 at $x = (\ln 3)/3$ **29.** Absolute maximum of 1.356 at $x = 0.6085$; absolute minimum of 0.5 at $x = -1$ **31.** Absolute minimum of 7 at $x = 2$; no absolute maximum **33.** Absolute maximum of 137 at $x = 3$; no absolute minimum **35.** Absolute maximum of 0.1 at $x = 4$; absolute minimum of -0.5 at $x = -2$ **37.** Absolute maximum of 0.1226 at $x = e^{1/3}$; no absolute minimum **39.** a **41. a.** Relative maxima of 413 in 1997, 341 in 2000, and 134 in 2004; relative minima of 290 in 1996, 313 in 1998, and 131 in 2003 **b.** Bank burglaries reached an absolute maximum of 413 in 1997 and an absolute minimum of 131 in 2003. **43.** The maximum profit is $700,000 when 1,000,000 tires are sold. **45. a.** 112 **b.** 162 **47.** 11 units **49.** 100 units **51.** 12° **53.** 21.92°C **55.** Maximum of 21.3 mpg at 43.7 mph; minimum of 17.3 mpg at 60 mph **57.** Use all 12 feet of wire for the circle. **59. b.** 1/2 **c.** To decide how to phrase a message to get maximum information content

Exercises 14.2 (page 884)

1. a. $y = 180 - x$ **b.** $P = x(180 - x)$ **c.** $[0, 180]$ **d.** $dP/dx = 180 - 2x; x = 90$ **e.** $P(0) = 0; P(180) = 0;$ $P(90) = 8100$ **f.** 8100; 90 and 90 **3. a.** $y = 90 - x$ **b.** $P = x^2(90 - x)$ **c.** $[0, 90]$ **d.** $dP/dx = 180x - 3x^2;$ $x = 0, x = 60$ **e.** $P(0) = 0, P(60) = 108,000, P(90) = 0$ **f.** 108,000; 30 and 60 **5.** $A(x) = x^2/2 + 2x - 3 + 35/x;$ $x = 2.722$ **7. a.** $R(x) = 160,000x - 100x^2$ **b.** 800 **c.** $640,000 **9. a.** $1400 - 2x$ **b.** $A(x) = 1400x - 2x^2$ **c.** 350 m **d.** 245,000 m² **11.** 405,000 m² **13.** $960 **15.** In 10 days; $960 **17. a.** 96 **b.** $46,080 **19.** 20 cm by 20 cm by 40 cm; $7200 **23.** 2/3 ft (or 8 in.) **25.** $3\sqrt{6} + 3$ by $2\sqrt{6} + 2$ **27.** Point A **29.** Radius = 5.206 cm, height = 11.75 cm **31.** Radius = 5.242 cm; height = 11.58 cm **33. a.** 12 days **b.** 50 per ml **c.** 1 day **d.** 81.365 per ml **35.** 12.98 thousand **39.** 237.10 **41.** Point P is at Point L. **45.** $(56 - 2\sqrt{21})/7 \approx 6.7$ mi

Exercises 14.3 (page 897)

3. c **5.** 310 **7.** 45 **9.** 95 **11.** 913 **13.** 10 runs **15. a.** $E = p/(200 - p)$ **b.** 25 **17. a.** $E = 2p^2/(7500 - p^2)$ **b.** 25,000 **19. a.** $E = 5/q$ **b.** 5 **21. a.** $E = 0.5$; inelastic; total revenue increases as price increases. **b.** $E = 8$; elastic; total revenue decreases as price increases. **23. a.** 0.071 **b.** Inelastic **c.** $1255 **27. a.** k **29.** It is negative.

Exercises 14.4 (page 903)

1. $dy/dx = -6x/(5y)$ **3.** $dy/dx = (8x - 5y)/(5x - 3y)$ **5.** $dy/dx = 15x^2/(6y + 4)$ **7.** $dy/dx = -3x(2 + y)^2/2$ **9.** $dy/dx = \sqrt{y}/[\sqrt{x}(5\sqrt{y} - 2)]$ **11.** $dy/dx = (4x^3y^3 + 6x^{1/2})/(9y^{1/2} - 3x^4y^2)$ **13.** $dy/dx = (5 - 2xye^{x^2y})/(x^2e^{x^2y} - 4)$ **15.** $dy/dx = y(2xy^3 - 1)/(1 - 3x^2y^3)$ **17.** $y = (3/4)x + 25/4$ **19.** $y = x + 2$ **21.** $y = x/64 + 7/4$

23. $y = (11/12)x - 5/6$ **25.** $y = -(37/11)x + 59/11$ **27.** $y = (5/2)x - 1/2$ **29.** $y = 1$ **31.** $y = -2x + 7$
33. a. $y = -(3/4)x + 25/2; y = (3/4)x - 25/2$ **b.**

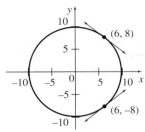

35. $y = -(2/11)x + 15/11$ **37.** $y = (11/12)x - 5/6$ **39.** $dy/dx = (3x^2 + a)/(2y)$ **41.** $dv/du = -(2v + 1)^{1/2}/(2u^{1/2})$
43. a. \$0.94; the approximate increase in cost of an additional unit **b.** \$0; the approximate change in revenue for a unit increase in sales **45.** $1/(3\sqrt{3})$ **47.** $ds/dt = (4s - 6t^2 + 5)/(3s^2 - 4t)$

Exercises 14.5 (page 911)

1. -64 **3.** $-9/7$ **5.** $1/5$ **7.** $-3/2$ **9.** \$384 per month **11. a.** Revenue is increasing at a rate of \$180 per day. **b.** Cost is increasing at a rate of \$50 per day. **c.** Profit is increasing at a rate of \$130 per day. **13.** Demand is decreasing at a rate of approximately 98 units per unit time. **15.** 0.067 mm per min **17.** About 1.9849 g per day **19. a.** $105.15 \text{ m}^{-0.25} \, dm/dt$
b. About 52.89 kcal per day^2 **21.** 25.6 crimes per month **23.** 24/5 ft/min **25.** 16π ft^2/min **27.** 2/27 cm/min
29. 62.5 ft per min **31.** $\sqrt{2} \approx 1.41$ ft per sec

Exercises 14.6 (page 919)

1. 1.9 **3.** 0.1 **5.** 0.060 **7.** -0.023 **9.** 12.0417; 12.0416; 0.0001 **11.** 0.995; 0.9950; 0 **13.** 1.01; 1.0101; 0.0001
15. 0.05; 0.0488; 0.0012 **17. a.** -4.4 thousand lb **b.** -52.2 thousand lb **19.** \$60 **21.** About 9600 in^3 **23. a.** 0.007435
b. -0.005105 **25. a.** 0.347 million **b.** -0.022 million **27.** 1568π mm^3 **29.** 80π mm^2 **31. a.** About 9.3 kg **b.** About 9.5 kg **33.** -7.2π cm^3 **35.** 0.472 cm^3 **37.** 0.00125 cm **39.** ±1.273 in^3 **41.** ±0.116 in^3

Concept Check (page 922)

1. False **2.** True **3.** False **4.** True **5.** True **6.** True **7.** True **8.** True **9.** True **10.** True

Chapter 14 Review Exercises (page 923)

1. Absolute maximum of 33 at 4; absolute minimum of 1 at 0 and 6 **3.** Absolute maximum of 39 at -3; absolute minimum of $-319/27$ at 5/3 **7. a.** Maximum $= 0.37$; minimum $= 0$ **b.** Maximum $= 0.35$; minimum $= 0.13$
11. $dy/dx = (2x - 9x^2y^4)/(8y + 12x^3y^3)$ **13.** $dy/dx = 6\sqrt{y - 1}/[x^{1/3}(1 - \sqrt{y - 1})]$ **15.** $dy/dx = -(30 + 50x)/3$
17. $dy/dx = (2xy^4 + 2y^3 - y)/(x - 6x^2y^3 - 6xy^2)$ **21.** 272 **23.** -2 **25.** $-8e^3$ **29.** 0.00204 **33.** 2 m by 4 m by 4 m
35. 3 in. **37.** 1789 **39.** 80 **41.** 56π ft^2 per min **43. a.** **b.** About the 15th day

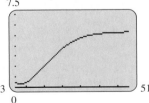

45. 8/3 ft per min **47.** $21/16 = 1.3125$ ft per min **49.** ± 0.736 in^2 **51.** $1.25 + 2 \ln 1.5$ **53.** 10 ft; 18.67 sec

CHAPTER 15 Integration

Exercises 15.1 (page 940)

1. They differ only by a constant. **5.** $6k + C$ **7.** $z^2 + 3z + C$ **9.** $2t^3 - 4t^2 + 7t + C$ **11.** $z^4 + z^3 + z^2 - 6z + C$
13. $10z^{3/2}/3 + \sqrt{2}z + C$ **15.** $5x^4/4 - 20x^2 + C$ **17.** $8v^{3/2}/3 - 6v^{5/2}/5 + C$ **19.** $4u^{5/2} - 4u^{7/2} + C$ **21.** $-7/z + C$
23. $-\pi^3/(2y^2) - 2\sqrt{\pi}y + C$ **25.** $6t^{-1.5} - 2\ln|t| + C$ **27.** $-1/(3x) + C$ **29.** $-15e^{-0.2x} + C$
31. $-3\ln|x| - 10e^{-0.4x} + e^{0.1}x + C$ **33.** $(1/4)\ln|t| + t^3/6 + C$ **35.** $e^{2u}/2 + 2u^2 + C$ **37.** $x^3/3 + x^2 + x + C$
39. $6x^{7/6}/7 + 3x^{2/3}/2 + C$ **41.** $10^x/(\ln 10) + C$ **43.** $f(x) = 3x^{5/3}/5$ **45.** $C(x) = 2x^2 - 5x + 8$ **47.** $C(x) = 3e^{0.01x} + 5$
49. $C(x) = 3x^{5/3}/5 + 2x + 114/5$ **51.** $C(x) = 5x^2/2 - \ln|x| - 153.50$ **53.** $p = 175 - 0.01x - 0.01x^2$
55. $p = 500 - 0.1\sqrt{x}$ **57. a.** $f(t) = 0.749t^2 + 1.626t + 2.645$ **b.** Approximately 220 million subscribers
59. a. $P(x) = 25x^4/2 + 10x^3 - 40$ **b.** \$240 **61.** $a\ln x - bx + C$ **63. a.** $N(t) = 155.3e^{0.3219t} + 144.7$ **b.** 7537
65. $v(t) = 5t^3/3 + 4t + 6$ **67.** $s(t) = -16t^2 + 6400$; 20 sec **69.** $s(t) = 2t^{5/2} + 3e^{-t} + 1$ **71.** 160 ft/sec, 12 ft
73. a. $B(t) = 314.5e^{0.02955t} + 477.8$ **b.** About 1,566,000

Exercises 15.2 (page 951)

3. $2(2x + 3)^5/5 + C$ **5.** $-(2m + 1)^{-2}/2 + C$ **7.** $-(x^2 + 2x - 4)^{-3}/3 + C$ **9.** $(4z^2 - 5)^{3/2}/12 + C$ **11.** $e^{2x^3}/2 + C$
13. $e^{2t-t^2}/2 + C$ **15.** $-e^{1/z} + C$ **17.** $(x^4 + 4x^2 + 7)^9/36 + C$ **19.** $-1/[2(x^2 + x)^2] + C$
21. $(p + 1)^7/7 - (p + 1)^6/6 + C$ **23.** $2(u - 1)^{3/2}/3 + 2(u - 1)^{1/2} + C$ **25.** $(x^2 + 12x)^{3/2}/3 + C$
27. $[\ln(t^2 + 2)]/2 + C$ **29.** $(1 + 3\ln x)^3/9 + C$ **31.** $(1/2)\ln(e^{2x} + 5) + C$ **33.** $(\ln 10)(\log x)^2/2 + C$
35. $8^{3x^2+1}/(6\ln 8) + C$ **39. a.** $R(x) = 6(x^2 + 27,000)^{1/3} - 180$ **b.** 150 **41. a.** $C(x) = 6\ln(5x^2 + e) + 4$ **b.** Yes
43. a. $f(t) = 4.0674 \times 10^{-4}[(t - 1970)^{2.4}/2.4 + 1970(t - 1970)^{1.4}/1.4] + 61.298$ **b.** About 181,000

Exercises 15.3 (page 960)

3. a. 88 **b.** $\int_0^8 (2x + 5)\,dx$ **7. a.** 21 **b.** 23 **c.** 22 **d.** 22 **9. a.** 10 **b.** 10 **c.** 10 **d.** 11 **11. a.** 8.22 **b.** 15.48
c. 11.85 **d.** 10.96 **13. a.** 6.70 **b.** 3.15 **c.** 4.93 **d.** 4.17 **15.** 12.5 **17. a.** $8 + 4\pi$ **b.** $4 + \pi$ **19.** 4π **21.** 24
23. b. 0.3025 **c.** 0.255025 **d.** 0.251001 **e.** 0.25 **25.** 23,413 million short tons **27. a.** About 1533 cases **b.** About 553
cases **29.** About 1900 ft **31.** 2751 ft, 3153 ft, 2952 ft **33. a.** About 1230 BTUs **b.** About 230 BTUs **35. a.** 9 ft **b.** 2 sec
c. 4.6 ft **d.** Between 3 and 3.5 sec **37.** 22.5 and 18 ft **39. a.** About 75,600 **b.** About 77,300

Exercises 15.4 (page 973)

1. -18 **3.** $-3/2$ **5.** $28/3$ **7.** 13 **9.** $-16/3$ **11.** 76 **13.** $4/5$ **15.** $108/25$ **17.** $20e^{0.3} - 20e^{0.2} + 3\ln 2 - 3\ln 3 \approx 1.353$
19. $e^8/4 - e^4/4 - 1/6 \approx 731.4$ **21.** $91/3$ **23.** $447/7 \approx 63.86$ **25.** $(\ln 2)^2/2 \approx 0.2402$ **27.** 49
29. $1/8 - 1/[2(3 + e^2)] \approx 0.07687$ **31.** 10 **33.** 76 **35.** $41/2$ **37.** $e^2 - 3 + 1/e \approx 4.757$ **39.** $e - 2 + 1/e$ **41.** $23/3$
43. $e^2 - 2e + 1 \approx 2.952$ **45.** $\int_a^c f(x)\,dx = \int_a^b f(x)\,dx + \int_b^c f(x)\,dx$ **47.** -8 **51.** -12
53. a. $x^5/5 - 1/5$ **c.** $f'(1) \approx 2.746$, and $g(1) = e \approx 2.718$ **55. a.** $(9000/8)(17^{4/3} - 2^{4/3}) \approx \$46,341$
b. $(9000/8)(26^{4/3} - 17^{4/3}) \approx \$37,477$ **c.** It is slowly increasing without bound. **57.** No **59. a.** 0.8778 ft **b.** 0.6972 ft
61. a. 18.12 **b.** 8.847 **63. b.** $\int_0^{60} n(x)\,dx$ **c.** $2(51^{3/2} - 26^{3/2})/15 \approx 30.89$ million **65. a.** $Q(R) = \pi kR^4/2$
b. $0.04k$ mm per min **67. b.** About 505,000 kJ/W$^{0.67}$ **69. a.** About 263 million; the total population aged 0 to 90 **b.** About
68 million **71. a.** $c'(t) = 1.2e^{0.04t}$ **b.** $\int_0^{10} 1.2e^{0.04t}\,dt$ **c.** $30e^{0.4} - 30 \approx 14.75$ billion **d.** About 12.8 yr **e.** About 14.4 yr

Exercises 15.5 (page 985)

1. 21   **3.** 20   **5.** 23/3   **7.** 366.2   **9.** 4/3   **11.** $2 \ln 2 - \ln 6 + 3/2 \approx 1.095$ **13.** $6 \ln(3/2) - 6 + 2e^{-1} + 2e \approx 2.605$
15. $(e^{-2} + e^4)/2 - 2 \approx 25.37$ **17.** 1/2   **19.** 1/20   **21.** $3(2^{4/3})/2 - 3(2^{7/3})/7 \approx 1.620$ **23.** $(e^9 + e^6 + 1)/3 \approx 2836$
25. $-1.9241, -0.4164, 0.6650$ **27. a.** 8 yr   **b.** About $148   **c.** About $771   **29. a.** 39 days   **b.** $3369.18   **c.** $484.02
d. $2885.16   **31.** 12,931.66   **33.** 54   **35. a.**

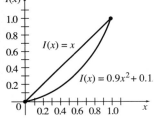

b. $(15, 375)$ **c.** $4500   **d.** $3375
37. a. 12   **b.** $5616, $1116   **c.** $1872, $1503
d. $387   **39. a.** About 71.25 gal   **b.** About 25
hr   **c.** About 105 gal   **d.** About 47.91 hr

41. a. 0.019; the lower 10% of the income producers earn 1.9% of the total income of the population.   **b.** 0.184; the lower 40% of
the income producers earn 18.4% of the total income of the population.
c.
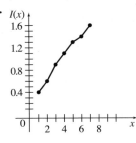
d. 0.15   **e.** Income is distributed less equally in 2005 than in 1968.

Exercises 15.6 (page 995)

1. a. 12.25   **b.** 12   **c.** 12   **c.** $22/3 \approx 7.333$ **3. a.** 3.35   **b.** 3.3   **c.** $3 \ln 3 \approx 3.296$ **5. a.** 11.34   **b.** 10.5   **c.** 10.5
7. a. 0.9436   **b.** 0.8374   **9. a.** 1.236   **b.** 1.265   **c.** $2 - 2e^{-1} \approx 1.264$ **11. a.** 5.991   **b.** 6.167   **c.** 6.283; Simpson's rule
13. b is true.   **15. a.** 0.2   **b.** 0.220703, 0.205200, 0.201302, 0.200325, 0.020703, 0.005200, 0.001302, 0.000325   **c.** $p = 2$
17. a. 0.2   **b.** 0.2005208, 0.2000326, 0.2000020, 0.2000001, 0.0005208, 0.0000326, 0.0000020, 0.0000001   **c.** $p = 4$
19. $M = 0.7355$; $S = 0.8048$ **21. a.**

b. 6.3   **c.** 6.27   **23. a.** 1.831   **b.** 1.758   **25.** About 30
mcg(h)/ml; this represents the total amount of drug available to the
patient for each ml of blood.   **27.** About 9 mcg(h)/ml; this represents the total effective amount of the drug available to the
patient for each ml of blood.   **29. a.** $y = b_0(t/7)^{b_1}e^{-b_2 t/7}$
b. About 1212 kg; about 1231 kg   **c.** About 1224 kg; about
1250 kg

31. a.

b. 71.5   **c.** 69.0   **33.** 3413   **35. a.** 0.6827   **b.** 0.9545   **c.** 0.9973

Concept Check (page 1000)

1. True **2.** False **3.** False **4.** True **5.** True **6.** False **7.** False **8.** True **9.** True **10.** False
11. True **12.** False **13.** False **14.** True

Chapter 15 Review Exercises (page 1000)

5. $x^2 + 3x + C$ **7.** $x^3/3 - 3x^2/2 + 2x + C$ **9.** $2x^{3/2} + C$ **11.** $2x^{3/2}/3 + 9x^{1/3} + C$ **13.** $2x^{-2} + C$ **15.** $-3e^{2x}/2 + C$
17. $e^{3x^2}/6 + C$ **19.** $(3\ln|x^2 - 1|)/2 + C$ **21.** $-(x^3 + 5)^{-3}/9 + C$ **23.** $-e^{-3x^4}/12 + C$ **25.** $(3\ln x + 2)^5/15 + C$
27. 20 **29.** 24 **31. a.** $s(T) - s(0)$ **b.** $\int_0^T v(t)\, dt = s(T) - s(0)$ is equivalent to the Fundamental Theorem with $a = 0$ and
$b = T$ because $s(t)$ is an antiderivative of $v(t)$. **33.** 12 **35.** $3\ln 5 + 12/25 \approx 5.308$ **37.** 19/15
39. $3(1 - e^{-4})/2 \approx 1.473$ **41.** $\pi/32$ **43.** 9π **45.** 5504/7 **47.** $5 - e^{-4} \approx 4.982$ **49.** 1/6 **51.** 32 **53.** 10.46; 10.20
55. 0.6011 **57.** 4.156 **59. a.** 0 **b.** 0 **61.** $C(x) = (2x - 1)^{3/2} + 145$ **63.** \$96,000 **65.** \$38,000 **67. a.** \$916.67
b. \$666.67 **69. a.** 21.684 billion barrels **b.** 21.684 billion barrels **d.** $y = -0.04911x + 2.4105$, 21.65 billion barrels
71. 782 **73. a.** 0.2784 **b.** 0.2784 **75. a.** \$2,728,871 **b.** \$2,728,871 **d.** $y = 7955.8x + 267,224$, \$2,727,226 **77.**
Approximately 4800 degree-days (the actual value according to the National Weather Service is 4868 degree-days).

CHAPTER 16 Further Techniques and Applications of Integration

Exercises 16.1 (page 1016)

1. $xe^x - e^x + C$ **3.** $(-x/2 + 23/16)\, e^{-8x} + C$ **5.** $-5e^{-1} + 3 \approx 1.161$ **7.** $26\ln 3 - 8 \approx 20.56$ **9.** $(x^2 \ln x)/2 - x^2/4 + C$
11. $e^4 + e^2 \approx 61.99$ **13.** $x^2 e^{2x}/2 - xe^{2x}/2 + e^{2x}/4 + C$ **15.** $243/8 - 3\sqrt[3]{2}/4 \approx 29.43$
17. $(4x^2 + 10x)\ln 5x - 2x^2 - 10x + C$ **19.** $(2/7)(x + 4)^{7/2} - (16/5)(x + 4)^{5/2} + (32/3)(x + 4)^{3/2} + C$ or
$(2/3)x^2(x + 4)^{3/2} - (8/15)x(x + 4)^{5/2} - (16/105)(x + 4)^{7/2} + C$ **21.** $2\sqrt{3} - 10/3 \approx 0.1308$
23. $16\ln|x + \sqrt{x^2 + 16}| + C$ **25.** $-(3/11)\ln|(11 + \sqrt{121 - x^2})/x| + C$
27. $-1/(4x + 6) - (1/6)\ln|x/(4x + 6)| + C$ **31.** -18 **33.** 15 **37. a.** $(2/3)x(x + 1)^{3/2} - (4/15)(x + 1)^{5/2} + C$
b. $(2/5)(x + 1)^{5/2} - (2/3)(x + 1)^{3/2} + C$ **39.** $(169/2)\ln 13 - 42 \approx \$174.74$ **41.** $15e^6 + 3 \approx 6054$ **43.** About 219 kJ

Exercises 16.2 (page 1024)

1. 9π **3.** $364\pi/3$ **5.** $386\pi/27$ **7.** $15\pi/2$ **9.** 18π **11.** $\pi(e^4 - 1)/2 \approx 84.19$ **13.** $4\pi\ln 3 \approx 13.81$ **15.** $3124\pi/5$
17. $16\pi/15$ **19.** $4\pi/3$ **21.** $4\pi r^3/3$ **23.** $\pi r^2 h$ **25.** $13/3 \approx 4.333$ **27.** $38/15 \approx 2.533$ **29.** $e - 1 \approx 1.718$
31. $(5e^4 - 1)/8 \approx 34.00$ **33.** 3.758 **35.** \$42.49 **37.** 200 cases **39. a.** $110e^{-0.1} - 120e^{-0.2} \approx 1.284$
b. $210e^{-1.1} - 220e^{-1.2} \approx 3.640$ **c.** $330e^{-2.3} - 340e^{-2.4} \approx 2.241$ **41. a.** $9(6\ln 6 - 5) \approx 51.76$ **b.** $5(10\ln 10 - 9) \approx 70.13$
c. $3(31\ln 31 - 30)/2 \approx 114.7$

Exercises 16.3 (page 1033)

1. a. \$6883.39 **b.** \$15,319.26 **3. a.** \$3441.69 **b.** \$7659.63 **5. a.** \$3147.75 **b.** \$7005.46 **7. a.** \$32,968.35
b. \$73,372.42 **9. a.** \$746.91 **b.** \$1662.27 **11. a.** \$688.64 **b.** \$1532.59 **13. a.** \$11,351.78 **b.** \$25,263.84
15. \$74,565.94 **17.** \$28,513.76; \$54,075.81 **19.** \$4175.52

Exercises 16.4 (page 1038)

1. 1/3 **3.** Divergent **5.** -1 **7.** 10,000 **9.** 1/10 **11.** 3/5 **13.** 1 **15.** 1000 **17.** Divergent **19.** 1 **21.** Divergent
23. Divergent **25.** Divergent **27.** 0 **29.** Divergent **31.** Divergent **33.** 1 **35.** 0 **39. a.** 2.808, 3.724, 4.417, 6.720, 9.022
b. Divergent **c.** 0.8770, 0.9070, 0.9170, 0.9260, 0.9269 **d.** Convergent **41. a.** 9.9995, 49.9875, 99.9500, 995.0166
b. Divergent **c.** 100,000 **43.** \$20,000,000 **45.** \$30,000 **47.** \$30,000 **49.** $Na/[b(b + k)]$ **51.** 833.3

Exercises 16.5 (page 1049)

1. $y = -2x^2 + 2x^3 + C$ **3.** $y = x^4/2 + C$ **5.** $y^2 = 2x^3/3 + C$ **7.** $y = ke^{x^2}$ **9.** $y = ke^{x^3-x^2}$ **11.** $y = Mx$ **13.** $y = Me^x + 6$
15. $y = -1/(e^{2x}/2 + C)$ **17.** $y = x^2 - x^3 + 5$ **19.** $y = -2xe^{-x} - 2e^{-x} + 44$ **21.** $y^2 = x^4/2 + 25$ **23.** $y = e^{x^2+3x}$
25. $y = x^4 - x^3 + x^2/2 - 1/2$ **27.** $y = -3/(3 \ln |x| - 4)$ **29.** $y = (e^{x-1} - 3)/(e^{x-1} - 2)$ **35. a.** \$1011.75   **b.** \$1024.52
c. No   **37.** About 13.9 yr   **39.** $q = C/p^2$ **41.** d   **43. a.** $I = 2.4 - 1.4e^{-0.088W}$ **b.** I approaches = 2.4.
45. a. $dw/dt = k(C - 17.5w)$; the calorie intake per day is constant.   **b.** lb/calorie   **c.** $dw/dt = (C - 17.5w)/3500$
d. $w = C/17.5 - e^{-0.005M}e^{-0.005t}/17.5$ **e.** $w = C/17.5 + (w_0 - C/17.5)e^{-0.005t}$
47. a.   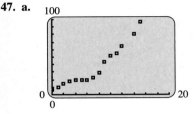   **b.** $y = 258.70/(1 + 31.40e^{-0.1930x})$

c. The logistic equation fits the data well.   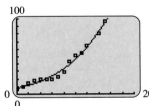   **d.** About 259

49. $y = 35.6e^{0.02117t}$ **51. a.** $k \approx 0.8$ **b.** 11   **c.** 55   **d.** About 3000   **53.** About 10   **55.** 7:22:55 A.M.

Concept Check (page 1055)

1. False   **2.** True   **3.** False   **4.** True   **5.** False   **6.** False   **7.** True   **8.** True   **9.** True   **10.** False   **11.** True   **12.** False
13. True   **14.** True   **15.** False

Chapter 16 Review Exercises (page 1056)

5. $6x(x - 2)^{1/2} - 4(x - 2)^{3/2} + C$ **7.** $-(x + 2)e^{-3x} - (1/3)e^{-3x} + C$ **9.** $(x^2/2 - x)\ln |x| - x^2/4 + x + C$
11. $(1/8)\sqrt{16 + 8x^2} + C$ **13.** $10e^{1/2} - 16 \approx 0.4872$ **15.** $234/7 \approx 33.43$ **17.** $81\pi/2 \approx 127.2$ **19.** $\pi \ln 3 \approx 3.451$
21. $64\pi/5 \approx 40.21$ **25.** 2,391,484/3   **27.** 1/5   **29.** $6/e \approx 2.207$ **31.** Divergent   **33.** 3   **37.** $y = x^3 + 3x^2 + C$
39. $y = 2e^{2x} + C$ **41.** $y^2 = 3x^2 + 2x + C$ **43.** $y = (Cx^2 - 1)/2$ **45.** $y = x^3/3 - 3x^2 + 3$ **47.** $y = 5e^{-x^2+3x}$
49. $y = x^4 + 2x$ **51.** $16,250/3 \approx 5416.67$ **53.** \$174,701.45   **55.** \$15.58   **57.** \$5354.97   **59.** \$30,035.17   **61.** \$176,919.15
63. a. \$10,099   **b.** \$71,196   **65.** About 27.7 years   **67.** 0.4798   **69. a.** About 8208 kg   **b.** About 8430 kg   **c.** About 8558 kg
73. a. $N = 329, b = 7.23; k = 0.247$ **b.** $y \approx 255$ million, which is less than the table value of 281.4 million.   **c.** About 289 million for 2030, about 303 million for 2050   **75. a.** $x = 1/k + Ce^{-kt}$ **b.** $1/k$ **77.** 213°   **79. a.** 158.3°   **b.** 125°   **c.** 133.3°

CHAPTER 17 Multivariable Calculus

Exercises 17.1 (page 1070)

1. a. 12   **b.** −6   **c.** 10   **d.** −19   **3. a.** $\sqrt{43}$ **b.** 6   **c.** $\sqrt{19}$ **d.** $\sqrt{11}$

5.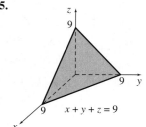

7.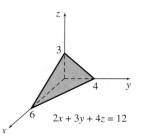

9.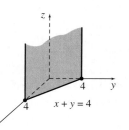

11.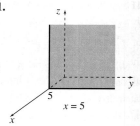

13.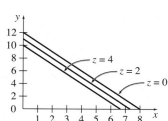

15.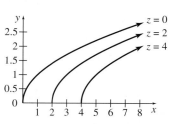

21. c **23.** e **25.** b **27. a.** $8x + 4h$ **b.** $-4y - 2h$ **c.** $8x$ **d.** $-4y$ **29. a.** $3e^2$; slope of tangent line in the direction of x at $(1, 1)$ **b.** $3e^2$; slope of tangent line in the direction of y at $(1, 1)$ **31. a.** 1987 (rounded) **b.** 595 (rounded) **c.** 359,768 (rounded) **33.** 1.416; the IRA account grows faster.

35. $y = 500^{5/2}/x^{3/2} \approx 5,590,170/x^{3/2}$

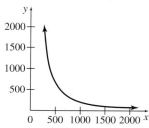

37. $C(x, y, z) = 250x + 150y + 75z$ **39. a.** 1.5 m per sec, 5.5 m per sec **b.** 1 m per sec **41. a.** 8.7% **b.** 48% **c.** Multiple solutions: $W = 19.75, R = 0, A = 0$ or $W = 10, R = 10, A = 4.59$ **d.** Wetland percentage **43. a.** 397 accidents **45. a.** $T = 242.257 \, C^{0.18}/F^3$ **b.** 58.82; a tethered sow spends nearly 59% of the time doing repetitive behavior when she is fed 2 kg of food a day and neighboring sows spend 40% of the time doing repetitive behavior. **47.** $g(L, W, H) = 2LW + 2WH + 2LH$ ft^2

Exercises 17.2 (page 1082)

1. a. $12x - 4y$ **b.** $-4x + 18y$ **c.** 12 **d.** -40 **3.** $f_x(x, y) = -4y$; $f_y(x, y) = -4x + 18y^2$; 4; 178 **5.** $f_x(x, y) = 10xy^3$; $f_y(x, y) = 15x^2y^2$; -20; 2160 **7.** $f_x(x, y) = e^{x+y}$; $f_y(x, y) = e^{x+y}$; e^1 or e; e^{-1} or $1/e$ **9.** $f_x(x, y) = -24e^{4x-3y}$; $f_y(x, y) = 18e^{4x-3y}$; $-24e^{11}$; $18e^{-25}$ **11.** $f_x(x, y) = (-x^4 - 2xy^2 - 3x^2y^3)/(x^3 - y^2)^2$; $f_y(x, y) = (3x^3y^2 - y^4 + 2x^2y)/(x^3 - y^2)^2$; $-8/49$; $-1713/5329$ **13.** $f_x(x, y) = 15x^2y^2/(1 + 5x^3y^2)$; $f_y(x, y) = 10x^3y/(1 + 5x^3y^2)$; 60/41; 1920/2879 **15.** $f_x(x, y) = e^{x^2y}(2x^2y + 1)$; $f_y(x, y) = x^3e^{x^2y}$; $-7e^{-4}$; $-64e^{48}$ **17.** $f_x(x, y) = (1/2)(4x^3 + 3y)/(x^4 + 3xy + y^4 + 10)^{1/2}$; $f_y(x, y) = (1/2)(3x + 4y^3)/(x^4 + 3xy + y^4 + 10)^{1/2}$; $29/(2\sqrt{21})$; $48/\sqrt{311}$ **19.** $f_x(x, y) = [6xy(e^{xy} + 2) - 3x^2y^2e^{xy}]/(e^{xy} + 2)^2$; $f_y(x, y) = [3x^2(e^{xy} + 2) - 3x^3ye^{xy}]/(e^{xy} + 2)^2$; $-24(e^{-2} + 1)/(e^{-2} + 2)^2$; $(624e^{-12} + 96)/(e^{-12} + 2)^2$ **21.** $f_{xx}(x, y) = 8y^2 - 32$; $f_{yy}(x, y) = 8x^2$; $f_{xy}(x, y) = f_{yx}(x, y) = 16xy$ **23.** $R_{xx}(x, y) = 8 + 24y^2$; $R_{yy}(x, y) = -30xy + 24x^2$; $R_{xy}(x, y) = R_{yx}(x, y) = -15y^2 + 48xy$ **25.** $r_{xx}(x, y) = 12y/(x + y)^3$; $r_{yy}(x, y) = -12x/(x + y)^3$; $r_{xy}(x, y) = r_{yx}(x, y) = (6y - 6x)/(x + y)^3$ **27.** $z_{xx} = 9ye^x$; $z_{yy} = 0$; $z_{xy} = z_{yx} = 9e^x$ **29.** $r_{xx} = -1/(x + y)^2$; $r_{yy} = -1/(x + y)^2$; $r_{xy} = r_{yx} = -1/(x + y)^2$ **31.** $z_{xx} = 1/x$; $z_{yy} = -x/y^2$; $z_{xy} = z_{yx} = 1/y$ **33.** $x = -4, y = 2$ **35.** $x = 0, y = 0$; or $x = 3, y = 3$ **37.** $f_x(x, y, z) = 4x^3$; $f_y(x, y, z) = 2z^2$; $f_z(x, y, z) = 4yz + 4z^3$; $f_{yz}(x, y, z) = 4z$ **39.** $f_x(x, y, z) = 6/(4z + 5)$; $f_y(x, y, z) = -5/(4z + 5)$; $f_z(x, y, z) = -4(6x - 5y)/(4z + 5)^2$; $f_{yz}(x, y, z) = 20/(4z + 5)^2$

41. $f_x(x, y, z) = (2x - 5z^2)/(x^2 - 5xz^2 + y^4)$; $f_y(x, y, z) = 4y^3/(x^2 - 5xz^2 + y^4)$; $f_z(x, y, z) = -10xz/(x^2 - 5xz^2 + y^4)$; $f_{yz}(x, y, z) = 40xy^3z/(x^2 - 5xz^2 + y^4)^2$ **43. a.** 6.773 **b.** 3.386 **45. a.** 80 **b.** 150 **c.** 80 **d.** 440 **47. a.** \$902,100
b. $f_p(p, i) = 99 - 0.5i - 0.005p$; $f_i(p, i) = -0.5p$; the rate at which weekly sales are changing per unit of change in price when the interest rate remains constant $(f_p(p, i))$ or interest rate when the price remains constant $(f_i(p, i))$ **c.** A weekly sales decrease of \$9700 **49. a.** 50.57 hundred units **b.** $f_x(16, 81) = 1.053$ hundred units and is the rate at which production is changing when labor changes by 1 unit (from 16 to 17) and capital remains constant; $f_y(16, 81) = 0.4162$ hundred units and is the rate at which production is changing when capital changes by 1 unit (from 81 to 82) and labor remains constant. **51.** $0.4x^{-0.6}y^{0.6}$; $0.6x^{0.4}y^{-0.4}$
53. a. 1279 kcal per hr **b.** 2.906 kcal per hr per g; the instantaneous rate of change of energy usage for a 300-kg animal traveling at 10 km per hr is about 2.9 kcal per hr per g. **55. a.** 0.01124 **b.** 0.7829 **57. a.** 4.125 lb **b.** $\partial f / \partial n = n/4$; the rate of change of weight loss per unit change in workouts **c.** An additional loss of 3/4 lb **59. a.** $(2ax - 3x^2)t^2e^{-t}$ **b.** $x^2(a - x)(2t - t^2)e^{-t}$
c. $(2a - 6x)t^2e^{-t}$ **d.** $(2ax - 3x^2)(2t - t^2)e^{-t}$ **e.** $\partial R/\partial x$ gives the rate of change of the reaction per unit of change in the amount of drug administered. $\partial R/\partial t$ gives the rate of change of the reaction for a 1-hour change in the time after the drug is administered.
61. a. $-24.9°F$ **b.** 15 mph **c.** $W_V(20, 10) = -1.114$; while holding the temperature fixed at 10°F, the wind chill decreases approximately 1.1°F when the wind velocity increases by 1 mph; $W_T(20, 10) = 1.429$; while holding the wind velocity fixed at 20 mph, the wind chill increases approximately 1.429°F if the actual temperature increases from 10°F to 11°F.
d. Sample table

T/V	5	10	15	20
30	27	16	9	4
20	16	3	-5	-11
10	6	-9	-18	-25
0	-5	-21	-32	-39

63. -10 ml per year, 100 ml per in. **65. a.** $F_m = gR^2/r^2$; the rate of change in force per unit change in mass while the distance is held constant; $F_r = -2mgR^2/r^3$; the rate of change in force per unit change in distance while the mass is held constant
67. a. 1055 **b.** $T_s(3, 0.5) = 127.4$ msec per ft. If the distance to move an object increases from 3 ft to 4 ft, while keeping w fixed at 0.5, the approximate increase in movement time is 127.4 msec. $T_w(3, 0.5) = -764.6$ msec per ft². If the width of the target area increases by 1 ft, while keeping s fixed at 3 ft, the approximate decrease in movement time is 764.6 msec.

Exercises 17.3 (page 1093)

1. Saddle point at $(-1, 2)$ **3.** Relative minimum at $(-3, -3)$ **5.** Relative minimum at $(-2, -2)$ **7.** Relative minimum at $(15, -8)$ **9.** Relative maximum at $(2/3, 4/3)$ **11.** Saddle point at $(2, -2)$ **13.** Saddle point at $(0, 0)$; relative minimum at $(27, 9)$ **15.** Saddle point at $(0, 0)$; relative minimum at $(9/2, 3/2)$ **17.** Saddle point at $(0, -1)$ **21.** Relative maximum of 9/8 at $(-1, 1)$; saddle point at $(0, 0)$; a **23.** Relative minima of $-33/16$ at $(0, 1)$ and at $(0, -1)$; saddle point at $(0, 0)$; b
25. Relative maxima of 17/16 at $(1, 0)$ and $(-1, 0)$; relative minima of $-15/16$ at $(0, 1)$ and $(0, -1)$; saddle points at $(0, 0)$, $(-1, 1)$, $(1, -1)$, $(1, 1)$, and $(-1, -1)$; e **31. a.** all values of k **b.** $k \geq 0$ **33.** Maximum profit is \$351,600, when $x = 12$ and $y = 30$. **35.** 38 units of electrical tape and 52 units of packing tape should be produced to yield a minimum cost of \$1832. **37.** 6 tons of steel and 3 tons of aluminum produce a maximum profit of \$216,000. **39. a.** 0.5148; 0.4064; the jury is less likely to make the correct decision in the second situation. **b.** If $r = s = 1$ then $P(\alpha, 1, 1) = 1$ **c.** $P(\alpha, 1, 1) = 1$ is a maximum value. **41. a.** 436.16 kJ/mol **b.** 137.66 kJ/mol **c.** Saddle point at $(1.75, 133°C)$

Exercises 17.4 (page 1104)

1. $f(8, 8) = 256$ **3.** $f(5, 5) = 125$ **5.** $f(5, 3) = 28$ **7.** $f(20, 2) = 360$ **9.** $f(3/2, 3/2, 3) = 81/4 = 20.25$
11. $x = 8$, $y = 16$ **13.** 30, 30, 30 **21.** 40 ft by 48 ft **23.** $x = 2$, $y = 4$ **25.** 189 units of labor and 35 units of capital
27. 45,000 m² **29.** Radius ≈ 1.585 in.; height ≈ 3.169 in. **31.** 5.698 in. by 5.698 in. by 5.698 in. **33.** 4 ft by 4 ft for the base; 2 ft for the height **35. a.** $F(r, s, t, \lambda) = rs(1 - t) + (1 - r)st + r(1 - s)t + rst - \lambda(r + s + t - \alpha)$ **b.** $r = s = t = 0.25$
c. $r = s = t = 1.0$

Exercises 17.5 (page 1109)

1. 10.022; 10.0221; 0.0001 **3.** 2.0067; 2.0080; 0.0013 **5.** 1.07; 1.0720; 0.0020 **7.** -0.02; -0.0200; 0 **9.** 0.12 **11.** 0.0311
13. -0.335 **15.** 20.73 cm³ **17.** 86.4 in³ **19.** 0.07694 unit **21.** 6.65 cm³ **23.** 2.98 liters **25. a.** 0.2649 **b.** Actual 0.2817;
approximation 0.2816 **27. a.** 87% **b.** 75% **d.** 89%; 87% **29.** 26.945 cm² **31.** 3%

Exercises 17.6 (page 1121)

1. $630y$ **3.** $(1/9)[(x + 42)^{3/2} - (x + 6)^{3/2}]$ **5.** $(2x/9)[(x^2 + 15)^{3/2} - (x^2 + 12)^{3/2}]$ **7.** $6 + 10y$
9. $(1/2)(e^{12+3y} - e^{4+3y})$ **11.** $(1/2)(e^{4x+9} - e^{4x})$ **13.** 945 **15.** $(2/45)(39^{5/2} - 12^{5/2} - 7533)$ **17.** 21 **19.** $(\ln 3)^2$
21. $8 \ln 2 + 4$ **23.** 171 **25.** $(4/15)(33 - 2^{5/2} - 3^{5/2})$ **27.** $-3 \ln(3/4)$ or $3 \ln(4/3)$ **29.** $(1/2)(e^7 - e^6 - e^3 + e^2)$
31. 54 **33.** 40/3 **35.** $(2/15)(2^{5/2} - 2)$ **37.** $(1/4) \ln(17/8)$ **39.** $e^2 - 3$ **41.** 97,632/105 **43.** 128/9 **45.** $\ln 16$ or $4 \ln 2$
47. 64/3 **49.** 1 **51.** 34 **53.** 10/3 **55.** $7(e - 1)/3$ **57.** 16/3 **59.** $4 \ln 2 - 2$ **63.** 13/3 **65.** $(e^7 - e^6 - e^5 + e^4)/2$
67. \$3518 **69.** \$933.33 **71.** 78.4 hr

Concept Check (page 1127)

1. True **2.** True **3.** True **4.** True **5.** False **6.** False **7.** False **8.** True **9.** False **10.** False **11.** True **12.** False

Chapter 17 Review Exercises (page 1128)

5. 23; 594 **7.** $-\sqrt{5}/3$; $\sqrt{5}/3$

9. **11.** **13.**

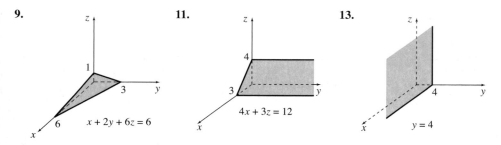

15. a. $4xy/(x - y^2)^2$ **b.** $-1/2$ **c.** 0 **17.** $f_x(x, y) = 20x^3y^3 - 30x^4y$; $f_y(x, y) = 15x^4y^2 - 6x^5$
19. $f_x(x, y) = (-6x^2 + 2y^2 - 30xy^2)/(3x^2 + y^2)^2$; $f_y(x, y) = (30x^2y - 4xy)/(3x^2 + y^2)^2$
21. $f_x(x, y) = (y - 2)^2 e^{x+2y}$; $f_y(x, y) = 2(y - 2)(y - 1)e^{x+2y}$ **23.** $f_x(x, y) = -2xy^3/(2 - x^2y^3)$;
$f_y(x, y) = -3x^2y^2/(2 - x^2y^3)$ **25.** $f_{xx}(x, y) = -6y^3 + 6xy$; $f_{xy}(x, y) = -18xy^2 + 3x^2$ **27.** $f_{xx}(x, y) = 2(3 + y)/(x - 1)^3$;
$f_{xy}(x, y) = -1/(x - 1)^2$ **29.** $f_{xx}(x, y) = 2ye^{x^2}(2x^2 + 1)$; $f_{xy}(x, y) = 2xe^{x^2}$ **31.** $f_{xx}(x, y) = -9y^4/(1 + 3xy^2)^2$;
$f_{xy}(x, y) = 6y/(1 + 3xy^2)^2$ **33.** Relative minimum at $(-9/2, 4)$ **35.** Relative maximum at $(-3/4, -9/32)$; saddle point at
$(0, 0)$ **37.** Relative minimum at $(11/4, -2)$ **39.** Relative minimum at $(-8, -23)$ **41.** Minimum of 0 at $(0, 4)$; maximum of
256/27 at $(8/3, 4/3)$ **43.** $x = 160/3$, $y = 80/3$ **45.** No **47.** -0.0168 **49.** 2.095; 2.0972; 0.0022 **51.** $(e^{15+5y} - e^{3+5y})/3$
53. $(2/33)[(7x + 297)^{1/2} - (7x + 11)^{1/2}]$ **55.** 395 **57.** $(e^3 + e^{-8} - e^{-4} - e^{-1})/14$ **59.** $\ln 2$
61. $(2/15)(11^{5/2} - 8^{5/2} - 7^{5/2} + 32)$ **63.** $(e^2 - 2e + 1)/2$ **65.** 308/3 **67.** 52/5 **69.** 1/12 **71.** $16(5\sqrt{5} - 1)/3$
73. 26/105 **75. a.** \$26 **b.** \$2572 **77. a.** Relative minimum at $(11, 12)$ **b.** \$431 **79.** 7.92 cm³ **81.** 15.6 cm³
83. 1.341 cm³ **85. a.** About 33.98 cm **b.** About 0.02723 cm per g; about 0.2821 cm/year; the approximate change in the length
of a trout if its mass increases from 450 to 451 g while age is held constant at 7 years is 0.027 cm; the approximate change in the
length of a trout if its age increases from 7 to 8 years while mass is held constant at 450 g is 0.28 cm. **87. a.** 2.828 ft²
b. An increase of 0.6187 ft² **89.** 20,000 ft² with dimensions 100 ft by 200 ft

CHAPTER 18 **Probability and Calculus**

Exercises 18.1 (page 1145)

1. Yes **3.** Yes **5.** No; $\int_0^3 4x^3\,dx \neq 1$ **7.** No; $\int_{-2}^2 x^2/16\,dx \neq 1$ **9.** No; $f(x) < 0$ for some x values in $[-1, 1]$.
11. $k = 3/14$ **13.** $k = 3/125$ **15.** $k = 2/9$ **17.** $k = 1/12$ **19.** $F(x) = (x^2 - x - 2)/18, 2 \leq x \leq 5$
21. $F(x) = (x^3 - 1)/63, 1 \leq x \leq 4$ **23.** $F(x) = (x^{3/2} - 1)/7, 1 \leq x \leq 4$ **25.** 1 **29. a.** 0.4226 **b.** 0.2071 **c.** 0.4082
31. a. 0.3935 **b.** 0.3834 **c.** 0.3679 **33. a.** 1/3 **b.** 2/3 **c.** 295/432 **35. a.** 0.9975 **b.** 0.0024
c. $F(x) = 1 - e^{-x/2}, x \geq 0$ **d.** 0.9502 **37.** c **39. a.** 0.2679 **b.** 0.4142 **c.** 0.3178 **41. a.** 0.8131 **b.** 0.4901
43. a.

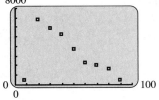

polynomial function

b. $N(x) = -0.00272454x^4 + 0.614038x^3 - 48.0160x^2 + 1418.53x - 7202.78$

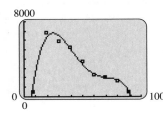

The function models the data well.

c. $S(x) = (1/304{,}337)(-0.00272454x^4 + 0.614038x^3 - 48.0160x^2 + 1418.53x - 7202.78)$ **d.** Estimates: 0.292, 0.192, 0.073; actual: 0.252, 0.209, 0.080 **45. a.** 0.2 **b.** 0.6 **c.** 0.6 **47. a.** 0.16 **b.** 0.14 **49. a.** 0.2829 **b.** 0.4853 **c.** 0.2409
d. $F(x) = 1.8838(0.5982 - e^{-0.03211x}), 16 \leq x \leq 84$ **e.** 0.1671

Exercises 18.2 (page 1156)

1. $\mu = 5$; Var$(X) \approx 1.33$; $\sigma \approx 1.15$ **3.** $\mu = 14/3 \approx 4.67$; Var$(X) \approx 0.89$; $\sigma \approx 0.94$ **5.** $\mu = 2.83$; Var$(X) \approx 0.57$; $\sigma \approx 0.76$
7. $\mu = 4/3 \approx 1.33$; Var$(X) = 2/9 \approx 0.22$; $\sigma \approx 0.47$ **11. a.** 5.40 **b.** 5.55 **c.** 2.36 **d.** 0.54 **e.** 0.60 **13. a.** $4/3 \approx 1.33$
b. 0.22 **c.** 0.47 **d.** 0.56 **e.** 0.63 **15. a.** 5 **b.** 0 **17. a.** 4.828 **b.** 0.0553 **19. a.** $\sqrt[4]{2} \approx 1.189$ **b.** 0.1836 **21.** 16/5;
does not exist; does not exist **23.** d **25. a.** 6.41 yr **b.** 1.45 yr **c.** 0.49 **27.** c **29.** c **31. a.** 6.342 seconds **b.** 5.138 sec
c. 0.7538 **d.** 4.472 sec **33. a.** 2.333 cm **b.** 0.8692 cm **c.** 0 **d.** 2.25 cm **35.** 111 **37. a.** 1.806 **b.** 1.265 **c.** 0.1886
39. a. 28.84 years **b.** 8.109 **c.** 0.2088 **d.** 28.27 years

Exercises 18.3 (page 1169)

1. a. 3.7 cm **b.** 0.4041 cm **c.** 0.2886 **3. a.** 0.25 years **b.** 0.25 years **c.** 0.2325 **5. a.** 3 days **b.** 3 days **c.** 0.2325
7. 49.98% **9.** 8.01% **11.** −1.28 **13.** 0.92 **19.** $m = -\ln 0.5/a$ or $\ln 2/a$ **23. a.** 1.00000 **b.** 1.99999 **c.** 8.00003
25. a. $\mu \approx 0$ **b.** $\sigma = 0.999433 \approx 1$ **27.** $F(x) = (x - a)/(b - a), a \leq x \leq b$ **29. a.** \$47,500 **b.** 0.4667
31. a. $f(x) = 0.235e^{-0.235x}$ on $[0, \infty)$ **b.** 0.0954 **33. a.** 0.1587 **b.** 0.7698 **35.** c **37.** d **39. a.** 28 days **b.** 0.375
41. a. 1 hour **b.** 0.3935 **43. a.** 58 minutes **b.** 0.09 **45. a.** 0.191 **b.** 0.246 **47. a.** 4.36 millennia; 4.36 millennia
b. 0.63 **49. a.** 0.29 **b.** 0.22 **51. a.** 0.5457 **b.** 0.003909

Concept Check (page 1176)

1. True **2.** True **3.** True **4.** False **5.** False **6.** True **7.** True **8.** True **9.** False **10.** False

Chapter 18 Review Exercises (page 1176)

1. Probabilities **3.** 1. $f(x) \geq 0$ for all x in $[a, b]$; 2. $\int_a^b f(x)dx = 1$ **5.** Not a probability density function **7.** Probability density function **9.** $k = 1/21$ **11. a.** $1/5 = 0.2$ **b.** $9/20 = 0.45$ **c.** 0.54 **13.** b **15. a.** 4 **b.** 0.5 **c.** 0.7071 **d.** 4.121 **e.** $F(x) = (x - 2)^2/9, 2 \leq x \leq 5$ **17. a.** 5/4 **b.** $5/48 \approx 0.1042$ **c.** 0.3227 **d.** 1.149 **e.** $F(x) = 1 - 1/x^5, x \geq 1$ **19.** $m = 0.5970; 0.0180$ **21. a.** 100 **b.** 100 **c.** 0.8647 **23.** 33.36% **25.** 34.31% **27.** 11.51% **29.** -0.05 **31. a.** Exponential **b.** Domain: $[0, \infty)$, range: $(0, 1]$ **c.** **d.** $\mu = 1; \sigma = 1$ **e.** 0.8647

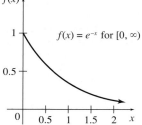

$f(x) = e^{-x}$ for $[0, \infty)$

33. a. 1 **b.** 0.4422 **35.** 0.406 **37. a.** $f(x) = e^{-x/8}/8; [0, \infty)$ **b.** 8 **c.** 8 **d.** 0.2488 **39.** 0.1922 **41.** 0.6321 **43. a.** 22.68°C **b.** 0.4819 **45.** 0.2266 **47. a.**

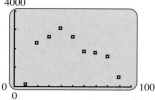

polynomial function

b. $N(x) = -8.53613 \times 10^{-4}x^4 + 0.196608x^3 - 16.6309x^2 + 577.248x - 4040.47$;

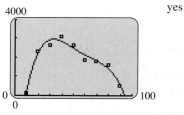

yes

c. $k = 1/167,355$ **d.** 0.1731; 0.2758; 0.3481; 0.1579; 0.2734; 0.3484 **e** 46.84 years **f.** 20.24 years **g.** 44.8 years **49.** 0.2206

Index

Note: n indicates footnote.

KEY DEFINITIONS, THEOREMS, AND FORMULAS

2.2 Row Operations

For any augmented matrix of a system of equations, the following operations produce the augmented matrix of an equivalent system:

1. interchanging any two rows;
2. multiplying the elements of a row by any nonzero real number;
3. adding a nonzero multiple of the elements of one row to the corresponding elements of a nonzero multiple of some other row.

2.5 Finding a Multiplicative Inverse Matrix

To obtain A^{-1} for any $n \times n$ matrix A for which A^{-1} exists, follow these steps.

1. Form the augmented matrix $[A \,|\, I]$, where I is the $n \times n$ identity matrix.
2. Perform row operations on $[A \,|\, I]$ to get a matrix of the form $[I \,|\, B]$ if this is possible.
3. Matrix B is A^{-1}.

4.2 Simplex Method

1. Determine the objective function.
2. Write all necessary constraints.
3. Convert each constraint into an equation by adding a slack variable in each.
4. Set up the initial simplex tableau.
5. Locate the most negative indicator. If there are two such indicators, choose the one farther to the left.
6. Form the necessary quotients to find the pivot. Disregard any quotients with 0 or a negative number in the denominator. The smallest nonnegative quotient gives the location of the pivot. If all quotients must be disregarded, no maximum solution exists. If two quotients are both equal and smallest, choose the pivot in the row nearest the top of the matrix.
7. Use row operations to change all other numbers in the pivot column to zero by adding a suitable multiple of the pivot row to a positive multiple of each row.
8. If the indicators are all positive or 0, this is the final tableau. If not, go back to Step 5 and repeat the process until a tableau with no negative indicators is obtained.
9. Read the solution from this final tableau.

5.1 Compound Amount

$$A = P(1 + i)^n$$

where $i = \dfrac{r}{m}$ and $n = mt$,

A is the future (maturity) value;
P is the principal;
r is the annual interest rate;
m is the number of compounding periods per year;
t is the number of years;
n is the number of compounding periods;
i is the interest rate per period.

5.2 Future Value of an Ordinary Annuity

$$S = R\left[\frac{(1 + i)^n - 1}{i}\right] \qquad \text{or} \qquad S = Rs_{\overline{n}|i}$$

where
S is the future value;
R is the payment;
i is the interest rate per period;
n is the number of periods.

6.1, 6.3 Truth Tables

The following truth table defines the logical operators in this chapter.

p	q	$\sim p$	$p \wedge q$	$p \vee q$	$p \rightarrow q$
T	T	F	T	T	T
T	F	F	F	T	F
F	T	T	F	T	T
F	F	T	F	F	T

7.3 Basic Probability Principle

Let S be a sample space of equally likely outcomes, and let event E be a subset of S. Then the probability that event E occurs is

$$P(E) = \frac{n(E)}{n(S)}.$$

7.4 Union Rule

For any two events E and F from a sample space S,

$$P(E \cup F) = P(E) + P(F) - P(E \cap F).$$

7.5 Product Rule

If E and F are events, then $P(E \cap F)$ may be found by either of these formulas.

$$P(E \cap F) = P(F) \cdot P(E|F) \qquad \text{or} \qquad P(E \cap F) = P(E) \cdot P(F|E)$$

7.6 Bayes' Theorem

$$P(F_i|E) = \frac{P(F_i) \cdot P(E|F_i)}{P(F_1) \cdot P(E|F_1) + P(F_2) \cdot P(E|F_2) + \cdots + P(F_n) \cdot P(E|F_n)}$$

8.2 Permutations and Combinations

Permutations Different orderings or arrangements of the r objects are different permutations.

$$P(n, r) = \frac{n!}{(n - r)!}$$

Clue words: arrangement, schedule, order
Order matters!

Combinations Each choice or subset of r objects gives one combination. Order within the group of r objects does not matter.

$$\binom{n}{r} = \frac{n!}{(n - r)!r!}$$

Clue words: group, committee, set, sample
Order does not matter!

8.4 Binomial Probability

If p is the probability of success in a single trial of a binomial experiment, the probability of x successes and $n - x$ failures in n independent repeated trials of the experiment, known as binomial probability, is

$$\binom{n}{x} \cdot p^x \cdot (1 - p)^{n-x}.$$

8.5 Expected Value

Suppose the random variable x can take on the n values $x_1, x_2, x_3, \ldots, x_n$. Also, suppose the probabilities that these values occur are respectively $p_1, p_2, p_3, \ldots, p_n$. Then the expected value of the random variable is

$$E(x) = x_1 p_1 + x_2 p_2 + x_3 p_3 + \cdots + x_n p_n.$$

9.2 Variance and Standard Deviation

The variance of a set of n numbers $x_1, x_2, x_3, \ldots, x_n$, with mean $\bar{x}$, is

$$s^2 = \frac{\Sigma x^2 - n\bar{x}^2}{n - 1}.$$

The standard deviation of the n numbers $x_1, x_2, x_3, \ldots, x_n$, with mean $\bar{x}$, is

$$s = \sqrt{\frac{\Sigma x^2 - n\bar{x}^2}{n - 1}}.$$

11.4 Derivative

The derivative of the function f at x, written $f'(x)$, is defined as

$$f'(x) = \lim_{h \to 0} \frac{f(x + h) - f(x)}{h}, \qquad \text{provided this limit exists.}$$

Rules for Derivatives

The following rules for derivatives are valid when all the indicated derivatives exist.

12.1

Constant Rule   If $f(x) = k$, where k is any real number, then $f'(x) = 0$.

12.1

Power Rule   If $f(x) = x^n$ for any real number n, then $f'(x) = nx^{n-1}$.

12.1

Constant Times a Function   Let k be a real number. Then the derivative of $f(x) = k \cdot g(x)$ is

$$f'(x) = k \cdot g'(x).$$

12.1

Sum or Difference Rule   If $f(x) = u(x) \pm v(x)$, then

$$f'(x) = u'(x) \pm v'(x).$$

12.2

Product Rule   If $f(x) = u(x) \cdot v(x)$, then

$$f'(x) = u(x) \cdot v'(x) + v(x) \cdot u'(x).$$

12.2

Quotient Rule   If $f(x) = u(x)/v(x)$, and $v(x) \neq 0$, then

$$f'(x) = \frac{v(x) \cdot u'(x) - u(x) \cdot v'(x)}{[v(x)]^2}.$$

12.3

Chain Rule   If y is a function of u, say $y = f(u)$, and if u is a function of x, say $u = g(x)$, then $y = f(u) = f[g(x)]$, and

$$\frac{dy}{dx} = \frac{dy}{du} \cdot \frac{du}{dx}.$$